THE CONTINENT OF EUROPE

MACMILLAN AND CO., Limited
LONDON · BOMBAY · CALCUTTA · MADRAS
MELBOURNE

THE MACMILLAN COMPANY
NEW YORK · BOSTON CHICAGO
DALLAS · ATLANTA · SAN FRANCISCO

THE MACMILLAN COMPANY
OF CANADA, LIMITED
TORONTO

THE CONTINENT
OF EUROPE

BY

LIONEL W. LYDE
M.A., F.R.G.S.

EMERITUS PROFESSOR OF GEOGRAPHY IN THE UNIVERSITY OF LONDON,
HONORARY MEMBER OF THE ROYAL HUNGARIAN ACADEMY OF SCIENCE

MACMILLAN AND CO., LIMITED
ST. MARTIN'S STREET, LONDON
1930

COPYRIGHT

First Edition 1913
Reprinted 1917, 1920
Second Edition 1924
Third Edition 1926
Fourth Edition 1930

PRINTED IN GREAT BRITAIN
BY R. & R. CLARK, LIMITED, EDINBURGH

PREFACE

I

In this series an attempt is made to treat the CONTINENTS OF THE WORLD from a double point of view. From the one, emphasis is laid only on what seems to be the essential individuality of the particular continent, e.g. the peninsular character and influence of Europe ; and areas which seem to be not quite typical, e.g. the British Isles and Russia, are treated in outline or with detail on such points only as have direct relation to that individuality. For similar reasons the countries of the core—Germany, Austria-Hungary, and Switzerland —are not treated in quite the same way as those of the circumference.

From the other point of view, in treating the typical political units, considerable attention is given to their political subdivisions, e.g. the Roman provinces of France or the modern Swiss cantons, especially when these illustrate principles or processes that are characteristic of the continent. Much emphasis is laid on the political unit, because I find it just as difficult to picture clearly the precise limits of a natural region—in Professor Herbertson's sense—as I find it easy to picture the delimited frontier of a civilised State. It is almost always the political control that gives the dominant note in the most important areas ; and, as the method of treating such areas should in each case, as far as possible, be appropriate to the dominant note, the political unit cannot be made subordinate without more being lost than is gained.

Besides, to most of us Geography seems to have neither meaning nor value apart from Man ; and so we usually think in political units as far as human activities are concerned. For the name of a political unit, e.g. France or Japan, is far more than a mere label of an atom of artificially partitioned land ; it contains a whole world of suggestion and association, and is an epitome of all that makes a nation—of things achieved,—of a type in art and literature, in science and politics,—of an ideal, the passionate desire to preserve and perpetuate which is the only thing deserving the name of patriotism.

v

I have attempted, too, to carry out an old conviction that geographic details are illuminating only when viewed as instances of world-processes, and that therefore the geography of any large unit should be approached through its world-relations. In this connection I think that nothing else possesses a tithe of the helpfulness inherent in the theory of the tetrahedral deformation of the Earth. The fact that some competent mathematicians believe that it has no sound physics or dynamics at the back of it, and assert that it has been wholly unfruitful in results, seems to me of less importance than its acceptance by so many great geologists, and its proved utility to geographers who approach their subject as essentially a human science.

After assuming four previous stages in the life of the Earth—a consolidation of meteorites into a globular unit, the separation of mineral crust from metallic core, the condensation of vapour over that crust, and the buckling of it into positive and negative land-forms—we have still to account for the distribution of these forms having taken a definite character. The essential details that have to be accounted for, form a sequence of what Professor J. W. Gregory calls "four homologies": the predominance of land in the Northern Hemisphere and sea in the Southern Hemisphere—the triangular shape of the great physical units, whether land or sea—the alternation of aspect, land tapering southwards and sea tapering northwards, resulting in a nearly complete ring of land round the north and an absolutely complete ring of water round the south—and so the antipodal position of land and water.

Any theory which attempts to account for these facts of distribution, has to deal with an Earth exhibiting the suggestion of four triangular faces which meet in six edges and project in four coigns; and such a distribution is essentially tetrahedral. Every spherical body which shrinks owing to contraction of its core, tends to become tetrahedral, for a sphere combines minimum surface with maximum volume, while a tetrahedron combines maximum surface with minimum volume; and collapse at one point must react at the antipodal point. But no body with a structure like that of the Earth could become a complete tetrahedron while rotating at a speed similar to that of the Earth. On the contrary, it must pass through alternate stages of collapse towards the tetrahedral, emphasising vertical lines in periods of violent disturbance, and of recovery towards the spherical, emphasising horizontal lines in periods of relative quiet.

In the case of the Earth, as long as the crust was thin, any shrinkage of core could only wrinkle the whole surface into forms that must always have been relatively "old"; but, as the crust thickened, active movement would be confined more or less to lines of weakness, which would be crumpled into forms that we may still call "young." And all the time, though the relative positions of land and water might change, the water held on the Earth's surface by attraction must always have collected where areas of crustal settlement decreased the distance from the centre of the mass. That is to say, many of the phenomena that have affected Man most—from the influence of the Himalayan uplift on the development of turf-forming grasses, not suited to huge mammals, to the concentration of volcanic activity at angular joints of great segments of the Earth's crust—have light thrown on them by this tetrahedral theory. They thus become simply examples of a law instead of isolated items that burden the memory.

Apart from any theory, too, it is in practice the painful and almost daily experience of glass-blowers that glass balls, when almost perfect, collapse into forms which definitely reproduce the relations of positive and negative land-forms on the face of the Earth; and the process is known in the trade as "tetrahedral collapse."

I have, therefore, adopted the theory as a working hypothesis.

II

EXTRACT FROM THE SECOND PART OF THE ORIGINAL PREFACE

My use of the word wyr *obviously needs some explanation. . . .*

We have had in our language for the last 600 years the word wyr. *It was originally applied—e.g. by Robert Bruce and King Edward I.—to an instrument used in the defence of a city-wall. This machine, heavily weighted, moved downwards and outwards in a circle; and on the outskirts of its circuit it might, and often did, cause considerable disturbance.*

Again, whirl *is more English than* cyclone; *and* wind-whirl *has the great advantage of suggesting—to young pupils—"whirl-wind." As these words in their full meaning cover all important "anti-cyclonic" and "cyclonic" phenomena, I have used them now for some years in lecturing; and I have retained them in this book, especially in the more general portion.*

NOTE TO THE 1924 EDITION

The changes brought about by recent events have been accompanied by some extreme interpretations of the principle of Self-determination ; and amongst minor inconveniences is the wholesale disappearance of many well-known and historic place-names from official maps.   In many cases they have been replaced by linguistic curiosities which it is not easy either to spell or to pronounce correctly, and which belong to languages that have no world-value for any purposes of international intercourse. Under these circumstances we may surely allow ourselves considerable license ; and if we may give an English pronunciation to Paris and an English spelling to Florence, we may take at least equal liberties about places of so much less importance.

L. W. LYDE.

UNIVERSITY COLLEGE,
LONDON.

NOTE TO THE 1930 EDITION

Except for a few statistics and one or two verbal changes no attempt has been made to remodel the Russian chapter or to bring it up to date, for the information accessible, though official, seems to be—so far as I have been able to test it—of doubtful value and accuracy. For instance, the relation of crops to precipitation (which can be judged from the verified figures of Rumania and South Russia for a quarter of a century) seems to have changed ! The chapter remains, therefore, like the pages referring to the political frontiers of pre-war Germany, as it appeared in the original edition (1913).

I greatly regret that in that edition there was a misprint in the chapter on Holland which, the Dutch officials informed me, has been copied in a number of small School books.   It referred to the percentage of the population living on barges.   An original badly written 1% was printed 10 p.c., and I overlooked the mistake in proof.   But I must add that the accusation, somewhat publicly and widely made, that I had done it intentionally to malign Holland, seems to me to border on insanity.   One does not discredit oneself intentionally.

Owing to the vast political changes I have found it impossible to bring some few of the statistics in the book up to date, as the official returns sometimes no longer include the same details, or are made up in a different form, or refer to different areas and different political units.

CONTENTS

Contents

ILLUSTRATIONS

Illustrations

CHAPTER I

WORLD-RELATIONS

IF the educational value and the economic utility of Geography, as a "human" science, are alike concerned with the making of mental pictures, perspective becomes at once an all-important consideration; and, if the physique and the climate of the great continental units may—on a working hypothesis—be intimately related to the process by which a cooling sphere is deformed towards the shape of a tetrahedron, the first step towards linear perspective is through a survey of World-relations.

The World-relations of Europe are both physical and climatic. **Physical** As soon as the secular cooling of the Earth began to modify its **Relation.** essential spherical characteristic of maximum contents with minimum surface, causes outside the practical concern of Man decided that the horizontal "triangle" of the tetrahedron should lie in what we now call the Northern Hemisphere. This involved a wide extension of land-surface into high latitudes and a marked tendency to uplift along the edges of the horizontal "triangle," such uplift in the particular geometrical form being necessarily about two-thirds of the distance from the common apex of the three perpendicular "triangles" to the opposite pole of the original sphere. It was fundamental, therefore, that the mass of the land in the Northern Hemisphere should have a marked east-and-west lie,—that its specific expansion should be poleward,—and that its most marked tendency to uplift should be fully 120° from the South Pole— actually between 37° and 45° N.

As the process of deformation matured, the sag in the centre of **Sequence** each "triangle" and the uplift of the edges became emphasised; **of Forms.** and we infer a natural sequence, the oldest folds of surplus crust merging generally in areas of lower elevation towards the sag and in lines of higher elevation towards the edge. So our World-relation involves, in the case of Europe, a belt of old folded highland merging northward in a vast area of lowland and skirted southward by a line of Young Folded Mountains.

Æ 1 B

**Comple-
mentary
Depres-
sion.**

The inevitable reaction from this process of maximum uplift further involves a complementary line of maximum depression—on the side away from the older folds and more or less parallel with the crest of the uplift. This prepares us for a considerable area of inland sea stretching east-and-west, probably broken into sections by old crustal blocks, such as form the core of the Iberian peninsula and the islands of Corsica and Sardinia; and round the margin of the intervening sections of sea, on the side away from the uplift, we expect the pressure of the foundered blocks to excite volcanic and seismic phenomena, as round the south of the Tyrrhenian and the Ægean seas.

**Climatic
Relation.**

The precise form of each belt in this sequence depends not only on the underlying structure, but also on the forces that have been acting on that structure, and on the time during which that action

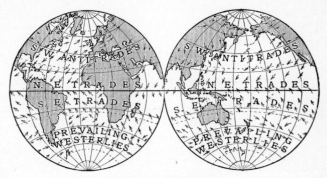

General plan of wind-system.

has been felt. In other words, the World-relation of the continent is climatic as well as physical. In the nature of things, an area lying on the eastern side of a great ocean and poleward of $37°$–$45°$ N. must have warm wet S.W. Anti-Trades blowing normally towards it; and thus two fundamental conditions for the presence of ice on a large scale—high latitude and heavy precipitation—are guaranteed. This would be the case even if there were no permanent wind-whirl (or low-pressure area) off Iceland—a possibility demanded by the assumption of some geologists that there could have been no wide glaciation unless the oceanic circulation had been interrupted by the existence of land and the vertical circulation of the atmosphere consequently much accelerated by "continental" influences.

**Precipita-
tion.**

We assume, then, heavy precipitation, cyclonic or otherwise, over the north-west of our area, leading to wide glaciation—at all events over the higher parts of the area; and, while all the higher ground, especially our ridge of Young Folded Mountains, may have had more or less independent centres of glaciation,—the Rhone valley having been covered with 5000 feet of ice—the great centre must have been where maximum rainfall and minimum temperature were combined. This occurs where the great lowland is skirted, on the brink of the Atlantic, by the Scandinavian highlands; and from this the ice-flow must have "radiated," and did radiate.

Again we are prepared for certain results. We are prepared to find, *e.g.*, that the great weight of ice depressed the north-west of the area, probably in many places below ocean-level,—that the regular wind-wyr (or high-pressure) movement over the interior lowland in winter would distribute glacier-silt to form loess, especially to south and south-east of the maximum extension of the ice-sheet,—and that the progress of the ice-sheet up-hill towards the south would be slow and short. This last consideration would lead us further. All pre-glacial organic forms which survived at all, must have migrated southwards before this ice-sheet; but the high ridge of Young Folded Mountains was also glaciated, and sunward of it was the complementary sea-filled depression. This double obstacle to movement southward and the narrowness of the belt between the two areas of glaciation suggest that we shall find relative poverty of native flora and fauna, owing to wholesale massacre in the Great Ice Age. Naturally, this is specially characteristic of Scandinavia. *Results of Glaciation.*

But the question of precipitation is of supreme importance quite apart from its relation to the action of ice. The most important single phenomenon in World-climate is probably the swing of the wind-system with the sun, leading to a swing of the rain belts and rain seasons. The northward movement of the sun in the northern summer carries the source of the Trade-winds north of the great tableland deserts, which lie in the broadest parts of the perpendicular "triangles" of the tetrahedron in latitudes south of $37°-45°$ N. Indeed, the deserts are largely caused by the Trade-winds, which are not only cold and dry so near to their source, but also moving from colder to warmer latitudes, and therefore able to hold more moisture than they can get. We are prepared, then, for an area of summer drought in Southern Europe; and this must have accentuated the poverty of the natural flora and fauna. *Swing of Wind-system.*

For, obviously, any plant or animal association must flourish best where conditions are most favourable to it; and, therefore, any such association must be most powerful, *i.e.* most difficult to oust, in its natural zone. But in the transition area between one natural zone and the next no natural association can be as stable as inside one or other of the natural zones; and thus these transition areas must have afforded early Man special facilities for pushing in himself and his domestic plants and animals. The most marked of all these areas is that between the Trades and the Anti-Trades, *i.e.* the "Mediterranean" latitudes; and in the case *Transition Areas.*

of the actual Mediterranean basin, as we have seen, other causes
had already led to relative poverty of natural flora and fauna.

Wind Control.

Outside the poleward limit of the Trades, we may expect that
the Anti-Trades should bring unfailing supplies of rain throughout
the year; but the same kind of continental conditions which
favoured a glacial sheet in the Great Ice Age, may favour semi-glacial
conditions every winter. In that case the interior lowland will be
covered with a sheet of cold heavy air, into which it will be
impossible for the warm light air of the S.W. Anti-Trades to intrude.
Only in summer, when the interior heats up and actually attracts an
inflow, will these warm light winds be able to bring their burden of
rain inland.

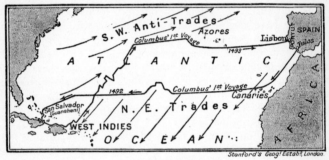

Columbus' first voyage.

Again we are prepared for certain results. We are prepared to
find, *e.g.*, that wheat-growing is much encouraged on the interior
lowlands by early summer rains,—that the summer-drought greatly
favours fruit-growing in the lee of the Young Folded Mountains—
that the complementary character of the seasons north and south
of these mountains, with its necessary accompaniment of complementary crops, must have led to intercourse between the two areas
in very early times.

Weathering.

One other point remains. We expect that the oldest foldings
of crust will have weathered most, and that their weatherings will
have gravitated northwards. If so, the lowlands will be modified
chemically and physically owing to the distribution—by wind,
water, and ice—of the denuded materials; and the old folded
highland will have been carved by deep sinuous valleys and other
signs of a river-system that is complex because imposed on a base
appropriate to vastly different conditions in ages long past.

World Site.

So far as the distribution of land on the Earth is concerned,
the western end of this old folded highland marks approximately
the mathematical centre of all the habitable surface; and, so far as
the distribution of water is concerned, it is the point from which

Trade-winds carry away in summer, and to which Anti-Trades [1] bring back in winter, over the narrowest and most important ocean on the face of the earth. To this the Discovery of America and the commercial history of England are significant and explicit corollaries; it also involves implicitly the conditions under which cryptogamic vegetation came to be buried under submarine mud in the process of being converted into coal, and under which land-locked basins came to be cut off so completely from the ocean that they became salt enough to be the source of the great salt-beds of Europe. Cf. p. 10.

All things considered, these are the two most important minerals in the modern development of Europe.

[1] This title suggests both the unity of the whole wind-system and the double antagonism between its two main manifestations—an antagonism of direction and an antagonism of character, as " *Not* steady," *i.e.* variable.

CHAPTER II

REGIONAL RELATIONS

WITHIN the World relation is the more intimate regional one, the local environment; and, in the case of Europe, the more important aspects of the precise site and surroundings are rather climatic and economic towards the north-west, and rather physical and political towards the south-east. The latter was the more important historically; for before the particularist Nomad of the ocean margin had expanded westward in his ships, the patriarchal Nomad of the continental steppe had expanded westward on his horse.

Ural-Caspian Gap. Oceans of sea and Saharan sand isolated the essentially European area on the north, the west, and the south. Only on the east was there a natural physical link with a neighbouring continent; and across the only part of this link which is neither mountainous nor forested, the Caspian Sea stretches the barrier of 700 miles of water from north to south. The character of the unforested lowland to the north of the Caspian is due largely to its emergence from beneath the waters of the Arctic Ocean—an emergence so recent geologically that the seals in the Caspian still retain almost all the normal "Arctic" characteristics. The low, smooth surface of this exposed sea-floor,—the desiccation involved in the disappearance of the great southward expansion of the Arctic Ocean,—and the constancy of icy winds in the winter from the Siberian Pole of Cold, all combined to preserve this Ural-Caspian gap as an easy steppe road into Europe. Mackinder has with reason called it " The Geographical Pivot of History."

Asiatic Inflow. The name Asia (*Asu* = " Sunrise ") was originally confined to the plains behind Ephesus, while all to the west of the Ægean might be called Europe (*Erib* = " Sunset "); and, of course, the Ægean itself made an unmistakable western frontier to Asia in this limited sense. In the larger sense, Asia, as a great home of Man, is separated from Europe, as another great home of Man, by this very thinly peopled steppe. The northern route into Europe over this lowland steppe from the " Land of the Horsemen," which was followed by the finer types of Yellow man,—Huns and Magyars, Bulgars and Finns,—

6

is easier than that southern route over the plateau steppe, from the "Land of the Camel-men," which was followed by the Turks. But the environment of both routes was pastoral and patriarchal, favourable only to nomad shepherds, eaters of meat and cheese, fighters for grass and water ; and any decrease in rainfall meant not only scantier supplies of water and grass, but also an increased percentage of bright sunshine, such as has, by its nerve-stimulus, largely accounted for the great movements of people over the vast grasslands of the world, whether steppes or savanas.   It was in the great cycle of drought, between 400 B.C. and 600 A.D., that hunger

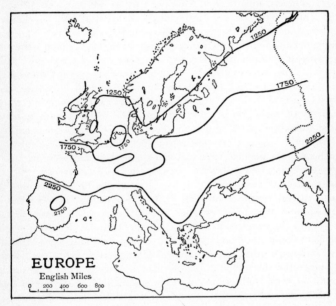

Distribution (in hours) of bright sunshine.

and actinic stimulus gave birth to the epoch-making migrations of Goths and Huns and Vandals, and to similar movements in Arabia, Persia, and Kashmir, of which Mahomet's was the most important.

The separation of Europe from Asia is, therefore, historic rather than geographical, political rather than physical ; and—although, as a matter of fact, at the summit of the two Trans-Ural railways, as on the summit of the Dariel Pass, there are sign-posts with "Europe" on one arm and "Asia" on the other—the weakness of any politico-historic influences is shown by the fact that the nominal frontier in the east runs neither along the Urals, where no continuous crest can be marked out at all, nor along the Caucasus, where the crest is a typical piece of sierra.   It is, indeed, a mere

Independ-
ence of
Europe.

compromise between geographical and political conditions; and where it is most important, at the Ural-Caspian gap, it is partly the course of the Ural river, *i.e.* a line towards which human movement is attracted from both sides rather than one from which human movement is diverted in opposite directions.

At the same time that specific development of the continent from the south to which its practical separation from Asia is due, had its own geographical base.

Pre-historic Inflow. The earliest debt of Europe to its southern neighbour was incurred in prehistoric times. The initial movements of the little brown-skinned, long-headed Gondwanas—as we may call primeval man—must have been entirely longitudinal, or at least isothermal, *i.e.* roughly east or west from the primeval race-home; and subsequent movements into Europe must have been much easier for the African branch over the two or three "Mediterranean" land-bridges than for any Asiatic branch across—or even round—the Kirghiz Sea. Indeed, two of the land-bridges, the "Italian" and the "Greek," led through a climate that was very favourable to the progress of early Man, being too transitional to encourage strong associations (cf. p. 3), and being kept equable by the great expanse of sea (now largely converted into steppe and desert) that stretched north-eastward up the Aralo-Caspian depression and south-westward over the Shari-Congo basin. It was, therefore, inherently probable that remains of very early Man would some day be found round the northern end of these bridges, *i.e.* on the Riviera, at Gibraltar, in Croatia, and that most progress should be made in those parts of the continent which had been earliest populated. Recent developments in the attitude of Historians to "Minoan" and "pre-Minoan" civilisation confirm the geographical probability.

Mediter-ranean and Early Man. Once the surface of the globe had approximated to its present condition, this Mediterranean area was still likely to favour progress in many ways. Its latitude guarantees absolute freedom both from continued high temperatures and from even occasional extensions of extreme cold; at the same time it involves alternate participation in purely temperate conditions, as dependent on the rainfall *régime* of the Anti-Trades, and in essentially tropical conditions, as dependent on the desiccating influence of the Trades.

In this area early Man was specially favoured, therefore, by the absence of the most adverse climatic condition, a hard winter; for the mountain uplift to the north protected him from the harshest phenomena of the so-called temperate zone, while the sea to the south preserved every year an almost tropical temperature long after the summer drought had given place to winter rain. There was, therefore, no frost to cut down crops, nor was there pressing need for fatty nitrogenous food. At the same time, the rainfall was so distributed as to check the growth of dense forest: there was no "closed association," for the struggle was not so keen that no new species could force its way in; nor, on the other hand, had the land been left intractable as the result of glaciation.

These two considerations are of great importance. North of **North v.** the Alps, even after the forest had been largely cleared, it took **South.** centuries for the ill-drained surface to become really fit for human habitation, so that it remained a land only of hunters and foresters long after southern Europe had been settled by tillers of the soil. And in that southern area, as the drought came just when the heat was greatest, and as the rainy season was cool, luxuriance of vegetation was impossible; for half of every year in the contest between man and nature, nature was passive or at best drowsy, and during that same period no tropical rain forbade man to make use of his most deadly weapon—fire.

Even so the case is understated. Far from tropical scenes of **Social** senseless competition, species are social; and, as these social species **Species.** included such food-plants as the olive and sweet-chestnut, man could find his daily food near at hand and in great abundance. Life thus became stationary, or at all events man had a fixed home, in which things could be kept; and at once savagery, with its lack of family ties and family goods, gave place to a civilisation based on the accumulation of wealth and the transmission of experience.

With the development of human activities in historic ages, the **Drought** sea and its non-European hinterland were still favourable to progress. **Control.** That hinterland included practically two areas in which the summer drought was so much extended as to be almost permanent drought, with a consequent imperious necessity for irrigation; and in each case the area was provided with a river-system the most conspicuous feature of which was an annual and beneficent flood. The most elementary processes of surveying the flood area—a natural and necessary occupation—involved the discovery of arithmetical and geometrical principles, as the beneficence of the flood involved an absence of cloud by day and by night; and the attraction of the stars to those who spent the night on the flat roofs appropriate to a rainless land, led to an early application of the arithmetic and geometry to the study of the stars.

Again, when Egypt and Mesopotamia had thus supplied the **The** dwellers on the Levantine coasts with a scientific basis both for **Levant.** navigation and for evolving a system of weights and measures, the Phœnician trader was still specially favoured by the geographical conditions of the area. Not only is the sea practically tideless, but it is also exceptionally safe at night; for the ordinary sequence of "land and sea breezes" is greatly quickened by the cloudless skies, and must involve off-shore drift at night. Nor was this all. In the clear air that is typical of the Mediterranean basin, the mountain peaks of distant lands were seen so distinctly—as Cyprus can be seen from the Phœnician coast—that they must have been at once a main incentive to early voyages of discovery, and an inestimable aid to navigation in days before the invention of any nautical instruments. The Peñas de Europa, though not actually on the Mediterranean, were for ages "The Lighthouse of Europe."

In early times, then, the Mediterranean race lived under conditions that did not strain their infant powers; and those of them who lived on the warm temperate shore had every opportunity of receiving stimulus and civilisation from their more advanced relations on the subtropical shore. It was an additional advantage that the intercourse was by sea, as that—in strong contrast to the steppe route in later times—favoured the inflow of ideas rather than people.

Lack of Stimulus. The very ease of life and navigation in the south, however, though favourable to early activities, was destined to be a drawback with the advance of civilisation, so that within 2000 years the centre of civilisation had moved to the north-west of the continent. There survival was only to the strong and fearless, and the most helpful features of the coast are the best proof of the hard conditions of life. Thus, it is specifically where a fractured plateau-scarp is exposed to wild storms and heavy precipitation in high latitudes that the combined action of ice and torrents develops such a nursery of mariners as a fiord system. Again, where the plateau gives place southward to plain, navigable rivers can give access to and from the ocean; and where the tough, old, folded highland is abruptly severed in the Armorican peninsula, abundant traces of Viking blood still show that the ria was a good substitute for the fiord.

Atlantic Margin. But all these things are more or less subordinate to the fundamental fact that we have here a piece of Atlantic margin; and the slight variation in the width of the S-shaped Atlantic suggests, even on a political map, that the shape bears no relation to the grain of the enclosing lands. On the contrary, these are abruptly cut short seaward—obviously as in Norway and Newfoundland, Brittany and Brazil, or otherwise, as where the North European plain drops from its submarine 100-fathom terminus. This ignoring of essential feature-lines has two important results which react on each other. The one is a great variety of coast—fiord and ria, estuary and gulf, peninsula and island; the other is access to and from an immense hinterland.

Atlantic v. Pacific. Here is the fundamental distinction between the Atlantic and the Pacific. The latter has had a simple history, its surrounding mountain-lines having been folded up continuously as its floor sank; and so its form is simple—a vast basin the edge of which is almost everywhere backed by mountains and festooned with mountainous islands. The Atlantic has had a complex history, in a succession of subsidences which broke across the grain of the land; and so its form is complex, finding its epitome and climax

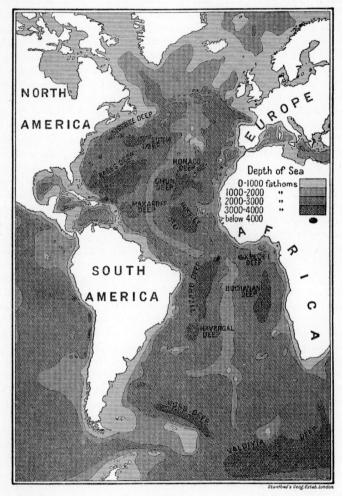

Floor of Atlantic, showing feature-lines.

in Europe, a "Peninsula of peninsulas." As the two basins are of approximately the same size, the smaller ocean must have the larger hinterland; and, having much the easier access to that hinterland by reason of its varied coast-line, it must be much the more important economically.

Sea Fish-ing.

The influence of such conditions on Man must naturally have been greatest where the conditions were most emphasised, *i.e.* in Europe; and in this connection the water-forms and land-forms are equally important. Geographically, a sea-fishery is the only firm foundation for a mercantile marine; and its essential conditions are profoundly favourable to the rise of pure democracy, based on the equality of man and man in the jointly-owned boat, and the equality of man and woman in the common home from which the fisherman is absent so often and so long that dual control must be evolved. No doubt, the depth and other conditions make the Mediterranean deficient in marine life of economic value, as it is in tidal power; but the North Sea is one of the finest fishing grounds on the face of the globe. The Atlantic tides are so strongly felt in the shallow enclosed area that there is great rise and fall of water-level in the long estuaries which feed the sea with river-mud and its accompanying fish-food, and the upper and lower strata of the water are so mixed as to make an absolutely homogeneous unit; the slightly submerged banks, especially the Dogger, are ideal fishing centres, having deep "pits" into which the fish can "drop" in cold or stormy weather; and the abundance of river-mud discharged into the sea, especially towards the south, where the shores are most densely populated, makes the submarine "deltas" ideal fish-nurseries. Cf. p. 16.

Peninsu-lar Dis-unity.

The land-forms, on the other hand, are predominantly peninsular; and, in the nature of things, peninsulas are essentially semi-submerged highland or mountain areas. They enjoy the climatic, commercial, and strategic advantages of a sea environment; but, unlike islands, their apparent unity of form is negatived by the normal presence of a mountain back-bone, which throws off human activities, like river-systems, in opposite directions. And, as their relative excess of length over breadth makes them difficult to govern from a single centre in early times, and gives them considerable difference of climate [1] and consequently of economic interests at the extreme ends, they are found to be adverse to political unity. This led to great variety of development between peninsula and peninsula as well as within the limits of each; and this variety led in turn to natural intercourse and mutual interchange of ideas and products.

Over Popula-tion.

Again, the area of the peninsulas is relatively small; but the climatic conditions were favourable to the growth of population in early times. The natural result was that the population reached "Saturation - point" somewhat prematurely, and the only remedy was emigration. How great the facilities for this were, may be gauged from the estimate that the development of coast is

---

[1] The normal direction of the great peninsulas (N.–S.) implies great latitudinal variation of climate.

sufficient to give one mile of coast to every 75 square miles of land ; and the political importance of this was greatly increased by the fact that the chief peninsulas show very marked differences of relief and climate, with corresponding differences of products and their attendant occupations. The various geographic units, therefore, not only developed more or less independently of one another, but also on independent lines ; so that the varied outline and the varied surface of the continent were reflected in a variety of social and political types which was very favourable to the progress of civilisation.

Under such conditions the Atlantic margin of Eurasia developed **Atlantic** a civilisation widely different from that of the Pacific margin,— **Civilisa-** a civilisation essentially based on variety, mobility, change ; and **tion.** this difference has been reflected in almost all the normal activities, *e.g.* the art of the two areas. Geographically, art is the child of energy and leisure, indolence and bustle being equally adverse ; and the prime defect of Western art reflects the peninsular environment of the artists. For the constant and rapid changes of life, with their concomitant changes of artistic ideals and fashions, have never given time for any one phase to develop a system of decoration completely suited to its subject-matter. In the Orient, on the contrary, Man's art, like his life, has known so little change that it has slowly evolved forms perfectly adapted to their subject and their functions.

CHAPTER III

MARGINAL AND MIDLAND SEAS

Marine Development. THE development of Europe, then, is intimately connected with its surrounding ocean and seas; but in this respect the White Sea and the Caspian have been of little importance, for the exposure to icy N. and N.E. winds in winter, the amount of fresh water sent down into them by rivers, the shallowness of all the White Sea and of the "European" part of the Caspian, cause them to be ice-bound for months every year, while the isolation, by latitude, of the White Sea, and by physique, of the Caspian, have further helped to minimise their utility. The Baltic and the Black Sea are more useful, but anywhere east of a line roughly joining the two great harbours of Copenhagen and Constantinople conditions are relatively unfavourable.

Black Sea. In the case of the Black Sea, for instance, there are practically few of the fishing phenomena which are the natural basis of commerce. It seems that, when the original crustal convulsion opened up the Bosphorus chink between the salt Mediterranean and the relatively fresh Euxine, the heavy salt water rushed into the latter and flooded its lower levels, killing off the native "fresh-water" fauna. One result of this was that the heavy salt water was suffused with sulphuretted hydrogen, and the lower layers have become lifeless. On the other hand, navigation is encouraged by a warm surface current, the ultimate result of somewhat complex conditions.

Black Sea Circulation. In winter the surface water reaches freezing-point, though it does not actually freeze except near the coast; and the reason for this is that the temperature of maximum density in the relatively fresh surface-water is considerably above 32° F. At this temperature, then, the heavy, chilled water sinks down on to the still heavier, though warmer, salt layers.

This locates the minimum deep-temperature in intermediate levels (25–50 fathoms). But when the greatest amount of fresh water is being discharged by the Dnieper and other large rivers, there is such a surplus as to give rise to a strong current of cool fresh water out of the sea. The pace and relative lightness of this keep it naturally in the centre and on the surface of the Bosphorus channel, while a counter current of warm salt water drifts into the Black Sea along the shores and on the bottom of the channel. This warm, salt, shore current not only keeps the strait unfrozen except at the rarest intervals of extraordinary winter cold, but also materially influences both the climate and the actual operations of navigation in the Black Sea. It is already divided into two before it leaves the Bosphorus, and this division is maintained in its passage over the shallow "North-European" (cf. p. 22) floor of the Black Sea, so that one branch eventually penetrates between the outflowing waters of the Dnieper and the Dniester to Odessa, while the other skirts Sebastopol. It is thanks to this that the Odessa harbour is seldom frozen up for more than a few days, and so the city is able to make full use of its position between two rivers whose mouths are intricate and difficult to navigate, and whose fresh waters are easily frozen.

The Baltic is still more important, especially in the history of **Baltic Sea.** civilisation. Its physical boundary is the partly submerged plateau on which Rügen and the Danish islands stand, and up to which there is a perceptible tide, amounting to 12 inches at Copenhagen; and the somewhat similar Åland ridge cuts off the Baltic proper from the Gulf of Bothnia. These submarine barriers have important effects on the circulation of the water somewhat similar to those in the Black Sea. Thus, the circulation inside the Baltic itself is mainly superficial, the heavier salter layers being so much blocked in as to be almost stagnant—a condition which is again adverse to marine life; but, as the Baltic—like the Black Sea in a less degree —receives much more water by rain and river than it loses by evaporation in such a latitude, over these stagnant strata there is a fresh-water current out into the North Sea except when the S.W. wind is blowing strongly.

Owing to the rotation of the Earth this current hugs the **Baltic** Swedish coast; and, being dependent on the summer rain and the **Circula-** melting of snow and ice, it varies so much in volume that there **tion.** is an inflow of what is called "Bank water" from the North Sea from September to April. This inflow, which seems naturally to come mainly from the deeper northern parts of the North Sea in late winter and early spring, and mainly from the shallower southern parts in the autumn and early winter,—and which is independent of a constant undercurrent into the Baltic of normal North Sea water,— has an important relation to the fishing industry.

Of course, extremes of temperature increase to the north and **Ice-bound** the east; but, except north of the Quarken Narrows, the interfer- **Coasts.** ence with traffic is less than might be imagined. Even in the Gulf of Finland, which is ice-bound for about 150 days every year, important traffic can be, and is, carried on by means of ice-breakers.   In hard winters the island-studded Åland Strait is covered with ice strong enough for heavy traffic; and the coasts between the strait and the Quarken Narrows are frozen up every year except where, in occasional years, ports with some exposure to Atlantic winds from the west and with salt "pits" to the east of them, *e.g.* Hernösand and Oxelösand, may remain open the whole winter (cf. Windau and Libau).   Otherwise, even between Stockholm and Visby, navigation is usually stopped from Christmas to Easter; and in severe winters there may be a good deal of loose, drifting ice in the Kattegat.   In the last 2000 years the entire sea has been frozen over perhaps half a dozen times—for instance, King Charles X. certainly *marched* his army across the Belts in 1658—and, with the constant accumulation of river-borne silt, the shore-waters are becoming so much shallower that they are more and more susceptible to frost.

North Sea.   West of the Copenhagen-Constantinople line conditions are not only favourable, but actually very stimulating, to human activity, especially in the North Sea.   This may be regarded as a shallow and often stormy sea which slightly covers, and entirely surrounds the large low "plateau" of the Dogger Bank; and, in the lee of this bank, the bed of the sea, which is part of the continental shelf having a fairly regular slope down from south to north, is scarred with a series of local depressions such as the "Silver Pit," the "Sole Pit," the Coal Pit, etc.

Southern Division.   The whole area may be divided into three parts, all of which converge on the Skager-Rak.   The south is the shallowest, with an average depth of only 20 fathoms; and, except in the pits, no part of the sea south of the Dogger has a depth of 30 fathoms.   This southern section is flooded, especially from the south-east, with quantities of deltaic mud, alive with the small organisms that make the best food for young fish.   It is, therefore, an ideal breeding-ground for fish; and its shores have naturally become the homes of amphibious races, such as the Frisians and Saxons, the English and the Dutch.   The Dover Strait is so narrow, and this part of the sea itself is so shallow, that the temperature of it is controlled mainly by the air above it.   It is, therefore, relatively cold in winter, when there is normally a cold outflow of air and water from the North European plain and its rivers, and so winter trawling is largely confined to the "Dogger"; while in summer the shallow waters off the continental coast are more frequented.   At all times, however, the tides so mix the upper and lower layers and the oceanic and continental waters that this shallow section is more or less homogeneous to the bottom.

Central Division.   The central section is roughly parallel to the east coast of Scotland, and has an average depth of 50 to 60 fathoms; and, as it is chilled towards the east in winter, and freshened towards the east in summer, and as the tide moves south-

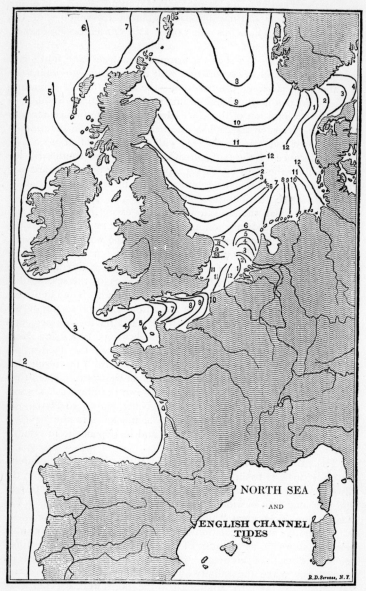

NORTH SEA

AND

ENGLISH CHANNEL
TIDES

B.D.Servoss, N.Y.

ward more slowly through the shallower Scotch waters than through
the deeper Norwegian waters, conditions are more favourable

both to the fish and to the fishermen on the west than on the east of the Long Forties Banks. This central section, like the southern, owes to the northern section its main supplies of the Atlantic element, which fills the "pits" with denser, because salter, but warmer water.

Tides. The tide enters this shallow, marginal sea from both north-west and south-west, and in conjunction with the currents determines the site and the season of the fisheries,—the herring fishing beginning off the Shetlands in June, and ending off Yarmouth in November,— as well as the position of the chief harbours and the inducements to fish. For over such a sea-floor the height of the tide determined both the area laid bare by the ebb, with its supplies of stranded fish, and the distance of the ports inland. And, as the southward tide naturally hugs the British coast (cf. p 15), while the northward tide works eastward, a circulatory motion is set up which is profoundly important in the distribution of fish.

Movements of Fish. The eggs of all the more important fish except herring float, and sea-fish begin to spawn when their food-supply begins to increase, i.e. in late spring and early summer, when the warm, salt, oceanic water is drifting food southward along the Scotch east coast. At the same time the inflow of cold and fresh water is driving the fish away from the east and towards the west shores of the sea, so that this western area is specially the spawning ground. The circulatory motion, therefore, carries the eggs away from England to the deltaic muds of the Dutch coast; they are hatched on the journey, and arrive at their destination as enormous shoals of tiny fish. Here their numbers produce such over-population that the food-supply (though very large indeed) soon begins to fail, with the result that the larger and stronger fish tend to migrate westward. From time immemorial, therefore, this must have drawn the finest fish towards the English coast,—even adult plaice being known to travel 200 miles in one season,—a fact of prime significance in the development of the English fishing industry and its dependent mercantile marine.

Mediterranean Sea. The part played by the Mediterranean has been very different. Not only does its basin form a distinct natural region between the Alpine uplift and the Sahara wastes; but also the sea itself is four times as long as it is wide, a great commercial advantage which has made it one of the great "high roads of civilisation." Its temperature, salinity, and circulation are, therefore, of relatively little moment, although, as a matter of fact, the tide at Venice sometimes reaches the height of three feet. Obviously latitude and distance from the Atlantic make the salinity and the temperature of the surface water decrease from the south-east to the north-west, except below the level of the sill which separates the Atlantic from the Mediterranean and forms the floor of the Straits of Gibraltar. Through these straits, as through the Dardanelles, there is a current of relatively fresh surface water into the Mediterranean, where the excessive loss by evaporation and the small contribution from the rivers lower the surface-level and increase the salinity.   There is a salt undercurrent outwards (cf. p. 15), but the inward surface current is much the larger and the stronger.   Indeed, it was the pace of this current that wrecked the ill-fated *Utopia* off Europa Point, as it is the weight of the out-current and the height of the Gibraltar sill which prevent the deep "Arctic" waters of the Atlantic from bringing their life-giving oxygen into the Mediterranean.

Both the north-western, warm-temperate, mountain-girt basin **Two** and the south-eastern, sub-tropical, gulf-girt basin have more pro- **Basins.** nounced articulation of outline and better economic outlets on the European than on the non-European side ; and in each case there is an island pivot.   From the natural centre of Sardinia—held in turn by Carthage and Rome, Goth and Byzantine, Vandal and Arab, Emperor and Pope, Aragon and Austria — Port Mahon invites to the Balearic islands and the Ebro valley, as Corsica does to the Apennine passes and the Lombard plain, or to the great through-route of the Rhone valley.   So the natural centre of Crete —held in turn by Greek and Roman, Saracen and Crusader, Venetian and Turk—commands the east-and-west bridge of the Cyclades and the north-and-south waterway of the Ægean to and from the Black Sea and the Morava confluence with the Danube.   Sicily, on the shallow saddle between these two deep basins, was the natural key to both, and was therefore held in turn by every dominant Power—Carthage, Greece, and Rome, Saracens, Normans, and Angevins ; and its command of both shores of Italy, and their relations respectively to Genoa and Venice, gave it as much political importance in ancient times as its natural fertility gave it economic importance, especially as an exporter of grain.

Since the opening of the Suez canal and the development of **Suez** prairie agriculture, however, the position has changed.   For the **Route.** whole produce of Sicily is absolutely immaterial to the world's grain-market ; and, on the other hand, the Suez route is unlike most other great water-thoroughfares, for it does not admit of Great Circle sailing, nor is it really oceanic.   It is essentially a coastal route, fed from a number of "bays" ; and the length of these leads to the development of a number of foci, *e.g.* Barcelona, Marseilles, Genoa, Naples, etc., more or less subordinate to a few others placed roughly on the horns of each "bay," *e.g.* Gibraltar and Malta (cf. Aden and Colombo).   All the Mediterranean coastlands are notably lacking in coal, but all along the European shores there are so many heavy cargoes out that cheap coal comes in everywhere ; for instance, coal is carried past Algiers to Constantinople at a lower rate than to Algiers itself.

"Atlantic" Climate.

The climatic influence of the Atlantic is indissolubly bound up with its economic influence, especially its facilities for commerce. In days when nautical instruments were very roughly made, and when ships were so few that there was little or no fear of collisions except in the Narrow Seas, it was a great advantage that the continental shelf drops to abysmal depths so abruptly 200 miles west of Land's End that there is a change of colour and of movement in the surface layers of the ocean,—a change so marked as to be unmistakable to the experienced eye. In later days, when artificial aids to navigation were multiplied, the Faroer plateau not only cut off the Atlantic—by the Wyville Thomson ridge—from the icy Arctic waters of the Norwegian Sea, but also provided a base for such a light as that of Rockall—with its curious resemblance to a ship under full sail, due to the dark stone of its hull-base being covered at the higher levels with the guano of billions of sea-birds. And, with the present development of international commerce, it is at least equally important that where the opposite coasts (of Newfoundland and Ireland) approach within the minimum distance of 1750 miles, there is a somewhat similar submarine ridge, the use of which is betrayed by its name of The Telegraph Plateau.

These advantages are emphasised by the fact that the Atlantic is by far the saltest of all the oceans, and that the maximum salinity in the North Atlantic occurs north of the tropic between the Sahara edge and the Dolphin Divide—the centre of which is marked approximately by its highest elevation in the Azores. A drift of relatively high salinity is therefore found to the east of the Dolphin Divide in Anti-Trade latitudes the whole way from the tropic to the Faroer ridge; and the influence of the Anti-Trades themselves, of the warm Gulf Stream Drift, and of this high salinity, cause icebergs to be practically unknown anywhere inside these limits.

Atlantic Winds.

Again, in days when steamers were unknown, the circulation of air over this same section of the Atlantic had an intimate relation to the history of geographical discovery. For the demand for air to fill the "vacuum" caused by the violent up-current over the heated desert of the Ibero-Saharan plateau so emphasises the normal down-current over the cool ocean that the wind-wyr round the Azores is abnormally large and strong; and the direction and regularity of the rotating winds not only account for the excellence of the port wine of the neighbouring coasts, but also provide that coast with a direct and unfailing link between the outward Trades and the homeward Anti-Trades (cf. p. 5).

With the substitution of coal for sails, and the consequent power of going "straight" independently of all winds and currents, the European harbours with the best access to coal are found to stand on or near a Great Circle which makes the shortest route from

Liverpool to Panama pass relatively "quite close" to such important

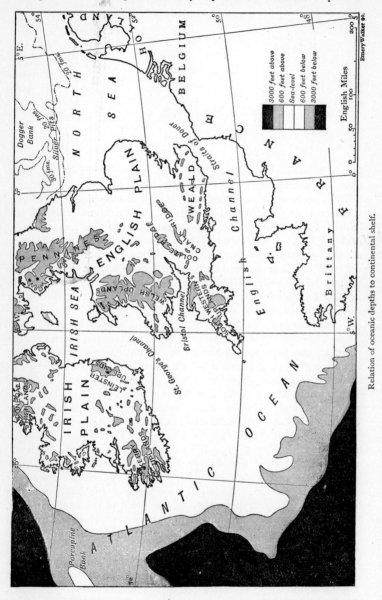

Relation of oceanic depths to continental shelf.

harbours as Halifax (N.S.), Boston, New York, Philadelphia, Baltimore, Norfolk (the U.S.A. coaling station), Havana, and Kingston.

CHAPTER IV

RELIEF

Latitu-
dinal
Division.

EUROPE is divided naturally into two distinct areas—a northern area of lowland, blocked westward by the old folded highlands of Scandinavia, and a southern area of old folded highlands, ribbed southward by young folded mountains; and the distinction is not limited to the land forms, but applies also to the marginal and midland seas. The North Sea, the Baltic, and the White Sea, are all shallow encroachments of the ocean on the northern lowland, not one of them more than 600 feet deep except in occasional troughs or pits; the Mediterranean, the Black Sea, and the Caspian, are all due to subsidences, and each of them has a depth of fully 6000 feet over quite a large area.

Dividing
Line.

The Caspian and the Black Sea have a special interest in this respect, because they actually contain submerged parts of the dividing line between the two areas. Thus, the geologically recent foundering of the "Black Sea" has abruptly cut off the European Balkans from their continuation in the Yaila Dagh, and the Yaila Dagh from their continuation in the Caucasus; and the latter range is abruptly cut off from the Asiatic Balkans by the subsidence of the "Caspian." In each case to the north of the divide, as in the Sea of Azof and the northern basins of the Caspian, the depth never exceeds 600 feet, and is typical of the northern lowland; and the land link of the Manych Depression between the two seas corresponds exactly to that of the Swedish Lakeland between the North Sea and the Baltic, as the freshness of the North Caspian water—which is quite drinkable—parallels that of the Bothnian Gulf.

Longitu-
dinal
Division.

There is an equally important, but not so obvious, structural division between east and west, the eastern half consisting of un-folded lowlands—where even earthquakes are unknown—merging to the north-west in an ancient mountain-system worn down into a peneplain, while the western half (west of 20° E.) consists of ancient "block and basin," merging to the south-east in young folded mountains, where there are at least four centres of volcanic activity, and earthquakes are an every-day occurrence.

The relation of this longitudinal division to the latitudinal **Divisions** explains what is most significant in the arrangement of the land *in re* **Man.** forms of the continent so far as man is concerned. Thus, we have

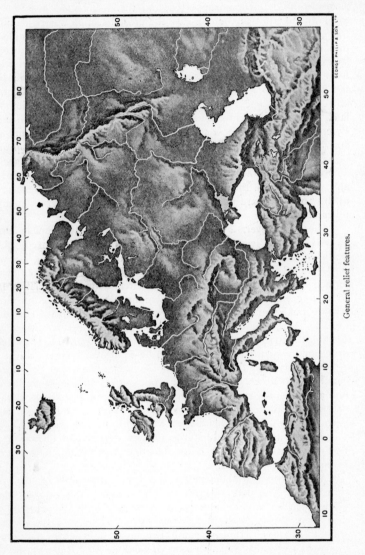

General relief features.

the North European or Swedo-Finnish peneplain flanked seaward by the Scandinavian Highlands and merging landward in the east European or Russian lowland, while the Mid-European or Franco-

German peneplain is flanked seaward by the Alpine system, and merges landward in the Great European plain. In both cases the relatively speedy contraction of the cooling interior of the earth left areas of the crust unsupported, and therefore bound eventually to tumble in; but in the one case the crustal section was rigid and fractured cleanly, while in the other it was flexible and crumpled into folds. In the one case, therefore, a fractured block has been so exposed to climatic influences as to have isolated man in the fiord environment which is the best nursery of individualism; in the other, sections of the folded chain have collapsed bodily, or odd links have been so worn and weakened as to give maximum facilities for human intercourse—by such gaps as that between the Pyrenees and the Alps, or such passes as those of the Simplon and St. Gothard. Further, the rigidity of the old Mid-European peneplain intensified the folding of the young Alpine chain to such an extent that whole blocks on the margins of the folds subsided; and here we find, therefore, small but profoundly fertile plains, as in the 20,000 square miles of the "Lombard," or the 40,000 square miles of the "Magyar" plain.

Soils. These, however, are mainly covered with alluvial soils; and alluvial soils are less lasting than the glacial and more mixed soils north of the Alpine folds. The fertility of these "strong" soils is due to the great variety of rock from which they have been formed in unglaciated areas, or to the direct action of glaciation in so mixing soils. And the great Scandinavian centre was in this respect much more influential than any of the subordinate centres, *e.g.* the Alps, not only because there the ice-sheet was thickest and most active, but also because the finest and most fertile glacial drift could, when dry, be transported by wind over a great plain.

Loess. Obviously, the dryness could only accompany high pressure conditions in which the wind in Europe moves in the same direction as the hands of a clock; and, therefore, the glacial silt would naturally be drifted all over the central plain, the burden of silt becoming lighter and lighter as the wind moved westward. It was inevitable, therefore, that the deepest deposits of loess would be to the south-east of the Baltic, but that deposits might be found as far west as Normandy.

Black Earth. Again, where the maximum southward extension of the ice (roughly 50° N.) left a series of lake-studded hills in latitudes where such an environment was very favourable to the growth of deciduous forests, dried humus was carried along with the glacier silt—to Russia, Hungary, and Rumania; and this not only increased its fertility and its power of holding water, but gave it the dark colour to which it owes both its name of Black Earth and its power of attracting heat. On the north Alpine foreland, however, such a clockwise movement of dry air could do little more than carry the finer and more valuable material back up the slopes down which it had come, while summer rains could do little less than wash it away down stream. We recover some of it in the Rhine gorge; but the morainic areas themselves have now typically poor and gravelly soil.

The prominent influence of the Scandinavian Highlands, apart **Scandi-** from their age, is due to their area (nearly 200,000 square miles). **navian** This is considerably more than double the area of the Alps; and **High-** the surface is so well adapted to holding snow that the Jostedalsbrae **lands.** glacier has an area of 600 square miles. Farther north, where decreased height and decreased precipitation are balanced by higher latitude and northern exposure, the difference in climate is suggested by the name of the Svartisan ("Black Ice") glacier, which still has an area of 400 square miles. The lakes of the Swedo-Finnish peneplain are correspondingly large, and lie round the edge of it, as the Canadian lakes lie round the edge of the V-shaped archean nucleus of the Hudson Bay area.

This Baltic edge is known as the glint line, and is due to the **Baltic** differential erosion of the archean rock and its neighbours; but in **Shield.** the Swedish lake-land it is covered with fertile recent deposits, while in Finland and Olonetz the glacial action is glaringly obvious in the areas of thick boulder-clay, the incoherent river-systems, the bare and scratched rock-surface, the thousands of lakes in the hollows worn by the ice in the huge flat slabs of granitic rock of which the country essentially consists. On the inner edge of the glint line in the south the terminal moraines are similarly responsible for the lake-dotted Baltic Heights.

The influence of the Ural system, though next in size to the **The Urals.** Scandinavian, has been less than that of any other mountain system in Europe. Indeed, it is only from the Asiatic side that they even look like mountains, although both on the mainland and in Novaya Zemlya they reach a height of 4000 to 5500 feet. But the fact that their steeper face is towards Asia, while their westward slope is so gentle that streams are navigable almost to their source, causes them to be an important climatic divide,—so much so that the ordinary European fruit trees, and such forest trees as oak and ash and elm, stop abruptly on their western slopes. They have also interesting climatic divisions from north to south, the northern section being mainly tundra and the southern being mainly steppe, while between the two the narrower and generally lower line is both "forested" and rich in minerals; and, as the piedmont valleys are also very fertile on both sides of this central part of the range, this section of it has become very important, and the continental frontier has been moved eastwards to include the whole geographical unit of the Government of Perm. The natural depression of the Ufa valley, a branch of which forms the southern frontier of this section, gives a line of least resistance for the railway from Ufa to Chelyabinsk.

Young Folded Mountains.

The total area occupied by the Alps, Carpathians, and Pyrenees is scarcely greater than that of the Scandinavian Highlands alone ; but, instead of being a lonely block, this Mediterranean system is essentially part of the great line of young folded mountains which stretches from west to east of the Old World, and played such an important part in the early distribution and specialisation of Man. Its influence has, however, been very different at different parts of the line ; for instance, within the nominal frontier of Europe the two terminal sections are widely different from the Alps.

Pyrenees and Caucasus.

The essential difference can be almost summed up in the statement that the control exercised by the Pyrenees and the Caucasus is specifically of a sierra type. Both are markedly straight, adhering closely to the normal east-and-west "tetrahedral" line. Both have a narrow crystalline axis which causes them to maintain a great average height, the Roncesvalles Pass being about 4000 feet and the Col de la Perche well over 5000, while the Dariel is nearly 8000, and the Marmison—between the headwaters of the important Rion and Terek basins—over 9000 ; and in each case the approach is complicated by the fact that on the gentler slope some of the highest summits stand well out from the main axis of the range, *e.g.* the extinct volcanoes of Elbruz and Kasbek on the north of the Caucasus, and Perdu and Maladetta (Néthou) on the south of the Pyrenees. In each case, too, more or less transverse spurs are so developed as to give a series of *culs de sac* of the "glacier-cut cauldron" type which is called a *cirque* ; and in the Pyrenean cirques the Christians held out against the Moslems in just the same way as, though with more success than, the Moslems held out against the Christians in the Caucasian cirques. To-day the Caucasus area contains representatives of very nearly every race and every language in Eurasia, and Andorra remains an independent republic in the Pyrenees.

Both systems agree, too, in the historic accident of having been truncated so abruptly that even round their ends access is far from easy, though the line from Derbent to Baku has an easier route across the Apsheron peninsula than the western line has from Ekatorinodar to Novorossisk, as that from Perpignan to Barcelona *via* the Col de Perthus (800 feet) has an easier route than that from Bayonne to Pamplona. Catalan speech is almost pure Provençal, and the modern industries of Barcelona are largely Provençal in origin as well as in character.

Sierra Control.

Further, the two systems agree even in their influence on the longitudinal movements of population ; for the easier access round the east end, which is partly due to the fact that both dissipate their energies eastward in developing width—in a double line—instead of concentrating them on a single upward growth, led to the Pre-Roman and Pre-Russian populations moving westward for safety. This westward movement took them into a land of so much heavier rainfall that the soil on the southern exposure in the lee of the range is enormously productive and largely covered with forest. Thus, the western end of the Pyrenees has an "Atlantic" rainfall of 5 feet, while the eastern end has a "Mediterranean" fall of scarcely twice 5 inches. This is exactly paralleled in the Caucasus, but the forest growth is even denser, being almost jungle, partly because of the better shelter in the lee of the higher range, and partly because of the greater abundance of underground water.

This, indeed, involves one of the few differences between the two systems. Both are curiously devoid of the lakes which are so typical of glaciated areas, and are such a protection from floods on the lower land ; but, while the limestone in the Caucasus absorbs the precipitation and passes it on so evenly that not only is the range—so far as the limestones extend—forested to the very top, but also waterfalls are practically unknown, in the case of the Pyrenees the upper streams become so much involved in the longitudinal folds of the range that they can only escape at rare intervals, and then in the form of a cataract. This flows generally over the edge of a cirque, as at Gavarnie, where there is a fall of 1515 feet. *Pyrenees v. Caucasus.*

The total result is that—in spite of the typical sierra narrowness of the ranges,—in spite of the high snow-line even on the northern slope (about 9000 feet),—in spite of the smallness of the glaciers, all the 900 in the Caucasus not having a larger total area than the Jostedalsbrae alone,—in spite of the fact than the Segre valley leads directly up to the Col de la Perche as that of the Terek does to the Dariel pass,—in spite of the fact that in other parts of the world railways use passes a mile higher than the Dariel and nearly two miles higher than the Col de la Perche—no railway till quite recently had been built across either range. *Cross Communication.*

The old connection between the Pyrenees and the Caucasus has been severed so sharply and in so many places that the complementary areas of summer-rain and summer-drought in Europe have always had more or less easy intercourse, such as is most effective in the development of civilisation ; and both the gaps in, and the varied course of, the connecting uplift are due to the same cause—the superior toughness of the older foldings. These tough old blocks are really just the roots of the old mountain system ; and the pressure from the south which forced up the flexible young folds was never great enough to overcome the resistance of the older rock to the north. Thus, the abrupt truncation of the Pyrenees shows that the range once extended eastward ; but the tough, massive block of the "Cevennes" plateau kept it so far to the south that the eastward extension was involved in the subsidence *Fold Gaps.*

of the western basin of the Mediterranean, and thus the Lower
Rhone valley became the chief link between central and southern
Europe.

Alpine Line. To the east of the Cevennes plateau the absence of resistant
rock allowed the young Alpine folds to make a marked bend northwards; but this was cut short by the tough "roots" of the Vosges
and Black Forest blocks, and the Alpine extension was forced eastward to the south of them.   Once past this obstacle, another northward bend was inevitable under the constant pressure from the
south, to be again cut short by the Bohemian plateau, which also
forms part of these Variscan fragments, as they are called.   Still the
field was not clear, for the low platform of western Russia belongs
to the same resistant series, and obstructs rather than guides the
Alpine development, so that the Carpathian extension was forced to
bend southward round the western scarp of the platform; and a
southward course was then maintained right up to the old block of
which the Rhodope mountains are the chief relic.   This again
involved the eastward bend of the Balkans, which were abruptly cut
short by the subsidence of the Black Sea, as the Pyrenees were by
that of the western Mediterranean.

Alpine Loops. Along the western edge of this "Rhodope" block, as along the
eastern edge of the old Iberian meseta, the Alpine energy was able
to escape; and the Nevada-Atlas remains of this movement are
looped up to the Alpine centre *via* the Balearic islands and the very
young Apennines, as the Dinaric-Pindus remains of it are looped up
via Crete and Cyprus and the Taurus to the Caucasus terminus.

Crustal Segments. Where the earth's solid crust is formed of angular segments
with great difference of level, as where the Calabrian and Tunisian
upfolds converge on the abysses of the western and eastern basins
of the Mediterranean, or where the Balkan and Anatolian segments
converge between the abysses of the eastern basin of the Mediterranean and the Black Sea, there conditions are found favourable to
the manifestation of volcanic and seismic phenomena.

Alpine Gaps. To the west of the Black Sea subsidence, as of the western basin
of the Mediterranean, there is what may be called a reactionary
westward loop of the main Alpine west-to-east line; and at the
critical point in the course, in each case, the loop was strained to
breaking-point.   Through the one gap the Danube gave a second
great link between Southern and Central Europe, and through the
other the Straits of Gibraltar gave Southern Europe access to the
Atlantic.

Alps Proper. A short survey of the general line of the Alpine uplift suggests,
then, that the widest development of the system will be found where
the tough old blocks lie farthest north, and that within this wider
area, *i.e.* the Alps proper, the folds will have a short northward and
then a long eastward lie.   Further, between the folds there are

likely to be deep longitudinal valleys, which should form the main channels of the hydrographic system; and where the back-pressure of the old rock to the eastward is felt, *i.e.* in the eastern half of the Alps, there is likely to be such dislocation of strata that "faults" may be more conspicuous than folds.

Captain H. V. Knox has illustrated very simply the relation of **Fold v.** the Alps to the old blocks on the west and north. On a table **Block.** covered by a thick cloth lay two books in the relative positions shown in the accompanying Figure: "A" to represent the Cevennes and "B" the Bavaro-Bohemian block. Place the hands flat on the cloth at C, and push the cloth towards D; it will at once ruck up into folds which are essentially similar to those of the Alps.

These folds in the case of **Internal** the Alps are of different types of **Divisions.** rock, the two inner folds being of crystalline rock and the two outer being of sedimentary rock. The two lines of crystalline rock are separated by a belt of mixed rock representing the older divisions of geological time known as the Age of Fishes and the Age of Reptiles; and farther to the west and north the rock is Mesozoic and Tertiary, representative of the Age of Reptiles and the Age of Mammals. We generally divide the surface of Switzerland, therefore, into four belts running approximately S.W.–N.E., *i.e.* between Lake Geneva and Lake Constance, and separating typically Romance and Teutonic peoples with typically Roman Catholic and Protestant creeds. The southernmost belt is a double band of crystalline rock; to the north and west of this comes a belt mainly of limestone; this is followed by the sandstone plateau of the Aar basin, which rises to the limestone ridges and valleys of the Jura.

In the inner crystalline belt we see the short northward lie in **Inner** the Cottian and Graian Alps, and the long eastward lie in the **Crystal-** Graian, Pennine, and Lepontine Alps; and the double-headed Dora **line Belt.** Riparia separates the Cottian and Graian, serving the one by the Genèvre Pass and the other by the Mont Cenis, as the double-headed Dora Baltea separates the Graian from the Pennine, serving the one by the Little St. Bernard Pass and the other by the Great St. Bernard, and as the double-headed Toce-Ticino separates the Pennine from the Lepontine, serving the one by the Simplon and the other by the St. Gothard. One of the trifles which are often so significant, because at first sight so immaterial, suggests a comment on the value of this double-headedness; the junction of the two St. Bernard routes on the Italian side seemed to the Romans so

important that they called their military depot at that point *Augusta*
—the modern Aosta.

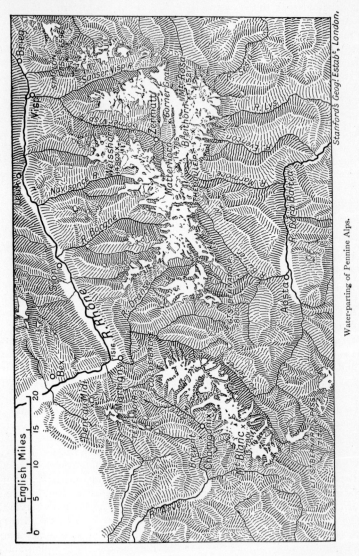

Outer Crystal-line Belt. In the outer crystalline belt we see the short northward lie in the Pelvoux and Mont Blanc masses, and the long eastward lie in the Bernese Oberland (crystalline only *east* of the Gemmi Pass) and the Alps of Glarus ; and the double-headed Isère separates the

Dauphine Alps from those of Savoy, the so-called "Mont Cenis" tunnel tapping its Arc tributary by burrowing under the Col de Frejus, while the sedimentary rocks along the whole northern face of the eastward lie have been eaten away to form the great longitudinal valley that is occupied up to the Furka-Pass divide by the Isère and the Upper Rhone, and down from the Furka by the Vorder Rhine and the Inn.   On the sandstone plateau of the Aar basin glacial activity has left such typical morainic lakes as those of Geneva and Lucerne at the outer foot of the crystalline belt, and those of Neuchâtel and Biel at the inner foot of the limestone Jura.

The conditions emphasised so far are essentially those peculiar **Eastern** to the Western or Franco-Italian Alps and the Central or Italo-Swiss **Alps.** Alps; and one fundamental distinction between these and the Eastern or Austro-Italian Alps is found in the fact that in the western and central sections there is really only one ridge to be crossed between the northern and southern plains, while in the eastern sections there are really three ridges, though the central one is of predominant difficulty.   It is natural, therefore, that the eastern rivers should more often rise in glacial lakes, as in the case of the Inn and the Adda, while the western rivers should more often flow directly from the glaciers.   Further, where maximum exposure to the north is combined with maximum access—up the great longitudinal valley—for the west winds, there we should find the greatest glaciation ; and it is only natural, therefore, that all the longest glaciers (Great Aletsch, the Unter-Aar, and the Fiescher) should be in the Bernese Oberland.

Now, though it is contrary to nature that a crystalline crest **Passes** should be easily worn down,—as witness the great snow-dome of Mont Blanc, the buttressed wall of Monte Rosa, the square pyramid of the Matterhorn, the triangular pyramid of the Weisshorn,—the normal activity of glaciers intermediate in character between the dry rigidity of the tropics and the constant fluidity of the Polar regions, can easily pare away the sides of a crystalline range, especially towards its ends.   And it was the thinness of the ends of the inner crystalline range that favoured the cutting of tunnels under the Simplon and the St. Gothard to replace the carriage roads which go over them at heights of just under 6600 feet and just over 6900. The Simplon tunnel, though the longest (over 12 miles), has the easiest gradient ; but the route in olden days involved too great a detour between North and South, and was therefore less used than the St. Gothard and the Brenner routes, which—like the Mont Cenis and Great St. Bernard—have been in constant use for 2000 years.   The most significant comment on the character of a transverse section of the Simplon route and on the imperative necessity of avoiding a detour is offered, perhaps, by the fact that the success of the Simplon tunnel has absolutely necessitated its practical continuation (in the Lötschberg tunnel, 9 miles), so as to shorten the route between London and Genoa by three hours.

Hanging Valleys.   Another effect of the old glaciation, almost equally important in facilitating communication, is the arrangement of all the typically U-shaped valleys in steps with broad floors. In the side valleys

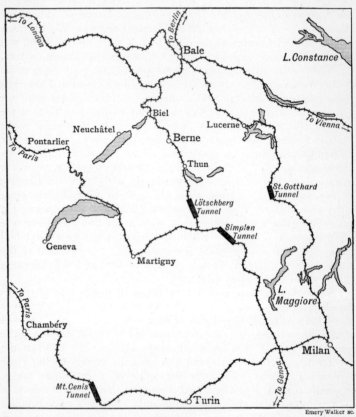

Swiss tunnels.

these steps down from the overhanging lip of the valley are usually marked by magnificent waterfalls, which in modern times are a great source of " power "; and above the lip is a bench or platform on which fine glacial silt makes a peculiarly fertile soil easily irrigated from the still existing glaciers. This is the real alp, where the altitude forbids any vegetation except of a lowly kind, but makes this—on the " loess "—of the finest possible character as food for cows. Similar alp pastures occur on the steps in the main valley, thus minimising or localising the difficulties of the ascent,

and providing natural facilities for the presence of houses and
supplies of food.

The origin of these discordances, or steps, is fully dealt with in **Protection**
Professor Garwood's article on the Protective Action of Ice ;[1] but **of Ice.**
their ultimate economic importance is connected with the fact that
they represent an old overflow of ice from an intermont basin or
valley, in the course of which the sides of the basin or valley were
so cut down that steps on opposite sides of the range were frequently
joined by a double glacier-cut gateway or pass.

The St. Gothard focus deserves a little more attention because **St.**
of its relation to the whole river-system. The chief rivers of the **Gothard.**
area follow the west-and-east valleys, but their régime has enabled

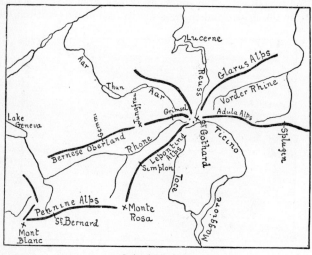

Swiss river-system.

them to cut back their heads to such an extent that the Rhone and
the Rhine have now reached opposite sides of the St. Gothard mass.
At the same time rivers are naturally thrown off northward and
southward from the main east-and-west axis of the system, *e.g.* the
Ticino and Reuss ; and this tendency affects even the great
longitudinal rivers directly they come between strata of different
resistance, so that the crystalline mass of Mont Blanc diverts the
Rhone across the softer limestone into Lake Geneva, as the Rhine
crosses it into Lake Constance.

The four rivers in question have now cut back their valleys to
the common centre of the St. Gothard, which has much the
heaviest rainfall in Switzerland (over 80 inches). The economic
importance of this is obvious ; and its political importance may be

[1] Cf. *R.G.S. Journal*, September 1910.

gauged from the choice of Andermatt, at the crossing of the Furka and St. Gothard roads, for a divisional head-quarters of the Swiss army.

Jura.

With increase of distance from the source of pressure in the south-east there is a decrease of both energy and complexity ; and in the extreme north-west the Jura present a profound simplicity, being just a score of parallel folds, every upfold being a ridge and every downfold a valley. This has materially hampered transverse traffic, though the elevation nowhere reaches 6000 feet ; and there is still need of some miles of tunnelling to "join up" the shortest route between Calais and the Lötschberg, and avoid the detour through the Weissenstein tunnel.

Eastern Alps.

A great contrast to the simplicity of this Franco-Swiss section is offered by the Austro-Italian Alps to eastward of the great transverse

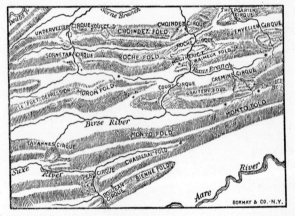

Typical piece of Jura.

depression marked by the middle courses of the Inn and the Adige, linked by the Brenner Pass (4470 feet). The feature-lines still run roughly east and west ; the predominant line is still crystalline ; and it is still flanked by a longitudinal, river-threaded depression. But the energy, instead of being concentrated, is dissipated in a fan-like expansion which is more pronounced than even that of the eastern Pyrenees and eastern Caucasus, and which more than doubles the breadth of the effective barrier ; this is naturally accompanied by such a decrease in height that even the crystalline High Tauern scarcely reaches 12,500 in the Gross Glockner ; and the medley of faults and fractures has greatly complicated the river-system, as the number of comparatively small peaks complicates the foregrounds in the ordinary summit views.

On the other hand, physical and climatic conditions are not un-

favourable to movement whether human or atmospheric (cf. p. 57). **The Brenner.**
The furrow along the northern foot of the crystalline axis gives at
least 250 miles of comparatively easy railway route between the
Arlberg Tunnel and the Schober ; the somewhat similar " Puster
Dal-Drave-Mur" furrow to the south of the Tauern axis gives
200 miles of good rail up to the Semmering, getting the through
traffic from Aalberg to Vienna by the easy route round the Eisenerz
("Iron-ore") Alps to the great steel-working junction of Leoben.
Both these routes are, of course, tapped by the great transverse
route through the Brenner, which owes much of its supreme importance to its character as a "saddle,"—bridging the broad double
line of the central Alps, and so giving a single pass across a two-
fold barrier,—but part of its importance to climatic causes.　It is so
low and so far from the Atlantic, and so much cut off from the wet
winds by the loftiest region of the central Alps, the Bernina and
Ortler groups, that the precipitation is exceptionally light, with
consequently a relative freedom from snow impediments and
avalanche dangers.　Its importance may be gauged from the
number of well-known passes which tap it, *e.g.* the Julier and Albula,
the Maloja and Bernina, the Stelvio and the Reschen-Scheideyck,
all carrying carriage roads.

Incidentally, too, the great valley has acquired importance from
the ease with which it gives access to some of the most varied and
beautiful types of Alpine scenery, *e.g.* bringing the wide lake-dotted
floor of the Engadine into close relation with the atmospheric
colour of the Dolomite pinnacles, the magnesian limestone having
a typically pearly or vitreous lustre with under-colours of red, brown,
green, grey, and even black, and weathering differentially into most
fantastic forms.　The effect is accentuated by the differential
fertility of the soft marl that is found alongside the hard dolomite.

The Carpathians repeat some of the typical phenomena of the **Car-**
Alps, but generally on a much smaller scale.　For instance, the **pathians**
main crystalline axis is discontinuous, appearing in the Little
Carpathians, Tatra, Central Carpathians, and Transylvanian Alps,
while the continuous outer sedimentary folds resemble those of the
Jura, and the inner belt is largely volcanic.　This last is the one
point on which the Carpathians repeat Alpine features on a larger
scale, for the volcanic belt which surrounds the south of the twin
crystalline ranges of the Tatra, and accounts for the mineral wealth
of the Gran basin, is much more extensive than that which skirts the
south of the Venetian Alps, where the intrusion of the volcanic is
into sedimentary rock, and so naturally does not lead to any great
mineral wealth.

The chief points in which the Carpathians differ from the Alps **Alps *v.***
are three in number.　In the first place, their greatest width **Car-**
corresponds with their greatest height, the High Tatra reaching **pathians**

nearly 9000 feet in Franz Josef, and the Transylvanian Alps reaching well over 8000 in Bucsecs, Mandra, and Negoi. Again, unlike the rest of this Alpine system, on both sides and in all directions they abut more or less immediately on fertile lowlands, so that the position and height and climate of any passes became of great importance in very early times. Above all, owing to their relative lowness and to their distance from the Atlantic, they lack the magnificent scenery which is typically connected with glaciation, huge snow-fields and glaciers, bold peaks and high waterfalls being alike absent, while the typical Alpine lakes are replaced by the water-filled "cups" of the Tatra granite. Only in the beauty of the volcanic Matra group and in the grandeur of the granite Tatra can the Carpathians at all rival the Alps.

Passes. The outer sedimentary zone, which forms the natural frontier of Hungary, though essentially continuous, throws off so many rivers in opposite directions to the lowland on each side that the range is passable at almost every point where two of these rivers diverge from the same part of the divide, *e.g.* the Gran and Poprad, the Vecsa and Opor, (*i.e.* practically the Vereczke Pass or "Magyar Gate"), the Theiss and Pruth (the Körös-mezo or "Tatar Gate"), and the Szamos and Goldene-Bistritz. In the extreme north-west the famous Jablunka ("Apple Tree") Pass leads down the Olsa valley to the Oder, as in the extreme south-east the Tömös Pass leads down the Prahova valley, and the Roteturm ("Red Tower") leads down the Aluta valley, to the Danube. Eastward from the "Apple Tree" Pass the climate of the sedimentary zone becomes more and more favourable to tree-growth. The monotonous sandstone of the East Beskids is redeemed by a covering of extensive forest; and it merges in the Carpathian Forest, the north-western buttress of Bukowina (Beech-Land), where the beech is the typical tree up to a height of 4000 feet.

The Plains. The rest of the continent may be roughly described as consisting of 2,000,000 square miles of plain, with great variety of soil and considerable variety of climate. The centre and eastern areas of the "plain" are so level that it is possible to travel by rail from Cologne to the Urals without going through a single tunnel; and in the more backward eastern parts this has given exceptional value to the rivers for navigation in the summer and sledge-transport in the winter. The western half is undulating, but the higher standard of civilisation has included extraordinary progress in the art of tunnelling.

There are areas along the North Sea and the Caspian which are below sea-level; but in the one case they have been reclaimed by the energy of the Dutch, and are protected by granite dykes where the natural sand-dunes of the low and windy coast are not continuous, while in the other they are due to the natural sinking of the Caspian.

The most valuable units are the Magyar Alfold, which was a sea in such recent ages that Transylvania is still rich in sea-flora, and small areas drained by man, such as the bed of Lake Copais and much of Italy. The draining of the Pripet-Beresina marshes in Russia, when completed, will add fully 20,000 square miles of valuable agricultural land and greatly facilitate traffic, though it must decrease the strategic value of this "rampart of White Russia."

The most important feature in the distribution of this vast area of plain is that its relation to the highlands has in no way deprived it of its essential character as a piece of Atlantic hinterland. For the distribution of the highlands puts no serious obstacle to access— climatic and commercial—to and from the great ocean, while the character of the highlands minimises the obstacle to communication between the northern and southern units of the continent. *Plain v. Highlands.*

At the same time the intervening nucleus of ancient rock has special economic importance because of its characteristic richness in deposits of metal, particularly round the edge, and because of its equally characteristic relation to beds of coal in the younger strata that flank it ; and, of course, where the metal and the fuel are adjacent, as at Creusot and Liège, great metallurgical centres were almost bound to spring up.

Three of the geological factors involved have a geographical significance. The scarp, as the actual line of cleavage, marks the line of maximum disturbance ; and such disturbance has a definite relation to the distribution of mineral wealth and to the development of natural depressions such as offer "lines of least resistance" for human movement, *e.g.* the Sambre-Maas valley. Moreover, a normal scarp gives, so to say, a section which betrays the contents of the whole block. *Line of Maximum Disturbance.*

But these old blocks are themselves only fragments of a great mountain system which has been weathered down in the course of ages into a peneplain ; and in this process any residual products must include the heaviest elements in the original mass, *i.e.* the metals. These have not only survived because most difficult to transport, but they have also been concentrated ; and they are naturally most abundant in the outlying parts of the existing core. Thus, iron and lead, copper and zinc, are found in the scarp above the Sambre-Maas gorge. *Residual Falls.*

Still more important is the fact that nearly all these deposits of metal are the result of igneous or aqueous activity, the scattered atoms having been first fused or dissolved at considerable depths, then transported to levels of lower temperature and lower pressure nearer the surface, and eventually deposited in cavities at no very great depth below that surface, because such cavities can exist only where there is no very great pressure. It is only by a strong, local, exceptional agent, *e.g.* working chemically by heat and mechanically *Subterranean Risings.*

by movement, that the earth's crust could have been, and still can be, drained of the metals that form such a tiny portion of it ; for— apart from aluminium, which forms about 8 p.c. of the crust, and iron, which forms about 4 p.c.—no other metal seems to form more than 0.07 p.c. (manganese).

Solvent Power. Most of the metal deposits of Europe have been precipitated from aqueous solutions ; and—however strictly meteoric water may be distinguished in theory from magmatic water—it is certain that the deep waters get some of their solvent power from carbonic acid, and that this must have been communicated to the superficial waters—and then passed on by them—from the decayed vegetation through which they percolated. Moreover, it is obvious that the mechanical erosion and the chemical corrosion of subterranean water depend largely on the pressure and the temperature, *i.e.* ultimately on the depth ; and that, as the water cools and so loses its power to solve, it loses also its power to rise, to erode, and to carry. Consequently, as the hot spring rises by a "line of least resistance," *e.g.* a fault fissure — such as is quite obvious at Aix-la-Chapelle, where the "waters" (Aix = *aquæ*) still have a temperature of from 110° F. to 136° F.—approach to the surface must involve first mineralisation of the transported elements and then deposition of them.

Deposition. Where this final part of the journey is through porous rock, *e.g.* the sandstone between Aix and Bonn, the metal may be distributed all through the strata ; where it is through very soluble rock, *e.g.* the limestone between Aix and Liège, it may be massed in a "cave" dissolved in the rock. But the essential facts are that heat and pressure favour solution, while decrease of either— still more of both—favours precipitation. The peneplain is the base of the old mass ; and the scarp not only gives a section of the contents, but is also the place where we expect to find both the residual metals from the higher levels of that old mass and the fault fissures which give the easiest line of exit for the subterranean waterways.

CHAPTER V

RELIEF CONTROL

(1) *Of Land Communications.*

THE distribution of the chief features of relief is as favourable to communication by land, both directly and indirectly, as to communication by sea. The indirect influence is based mainly on the concentration of great variety of relief within small area, and the consequent variety of economic development. For each natural unit of relief has its own natural product—plant, and beast, and man; and, in each, life has depended on response to the prevailing control. *Indirect Influence.*

In the case of man, necessaries of sustenance in any of these areas have involved certain occupations, *e.g.* pastoral, involving daily care of animals that must be milked at regular times, or agricultural, in which there may be a rush of work followed by a spell of holiday. Such occupations perpetuated through generations develop certain fixed habits, which crystallise into definite characteristics, *e.g.* a power of continuous application or a gift for almost superhuman effort on an emergency; and these express themselves in social and political institutions, as when mere babes in Cornwall show, in their play, a power of controlling a gutter-torrent which only grows out of centuries of mining experience, or when constitutional government seems everywhere to have grown out of the domestic organisation of a fishing race. Cf. p. 12. *Occupational Control.*

The close proximity of different economic types, then, must have led in very early times to constant intercourse, to exchange of products (barter) and ideas, and so to the development of facilities for such exchange. And the position has been emphasised by the fact that the whole continent may be roughly divided into two supplementary areas, one of summer-rain and the other of summer-drought, with corresponding needs and products. *Supplementary Areas and Types.*

The direct influence of the relief control is also best seen in a comparison of the two areas, for the area of summer-rain includes practically the whole plain of Europe, while that of summer-drought consists largely of mountainous peninsulas. *Direct Influence.*

39

Great Plain

The essential significance of the great east and west plain is implied in the statement, that it is possible to travel by rail from the extreme south-west of France, *via* Paris and Berlin, to the extreme north-east of Russia without going through a single tunnel and without ever being 600 feet above the sea.   And it is precisely

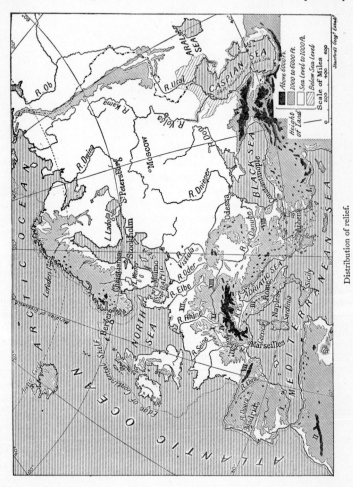

Distribution of relief.

this fundamental fact that makes comparisons between Central Europe and England often so absurd.   For instance, the nationalisation and reconstruction of our canal system have been strongly recommended to the English public by utterly misleading statistics drawn from Holland and Germany.   The *Daily Chronicle* pointed out that the Aire and Calder Canal " could be made fit for all necessary traffic at a cost of £1,000,000 per 100 miles"; and statistics were quoted from the canal traffic between Berlin and Hamburg. But the Aire and Calder Canal is the levelest canal in England, and the access to fuel and water make it the cheapest to work; and, while there are only 3 locks in the 230 miles between Berlin and Hamburg, the average in England is 1 lock for every 2100 yards.

From the Franco-Spanish frontier at Hendaye, where the **East-and-** Spanish 66-inch gauge stops, a uniform 56½-inch gauge con- **West** tinues as far as Warsaw, where the Russian 60-inch gauge begins; **Railways.** and the line of through communication between, *e.g.* Bordeaux and Warsaw, offers a significant comment on the relief and on its relations to historic movements of people. By the gap of Charente and the gap of Poitou, along the northern foot of the Ardennes and of the Westphalian Highlands, crossing the Seine at the Isle of Paris and the Elbe at the Isle of Magdeburg, it follows the line of least resistance which, just because it is that, is marked by a series of great towns. Thus the line of least resistance comes to be the line of most utility.

Every one of the important rivers crossed on this route is **Rivers of** navigable so far as relief is concerned. Thus, the Loire is naturally **Plain.** navigable far above Orleans, though its variation in volume, and the power of the flood from the crystalline upper part of the basin to choke up the lower course by debris torn from the Tertiary strata in its middle course, have forced regular navigation on to lateral canals; the Seine has a minimum depth of 10 feet up to Paris, 220 miles from the English Channel; ocean steamers ply regularly to the great junction of Cologne; the Weser is navigable to above the Westphalian Gate, near Minden; and all the other rivers crossed are navigable to above the German frontier. The alternative route through Brussels and Hanover is based on historic rather than physical considerations, but its ease may be gauged from the route of the great east-and-west canal system of Germany.

The great foci of this west-and-east belt of rail are Paris, Berlin, **Cross** and Warsaw; and it is important to notice their relation respectively **Distances.** to the shortest distances across the continent from north to south. Obviously, these cross routes join the Baltic to the Black Sea and the Adriatic, and the North Sea to the Adriatic and the Lion-Genoa Gulf. And political considerations encourage duplicate routes. Thus, the direct distance from Odessa to Danzig is practically the same (750 miles) as to Riga; but the Dniester valley leads to a route that is largely Teutonic, while the Bug valley gives easier gradients through one that is wholly Slav. Again, the direct distance from Stettin to Trieste is only 550 miles, while that from Lubeck to Venice is 650; but the detours necessary on the more easterly route make both routes actually the same distance (850), and the gradients from the Oder to the Danube by the Moravian Gate are easier—and therefore strategically more dangerous—than those by the shorter Saxon Gate route, and the Brenner Pass was really easier than the Semmering. From the Narrow Seas the competition, both political and economic, is still more severe; and this gives special advantage to the route between Calais and Marseilles *via* the Rhone valley, which is both the shortest (not much more than 700 miles of rail) and all French. On the other hand, the fact that Antwerp can approach the St. Gothard tunnel best *via* the

Simple relief of France.

Rhine valley minimises the 100 and odd miles of extra rail from Hamburg on the journey to Genoa, making Genoa almost an outpost of Frankfort-on-Main.

Cross Routes. The chief cross routes, except the low 300-mile railway between Bordeaux and Cette, utilise the same lines of least resistance. The Orient express route to Constantinople threads the middle basins of both Rhine and Danube, again making Frankfort important. In the west the parallel "Suez" route threads the Seine and the Upper Rhone basins. To the east parallel routes join Hamburg to Odessa by the Oder valley outside the Carpathians, *via*

Berlin, Breslau, and Cracow, and Bremen to Constantinople by the Elbe valley inside the Carpathians, *via* Dresden, Vienna, and Belgrade.

Obviously, the shape of the continent makes the saving of distance by rail over that by sea so great towards the east, saving 4000 miles between Riga and Odessa, that even very inferior services by rail can still command the traffic ; but in the west the saving is comparatively so small that the service must be good to attract the traffic in anything except mails and passengers. As far as World traffic is concerned, this is emphasised by the high dues on the Suez Canal, which are calculated to be equivalent—for ordinary freight—to at least 1000 miles of detour ; and, on the other hand, uniformity of gauge has almost obviated break-of-bulk by rail, so that even in this respect sea-transport is losing its chief advantage for long-distance work. For instance, during mid-winter cauliflowers come into Covent Garden from Naples *without break-of-bulk*, the result being that they can be sold wholesale at about ten-pence per dozen ! *Rail v Sea.*

The position of inland waterways is little better, even in countries so favourable to inland navigation as France and Germany. For obviously the size of a lock varies with the water-supply, and the demands on the available amount are growing rapidly. In France, for instance, about 25 per cent of the total population is urban, and about 25 per cent of all the " power " used in mechanical industry is water-power. In Germany the urban population is nearly 30 per cent of the whole, and water-power is responsible for about 20 per cent of the total power. The demand for water is, therefore, increasing most in precisely those centres which the canals would feed. In other respects, too, canals are losing ground in the face of modern conditions and methods of carrying on trade. They are too cumbrous and immobile, especially in the matter of terminal accommodation ; it is difficult to maintain on them either speed or punctuality ; and the modern trader prefers a quick sale of small lots to the warehousing of a quantity for a considerable time. In this connection, it may be noted that in the United States by 1910 more than 2000 miles of the older canals had been actually abandoned. Cf. p. 212. *Canal Water Supply.*

Two qualifications must be added. Where relief, as in France, guarantees a reliable rainfall in the upper basins of rivers that are navigable for a large proportion of their total length, there canals may be most useful in joining the head-waters of such rivers. Thus the navigable Saône is joined to the Loire *via* St. Etienne and to the Yonne *via* Dijon ; France has over 5000 miles of navigable river thus joined by 2000 miles of canal. Similarly, the rivers of Germany supply fully 6000 miles of navigation, linked by about 1500 miles of canal. *Link Canals*

The other qualification is in regard to ship-canals, such as the

Ship Canals. Manchester and Kiel canals. Such canals are essentially short links of deep water, either joining two neighbouring seas or extending one sea inland. The Manchester Canal extends sea-traffic 35 miles inland and has a depth of 28 feet; the Kiel Canal crosses the 60 miles between the North Sea and the Baltic with a minimum depth of about 43 feet, saving two days on the sea-route between Kiel and Brünsbüttel.

Danube Route. These great thoroughfares illustrate the permanence of relief control, for they were the scenes of great movements of people in

The Kiel and Hanover Canals.

early historic ages, as they have been of rail and canal development in modern times. Apart from the evidence that prehistoric man had settled on the loess near Krems and on the Neusiedler See, the Danube was the most important of the early thoroughfares, because it essentially links Europe to Asia. Huns and Avars, Slavs and Magyars, followed it westward; Carlovingians and Bavarians, Crusaders and Habsburgs, followed it eastward. Indeed, the number of sanctuaries that line its Roman bank shows how important a route it was from the days when, like the Rhine, it formed part of the great Roman frontier against the Barbarians. The sites of Blenheim and Traunbruck, Wagram and Mohacs, give similar testimony. In fact, as was pointed out long ago, it was precisely the constant use of the valley as a line of passage that made it unsuitable for a political frontier ; so that, while its chief Alpine tributaries are peculiarly prominent as frontiers—*e.g.* the Iller between Würtemberg and Bavaria, the Inn between Bavaria and Austria, the Enns between Upper and Lower Austria, the Leitha between Lower Austria and Hungary, the Drave between Hungary and the Croatia-Slavonia region of Jugo-Slavia—the main stream makes a great central line of attraction to which human activities gravitate, in Hohenzollern and Würtemberg, Bavaria, Austria and Hungary ; and on it now stand no less than three political capitals.

The valley of the Rhine, before the river became the Roman **Rhine** frontier, had been a great funnel for Celtic and Teutonic move- **Route.** ments ; and the Romans, as Mackinder says, bequeathed to the French the theory that it was the natural frontier of France, and so laid the foundation of its political importance during the last 1000 years. That importance is largely summed up in the history of the strategic centres, *e.g.* Basel and Strasbourg, Mainz and Coblenz, which mark the essentially Roman or Franco-German part of the river. Charlemagne's choice of Aix-la-Chapelle as his great centre was almost a forecast of the series of battlefields that would mark the line of least resistance between the Latin West and Teutonic East below the northern foot of the Ardennes, and of the commercial struggles between Rotterdam and Antwerp for the hinterland of Cologne.

The Rhone valley was still more important in the early develop- **Rhone** ment of Europe ; and the Burgundy Gate played, in the earlier **Route.** struggles between France and Germany, the part played by the Lorraine Gate in modern times. On this the rivalry of Dijon and Arles, as the shape of the old Kingdom of Lothaire and Duchy of Burgundy, is a significant comment. And that the Ebro valley had a similar importance in Spain may be inferred from the fact that the river gave its name to the whole Iberian peninsula.

CHAPTER VI

RELIEF CONTROL

(2) *Of Distribution of Population.*

RELIEF control of human activities rests on the relation between the origin and the character of the relief. It is in the Danube valley that the earliest remains of Man in Central Europe have been found, and they were found in loess.

666.   The "Mark of the Beast" is a very good high land-mark and low water-mark in the development of life ; for the oldest forms of

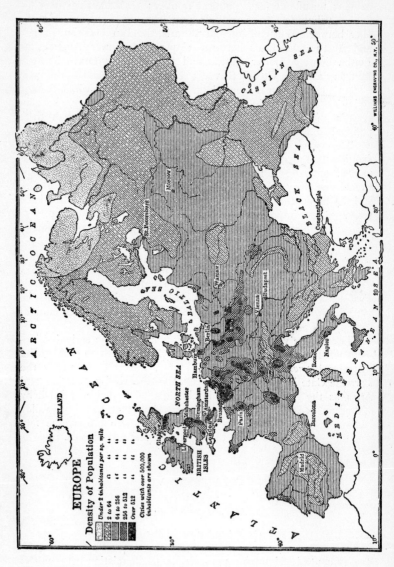

life seem to have been of marine origin and to have originated in depths less than about 666 feet, while the great development of land fauna has been confined to altitudes less than about 666 feet.

It at once becomes significant that three-quarters of the total area
of Europe may be classified as plain, and that even Supan estimated
the average elevation of the whole as under 1000 feet, while
Humboldt estimated it as only 675 feet. The climatic control implied
in this, we may discuss elsewhere (cf. ch. viii.); but the relief control
may be so far dissociated from the climatic control as to allow us
to trace a foundation for the relation, *e.g.* of the savage European
to mountain and plain, and of the civilised European to coal
and iron.

The general level of the continent being favourable for the **Early**
development of plant and beast life implied, considering the latitude, **Mammals.**
a minimum difficulty in Man's hunt for food; and this was further
facilitated by the fact that the glaciation of the area had decimated
the larger beasts, *i.e.* those usually most dangerous to Man. Under
favourable conditions, then, large beasts would have monopolised
the food supplies, but under unfavourable conditions they suffered
most; for a small diminution of supply pinched them soonest, and
their relatively small numbers—implying that they were unprolific
because voracious—minimised the chance of their occasional
progeny including any "freaks," whose modified structure would
enable them to survive under the changed conditions. Cf. p. 76.

Over this vast plain the soil is almost everywhere not of local **Soil.**
origin; it was brought to its present location by ice or rivers. The
maximum extension of the ice covered nearly all the great plain
except in France, and the debris carried by it was deposited in
various forms—*e.g.* sheets of clay, layers of sand, piles of gravel, the
heaviest material being deposited nearest to the centre from which
the ice-sheet radiated (cf. p. 3). The glacial clay is naturally
heavy and impervious, hard to cultivate and water-logged, and
produces little but humble peat-producing vegetation; so that areas
of this kind did not favour dense populations. The sand and gravel
are light and dry, but are neither rich in plant food nor tenacious
of water; so that hills of this coarse material would produce little
but conifers. But clay flats might lie in the lee of limestone hills,
from which the solvent lime might be torn by the ice itself or might
gravitate after ordinary weathering; and this at once would make
the clay fertile and porous. Or river-floods might spread rich and
easily worked alluvium over the clay flats, and the river-valley was
certain to attract an early population.

As the maximum effects of the glaciation were towards the **Nordic**
north-west, that area would be longest in becoming habitable— **Race-**
except so far as the land-waste encouraged a most prolific abundance **Home.**
of food-fishes, as illustrated by the superabundance of "fish"
remains in the kitchen-middens, *e.g.* of Denmark; and, on the other
hand, a glance at a geological map will show how the distribution
of "limestone" ridges and rims, *e.g.* in Denmark, Scania, and

Central Europe, was bound to quicken human settlement below and within them, and how the variety of rock generally was bound to yield a strong blended soil to the various lowlands and basins. On the more fertile parts of this central plain, especially on the patches of loess (cf. p. 24), the Nordic race attained its essential character ; and, as it developed and became largely urban in habit, the less fertile and more intractable areas were taken in hand, *e.g.* marshes drained and dense clay rendered pervious by lime and stable manure and other solvents, until the whole plain has been made fertile artificially.

South of the young Alpine system, where the Mediterranean race

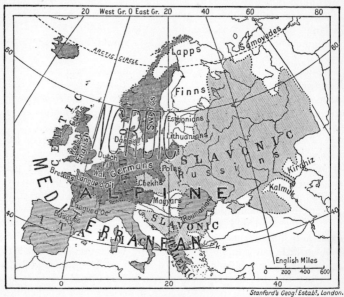

Racial Europe.

Stanford's Geog! Estab!. London.

Mediterranean Race-Home. found its area of characterisation, conditions were very different. The absence of glaciation and the smallness of the river-basins make the soil essentially residual and local ; the variety of rock and the widespread presence of limestone guaranteed fertility, while heavy weathering guaranteed depth. This was increased by the amount of alluvium, for the long dry summer involves heavy weathering, and so prepares abundance of loose material for the autumn floods to transport down the yellow Tiber and many another river. Indeed, when Olympia was unearthed, at the expense of the German Government, thirty years ago, it was found to have been buried, not under a vast volcanic outflow, but under terraces of river-borne mud ! Again, the Alpine uplift guaranteed both shelter and unfailing supplies of water. These conditions were very favourable to early Man, and suited his primitive implements; but they had their drawbacks. The local soil has not the " strength " of the intractable glacial blend—so that it wears out more quickly; and the local race has not the Nordic tolerance of cold and relative immunity from lung disease. If the Mediterranean race spread to higher latitudes, therefore, it could only be by creeping along the mild coast-lands of the Atlantic; and the progressive deterioration of the local soil would mean a relative, if not an actual, decrease in the economic importance of the area. Such deterioration, too, if and when matured, might be reflected in the condition of the cultivators themselves.

Between the Nordic plain and the Mediterranean peninsulas lies the zone of ancient crystalline cores on which the Alpine Round-heads found a congenial home. These crystalline rocks are rich in metals, but naturally poor in organic materials; and their wealth of metal occurs along the fractured scarps rather than on the core, *i.e.* along the "shores" of the primary axial peninsula of Europe, brought there by hot springs in working their way out from great depths by lines of least resistance. The heat to which these springs owe their actual existence, enables them also to transport many minerals which would be quite insoluble in cold water; but, as we have seen, any lowering of temperature tends to arrest the ascending current and destroy its chemical or corrosive power. Such lowering of temperature may be found in a subterranean fissure or cave; it must be found near the surface of the earth and on approach to the outside air. In either case precipitation begins, and the mineral is deposited *in loco* (cf. pp. 37, 38). *Alpine Race-Area.*

Further, when such a mineral-filled fissure is actually exposed on the scarp of a fractured block, *i.e.* a line where resistance has obviously been strained to breaking point, differential weathering will almost certainly follow, with the result that the lode will show as a ridge or a trough. In other words, the mineral is not only most abundant where it is most accessible, but also is so situated as naturally to attract attention. Thus, few useful metals are found even in the crystalline part of the Young Folded Mountains, for their thinness and their physical history are not favourable; but nearly all the useful metals are found in the rims of the old blocks, especially in Central Europe. For instance, the scarp of the meseta yields mercury near Almaden, lead near Linares, copper at Rio Tinto, tin in Galicia, and zinc in the Basque Provinces; lead and copper occur in Brittany and round the central plateau in France; zinc, lead, and tin are found on the north-west and the north-east of the Variscan fragments. *Location of Minerals*

Geologically nearest to these old metalliferous rocks in time and place are the old sedimentary rocks that contain salt and coal, and *Coal and Salt.*

E

iron is often associated with the coal.   Salt is worked in Catalonia, near Nancy, at Stassfurt and Spessart, at Wieliczka and Salzburg— in each case in the "lee" of Variscan fragments.   The coal has similar associations, *e.g.* in the Asturias, in the Upper Loire basin, in the valleys of the Meuse and Ruhr, on both sides of the Erz and of the Riesengebirge, and along the eastern edge of the Russian platform (cf. p. 28).   And in each case valuable deposits of iron were within easy access of the coal.

Continu-ity of Control.   Special importance should be found to attach to areas where tongues of the fertile plain intrude into the carboniferous basins that flank the metal-bearing fragments, *e.g.* in Rhine-land ; and the working of the coal and the subsequent industrial developments could not cause in such old agricultural areas the dislocation of population and the transference of political power that were associ-ated with the Industrial Revolution in England.   Such conditions supply the best possible guarantee of stability and prosperity to any new industry naturally evolved on the spot and gradually replacing the old one.   The modern supremacy of Birmingham and Sheffield in the hardware industry is due to somewhat similar conditions of Geographical momentum, except that in their case the iron industry was present in very early days.

Density of Popula-tion.   Marshy lowlands in the latitude of the North European plain must naturally be forested—a condition adverse to density of population, though probably favourable to the development of fine physique in the individual (cf. p. 10); and primitive Man in temperate forests supported life by hunting and fishing—occupations adverse to density of population.   Practically, therefore, relief control was more adverse to dense population in Cis-Alpine Europe than in the Mediterranean basin ; and it was equally adverse to movements of population except where climatic control was responsible for vast grass-lands in the eastern parts of the plain, or along the bridge of old blocks between the grass-land and the Alpine wall.   At the same time, these conditions, so adverse to early Man, are precisely those which have now given Cis-Alpine Europe supremacy over Southern Europe.

CHAPTER VII

CLIMATE

EUROPE occupies an essentially transitional position—between the vastest land mass in the World and one of the largest oceans, and between the Trades and the Anti-Trades. This, as we have noticed (cf. p. 3), was one of the great features of the area that were favourable to the progress of early Man; and its influence is essentially climatic. No equal area in similar latitudes elsewhere on the face of the globe has such an equable climate, or is so markedly transitional. Transition Area.

For instance, the average annual temperature is essentially "intermediate," and diminishes steadily from south to north; the winter temperature is nowhere really extreme for any length of time, and diminishes steadily from west to east; the summer temperature, again, is nowhere really extreme for any length of time,—very little of the continent having a summer *season* of over 68° F.,—and diminishes steadily from east to west. So with rainfall. Very little of the continent gets more than 60 inches a year, and very little gets less than 12 inches; and while two-thirds gets summer rain, one-third gets winter rain, the seaward end of each belt (of summer rain and of winter rain) getting also autumn rain. Temperatures and Rainfall.

The really dominant agent in this distribution of equality is the wind, the favourable influence of which is greatly accentuated by the general east-and-west lie of the feature-lines and by the extension of marine influences eastward along the Mediterranean basin. And this wind-borne oceanic influence exercises such a distinguishing control over the area—raising the average temperature in the north and lowering it in the south—that, on this ground alone, Europe may be treated as a separate continent. Wind.

Everywhere on the face of the Earth the most important single phenomenon is probably the swing of the wind-system with the sun; but this is obviously of special importance in Europe, and through European influence it affects indirectly the civilisations of areas held, or originally colonised, by Europeans in other continents. One of the strongest reasons for avoiding the modern Swing of Winds.

fashion of using the name "Westerlies" instead of the old "Anti-Trades," is the obvious emphasis that the latter puts on the relation between the two great manifestations of the single wind-system, the one towards the equator and the other towards the poles from a common starting-point. When the equator of heat corresponds with the equator of size—at the equinoxes, these climatic phenomena are symmetrical north and south of the equator, and the common starting-point in each hemisphere is near the tropic.

Summer Drought.   This implies that the attractive range of the high-temperature and low-pressure centre is considerably over 1000 miles; and,

Walker & Cockerell sc.

Currents of North Atlantic.

therefore, when the equator of heat is 10° N. even over the centre of the Atlantic Ocean, and 25° N. over the centre of the Sahara, the source of the Trades must be at least 35° N., and may be even higher than 40° N. In other words, all the south of the Mediterranean basin must be, and a large proportion of the whole basin generally is, in summer within the Trade-wind sphere. And as these winds near their source, *i.e.* where they fall on to the surface of the lithosphere from the upper layers of the atmosphere, are cold and dry, and as they blow from colder to warmer latitudes, so far from bringing rain, they can always hold more moisture than they can get. The mass of the Mediterranean basin is, therefore, doomed to summer-drought.

In winter, on the contrary, this northernmost extension is **Winter** equally far south of the northern tropic; and so all the Medi- **Rain.** terranean basin is brought well within the influence of the Anti-Trades, and their essentially oceanic character is preserved far to the eastward owing to the eastern extension of the Atlantic Ocean in the Mediterranean Sea. The whole of the Mediterranean basin, therefore, enjoys winter rains; and these are heavy enough to give, *e.g.*, Naples a total annual fall 7 or 8 inches greater than that of London. Cf. p. 55.

Of course the character of the wind, as a physical fact of, or **Atlantic** element in, climate depends on its normal direction, as a physical **Drift.**

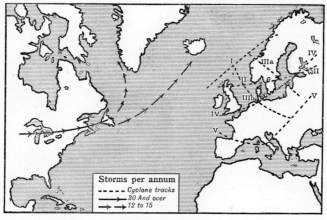

Atlantic storm tracks.

factor in, or cause of, climate; and its normal direction in this case brings it across the vast area of relatively warm water which accumulates in the north-east of the Atlantic. The so-called " Gulf " water, as a stream, is practically not found east of Labrador or north of the Azores; but, as a drift, it is found as far east and north as Spitsbergen, the average winter temperature at Mussel Bay being not 2° F. below the average annual temperature (16° F.). Even in February the surface temperature of the ocean as far north as the Azores is fully 64° F., and in August the same temperature is found as far north as the coast of Brittany.

Off such a large area of relatively warm water an equally large **Atlantic** amount of water-vapour must be carried; and the normal direction **Hinter-** of the wind carries this, with the heat which it implies, to an ex- **land.** ceptional distance inland because the distribution of relief is that of a typical Atlantic hinterland, although, of course, the actual rainfall decreases eastwards—*e.g.* Athens (15 inches) not having quite half that of Malaga. But this normal direction of the wind must be carefully related to the "permanent" wind-whirl off Iceland and the "permanent" wind-wyr off the Azores, the influence of each being sensibly accentuated by the seasonal changes of pressure in the north-east of Asia.

Iceland Whirl. In winter, when North America and Northern Eurasia are covered with blocks of cold air, the Icelandic wind-whirl is exceptionally active, and its gradients are very steep; and cyclonic storms are constantly following one another along the edges of the

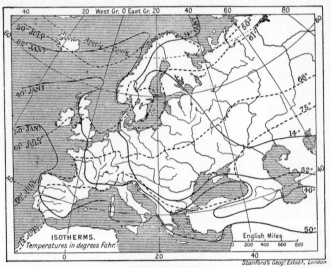

ISOTHERMS.
Temperatures in degrees Fahr.

European temperatures.

atmospheric "trough," especially when the North Sea has been flooded with warm water in the late summer. The winds in this whirl, then, are warmed by the ocean's retention of its summer heat, by the "Gulf" drift, and by their southern origin; and for the same reasons they are saturated with vapour, which they must drop as they move from warmer to colder latitudes, or from warmer to colder altitudes—whether up a mountain-side or up a low-pressure funnel (cf. p. 57). In theory, therefore, strong, warm, rain-bearing winds should be constantly rotating (in a direction contrary to that of the hands of a clock) round the Icelandic centre of low pressure; and these winds would obviously reach places due south of the centre as west winds, places due east as south winds, and places between south and east as successively W.S.W. and S.W. winds. Under these circumstances the whole oceanic margin of Europe must tend to have mild and rainy winters, especially after a hot and dry late-summer, and the isotherms over it will run as nearly parallel to the isobars as the local relief will allow.

All along the west of the continent and along the north of the Mediterranean extension of the Atlantic, then, we expect to find heavy rains, especially in winter, the extreme fall amounting, *e.g.*, to 197 inches on the summit of Snowdon and 179 on the Dalmatian scarp behind Cattaro. The same areas will have a high winter temperature, and will be subject to cyclonic storms (cf. p. 90). The greatest contrasts will be found, on the contrary, where high latitude coincides with maximum distance from the ocean or with deprivation of ocean influence, as in the lee (*i.e. north-east*) of the Scandinavian plateau, and where low latitudes coincide with minimum distance from the ocean, as in the lee (*i.e. south-west*) of the Iberian plateau. *{Extremes of Rainfall and Temperature.}*

The heavy winter rainfall in the Straits of Gibraltar is due partly to the diversion of the outermost whirls of the Icelandic system between the lofty Nevada and Atlas into the warm Mediterranean basin, and partly to the natural flow of the Azores wind-wyr clockwise in the same direction. This Azores wind-wyr, however, in winter is naturally weak, so that it does little to supplement or reinforce the Icelandic whirl, while both of them are powerless to push into the heart of the continent against the heavy block of cold air that is sitting over it and in the teeth of the outflow from the Siberian "pole of cold," which has recorded a winter minimum of − 92° F. *{Azores Wyr.}*

Under these circumstances, the cold "continental" air must have a minimum power of holding moisture, while precipitation must be mainly in the form of snow ; and, on the other hand, the winter storms, which cannot penetrate the continent, must be diverted northward along the west coast or eastward along the south coast, carrying exaggerations of the oceanic influence alike to the English Channel and to the Adriatic. In all areas, too, where the sea is still evaporating rapidly after the neighbouring land has begun to cool rapidly, as roughly west of 15° E., the natural result will be regular autumn rains as well as winter rains. But east of that longitude a small area of shallow "fresh" sea, such as the Baltic, is powerless to retard the time of minimum temperature, and would be powerless even if it remained absolutely unfrozen. As a matter of fact, very soon after mid-winter the whole Baltic basin is cold and dry. It is characteristic that a normal range of temperature on the Scotch coast of the North Sea (21° F.) should be just half that in the same latitude on the Russian coast of the Baltic. *{Seasonal Rainfall.}*

The conditions in summer make the Azores centre dominant and the Icelandic centre relatively feeble; for the pressure in the latter is abnormally high—for a low-pressure centre,—and the *{Summer Conditions.}*

Azores centre has moved north, *i.e.* nearer to Europe, with the whole wind-system. In theory, then, cool, dry, and relatively gentle winds should be constantly rotating clockwise round the Azores centre of high pressure; and these winds should reach places due north of the centre as west winds, and places north-east of the centre as north-west winds. At the same time over the heated continent there is such a low pressure that winds off the cooler ocean are

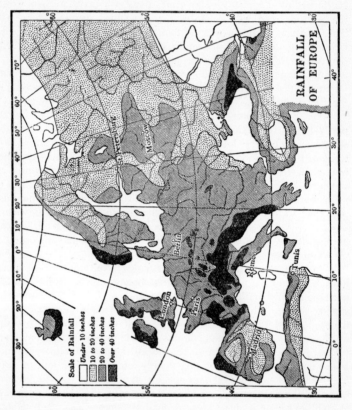

attracted strongly inwards. Such cyclonic storms as may occur, then, are likely to pass over the central plain, and in any case the wyr influence is cool and dry. In other words, the typical summer wind in North-West Europe is from west or north-west on 37 days out of 100, as against a south-west wind on only 22 days, and that westerly or north-westerly wind brings us relatively little rain. This is more or less true also even of Eastern Europe. For the summer rains there are mainly of local origin, the moisture evaporated off the large areas of local water during the long calm

broiling summer days being precipitated at night or in thunderstorms.
This may mean that the rain does not come often enough, and is
too violent when it does come.

The land being now warmer than the ocean, and its temperature **Iso-**
increasing with distance from that ocean, the isotherms begin to **therms.**
bend northwards directly they touch land, so that, while the winter
lowest mean was on the Finland plateau, the summer highest mean
is on the Kirghiz steppe. But, the sun being now the dominant
influence, as the sea is in winter, the isotherms never diverge much
from the sun-line, *i.e.* run more or less parallel to lines of latitude
instead of more or less parallel to the ocean-coast. In a word, they
are "sun-lines" in summer and "sea-lines" in winter.

The high temperature and the low level—actually below the **Summer**
sea-level—in south-eastern Russia so increase the capacity of the **Rain.**
air there for holding moisture that by midsummer it seldom reaches
even dew-point; still less is there rain. But elsewhere the high day
temperatures lead to quite a considerable rainfall associated with
local convection currents; cyclonic rains are widespread; and there
are heavy relief rains over all the Alpine system.

Where cyclonic and relief conditions are complicated, very
heavy rains occur in summer over Central Europe, *e.g.* in the Oder
basin, but they occur under what are more like winter conditions.
That is to say, a belt of high pressure covers the Great European
plain, while one of low pressure spreads southward from the Baltic
towards the nearest parts of the Mediterranean, from which a
similar low-pressure area is spreading northward. The lofty snow-
clad Alps form an insuperable barrier to this northward movement
of light air, causing a détour over the lower eastern outliers of the
system (cf. p. 34). To the east, then, the whole Sudetic system,—
which nowhere much exceeds 5000 feet,—while not an insuperable
obstacle, so intensifies the cyclonic uplift that *over* 21 *inches of rain
have fallen in twenty-four hours* on the top and northern slopes of the
Riesengebirge. Incidentally, too, this shows how inert a wyr is,
and how little part it usually takes in the circulation of the air
round it. It also shows how the upward movement of the air is
continued beyond, *i.e.* to leeward of, the actual crest of the obstructing mass, so that the heaviest precipitation is on the lee side. So
the Snowdon maximum is at Glaslyn, in the lee of the summit.

As a rule, average temperatures and average rainfalls are very **Averages.**
misleading, many areas never having—except for a day or two in
spring or autumn—their mean annual temperature; but in the case
of an essentially transitional and peninsular area general or average
conditions may be emphasised.

In Western Europe generally, then, the dominant wind is from **Direction**
some point in "west" for 53 out of every 100 days, south-west on 25 **of Wind.**
of them, due west on 17, and north-west on 11. In Eastern Europe,

on the other hand, it is from some point in "east." Again, a north wind, like a west one, is much commoner in summer than in winter ; and both bring cooling influences then, especially in the west. Consequently the range of temperature is least on the ocean margin, especially towards the north-west.

Exceptions. To these general rules or processes of atmospheric circulation there are some important exceptions or modifications, but they are essentially local and temporary. They are all related to one or both of the fundamental conditions—a local area of low pressure and a local area of high relief. And, as they are exceptional,— to the normal paths of the air-currents, which are also parallel to the great feature-lines,—they must obviously have a northern or a southern component. Those with a southern component are usually of the föhn type, and those with a northern component are usually of the mistral type.

Föhn. The föhn, which is typically a winter and spring phenomenon, is certainly a direct result of a local high pressure, but it is indirectly related also to the local high relief and to a distant low pressure. When a strong system of low pressure coming in from the Atlantic is divided in such a way that one branch is drawn in over the Mediterranean while the other works up the English Channel, there seems little chance of the two being re-united except by a route immediately west or immediately east of the main Alpine block (cf. p. 57) ; but if the Mediterranean current is persistent, local conditions of relief and pressure may combine to minimise the obstacle of the Alpine block itself, especially in the neighbourhood of the great central depression of the St. Gothard, *i.e.* at the northern apex of the Italian watershed in the deep Ticino valley between the Pennine and the Lepontine Alps.

The initial movement in a föhn, therefore, seems to be a horizontal "impulse" of the air on the higher levels towards the north, and then a gravitation of the same cold heavy air down the northern slopes. This gravitation at first takes it apparently *over* still colder and heavier air that is lying stagnant in the valleys below, but the moving cold air is followed by moving warm air ; and the latter is almost certainly part of the Mediterranean low-pressure current, though the latter is not evident at first in the lower strata of the air on the south side of the Alps. Indeed, the temperature in the lower strata to the south often remains very low, because the cold heavy air is "lodged." On the contrary, it seems to be the activity of the warm current at the higher level that gives the initial "impulse" to the cold air just below it on the heights.

The ascent of the warm current, however, is accompanied by heavy rain, and the freeing of a corresponding amount of latent heat ; and, thanks partly to the action of this heavy rain in degrading, the down-grade of the Reuss basin towards the northern centre of low pressure begins at once. To the initial momentum of the air-current is now added the attracting power of the low-pressure centre to the north, so that the down-current is always violent; indeed, it has done so much harm in this way that in the Canton of Uri there are regulations about the extinguishing of all fires on news of the föhn's approach. But, in spite of the danger from fire, it is hailed with joy in the spring, because not only is it extraordinarily dry, but also its original temperature has been increased—often 100 per cent—by the compression under the heavier barometrical pressure during its descent; it is, therefore, so dry and so warm that it becomes a veritable "eater of snow." It is to this that it owes its name of föhn ("favouring"). In the naming of the similar "Roteturm" wind in Transylvania more emphasis has been given to its "gap" character, as related to the Red Tower Pass.

The southerly sirocco of Sicily and leveche of Spain differ from **Sirocco.** the föhn in origin and therefore in character. They are essentially Saharan winds—hot, dry, and full of dust; and the dust collects so much vapour in passing over the Mediterranean that they are almost always hazy or foggy. They may occur at any season of the year, but are most common about the time of the spring equinox. Then the northward movement of the sun is apt to induce local areas of very low pressure in the Shott depressions in the lee (*i.e.* south) of the Atlas; and the normal anti-clockwise rotation round these centres carries the heat and fine sand as far east as Malta and as far west as Almeria. The terrific heat—which sometimes exceeds 93° F. *at midnight*—has a deadly effect on vegetation, *e.g.* vines or olives in blossom; but the area affected is fortunately confined to the southern latitudes of the Mediterranean. The name *sirocco* is, however, applied in the northern latitudes of the basin, as *solano* is in Spain, to the ordinary eddies in the main air-current of the Anti-Trade. These eddies, of course, have a southern component in them; but they are normally mild, rain-bearing winds, which are seldom violent and do much good.

Somewhat the same distinction may be drawn between the *bora* **Bora and** ("North Wind") and the mistral ("Masterful Wind"), the former **Mistral.** being more of a "gap" wind. Indeed, there is no question that it is often the ordinary north wind blowing with special force through the few gaps which do exist in the Alpine barrier, *e.g.* over the barren Karst saddle towards the Adriatic low-pressure centre. At other times, like the mistral, it is a local movement, due to the great differences in the day temperature on the sheltered strip of coast and on the snow-clad Alps or Cevennes. In consequence, though piercingly cold, it is essentially a healthy dry wind, accompanied by cloudless skies and other conditions favourable to the cleansing and warming of the soil. For the same reason, too, it usually stops at sundown. And it is very suggestive of the continental conditions of Spain, as contrasted with the peninsular conditions of France, that at the mouth of the Ebro, as the *cierzo*, it is mainly confined to autumn and early winter, while at the mouth of the Rhone it is most violent in late winter and spring.

Three Climatic Areas.

There are, then, three main climatic regions in Europe—the Atlantic, the Continental, the Mediterranean ; and these are so complementary of one another, and the total area of their distribution is so small, that they greatly favoured that interdependence and mutual intercourse which were the great impulse to civilisation in early days. The Atlantic region is specially marked by even temperature, the mean temperature seldom falling below 32° F. for more than one month in the year and seldom rising above 64° F. for more than one month, and by evenly distributed rainfall, the amount being everywhere greatest in autumn. The Mediterranean region is specially marked by the absence of serious frost, 50° F. being a typical winter temperature alike in Valencia and Calabria, Corsica and Crete, and by the absence of summer rains except along the northern heights, which are also specially instrumental in excluding the cold northerly winds in winter. The Continental region is specially marked by extremes of temperature, at least three consecutive months averaging below 32° F., and at least three averaging above 64° F., and by scanty rainfall, very little of the area having 30 inches and much of it not having even 20. Western Europe is, therefore, climatically complementary of Eastern Europe, especially in the matter of temperature range, as Northern Europe is of Southern Europe, especially in the matter of seasonal rainfall.

Supremacy of Europe.

Climate, therefore, like position and relief, has greatly favoured the development of the continent as a home of Life, so that Europe has been far ahead of all the other continents in this respect. The scene of the most complicated mountain-building, it has the most complicated outline ; and variety of outline and of relief and of climate has combined with smallness of area to crowd species in such a way as to give maximum struggle for existence under conditions where success was not impossible. Such a concentration of stimulus means maximum advance amongst the organisms that do survive.

CHAPTER VIII

CLIMATIC CONTROL

(1) *Of River Régime.*

THE geographic control of river development is, of course, physical **Two** as well as climatic; but the chief features of relief are so distributed **Centres.** in Europe that their influence mainly, and directly, accentuates that of the purely climatic phenomena. Thus, it is obvious that most of the important rivers radiate from one of two centres, the low Valdai plateau and the comparatively high Alpine system; and the much greater height is accentuated by the much closer proximity to the sea. The summit of the Valdai (1150 feet) bears the same relation even to European Russia alone as a 10-inch brick on its end bears to 1,000,000 acres; and it stands 1000 miles even from the North Sea. About 160 separate peaks in the Alps have a height at least ten times that of the Valdai, and far more than half of them are well within 500 miles from the Atlantic itself.

There is, therefore, an immediate relation between the size of **Size of** the river-basins in Europe and their available precipitation. The **Basins** largest basin on the Atlantic sea-board, that of the Loire, has an area of about 45,000 square miles; the basin of the Rhine is nearly double that (86,000); the Danube basin (312,000) is nearly four times that of the Rhine; and the Volga has a basin of about 565,000.

Now the annual range of temperature over the Atlantic in the **Range of** latitude of these rivers is less than 10° F., and is accompanied **Tempera-** by—indeed, it implies—a very high relative humidity. But the **ture.** daily range of temperature in the basins themselves seems to be greater than anywhere else in the world within similar latitudes, and there is a maximum variability of weather generally. Through-out the whole area the departure from normal is towards warmth, *i.e.* the encouragement of evaporation, the excess towards the north-west being sometimes as much as 40° F.; and this implies an abnormal capacity of the air for absorbing moisture.

Again, though the continent is temperate in its mean annual temperature, both statistically and as illustrated by physiological effects, it is essentially intemperate in many of its phenomena. Even in England in the year 1911 between April and August the maximum daily temperature varied between 11° F. and 100° F. ; and over the whole continent—in strong contrast to similar latitudes in the southern hemisphere—the normal interaction of land and sea creates maximum disturbance.   This must be related to the retardation of maxima and minima temperatures.   In the essentially continental part of the continent maximum or minimum temperature is retarded for one hour past midday or midnight and for one month past midsummer or midwinter, while in the marine part it is retarded for two hours and two months respectively.   And this will ensure—amongst other results—maximum rainfall, mainly by convection, about two hours after midnight, and mainly in thunderstorms, about two hours after midday.   It will also ensure rather similar temperatures in continental springs and autumns, but rather dissimilar temperatures between spring and autumn on the Atlantic sea-board.

Precipitation in Winter. This, of course, instantly affects precipitation.   The Anti-Trades have come so far in winter that "they have got into their stride," but they are greatly interfered with by the seasonal changes of temperature over the land.   The land temperature then is not only a most effective precipitating medium, but relief influences are also most accentuated ; and the low temperature and consequent high pressure force the whole air-current into lines of least resistance, which come to be called "cyclonic tracks."   We thus have a constant succession of more or less violent storms passing up the English Channel, forming almost as sure a line of defence for England as the channel itself ; and all the sea-board rivers, whether Atlantic or Mediterranean, get an abundant winter rainfall, while continental basins are starved.   [See p. 53.]

Precipitation in Summer. The latter have their turn in summer, when the high temperature and consequent low pressure involve a maximum capacity in the air for absorbing moisture and a maximum tendency towards convection.   These conditions combine to give the interior an abnormal rainfall in summer, but coupled with the disadvantage of the fall being too heavy and too local in both time and place, and therefore likely to cause serious floods in small or discordant basins. Thus, the north-western basins get an average of 10 per cent (of their total rainfall) in each of the five months September to January, while the central basins (north of the Alps) get an average of 12 per cent in each of the three months June to August, and not more than 7 per cent in any other three-month period.   Reflected in the régime, *e.g.*, of the German and the Russian rivers, this means that the former get equal supplies in spring and in autumn (cf. p. 55)

and twice as much in summer as in winter, while the Russian rivers
get 3 per cent more in autumn than in spring and 130 per cent
more in summer than in winter.

There will be, then, great variety of régime, not only as between **Varied**
rivers in different parts of the continent, but also as between **Régime**
different parts of the same basin, if a large one ; and a basin of
insignificant size at a considerable height near the Atlantic may
contradict a huge basin of low level in the interior in almost every
possible phenomenon.

North-Eastern France.

In both cases, however, the proportion of the actual rainfall over **Surface**
the basin which actually reaches the river, depends largely on the **Control.**
character of the surface, *e.g.* whether once glaciated or not, pervious
or impervious, and on the extent to which that surface is covered
with vegetation ; and this important consideration of vegetation
itself largely depends on the character of the surface and on seasonal
changes of climate. For instance, on the bare granitic hills of
the Loire basin in winter, some 75 per cent of the total fall feeds
the river, while on the porous plain of the deciduous forests in
Russia not 15 per cent seems to reach the river in summer ; and
the economic effect is further emphasised by the fact that the

smaller basin would in any case tend to have the more variable flow in the navigable part of the river.

Valdai System. Of course, the rivers of the Valdai area must be long and slow; but no part of their watershed has a normal rainfall of more than 40 inches, over 99 per cent of their basins it is not even 30, and over all the unforested parts evaporation is very rapid. They are, indeed, navigable for a very large proportion of their length, but for a relatively small proportion of the year. For instance, the Volga, in spite of the huge size of its basin (cf. p. 61), rises at only 550 feet above sea-level (633 feet above Caspian level); and it is navigable for 2260 miles out of 2325, but is ice-bound for 139 days at Kostroma and 107 at Tsaritsyn. All these "Valdai" rivers are ice-bound for a large part of the year; and the time in question lengthens towards the north and the east. This involves peculiar dangers from flooding. In the case of the northward-flowing rivers, their upper reaches always thaw before their lower reaches, causing most detrimental floods in the northern part of their basins; and a similar phenomenon is found on the eastward-flowing part of the Volga, the ice breaking up a fortnight earlier at Tver than at Kostroma.

Volga. This eastward section of the Volga goes through numerous morainic marshes, too, and spring comes so suddenly that on the vast forested lowland the melting snow can neither gravitate away nor be evaporated quickly enough to avoid further flooding—for miles over its low left bank. On the other hand, over the thirsty steppe evaporation and percolation are both so active that the river eventually discharges not much more than half the amount discharged by the Danube, which has a basin not much more than half the size of the Volga basin. The Volga is more or less typical of the continental part of Europe, though it belongs to the latitudes where there is extreme heat rather than extreme cold. But they are all ice-bound in winter, and their basins are so cold that, even where rain falls, it does not run off; they all flood suddenly when the ice and snow are melted in spring, and they all are fed with sufficient summer rain.

"Alpine" System. The rivers of the purely marine area enjoy more or less even rainfall throughout the year, but low temperature increases precipitation and decreases evaporation in the cold season; so that they are all normally low in summer, though small floods occur occasionally, and all normally high in winter and subject then to heavy floods. Such a régime, only greatly accentuated, is found throughout all the summer-drought area, where in summer many of the rivers become discontinuous.

Seine. The Seine is a good instance of the marine type under simple conditions. Its basin is no larger than Scotland (about 30,000 square miles), and no part of its watershed has an elevation of over 2500 feet; but only two-thirds of the basin consists of permeable rock, all the Yonne feeder and part of the Marne feeder being impermeable. Owing to the small size of the basin and the lowness of the watershed the same meteorological conditions usually prevail over all parts of it at the same time, and the torrential tributaries can send flood-water from the margin of the basin to Paris in four days. Heavy rains over the torrential tributaries imply heavy rains over all the basin, but the non-torrential tributaries cannot send flood-water from their basin-margins to Paris in less than a week. The simultaneous occurrence of heavy rain over all the basin—especially if snow is melting under the influence of the warm south-

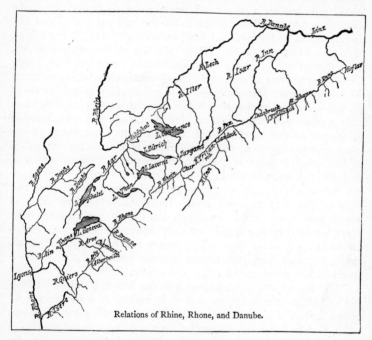

Relations of Rhine, Rhone, and Danube.

west wind—involves, therefore, sudden floods or a succession of floods on each of the torrential tributaries, and a certainty of a slow subsequent rise on each of the non-torrential streams; and meantime the continuous rain has *saturated* small subsidiary depressions in the centre of the basin, *e.g.* the Brie, thus making them temporarily impermeable. The simplicity of the phenomena enables the ultimate flood at Paris to be foretold at least a couple of days in advance, which minimises the loss of life; but the only means of stopping the flood, at a time when evaporation is sluggish and plant-life is inactive, would be to divert the Yonne bodily into the Loire.

The Rhine gives an illustration of a larger basin with a more

Rhine. complex régime. Its upper course is fed from glaciers and permanent snow, its middle course is among hills covered with snow in winter, and its lower tributaries are rain-fed; the glaciers and permanent snow melt fastest in summer, the temporary winter-snow on the lower hills melts in spring, and the north-western part of the basin receives autumn and winter rain. We expect, therefore, a summer maximum where the Rhine itself is joined by its great glacier-fed tributary, the Aar - Reuss, at Swiss Coblenz ("The Confluence"), *i.e.* opposite Waldshut. This summer maximum, which gives a navigable depth of about 5 feet from Basel to Strassburg, implies a winter minimum (of 3 feet) over the same area, or rather as far as the mouth of the rain-fed Ill. From the mouth of the Ill northwards the minimum depth is not below 5 feet; and, after the "confluence" of the Moselle at the other Coblenz, the inflow of rain gives a winter maximum of never less than 9 feet. The spring-melting of the snow in the Neckar valley largely accounts for the fact that Mannheim—with a minimum dredged depth of $7\frac{1}{2}$ feet—does an annual river-borne trade of over 6,500,000 tons; and it equalises the variation (20 feet) between the summer maximum of the upper ice-fed and the winter maximum of the lower rain-fed reaches. The total result is that, below the inflow of the rain-fed Nahe at the old Roman port of Spires, vessels of at least 500 tons burden can ply without difficulty, while below the inflow of the snow-fed Main the burden rises, for at least 200 days in the year, to 2000 tons. Incidentally, too, this influx of winter and spring floods converges on the Bingen narrows, with a consequent current-speed normally above 6 miles an hour—necessitating powerful tugs and stationary hauling-gear for up-stream traffic, but supplying one reason why the estuary of the Rhine is so much less silted up than that of the Elbe.

Rhone. The Rhone may be compared with the Rhine, if only to criticise the prevalent misconception that it is useless as a waterway. Of course, it has obvious drawbacks. Though its length is only 500 miles, it rises 6000 feet above the sea; and, as it is fed from what is at once the highest part of the Alps and that nearest to the Atlantic, its volume and its pace must be great. No doubt, too, the ice-fed Durance joins the main stream too near its mouth to avoid complicating conditions in the delta, and the Ardèche joins it too near for its melted snow to be of much use for navigation. On the other hand, about 4700 feet of the total fall is accomplished in the 105 miles down to the Lake of Geneva; the river is fed from 405 square miles of glacier; and its fall from Lyons to the sea is only 530 feet in 230 miles. Again, while all the ice-fed streams flood in summer, the rain-fed ones flood in winter and the snow-fed in spring, so that the Saone and the Ain, like the Neckar and the Moselle in the case of the Rhine, help to keep the volume more or less uniform throughout the year. These conditions combine to give the Rhone almost always a minimum depth of $4\frac{1}{2}$ feet—which is enjoyed by the Elbe for only 200 days in the year and by the Oder for only 127; and the one great injury from the ice-fed torrents, an undue widening of the bed by the heavy floods, has been artificially corrected in such a way that the concentration of energy in a single channel enables the river to carry away its heavy burden of shingle and gravel.

The Danube has a still more complex régime, as might be **Danube:** inferred from the fact that it twice cuts across the great Alpine **Upper** barrier. In the upper part of its basin it is fed with winter-rain **Course.** from the Black Forest and by melted snow in spring from the

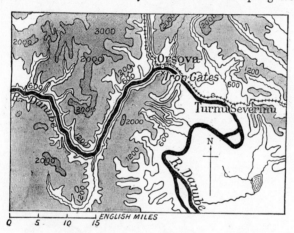

Iron Gates on Danube.

Alpine foreland; and, as this part of its course gets little actual supply of rain in the time of maximum evaporation and maximum plant-energy, it has a minimum flow in summer. It suffers further, in this section, because during drought the head stream disappears bodily underground, sometimes for three or four months; and, when it reappears 8 miles to the south and 560 feet lower, it enters *Lake Constance, i.e.* flows to the North Sea, not the Black.

At the first Alpine barrier the river is joined by its great ice-fed **Middle** tributary the Inn, which has a length greater than that of the **Course.** Danube proper above their confluence at Passau; and the whole river assumes an Alpine régime, showing a summer maximum at Vienna and receiving the "Danube" as a truncated stream now rising in Würtemberg, not in Baden. Once inside the mountain-barrier, it becomes a more or less typical Steppe river, suffering great extremes of climate; and, as it is now fed mainly by winter-snow and river-ice, it has a spring maximum, the melting of the ice-fields—

where the river deployed in several channels (now converted into one) on to the Hungarian plain—having caused formerly very destructive floods, *e.g.* in 1838 at Budapest.   But the melting of the hill snow and the lowland ice, and the normal occurrence of

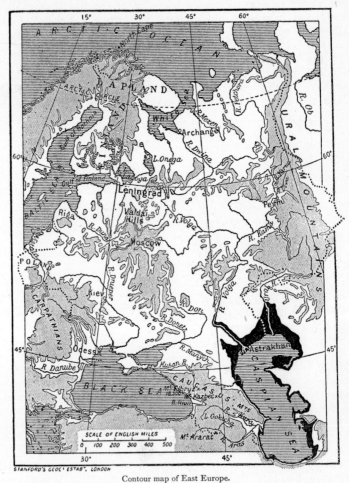

Contour map of East Europe.

The lightly shaded areas are more than 600 feet in height.   The Caspian Sea is 84 feet below sea-level.

early summer rains, are followed by such high temperatures that the air has a maximum capacity for absorption at the same time that plant-activity is at a maximum; and the river shows a late-summer and early-autumn minimum at Belgrade.

After crossing the second Alpine barrier (Kazan—Orsova), the

great difficulty is temperature, not precipitation. In the continental **Lower**
climate the transitional seasons are so short that navigation is very **Course.**
precarious ; for instance, in 1902 the winter began with such a
sudden and extreme frost that 38 steamers were frozen up between
Braila and the coast, where the river is navigable by ocean vessels
of 4000 tons register, and more than 120 loaded barges suffered
a similar fate between Braila and Rushchuk, where the barges have
a capacity of up to 2000 tons. On the contrary, the large amount
of underground water—with a normal and constant temperature
of 48° F.—received by the river between Vienna and Pressburg
creates a winter harbour that is almost entirely free from ice ; and
it was here that the old Roman road from Aquileia found a terminus
in Carnuntum.

CHAPTER IX

CLIMATIC CONTROL

(2) *Of Vegetation.*

WE have already noticed how early Man must have had most **Early**
chance of intruding, with his domestic plants and animals, in a **Man.**
transition area, and how markedly Southern Europe is such an area.
But the mere absence of the more adverse conditions is not, by
itself, sufficient to account for the very early growth of civilisation
in the Mediterranean basin. And we may examine in some detail
both the phenomena
which account for the
absence of the unfavour-
able conditions, and
those which account for
the presence of favour-
able ones.

Existing Glaciers.   Ancient Ice Sheet.

All organic forms, **High v.**
whether plant or beast **Low**
or man, have much in **Forms.**
common ; and their in-
terdependence implies,
on the one hand, more
or less common climatic
conditions, and, on the
other hand, the sub-
servience of the lower forms to the higher. From one point of
view, Man had to oust the essentially "wild" plants and beasts that
were in possession of an area ; from the other point of view,

survivors or intruders must be his servants. This was easy in Europe, for, in the first place, the Great Ice Age had decimated the native flora and fauna of Europe ; and survival had been easiest where it is more or less true to say that subsequent progress was most difficult, *i.e.* in the Mediterranean basin. The evolution of Europe as a continent has been intimately bound up with the movements of shepherds from the grass-lands of Asia into the fruit-garden of the Mediterranean on their way to the forests and fisheries of North-West Europe.

Seasonal Climate. Europe lies mainly in purely temperate latitudes, but also partly in essentially transitional latitudes. In both there are seasonal variations of temperature and of rainfall, and these are the two essential conditions in the evolution of those plants which are most useful to man. The greater differences of rainfall are in the south, and the greater ranges of temperature are farther north. The net result is more favourable to the north than to the south ; for the absence of moisture, which is the fundamental check on the growth of plants, comes in the south at the time when otherwise the heat is most favourable to such growth. In the north, on the contrary, the shortness of the summer season is more than compensated by the length of the summer day ; and the occurrence of the rainfall and the heat simultaneously gives to both a maximum utility. But this could not be effective until the more adverse results of the old glaciation had been modified or removed ; and one agent in this process was the gradual desiccation that has been spreading over the Old World, and that has progressively handicapped the Mediterranean peoples.

Cultivated Plants. Now, the rainfall in most parts of Southern Europe is scanty in amount and strictly seasonal in character, and these conditions are so adverse to forest growth that continuous forests are rare ; and this must have left a relatively large area free for cultivation, so that cultivated plants appeared in the Mediterranean basin ages before they appeared on the European plain. But, though the rainfall is adverse to continuous forest, the absence of any cold wind in the dry season and the presence of sufficient warmth in the wet season render the limited supply adequate for discontinuous, or " orchard," trees, provided that they are adapted to resist drought. The various processes by which this adaptation is secured, include lengthening of root, restriction of height, thickening of bark, development of thorns, toughening of leaves, secretion of volatile oil, and other means of resisting or evading the evaporating power of very dry air or of drawing water from great depths. And no typical plants have survived in the Mediterranean basin without fulfilling one or more of these conditions. The olive, the cork-oak, the vine, and—in the rainiest areas—the sweet chestnut are typical.

The olive is probably the most important, as it is the most

typical. Like many other natives of summer-drought, *e.g.* the box **The** and the yew, it develops a rich colour in the wood, and grows so **Olive.** slowly that its wood takes a most beautiful polish, and the tree itself attains a prodigious age (1000-1200 years). But the greater violence of the wind where there is no ground-friction, the more rapid transpiration of the leaves at this higher level, and the lower humidity of the air at that level, all combine to restrict its height usually to under 30 feet; and even this height seems to be reached only by the help of man. The small size of the narrow "willow" leaf, the hoary hue of its under side, and the fact that it is ever-green, all combine to minimise transpiration in the hot dry-season and to facilitate assimilation in the cool wet-season. The tree never suffers from physiological drought, because it cannot live at all where the temperature is too low for it to assimilate in the cold season; and its root-system is so enormously developed that it is able to draw water from depths where actual drought cannot reach, while the stem up which the water passes may have a girth of over 20 feet, *i.e.* equal to the height of the tree! And olive-oil is the milk and cream, the butter and cheese, of this typically summer-drought area.

Plants of humbler habit, with no woody stem to defy climatic **Humble** injury, are also largely found in the Mediterranean area; but they **Plants.** have survived only in virtue of aromatic properties or some pro-vision for storing water, as in the case of laurel and oleander, lavender and myrtle, garlic and asphodel. And the destruction which man has undoubtedly caused amongst forest growths in historic times, has probably been equalled by that caused by goats amongst the humbler plants, so that the survivors are typically unpleasant to handle, being covered with hairs or spines or resin, or in some other way made distasteful to the goats.

Of course, the great variety of level involves considerable **Natural** variety of temperature, and this means variety of vegetation—from **Grasses.** palm trees to pines; and, on the other hand, the most important areas are largely alluvial floors of valleys that are surrounded by lofty mountains, from which the alluvium has itself been carried, and from which it is watered to an extent that bears no obvious relation to the local rainfall. But neither the alluvial flats nor the relatively large supplies of water in the subsoil are very suitable for, or very favourable to, the shallow-rooted grasses, so that there is bound to be a deficiency of natural pasture except on the fertile soil of the glacial platforms.

The case is different with the cultivated grasses, especially **Culti-** barley and wheat, both of which are natives of the Mediterranean **vated** basin. Neither of them needs the great heat which is typical of **Grasses.** the basin in summer, but the effective value of which is lost because the drought makes summer the time of rest for plants. The early growth of both is encouraged by the mild moist winters, while the spring heat "forces" them on so quickly that they are mature before the drought is at hand; and by that time the perfection of ripening depends precisely on the presence of dry warm weather, which also facilitates harvesting.   There is, therefore, every encouragement for man to cultivate annuals of this kind on the precious alluvial plains.   In other words, he can easily provide himself with corn and wine and oil; and on such of the alluvial plains as had been originally forested, and so were rich in fibrous leaf-mould, *e.g.* Northern Italy, he could grow the flax which he needed for clothing.

Fruit.   To these fundamental necessaries he could easily add various pulses and flavourings, *e.g.* the garlic, and all kinds of nuts and stone-fruits; and in later times the areas which enjoy early summer rains, were found to be as favourable to maize as those enjoying only winter rains were to tobacco.   But the typical control is seen in the fruit-growing—with irrigation.   Nearly all stone-fruits are natives of South-Western Asia, as the various citrus fruits are of South-Eastern Asia; and the easy cultivation of the ordinary arable land, and the rapid growth of the ordinary annual crops, left the leisure that was necessary for the cultivation of fruit and for attending successive harvests, *e.g.* vine, fig, olive.   At the same time, the essential problems of irrigation were the same there and then as they are now in California, and the family was neither capable of being, nor allowed to be, the irrigating unit of labour— a result somewhat adverse to family life (cf. p. 74), as the relative lack of rain was to density of population.

Northern Europe.   One of the great natural advantages of Europe in early days was that the southern part is in climate and crops more or less complementary of the northern.   Here almost the only drought is physiological, for every normal winter is cold enough to stop vegetation.   Under normal conditions, then, the annual plants must be such as mature in summer, or they must be treated so as to evade the typical winter conditions; and this involved such change of exposure or season as, *e.g.*, in planting vines on hill-slopes facing south-east or sowing wheat in spring instead of autumn. But the ordinary succession of climatic phenomena was intimately associated with the calm heavy air of a high-pressure centre in winter and with the light rain-bearing inflow to a low-pressure centre in summer; and the absence of wind in the cold season was as favourable to the growth of forest as the presence of rain was in the warm season.   A very large proportion of the area was, therefore, bound to produce temperate forest.

"Forest" Crops.   But the summer was not long enough, nor was the temperature high enough, for the favouring rain-supply to produce dense vegetation; and Man intruded without much difficulty, marking his arrival by such encroachment on the forest as handicapped it

in its natural struggle with other forms of vegetation. Thus the
various grasses, natural and artificial, which do not need much heat,
and which do not mind more or less constant rain, were encouraged,
especially oats and rye ; and the fibrous floors of the old forests
were equally favourable to flax and hemp, as they have been in

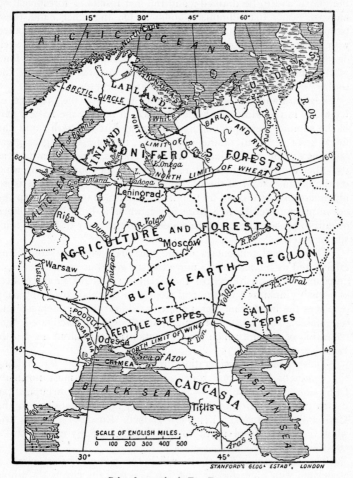

Belts of vegetation in East Europe.

later times to various root-crops that are tolerant of little sunshine
and much rain, *e.g.* potatoes and turnips. The flax was less
valuable than in the Mediterranean basin, however, because the
climate was so favourable to natural pasture that wool was both
abundant and more suited to the requirements of Man in the long

cold winter; and the same conditions increased the demand for animal food, thus incidentally involving a type of occupation very favourable to the development of family life.

"Social" Forests. At the same time life was relatively hard. One legacy of the old glaciation was an intractable soil; the forest had to be cleared; the marsh had to be drained; and the first results of forest-clearing increase rather than diminish flooding. On the other hand, these temperate forests are social, a fair variety of types being combined with a large continuous area under each type; and under such circumstances enormous herds of swine found abundance of food in the continuous oak and beech forests, and the variety of the timber was sufficient for ordinary domestic purposes.

Prairie and Steppe. Eastward and south-eastward of the forest area the presence of icy winds in the winter and the absence of rain in the hottest part of the summer were profoundly adverse to forest growth; and the forest gave place to prairie and steppe, the one offering as great facilities for the cultivation of artificial grasses, especially wheat, as the other did for natural pasture. There is, of course, strong wind on the ocean margin of the old forest area; but its strength is so much lessened by ground-friction that it did little more than keep the ocean margin usefully free from forest, while it brought abundance of rain to replace the moisture which it carried away from the transpiring trees.

Domestic Cattle. The pastoral tendencies of the grasslands were far from being annihilated as the shepherds moved westward; but obvious changes crept in. The lush grass of the Atlantic sea-board produces beef of a quality unknown on the real steppe, so that the cow completely displaces the mare from her premier position on the steppe; and the stabling of most domestic animals greatly facilitated that collection of manure which has revolutionised agriculture in North-West Europe.

Zones of Vegetation. These general considerations may afford ground for dividing the continent into formal zones of vegetation, the most northerly being the useless Tundra — the cold desert which occupies the northern margin of the Russian lowland, and overlaps on to the Ural and Scandinavian heights. Indeed, Russia—spanning the whole continent from north to south—gives a fairly correct bird's-eye view of all the zones.

"Coniferous" North. The Coniferous Forest, in which the non-coniferous birch is associated with pine and fir and larch, practically covers the whole area southward from the Tundra at least as far as the latitude of Öslo–Leningrad (60° N.), the fir being specially dominant round the Gulf of Bothnia. The subsidiary forest products include resin and tar, potash and pulp; but agriculture is more typical of the deciduous forests, while the clearings are typically devoted to oats, barley, rye, and potatoes.

The Deciduous Forest remains only "in samples" except in Russia, where it still covers much of the land between the latitude of Leningrad and that of Kief. The southern limit of the area is partly physical and partly climatic. In the west it runs along the northern edge of the Young Folded Mountains, and in the east along the southern edge of the old glaciation; and inside these latitudinal extremes it is roughly bounded longitudinally by lines within which there is a winter temperature below 32° F. for at least two months, and a summer temperature above 64° F. for at least two months, with a mean annual rainfall of rather more or rather less than two feet. Where relief decreases the temperature and increases the rainfall, as along the Vosges and the Black Forest, the Erz Gebirge and the Sudetes, deciduous trees give place to conifers; and where late glaciation has left a marshy and intractable soil, as along the south shore of the Baltic, conifers and heaths occur, as also on the windy flats that border the North Sea. But agriculture is widely developed over the cleared parts of the area, the chief grains being wheat and rye and the chief roots being beet and potatoes; and the pastures, which are largely artificial, have been so much improved by systematic grazing and regular mowing that they are exceedingly rich. {.sidenote "Decidu-ous" Centre.}

The Evergreens of the Mediterranean basin coincide with the area of summer-drought, which practically includes all the land that drains into the Mediterranean proper. But altitude gives great variety, the trees at the highest levels being coniferous; and the actual uplift gives great protection to the coastal valleys, so that— with irrigation from the snow-capped heights—even tropical plants can be cultivated. Not only so, but these are of unique excellence; for instance, the finest rice in the world is grown in Lombardy— illustrating the general law that the farther from the equator grain can be ripened properly at all, the more perfect does it become. All the typical trees and shrubs are sombre-coloured, for only those survived which were able to exclude—by means of colours from the lower end of the spectrum—the dangerous ultra-violet rays of sunshine; and there is considerable localisation of type, *e.g.* cork and various kinds of "alfa" being more dominant in the "African" climate of Iberia, while olive and mulberry are more dominant elsewhere. The various evergreen shrubs of the citrus genus are very typical, especially oranges and lemons. Their restricted height, the colour and texture of their bark, the shape and glossy surface of their leaves, their secretion of volatile oils, their protection of their green shoots by axillary spines, all make them more or less in-different to summer drought so long as copious autumn and winter rains come in time to "flush" their fruit with juice. {.sidenote "Ever-green" South.}

The Steppe of South-Eastern Europe is said to be a sort of continental extension of the Mediterranean domain, as the North- {.sidenote "Inter-mediate" Steppe.}

European heaths are said to be a maritime extension of the Steppe proper. It certainly is characterised by many typical Mediterranean plants, especially of the bulbous habit; but this is a natural control of the climate. Steppe is essentially land in temperate latitudes so far from the ocean, or so much cut off from oceanic influence, and so much exposed to wind in winter, that its climate is adverse to all plants except such as can *evade* the extremes of temperature and drought. It is found inside the Alp-Carpathian ring of mountains and in similar latitudes in Russia; and the fact that its northern limit coincides roughly with the northern limit of loess, *i.e.* the southern limit of morainic deposits, has led to its being connected with the fine character of the loess. But it is almost certainly a joint result, with the loess, of the dry winter wind which distributed the glacier silt (cf. p. 24). It is naturally desert in summer, in autumn, and in winter; but in spring the melted snow makes it "blossom as the rose," with dark-red tulips, peach-red almond-shrubs, pale-red woodbine. And its better-watered areas, especially in Hungary, repay richly cultivation under grain.

CHAPTER X

CLIMATIC CONTROL

(3) *Of Beast and Man.*

Ice Age. THE Great Ice Age scarcely affected fish and birds, but it worked havoc among land mammals—in proportion to their size and appetites and in inverse proportion to their intelligence and powers of loco-motion. Indeed, the extraordinarily rapid progress of early Man subsequently cannot be dissociated, on one hand, from the wholesale massacre of the stupid during the glacial epochs, and, on the other hand, from the typical agility and intelligence of arboreal mammals. But Man is innately adaptable and omnivorous as well as intelligent, and must have come best out of the struggle, while the purely herbivorous beasts of the more southern latitudes must have come out of it worst. For the advancing ice drove many typical plants to practical annihilation in the Mediterranean; and the smaller and more abstemious beasts which survived must—in the process of adjustment to new sources of food—have lost some of their old advantage of superior strength, and have been very much at the mercy of man. Cf. p. 47.

Social Species. The importance of this depends partly on the fact that, far from tropical scenes of senseless competition, species are few but social; and the old civilisation and the dense population of Europe have involved the disappearance of such species as could not be brought into due subjection (cf. p. 69). For instance, the demand for beech-wood of a character appropriate to—because produced by—areas of close foresting has led in chair-making areas to the whole-sale destruction of nut-eating animals, *e.g.* squirrels, whose appetites interfered with the natural increase of seedlings. Exactly opposite conditions gave rise to the pre-war law in Russia prohibiting access for three years to certain forest-areas favourable to the sable.

As almost the whole continent may be described as natural **Fauna.** forest or mountain zone, we should expect that the natural fauna would be either of the forest type, *e.g.* the wolves and bears of Russia, or of the montane type, *e.g.* the chamois and ibex of Switzerland; but the domestication of the important hoofed animals and the cultivation of artificial grain have given special opportunities for the spread of rodents, by decreasing the old competition on their grass-land home, whether steppe or alp (cf. the Alpine marmot), and increasing their artificial supplies of food.

Unfortunately for Man, from the need for fertility to discount **Steppe** the appalling mortality in the times of keenest competition, many **Organ-** of these animals, *e.g.* the rat and the rabbit, have inherited, as the **isms.** Negro has in his age-old struggle with noxious microscopic fauna, extraordinary reproductive power ; and, as they are all wholly or partly vegetarian in diet, they have become a very serious tax on agriculture, especially where there has been foolish and wholesale decimation of such essentially useful birds as owls. Locusts and grasshoppers are similarly prolific steppe organisms. It was estimated that the British operations in Cyprus exterminated in two years 250,000,000,000 locusts—whose "music" is simply the noise of millions of ceaselessly moving jaws.

In his war with such pests, including the few noxious reptiles **Birds.** which survived glaciation—though they have never flourished since then in Europe as they have in the hotter parts of the Old World—Man has been greatly helped by the rich bird fauna. And this richness is due partly to the large area of original forest, and partly to their greater mobility in the face of glacial movement or human hunters, but mainly to the fact that the Nile valley has provided a unique line of migration between the breeding-grounds and the winter-quarters of many species. There has been also a somewhat similar migration westwards towards the Atlantic in winter ; so that there is a zone of rich bird fauna all the way from England *via* the Atlantic and Mediterranean coast-lands and the Nile valley to the Ethiopian highlands. Indeed, the choice of the island of Capri by Tiberius as the site of his famous palace, was due partly to the excellence of its vineyards and partly to the fact that it was—as it still is—a regular resting-place for quails on their northward migration. Amongst the birds which do not migrate far southward, *e.g.* ptarmigan, there is a change of colour—to white or nearly white—in winter; and the change is protective against radiation of heat as well as against enemies.

Man. Man, as the culminating product of the various controls, is of three main types—Nordic, Alpine, and Mediterranean; and his dominant control is climatic, the direct influence showing specially in colour and the indirect in physique. And we may make two assumptions about his theoretical development and characterisation : (1) his early progress must have been easiest where conditions approximated to a natural evolution, but (2) his ultimate progress should be greatest where conditions strained his powers without overstraining them. If these assumptions are justified, the optimum result should be found where the two sets of conditions were combined; and we should, therefore, find the highest type evolved in the forested areas of cool-temperate latitudes.

Arboreal Type. Primeval man—whom, without necessarily accepting all or any of the suggestions about a probable Gondwanaland, we might call a Gondwana — was certainly evolved in a region of such high temperature and high relative humidity that it was forested; and the Gondwana was, therefore, brunet in colour and arboreal in habit. The brown pigment is still found in the epidermal cells of all peoples on the face of the earth, even the blondest; and infants can support their own weight unaided if suspended by the fingers. This, though obviously an anachronism now, like such other transient infantile traits as extreme long-headedness and a concave nose, is an appropriate and significant accomplishment in the highly evolved descendants of arboreal primates. Man, in his individual development, has to climb his own genealogical tree; and, during the Age of Fear, survival was naturally to those children of the Tree-Dwellers that were blessed with the most prehensile fingers. But, obviously, their forms as well as their fingers were adapted to their arboreal environment; and the habitual conformity of the human skull to the general plan of the human body at once becomes of prime importance. For arboreal environment involves simian physique, which implies an elongated body; and to this the skull would unquestionably conform.

Colour Modification. Primeval man came into Europe, therefore, from the south; he was brown-skinned and long-headed; like nearly all other tree-dwelling mammals, he was markedly social and quick in mind and body; and he instinctively avoided the unforested highlands. But he arrived in days of heavier rainfall and higher relative humidity; and, until he had himself made effective attacks on the native forests, he found a congenial home in the Mediterranean basin. There were also, as we have seen, lines of easy movement from this area into the northern forest areas, especially in the Atlantic half of the continent. In each case the new environment must have tended to arrest or to develop fundamental traits, and to do this in different degrees and in different directions; and the predominant factor in the differentiation was the essential contrast of summer-rain and summer-drought with their implicit differences of relative humidity, *i.e.* capacity for obstructing the ultra-violet rays of sunlight. Summer-drought, with its high actinic power, tended to blacken in the lower latitudes; summer-rain, with its high opacity, tended to bleach in the higher latitudes. For the increased activity of the lungs, in the presence of the relatively little and feeble sunshine in the summer-rain area, favoured the lighter colour of the skin; the increased activity of the intestines, in the presence of the relatively great and strong sunshine of the summer-drought area, favoured the darker colour. Nordic man, therefore, became fair, while Mediterranean man became—or remained—very dark, the shade deepening eastward with the decrease of relative humidity.

Under these circumstances the survival of the fittest meant the **Need of** survival of those who were appropriately coloured. For human **Pigment.** protoplasm is normal only at a temperature of about 98°–99° F., and even infra-red rays can disturb it seriously if it is not protected by a sufficiently pigmented cover, *i.e.* skin, because the normal temperature of the body is increased perceptibly by an increase in the temperature of the surrounding air. The actual process is illustrated in Europe by the distribution of freckles or ordinary sunburn. This is a pathological phenomenon, *i.e.* an injury, caused only and directly by the short actinic rays, and is therefore a sign of incomplete adaptation to environment; it seldom occurs in dark-skinned persons, and can be prevented in the fair-skinned by a slight staining of the skin. Natural skin-pigment is evolved as a similar protection, and therefore varies with the need, *i.e.* the intensity of the sunshine, as conditioned by the altitude of the sun and the humidity of the air " blanket."

In this connection the forest was of prime importance. It **Forest** meant the direct presence of tree-shade, and it implied a relatively **Influence.** high humidity; and the relative humidity must always be high where, as in Europe outside the Mediterranean basin, moist winds blow regularly towards higher latitudes. Here, too, even apart from the question of humidity, neither heat nor light is intense, so that dark skin was not needed to increase radiation of heat and protect from light, while fair skin was needed to minimise radiation of the relatively deficient heat, especially in the typical gloom of the fiords and forests of North-West Europe, which are also in the normal path of cyclonic systems.

The southern frontier of the White man, then, roughly coincides **"White"** with the southern frontier of Bear-Worshippers because it is the **Man.** southern frontier of temperate forest. And, in view of the great importance of the angle of ray-impact and the thickness of the atmosphere, we may fix the natural limits of the normal or average White man in Europe as such parts of latitudes 45° to 55° N. as are maritime or forested; south of this he is blackened, and north of it, *i.e.* north of the latitude of Copenhagen, he is bleached. This is equally true of Asiatics moving westward, *e.g.* the Magyars, and of the original Brown man after movement northward. The case of the Finns is profoundly significant, *if* it is a case of the lank-haired race intruding into the domain of the wavy-haired; for in that case the Finns' hair has regained its original morphological wave, and lost the physiological coarseness that it acquired in the Yellow man's intemperate climate (see Note, p. 81).

Hair. This would be strong evidence against the belief that the wavy European hair is of secondary origin, derived from the crossing of

Geometrical centre of Europe.

distinct primary types of man, Black and Yellow; but in any case we would accept, as conclusive evidence of priority, the closer agreement between the wavy European hair and that of other primates. And, as the Black man is further than the Yellow man from the higher apes in this respect, we assume that the former has suffered more variation, *i.e.* degeneration, from the original type. We, therefore, expect such foreign influences as have been really effective or civilising to have reached Europe from the east rather than from the south.

Alpine Man. There has been such an intrusion from the east in the case of Alpine man; and he is still largely a Yellow or "parchment-skinned" man. Unlike the Nordic man and the Mediterranean man, he has his area of characterisation outside the frontiers of Europe—on the vast intemperate grass-lands of Asia. He is, therefore, a man of the alp rather than of the Alps; he flourishes only on the grass-land, whether lowland steppe or montane alp, and dies out rapidly even on the foothills—the *forested* foothills—of the Alps. But he is, of course, at home on the Russian and Hungarian steppe, as on the Bulgarian plateau; and in each case the park-land between grass and forest weaned him gradually from the lower civilisation of the pastoral nomad to the higher civilisation of the tiller of a forest-clearing. As the domesticator of the wild ox and the wild horse, which were natives of such park-land, this Round-head was the greatest of all the benefactors of Europe; and it was mainly his artificial mobility, as a user of domestic animals, that enabled him to impose his rule and language on the dense population of fruit-growers in the area of summer-drought. The Achaeans were characteristically known as "Tamers of Horses."

Access from the Danubian steppe was physically almost as easy into Italy as into Greece, and the Italian route had the climatic advantage of being skirted by almost continuous alp; it was, there-fore, more suitable to the Itali ("Cattle-men") branch of the Round-heads than the Greek route was to the Achaean branch. Not only was the route suited to Cattle-men, but so also was its destination. The alp pasture is essentially rich, and the essential products of it are cattle, not sheep and goats; and 25 per cent of Italy is still pastoral, the main stock being cattle. So the Round-heads, in occupying the unforested highlands which had been instinctively avoided by the Long-heads, possessed themselves of an unoccupied territory which was admirably suited to their own hereditary needs, and which commanded the best route between the centre of the summer-drought area and the centre of the summer-rain area. In spite, therefore, of their small numbers, they were able to impose control—political, economic, and even linguistic—over the far more numerous and more civilised Long-heads of the Fruit-land; and it is interesting to notice that the geometrical centre of Europe, as a continent, is the original spot where Nordic, Alpine, and Mediterranean men naturally met.

NOTE

Ripley's alternative to the accepted view of the Finns as Ural-Altaic in physique as well as speech is stated in the chapter on Russia; but he ignores the significance of their hair being very *lightly* waved.

CHAPTER XI

THE ITALIAN PENINSULA

Central Site. THE race-home of the old Romans is the centre of the most clearly characterised natural region in the Old World; it is "a long pier-head of Europe," almost joining the snowy Alps to the sandy Sahara, and almost cutting off the larger, sub-tropical, gulf-girt basin of the great midland sea from the smaller, warm-temperate, mountain-girt basin.

Typical Area. It is in several ways the most typical country of Europe, as a "peninsula of peninsulas." For it combines within its frontiers the three great types of land form—continental, peninsular, and insular, and the two great contrasts of the European climate—summer rain and summer drought; and these advantages helped to make it the centre from which the continent was evolved as a political unit, for its position gave great facilities for passing on the culture borrowed from the sub-tropical basin to the hinterlands of the warm-temperate basin, especially *via* the Ebro and Rhone valleys.

World Influence. In modern times the Suez Canal has enabled it to resume this task in the economic world, and has restored to it most of the influence of which it was deprived by the discovery of the Cape route to India. Possibly it would never have lost that influence if the Italians had not actually tried to prevent Atlantic expansion and to perpetuate Mediterranean methods of navigation with their circumscribed sphere. The World reaped the benefit of their long experience in navigation, but only through individuals such as Columbus and Cabot; and Italy herself has paid the penalty of arriving too late in the field of colonial expansion.

World Centre. As the centre of the Old World, Italy acquired a World-dominion focused at Rome : all roads led to Rome, the capital of the Republic, of the Empire, of the Church ; and world-mastery became a tradition. Roman citizenship, therefore, became of infinitely more importance than race or—at first—than creed; all races and all creeds were tolerated ; and the one vital need was for means of reaching them all. The control exercised by these conditions is visible on all sides, *e.g.* in the self-centred egotism of the people; the number of

"foreign" emperors or hybrid marriages; the tenacity with which
Venice and Genoa remained friendly with the Saracens while acting as
transport contractors for the Crusaders; the success of the modern Italian as a colonist—in colonies belonging to nations earlier in the field.

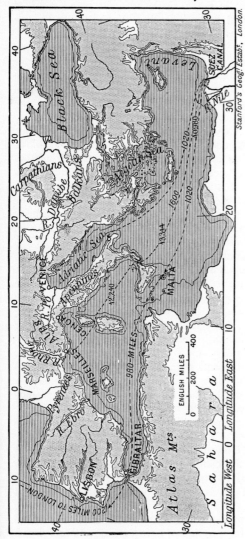

Mediterranean area.

The triple variety of land forms must have involved certain differences of human development inside the area; and these differences of local environment were bound to be accentuated by differences of foreign environment — French and Austrian, Greek and Spanish, all more or less connected with the Alpine uplift, or African and Arab, influences from the desert, the Arabian influence ideally illustrated in the cathedral of the ill-fated Messina.   **Foreign Environment.**

The presence of the sea on three sides, as in France, gave facilities for commerce in three directions, and wide commerce is always favourable to tolerance and cosmopolitanism; but it also isolated the area in such a way as to render defence relatively easy   **Sea Frontier.**
and to encourage political unity, at least in language and creed.
The sites of nearly all the chief towns, the routes of the chief
railways, the presence of "sea-coal" everywhere, the number of
fishermen (over 160,000)—though they "fish" mainly for coral and

sponge—all illustrate the sea control.   It should be noticed, however, that the number of good harbours is very small, especially on
the Adriatic, where there is not a single adjacent island south of
Rimini nor a single natural harbour south of Venice ; even the few
that do exist have curiously limited hinterland ; except in the Po
basin, there is practically no hinterland with water-transport ; the
great excess of imports over exports in weight makes it very difficult
for vessels to get return cargoes ; and the economic position of the
country with regard to the Suez route and between the industrial
west and the raw materials of the east tends to minimise the
importance of the purely domestic and national trade.   Yet, thanks to
the great Alpine tunnels, Genoa in 1925 became the *first* Mediterranean port (8,200,000 tons), about 1,000,000 tons ahead of Marseilles.

Land Frontier.   The land frontier has always been a real protection and an
isolating medium, and has encouraged unity—linguistic, if not always
political—to the south of it ; but the fact that these tunnels run
under passes that have been in constant use for centuries—the
Mont Cenis and the St. Gothard for certainly 2000 years—suggests
that the isolation has never been complete politically or economically.
The reason for this is obviously in the physical character of the
barrier.   It is concave towards Italy, and steeper on the Italian than
on the non-Italian side.   The early melting of the snow and ice
on the south side led to very heavy weathering, which involved a
steep climb up from the south, while the approach to the scarp from
the north, *e.g.* by the Brenner route, was gradual and easy—falling
nearly 1000 feet more in the first 80 miles south from the Brenner
than in the first 80 miles north from it.   Further, the convergence
of the valleys on the concave side always made it easier to invade
Italy from France or Austria than *vice versa*; indeed, it was
impossible for Italy to move by more than one route at a time, for
increase of distance from the base involved increase of distance
between the routes.   Economically it is specially important that the
basins of the three great rivers, Ticino, Adda, and Adige, give
access almost due north and south.

Frontier Line.   The precise frontier illustrates one result of the political disunion
which we may presently associate with the internal relief of the land,
for that disunion enabled the highlanders to encroach on what was
linguistically Italian.   Towards France it is approximately the crest
of the Alps ; but two things are significant.   On the one hand,
barren, lonely heights can watch and control—for good or ill—the
valley roads ; and thus the position of Savoy astride of Mont Blanc
was so dominating that it enabled a Savoy king to give unity to
modern Italy by taking advantage of political trouble on the outward
flanks of the Alps in 1860, 1866, and 1870.   Savoy, however, was
naturally the price that had to be paid to the French for their help
towards the first great effort in 1860.   On the other hand, the

seaward end of the actual frontier-line should be the ridge of the Maritime Alps which forms the water-parting between the Roja and the Paillon basins, and which reaches the sea at C. Martin. Similarly in the east the seaward end should be the water-parting ridge of the Julian Alps where they abut on the extreme north of the Gulf of Trieste.

The approaches to the great Trans-Alpine railway routes introduced other factors. The whole of the Ticino and the Adda basins is linguistically, and should be politically, Italian, but is content to be Swiss; the Adige valley, like the Danube valley, has been too much of a thoroughfare to give any natural site for a frontier, but Austria gained immense military superiority by pushing south of the water-parting. In 1919 Italy gained nearly 9000 square miles of territory and over 1,500,000 of people, including 250,000 Germans; and, even if her natural frontier is *not* east of the Julian water-parting, Italians, like ancient Romans, have a real power—quite unknown among Germanic peoples—of assimilating alien types. Economically, if not politically, the whole of the Adige basin is appropriately in Italy; but the linguistic frontier is just north of Trent, although the mountaineers have overflowed on to the fertile lowland of the Po.

The most important features of the internal geography are the **Small** size, the shape, and the natural divisions. The small size, now just **Area.** that of the British Isles, was an unmixed benefit in early historic times; it involved easy knowledge of the land and its people and possibilities, it necessitated the concentration which developed a national type, and it based this type on a civilisation in which— owing to the restricted area for food-supply—artificial and sedentary modes of supplying the needs of life were early substituted for primitive and nomad modes.

As far as the shape is concerned, the fundamental characteristic **Length v.** is a disproportion between length and breadth, whether viewed as a **Breadth.** whole or as two areas, continental and peninsular. Its greatest length is about 700 miles, *i.e.* a little longer than Great Britain, while its average width is not a quarter of that. The continental basin alone has an extreme "length" from east to west (350 miles) at least three times its average "width" from north to south; the peninsula is normally less than 100 miles wide from east to west, and even that is "halved" by the Apennines. The area was, therefore, too long for its width to be easily ruled in early days from a single centre, especially while the Po valley was still forested and water-logged. It was this difficulty which forced on the Romans the necessity for covering the whole land with a skeleton of great roads, properly paved and bridged, and running—as no doubt the Tiber valley suggested from the very first—up the great river-valleys; and it was significant that they probably took their name from the *roma* or *groma*,

" the four cross roads " which crossed at the Forum, and that their priestly kings were essentially pontifices, " bridge-builders."

Natural Divisions.   Peninsular isolation with varied relief is most favourable to the development of marked individuality in a people.   And the natural division into three separate areas accentuates the differences of climate, with the consequent differences of occupations and interests, that are implied in the great length of the country from north to south ; and it was on these differences that the political disunity of the area was based.

Continental Plain.   By far the most important division, except in actual size, is the continental one ; and it may itself be subdivided into two parts of very unequal importance,—the old basin of the Po, which lies west

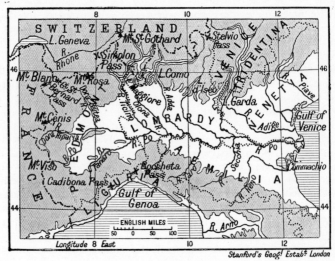

The Po and Piave basins.

of the old mouth of the river at Ferrara, being very much more important than the " Venetian " plain.   This importance is essentially based on its character as an old gulf of the Adriatic filled with alluvium from the mountains that shut it in on north, west, and south ; and this in turn accounts for its low and level surface, its fertility and ease of cultivation, and its original superabundance of forest and marsh.   The overwhelming importance of the Alps over the Apennines in this connection depends on their greater height, their greater exposure to the wet winds, their greater steepness ; the Po drops 5000 feet in its first 20 miles ; the rainfall on the northern boundary of the plain is always over 40 inches, while that on the southern boundary is sometimes only 20 ; and the average height of the glaciated Alps is over 12,000 feet, while that of the

Apennines is under 6000.   The force of the Alpine inflow is, therefore, so much stronger than that from the Apennines that the Po is shoved southward to the very spurs of the latter, as under similar circumstances the Danube is shoved southward against the Bulgarian scarp and the Ganges against the scarp of the Dekkan. And this southward movement of the line of the river involves the greater width of plain having a slight southward, *i.e.* sunward, slope close enough up to the Alps to get the maximum of shelter.

These conditions, accentuated by the low level, the natural **Its River** fertility, and the ease of cultivation, have made the area enormously **Régime.** productive in modern times, as they made it enormously attractive to round-headed mountaineers in early times ; but they imply reasons for the late political and economic development of the plain. For the number of rivers feeding the main stream from the north involved a maximum number of obstacles to communication east-and-west, while the forest and marsh were equally adverse to communication north-and-south.   Such an area was bound to have a low swampy "island and lagoon" coast ; and its condition and even its size were bound to be much changed by the banking of the Po, east of the last spur of the Apennines near Piacenza.   This was rendered necessary by the régime of the river, which—though nominally navigable by steamer to Valenza—is rough at high water and silted at low water ; and the embanking was both a protection against flood and a means of confining the low-water current so as to give it a maximum scouring power.   The consequent facilities for irrigation account for the high value of the rice crop (averaging 1,000,000 tons a year) ; but the fertilising floods, instead of being naturally spread over the riverine lands, are now carried down to the sea, extending the delta so rapidly that the Adriatic coast is now 20 miles from Adria, and the river-bed has been so much raised at the head of the delta that the town of Ferrara is actually below the water level.

Historically, the political importance of the basin has been **Its His-** greater even than its economic importance, for the Alps played a **toric Im-** part similar to that played by the Appalachians in the early history **portance.** of North America.   They were a useful check on the premature expansion of the Romans, as in the Middle Ages on the " Roman " claims of the German Emperors ; and when they did let movements of people in or out, it was only in small groups and at considerable intervals of time and place.   The Po basin thus became a natural transition area politically as well as physically.   To this day purely Teutonic features may be traced round the Italian outlet of the Brenner route, as purely French dialects are used in Piedmont, and as markedly round heads are found over the whole plain—thus incidentally minimising ethnic difficulties at the various times when the plain has been politically attached to a purely Continental Power located in Alpine Europe.   All the various elements—

including Saxon, Slav, and Bulgar—even of the Lombard invasion—
were apparently absorbed by the dense population into which they
intruded; but they infused that population with influences, physical
and otherwise, which accentuated the natural differences between
Northern and Southern Italians as based on the natural differences
of geographic environment.   The same essential conditions underlie
the saying that "The Po valley has been the cockpit of Europe."

Peninsu-   The peninsula is threaded by the Apennines from the Altare
lar Relief. Pass to Cape Spartivento, presenting a steep face to the nearer

| | Apennine forelands | Alluvium |
| Remnants of Tyrrhenian crust block. |
| Fold system of Alps and Apennines. |

Tectonic map of Italy.

coast, *i.e.* to the Adriatic in the northern half and the Tyrrhenian
Sea in the southern.   Similarly, in Liguria, where the range is
steepest, there is practically no coast strip at all.   Indeed, it is the
steepness and the increase of height eastward of Genoa—up to 7000
feet—that make the Riviera di Levante so favourable to the growth
of olive and orange, and that account for the uniformity of human
type and the purity of the Italian language to the south.   At the
head of the gulf, the Altare, Giovi, and Bochetta passes facilitate
access inland—by tunnels now—from Savona to Turin and from
Genoa *via* Novi to Turin and Milan; and a tunnel under the La

Cisa Pass, which separates the Ligurian from the Tuscan Apennines, gives a good route between the land-locked gulf of Spezzia and the Parma valley.   The slopes of the range are extensively forested, mainly with chestnut, oak, and beech; and their upper slopes give excellent pasturage.

The Tuscan and Umbrian sections of the range form the most **Main** important part, not only because here their gentler slope opens out **Water-** westward—while their steeper slope is so inaccessible that it is still **shed.** the site of the independent republic of San Marino—but also because the diversion caused by the hard old rock of the Etrurian " remnant" gave the range its greatest eastward detour just where the wettest winds that ever reach Italy—north of the Barbary and Corsican heights—first strike land.   Inside this great detour, then, there are both room and rain sufficient for largish rivers, the Arno and the Tiber; the hard old rock is rich in mineral wealth, *e.g.* at Carrara and Massa and in the Catena Metallifera; and the Chiana depression between the old rock and the new is so level that water flows, according to the wind, into the Arno or the Tiber.   Similarly, in Latium to seaward of the Tiber valley there is a line of hills independent of the Apennines; but in this case they are volcanic, *e.g.* Monte Amiata, and the volcanic action is seen all over the undulating plain of the Roman campagna, showing itself in such typical crater lakes as that of Bolsena.

Farther south the range is divided into three separate chains, **Central** rising from 7000 feet in the west to 8000 in the centre, and to **Apen-** nearly 10,000 in the east.   Down the windward slope flow such **nines.** rivers as the Nera and the Anio, and between the western and central ridges there are such natural basins as that of Lake Fucino or Celano; while between the central ridge,—where Terminillo and Velino are snow-capped from November to May,—and the Gran Sasso-Maiella barrier the Aquila valley is the coldest place in Italy. Lake Fucino, which is exactly in the middle of the peninsula, is about 2200 feet above the sea; and Aquila is 200 feet higher still. This central belt is not so difficult to cross as it might seem at first sight, however, because the rivers take the sudden bends so characteristic in limestone, *e.g.* the Aterno between the Gran Sasso (9560 feet) and Maiella (9170); and thus communication between the two fertile lowlands on each side is facilitated even for railways, as it was for the old Roman roads, *e.g.* the Via Salaria.

Farther south still the three parallel chains are broken up into **Southern** somewhat incoherent groups, closing in on the west and opening **Apen-** out towards the Adriatic.   On each side there is again the appear- **nines.** ance of independent heights, *e.g.* M. Amiato and M. Gargano, isolated from the Apennines by lowland—the Campanian plain and the northern tongue of the Apulian plain.   But, while the latter continues to the "heel" at Otranto, the "toe" of Calabria is

entirely mountainous, and from the Sila forest (6300 feet) to the
sea consists of the same ancient rocks as the Etrurian remnant.

Temperature. Climatically, the typical Mediterranean features of dry heat and
a cool rainy season are modified by local relief. As in India, the
lower level and remarkable shelter of the northern plain compensate
for its higher latitude, while the higher level of the southern
peninsula is accompanied by greater exposure; so that there is
some unity of average temperature over the whole area—the mean
temperature of Udine not differing 10° F. from that of Syracuse.
But the Po basin is so much cut off from oceanic influences that
it has considerable extremes, Milan having a normal range of
over 40° F. at a height of under 500 feet above the sea. On the
contrary, the narrowness of the lowland strip on each side of the
Apennines minimises the effect of the summer-drought, although
even in Tuscany camels are not unknown.

Rainfall. The rainy seasons are, however, not purely of the Mediterranean
type. North and east of the Apennines the rainy season is late

The malarial districts of Italy, shown
in stipple.

autumn, when the land has already
cooled and the relative warmth of
the Adriatic leads to local low-
pressure phenomena—which have
a significant relation to the unique
development of seamanship amongst
the Slavs of the Dalmatian coast;
but south and west of the Apennines there are also winter rains,
and there are even heavy summer
rains (25 per cent of the total)
along the foot of the Alps, *e.g.* at
Milan, while in the extreme south
there may be summer rains (3 per
cent of the total) from the Trades,
e.g. at Syracuse. It is largely the
autumn rains, acting on decaying
vegetation along the banks of silted rivers from deforested highlands, that account for the prevalence of malaria, to which 80 per
cent of the southern Italians have been subject in recent years, with
20,000 deaths every year. Obviously, the disease has had most power
where the fresh south-west wind has least, *i.e.* in the lee of Corsica
and Sardinia, *e.g.* the Maremmas, the Campagna, and the Pontine
marshes; and these are the very places where otherwise the combination of heat and moisture might be, and is gradually being made,
most favourable to agriculture.

Scenic Effects. The variations of temperature are curious, the range being
greatest where the rainfall is greatest and most evenly distributed;
and it is this abnormality that largely accounts for the productive-

ness of the northern plain, as also for some of the scenic effects in the Alps. For the great range of temperature, with its slight effect on the ice and its marked effect on the soil of the heights, involves great disintegration; and the removal of the disintegrated material leaves sharp peaks and ragged edges, and is said to fill the glacial lakes at the foot of the range with the mica—in suspension—to which their intense blueness may be attributed. It is not easy, however, to trace the source of the said mica in the case of Lake Como, which is the deepest lake, some 900 feet *below* sea level.

The question of shelter is very important both directly and **Shelter.** indirectly. Indirectly, in the case of the Alps, it is dependent on conditions favourable to the development of the föhn wind (cf. p. 58); directly it is responsible for, *e.g.* the distribution of rice and olive. Thus, in December, Florence is 5° F. warmer than Bologna, and Genoa is 5° F. warmer than Florence; and the Tuscans need a charcoal-burning hand-stove when the Tramontano ("Wind from across the Mountains") blows,—as the Dutch need a peat-burning foot-stove against their ground-damp,—and their characteristic clothing is of linen in summer and fur in winter. So, on Lake Como the sites of Bellano looking north and Varenna looking south have given rise to the saying: "If you wish to anticipate Hell, go to Bellano in winter and Varenna in summer." And there is a similar saying about Arona and Angera on Lake Maggiore. Thus, olives are found right up under the Alps (46° N.), and then disappear, only reappearing south of the Apennines; for the winter cold—which accounts for the terrible suffering of the poor in winter—in the south of the Po plain is fatal to them, although the summer heat in the same place is great enough for rice. The worst cold, however, is in the intermont valleys in the east of the peninsula that are exposed to the Bora in winter, *e.g.* Aquila and Potenza; for the mountains are covered with snow—heavy falls occurring even in June—the valleys open northward, and the constant Low-Pressure system on the Adriatic naturally involves northerly winds on the west of the whirl. In Naples, *i.e.* the same latitude as Potenza, "cold is a word."

Everywhere, however, there is a very large percentage of sunshine, **Sunshine** from 45 to 54 per cent of the possible total for the latitude; and this means an average of fully three hours more sunshine every day all the year through at Rome than, *e.g.* at York. Indeed, the Roman's horror of rain—as illustrated by the fact that every other carter, peasant, and beggar carries an umbrella, as every other horse, donkey, and ox wears a mackintosh—is mainly due to its association with the cold and sunless season. On the other hand, the association of heat with the absence of rain leads to a great deal of outdoor life, *e.g.* in café and promenade, and accounts for the wonderful preservation of old buildings—where man has let them alone—in contrast to their speedy weathering in climates where the expanding power of heat is associated with the denuding power of rain, *e.g.* on the Thames Embankment, where Cleopatra's Needle has weathered more in the last 1800 weeks than in the previous 1800 years.

Farming. Under such circumstances, it is not surprising that, in spite of the large proportion of useless land ($8\frac{1}{2}$ per cent), more than 30 per cent of the total population is engaged in agricultural or pastoral occupations; grain and grass, fruit and fibres, are all typical; and in regard to all there are peculiar advantages and disadvantages. The latter are largely historical. On the one hand, reckless destruction of forest has led to such silting-up of

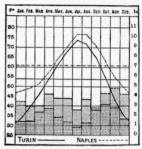

Rainfall and temperature of Turin and Naples.

rivers and water-logging of riverine lands that malaria either makes large areas quite useless or compels the cultivators to live at a considerable distance from their work, involving an immense waste of time and toil in getting to and from it; and this is complicated by drought in the peninsula and by hailstorms in the north—when a cold upper current from the Alps drops into the "hot-house" of the Po plain. The south is cursed, too, by the inheritance of Bourbon methods of holding land, under which an absentee sublet a large estate to be worked by hired labour; and it was specially in the Bourbon area that the land was deforested to pay Bourbon taxes,—that need for mutual help against the infamous Bourbon police led to the formation of secret societies,—and that questions of Temporal Power made it impossible for a good patriot to be a good "Christian," and made brigandage profitable.

Tuscany. On the other hand, much of the land is naturally very fertile, especially in the volcanic area round Naples, on the mixed soil of Tuscany, and in the alluvial north, where vines may be seen climbing up mulberry trees which overshadow growing maize. The climate encourages the use of vegetable rather than animal food, and this in turn encourages a dense population, so that neither labour nor market is lacking; and fortunately where the average conditions are naturally best—in Tuscany,—historically the system of holding land has practically combined the advantages of "large" and "small" farming. For both landlord and tenant are directly and jointly interested in the land; the mixed crops and the normal rotation give work evenly distributed all through the year, *e.g.* harvest varying from wheat in June, through wine, to oil in December, and the consequent wide experience trains an adaptable as well as an industrious type of man. Indeed, the good reputation of the Italian colonists in the New World a generation ago was largely due to the considerable percentage of Tuscans, driven to emigrate by the smallness of their farms (30 acres) and the consequent small demand for labour.

The most important cereal is wheat, which occupies 32 p.c. of **Wheat.** the arable land, and averages now 18 bushels per acre. The low pre-War yield was partly due to the fact that in Tuscany it is grown as a spring crop, and is intentionally "crowded," with the result that there is a very quick growth of the "leggy" and pliable kind needed in the straw-plait industry of Leghorn, Pisa, and other Tuscan towns. Somewhat similar conditions prevail in the north of the Venetian plain, *e.g.* near Vicenza, the straw-plaiting itself being a domestic and rural industry, while the making of the hats is a factory and town industry, *e.g.* at Marostica. The girls who pull and plait the straw seem also to attend to its cultivation on the barren foothills of the Piave basin, where climatic conditions made the grain as valueless as the straw is valuable—for its pale colour, its elasticity, and its lustre. The hard wheat of the more droughty areas, *e.g.* Apulia, is specially used in the making of macaroni and other alimentary pastes; and much the same conditions are found just in the lee of the Apennines, *e.g.* round Parma. It was the large industry in such pastes that accounted for the huge imports of wheat before the War; the annual import now is scarcely 2,500,000 tons.

Maize is a typically summer crop of the moister lands, as wheat **Maize.** (for grain) is a winter crop of the drier lands; it occupies nearly half as much area as wheat, but is much more widely spread. Indeed, it is cultivated almost everywhere as an alternative crop, partly because it can follow, *e.g.* hemp, so that two crops can be reaped off the same land in one summer,—partly because it is very prolific, giving a large return on a small expenditure,—and partly because maize polenta is essentially *stodgy*, so that a little goes a long way. The poor quality of the grain, however, in many parts is so deleterious that it renders the peasants too weak to resist the poisonous attacks of the sand-flies which carry pellagra.

The high spring and autumn temperatures in the Ticino **Rice.** lowlands, the facilities for irrigation, and the high latitude, combine to make the rice of supremely good quality in Lombardy and Piedmont. Good rice is also grown round Ravenna and Salerno, and the Italian peasant is accustomed to laborious cultivation, such as rice needs; but the attraction of mosquitoes to the rice-lands and the competition of monsoon lands, where natural floods restore the land annually after the ravages of such an enormously prolific crop, are leading to a considerable reduction in the rice area. At the same time, better cultivation has slightly increased the yield per acre. Novara and Pavia are much the most important provinces in acreage and total yield, the yield per acre being usually highest in Pavia and Mantua; the total acreage is *c.* 350,000.

Pasture : Cattle.

Pasture stands next in importance to grain-growing, and the relative value of the various kinds of stock—as compared with the British—is a significant comment on relief, climate, and distribution of population. Thus cattle, which are much the most important,— before the war valued at £90,000,000,—stand to British cattle as 7 to 7, while sheep are only as 11 to 24 ; and this represents roughly the relative value of irrigated (naturally or artificially) and un-irrigated pasture. The natural water-meadows along the banks of the Po are mainly devoted to dairy cattle, especially in Emilia ; and irrigated meadows both in Emilia and in Lombardy are similarly used. The milk is everywhere made into cheese, which in Emilia takes its name usually from the old Duchy of Parma,—though now made specially round Lodi,—and in Lombardy takes its name from the town of Gorgonzola. In the Tuscan and Roman maremmas, as along the Chiana valley, the natural water-meadows are devoted especially to the fattening of foreign cattle, *e.g.* from Switzerland. In the north, too, a great deal of hay is made, irrigated meadows yielding sometimes nine crops in as many months.

Pasture : Sheep.

Sheep-farming is still largely a semi-nomad occupation and confined to the drier parts of the country, for the flocks are brought down to the plains in winter, falls of snow on the Apennines being so heavy that in some villages communication between house and house can only be conducted by tunnels through the snow. The chief centres are the Alpine slopes of Piedmont, which are very much in the lee of the Alps,—the Central Apennines in Umbria and Abruzzi, — and the Southern Apennines in Apulia, Basilicata, and Calabria, where, however, the weight of washed wool per sheep is small. In the northern half of the country the local supplies of wool support local woollen industries, especially in Piedmont and Tuscany (cf. the old Banker wool-merchants of Florence) ; in the southern half — where the bright light is particularly favourable to the bleaching of the skins—the chief "pastoral" industry is in glove-dressing, Naples handling often 3,000,000 sheep and goat skins a year, and converting the very tough gut, *e.g.* of Foggia, into violin-strings by treating it with the local sulphur. The number of sheep, and still more of goats, is decreasing, however, largely owing to new forest laws ; for sheep and goats have been the greatest enemies to the survival of forest. Tuscany and Latium produce the largest quantity, while Piedmont and Venetia show the heaviest weight per sheep. In consequence of the decreased supply at home, there is a growing import of wool (raw, washed, and combed), mainly from Argentina, Australia, and France ; but the best lamb-skins in the world (for gloves) still come from Italy.

The Vine.

The vine is cultivated practically throughout the whole country, and wine is the universal drink ; but the area under vineyards is relatively small in the north. The large percentage of bright sun-light, the high September temperature (60° F. being an optimum), the abundance of cheap labour, the cool equable cellars in the tufa or the natural crotti in the limestone, the local supplies of sulphur for treating the vines, are all favourable to the wine industry; and Italy stands second in the whole world for quantity. But the quality is inferior. This is to some small extent due to the latitude, which is really favourable only to the heavier type of white wine, *e.g.* Marsala, and which does not guarantee a dry harvest-time (September–November, according to locality); but it is mainly due to bad methods. The large owners are "too proud" to purify—they call it "adulterate"—their wines, while the small owners are too ignorant and too poor to store the wine properly or to treat the vines properly; so that the wines will rarely keep for any time. The best "export" wines come naturally from the least backward provinces, *e.g.* the Asti of Piedmont and the Chianti of Tuscany; but some of the local growths that are used locally, especially those of Capri and Vesuvius, have a great reputation. Over-production was a real danger, but has been minimised by the ravages of the phylloxera and peronospora. Cork and vat-wood (chestnut) are local products.

The olive is more characteristic than even the vine, and—like **The Olive** the chestnut—an essential part of the people's food; and Italy stands next to Spain in the world for the quantity of olive-oil pro-duced, and equals France in quality. In the south the tree flourishes without any shelter, and there are continuous woods of nothing but olives, *e.g.* round Bari and Lecce; and in some parts *e.g.* at the shipping-port of Gallipoli, there are wonderful "natural cisterns" in the limestone available for the clarify-ing of the oil. Here, too, the winter rains guarantee "power" for the mills exactly at the right time; and there is abundance of cheap labour,—from labourers willing to pick for nineteen or twenty hours continuously! But the olive, like the vine, is a warm-temperate rather than a sub-tropical product; and the finer oil comes from the higher latitudes. The tree can flourish in latitude 46° N.—right up under the Alps, but disappears from the Po plain, where the climate is too extreme; and even when it first reappears, south of the Apennines, it requires some protection in the areas which produce the finest oil. The superiority of the Tuscan oils, *e.g.* from Lucca and Pisa, is due partly to the under-ground heat, which is also evidenced by the number of thermal springs. The finest quality is won by hand-crushing, as the finest wine is made by foot-crushing, for machinery in each case is apt to bring out unpleasant astringent properties. The wood of the olive, like that of the walnut for which Italy is also famed, shows the influence of summer-drought on colour. Cf. p. 71.

Citron.   The various kinds of citron, or *agrumi*,—all, like maize and tobacco, relatively modern importations, but from the Old World, not the New,—are specially important in the south; and even there they are largely confined to the hinterland of the Tyrrhenian Sea, where the "intermediate" climate produces, *e.g.* oranges intermediate in type between the insular "St. Michaels" and the semi-continental "Jaffa." As oranges—though not lemons—are all ripe at once, there is need for abundance of cheap labour; so that this industry is again suited to the country. The winter rains, too, supply the means of irrigating; but this is not an unmixed advantage. It quickens growth, but tends to incomplete ripening, which makes the fruit less palatable, or to excess of juice, which makes it travel badly. Various processes in the citric-acid trade are centered at Messina and Palermo. Like the almonds, *e.g.* of Bari, and the figs, *e.g.* of Catanzaro, oranges and lemons enter very largely into the foreign commerce of the country.

Silk— Mulberry.   The mulberry is as wide-spread as the vine and—though also a modern importation—as characteristic as the olive; and Italy holds the first place in Europe and the third place in the world for the quantity of silk produced, while it holds the first place in the world for quality. Both the human and the climatic notes are important. The tree flourishes best in damp heat, but the silk-worms' eggs keep best in dry heat; and irrigation obviously bridges the gulf. The shelter of the Alps, especially in the Ticino basin, guarantees the necessary six or seven weeks of hot spring (60° F. being desirable). The northern plain supplies an abundance of the essential cheap labour, with the necessary qualifications of delicate fingers, patience, and assiduous carefulness,—mainly for rearing the silk-worms, but also for picking and cutting up the leaves, etc. The maximum of regular showers in conjunction with perfect shelter makes Lombardy more favourable than Piedmont, *e.g.* Bergamo having an almost ideal situation; but both provinces have had valuable external influences, French and Swiss, and the most important area is along the provincial frontier in the Ticino valley. On the other hand, the summer in the Mediterranean is naturally too dry to allow usually of more than one crop of leaves being taken in the year, which means only one generation of silk-worms; and this accounts for the almost total absence of "silk" over the whole belt of minimum rainfall which lies—in a straight line—between the south-west of Tuscany and the south-east of Apulia, in the lee of Corsica and Sardinia to the north-west and in the lee of the Apennines to the south-east. These conditions limit the available time to the spring months, *i.e.* precisely the time when other farm work is most pressing; so that the industry suits only small holdings, especially those where most of the labour can fall on women and children.

Somewhat similar considerations enter into the question of the **Hemp and** distribution of fibres. No doubt, the site of the old forested marsh, **Flax.** especially where the Po plain opens out east of the Adda confluence, provides the firm, moist, fibrous soil which is most favourable to flax and hemp; and the warm-temperate conditions of the north tend to fineness of fibre as the sub-tropical conditions in the south tend to abundance of oil, so that Cremona is as famous for its linen and Bologna for its cordage, as Naples—with its local cork and sulphur —is for paints and linoleum. But the essential consideration is a standard of civilisation so low that women are allowed to do heavy field labour.

The question of cotton-growing involves different considerations. **Cotton.** Herbaceous cotton—like the excellent "Levant" tobacco which is raised on the unirrigated sheep-pastured lands of the "Two Sicilies" —is evidently suited to both soil and climate in the south, and large quantities were grown, especially during the American Civil War; but by 1870 U.S.A. cotton was on the market again, and the Franco-Prussian War brought to a head the critical period in which the phylloxera trouble had involved French wine-growers. A large proportion of the old cotton-lands in Italy was, therefore, put under vineyards; and a return to cotton-growing is rather impeded now by the proximity of Egypt.

The distribution of minerals may be associated with the presence **Minerals.** of old crystalline or new volcanic rock; and, as the amount of old rock is very limited except in Sardinia, we cannot look for much metal. The volcanic products include sulphur, borax, and pumice; the sulphur (now only 12 p.c.)—specially valuable for medicinal purposes because (perhaps *not* volcanic in origin) of its freedom from arsenic, as the Lipari pumice is free from crystals—is most abundant in Sicily, *e.g.* at Girgenti and Catania; while the borax comes mainly from the Volterran district of Tuscany, famous also for its alabaster (a sulphate of calcium). As to metals, Sardinia is rich in all kinds, *e.g.* iron and lead, copper and zinc, especially on the Iglesias scarp; and the metalliferous rock reappears in Elba, where it is very rich in fine iron, and in the Tuscan mines, which include tin and mercury[1] (Monte Amiata). The influence of igneous intrusion is also seen in the marble of Carrara and Massa. Iron of an inferior quality is found in Lombardy, and the presence of both iron and silicious schist (for grindstones) in the Val Trompia led to the early sword-making industry of Brescia. Milan, with equally easy access to charcoal and better iron (near Bergamo), developed on similar lines.

The fundamental defect in the natural resources of the area is **Coal v.** the total absence of coal except for some deposits of lignite, *e.g.* **Water-** near the edge of the old rock in Tuscany, especially in Arezzo, **Power.** Pisa, and Grosseto; and this has not only retarded the growth of

[1] With Idria (cf. p. 105) Italy now produces *c.* 50 p.c. of the world output.

manufactures, but has also increased the reckless use of wood. The Government, however, is doing its best to stop the waste of wood and to reafforest; and the scarcity of fuel, which still involves an annual import of *c.* 12,000,000 tons of coal (including "Reparations"), is almost compensated for by the development of water-power. For this there are quite exceptional facilities, which the reafforestation can only increase; and the proper utilisation of the streams at higher levels for industrial purposes would naturally improve the facilities for using them at lower levels for agricultural purposes. For instance, the diversion of the river Sele from the Tyrrhenian Sea to the Adriatic has not only supplied two droughty provinces with much-needed water, but also led to a material improvement in the drainage of the malarial plain of Salerno.

Distribution of Water-Power. It is estimated that the total amount of hydraulic power available reaches 8,000,000 h.p., at least half of which can be supplied by "efficient" waterfalls (numbered at over 24,000); and of the total in use nearly 75 p.c. is distributed in Northern Italy, and well over 22 p.c. in Central Italy. Already the fuel question has been practically eliminated in the cotton industry; and similar developments are going on in all sorts of industries in all parts of the country, *e.g.* at Genoa and Spezia, Brescia and Bergamo, in the dyeing of Schio, the woollen industry of Novara, the cheese-making of Lecco, the manufacture of aluminium from the Aquila bauxite, the steel-works of Terni. Indeed, in Northern Italy not only all the small cities, but groups of villages also, are supplied with power in this way; the *per caput* consumption here (500 kw. hours, *i.e.* 10 times that in Southern Italy) has doubled since 1914. The total amount of power already at work is over 3,500,000 h.p., of which only 1·8 p.c. is used for lighting purposes.

Town Sites. One of the chief considerations in the economic distribution of people is the proximity of this water-power to the most productive agricultural areas, and the advantage of this has been increased by the fact that the great historic towns are normally found on "Piedmont" sites between the source of power and the source of food. For instance, the typical site in the north is above the swamp of the old "Gulf" plain, below the mountains, where a valley deploys from the latter on to the former, and at the lowest point in the transition "Piedmont" area where the river, if present, could best be bridged, *e.g.* Milan and Brescia, Verona and Vicenza, or Piacenza and Parma, Modena and Bologna. At the eastern end of each line there was an obvious alternative between clinging to the valley-mouth, *e.g.* at Treviso and Rimini, or making a direct line for the sea, *e.g.* at Venice *via* Padua or at Ravenna. Of course, towns were bound to spring up along the line of the main river; but there, too, the sites show the importance of the bridge and of avoiding the swamp, all the chief towns being characteristically east of a confluence, so saving one bridge and avoiding the marsh between the converging rivers. Thus, Pavia is to the east of the Ticino, Piacenza east of the Trebbia, and Cremona east of the Adda.

Milan, or Mediolaneum, as the "Middle-plain" site, illustrates **Milan.** almost every point at issue. It stands about 500 feet above the sea, in the middle of the fertile Lombard plain, about half-way between the 300-foot contour that edges the Po flats and the 600-foot contour of the Piedmont terrace. It is thus between pastoral and agricultural, montane and lowland, areas, where summer-drought is unknown, and yet where—thanks partly to the smallness of its local stream, the Olona—floods are also unknown. Its facilities for communication no doubt reflect the strategic dangers which in olden days made the forging of sword-blades the typical industry, as the tallness and relative fairness of the surrounding population reflect the ease with which "Long-beards" pressed southward *via* the Rhine and Rhone and Inn basins. It is still a great agricultural market, but silk has become more important than flax; and it is still a great nodal junction, but cutlery has displaced armour, as motor-cars have displaced the old mule transport. The causes of its slow development in the past imply, therefore, the causes of its modern success; free communication and diversity of economic interest, local and international, have raised it to a great metropolis with a population of about 960,000.

Its natural rivals were the two "End-plain" sites of Turin and **Turin.** Venice. The position of Turin upon "Piedmont" levels and between two great converging rivers suggests at once an essential difference of environment. With double access *via* Susa to the Lower Rhone, and at the head of navigation on the joint river, it too had a geographic nodality; but the purity of the Alpine Round-head type in the local population implies an isolation which made it a safe capital for Piedmont and even for Italy during the early struggle for unity (1860–1861), as its old name Augusta *Taurinorum* implies a pastoral rather than an agricultural area. It is still the headquarters of the woollen industry.

Venice presents a direct contrast to Milan, for the conditions of **Venice.** its old success have been its greatest drawbacks in modern times, though it still remains the seaward end of an important west-and-east land route and the landward end of an important south-and-north sea-route. Its site is 120 islands on the edge of 200 square miles of lagoon, which once formed the central sea of the "Seven Seas" between the famous old Roman port of Aquileia and the old Ostro-Goth capital of Ravenna, each now 6 miles inland. These islands are inside the incomplete storm-beach of the Lido; for it is precisely here that the gales from the constant Low-Pressure system over the Adriatic in winter drive the surf against a sloping shore of coarse shingle—rich in material for mosaic-work—while the south-

ward trend of the tide down the western coast of the Adriatic has prevented the silt of the Po and the Adige from filling up the gaps in the
beach. Three or four good channels, therefore, remain open, the best
being in the lee of the rialto ("high bank"); and this has now been
artificially deepened to 30 feet, while the lagoon has been joined to
the mainland by a railway bridge of 222 arches (2¼ miles).

Here was a natural refuge, *e.g.* from Hun and Lombard, with
enough tide to puzzle the dwellers round the "tideless" Mediterranean,
so protecting it by land and sea, *e.g.* from Pepin and the Genoese,
and to make it fairly sanitary. Made naturally healthy by the
fresh winds to which the beach owed its very existence, and rich in
shore-feeding fish, *e.g.* red mullet, and in the means for evaporating

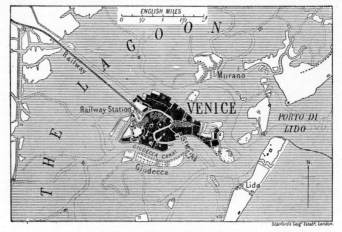

Venice: the islands, canals, and lagoon.

the invaluable salt, Venice began its career early, and got an
initial advantage which it preserved for centuries. All raids on
Italy after the fifth or sixth century helped to build up Venice,
with a population of refugees devoted to personal liberty and so to
republican forms. Easy access to the sea that led to the fabulous
East, and across the fertile plain to the Alpine passes, gave her
command of the greatest medieval trade-route, *e.g.* for transport of
Crusaders seaward, or of costly gems and spices landward; and the
Orient trade brought such wealth and consequent leisure as to favour
the local development of artistic industries, *e.g.* in damask, glass,
and gold lace.

**Other
Plain
Sites.**

Of the other well-known cities on the northern plain, most
have had their real importance exaggerated by strategic considerations which have been essentially adverse to them, *e.g.* Mantua and
Verona (in its river-loop); and the best natural site, that of Bologna,

has suffered from the relative ease of communication between continental and peninsular Italy, as illustrated by the absence of "Alpine" intruders in the north-west of Tuscany and the constant presence of them in Umbria and the Marches. In the time of the
Ostro-Goth emperors, however, Bologna, like Ravenna, profited by proximity to Byzantine influences, seen at Bologna in its possession of the oldest university in Europe, and at Ravenna in the remains of Byzantine architecture. The peaceful development of modern times involves the manufacture of flax products at Bologna and Ravenna, as of hemp products at Cremona and Mantua ; and the Poretta

The Quadrilateral.

Pass to the Arno valley has made Bologna an important cross-country railway junction.

The peninsula cities illustrate the same general controls, and have **Peninsular Sites.** somewhat similar inter-relations, *e.g.* between Rome and Florence, Naples and Genoa; but their history has been materially modified by the peninsular isolation, as illustrated by the purity of the long-headed Mediterranean race and their Italian tongue. In the case of Florence and Rome this isolation has been accentuated by the paucity of natural harbours both in front and in the rear, and by the practical absence of water access, though both cities stand nominally on navigable water, and had seaports in Pisa and Ostia.

Rome, like Venice, had an early start; and the volcanic hills on **Rome.** which it stands gave it as much protection after 400 B.C. from destructive floods and malaria as in earlier times from fertilising floods and political foes. It had the advantage of being on the edge of Latium, the "Broad-plain," which meant both fertility and a navigable river; and the presence of islands in the river greatly facilitated the first engineering works of the bridge-builders. The distance from the mouth of the river (14 miles) was a great protection against pirates and invasion, even in days when vessels drawing 12 feet of water could come up to the island on which stood the temple of Æsculapius, the Healer. The volcanic rock was easy to quarry and to cavern (cf. the Catacombs), the river itself protected most of the city from attack from over the broad plain, and the position was fairly central for the peninsula proper.

Florence, like Milan, though for a different reason, started late; **Florence.** indeed, it is scarcely mentioned before the days of Sulla, and could not have existed before the draining of the lake which once covered the lowlands (25 miles long and 11 wide, and under 200 feet above sea-level) between Florence and Pistoia.   The old tramontana road, therefore, crossed the Apennines by the La Futa Pass, not by the modern railway route *via* Pistoia and the Reno valley.   Nor was the district much thought of by the Etruscans—though relics of an old cyclopean fortress still crown the hill of Fiesole (970 feet)— because it is away from the metalliferous strata.   At the same time Tuscany is essentially the heart of Italy, as the Tuscan dialect is the best Italian ; and one reason in each case is the isolation of a fertile area.   How great this isolation is naturally may be gauged by the sharp distinction between the Alpine Broad-heads on the Emilian slope of the Apennines and the Mediterranean Long-heads in the Arno basin ; indeed, there is anthropological evidence that every- where north of Rome intruders normally entered the peninsula from the north-east corner by land, as south of Rome they entered from the south-east by sea.   Florence was thus a natural site for the capital of Italy, as it actually was in the second era of the struggle for unity (1865–1871) ; and Tuscany inherited something from the early days of Etruscan civilisation, which seems to have had some relation to the meeting of Alpine and Levantine traders round the richest mineral deposits known on the Orbis Terrarum.

Genoa.   Genoa, like Milan, as suggested by the presence of broad-headed intruders, is a gap city ; and it owed its old supremacy to its monopoly of the one good harbour on an inhospitable coast, to its easy access inland, and to its local supplies of timber for shipbuilding. But its modern development is mainly due to entirely extraneous causes—the cutting of the Suez Canal and the Alpine tunnels ; and, but for local obstacles, it would have been greater even than it is. The home hinterland is not large enough (perhaps a population of 9,000,000), and its industries are not such as to supply the port with an export trade anything like equal to its import trade ; and while the imports are mainly heavy and bulky goods, coal and iron, timber and grain, which—especially in view of the costly railway transport through the Alpine tunnels—must travel by water, the exports can afford to go by land, *e.g.* silk and olive-oil, eggs and fruit.   The result of this was such congestion in the port itself and on the lines through the Apennines that even in 1913 it could not serve its foreign hinterland properly ; for instance, Russian grain reached Switzerland in the proportion of about 100,000 tons *via* Rotterdam, 90,000 *via* Marseilles, and only 55,000 *via* Genoa. The same was true, *e.g.*, of the cotton imports into Zurich, though Genoa is much the nearest cotton-port.   Indeed, some cotton reached even the Po valley *via* Bremen.   Part of the difficulty was caused by the opposition of the local Labour Associations to the increase of railway facilities, especially between Genoa or Sampierdarena and the great junction of Novi ; but the great difference in the outward and inward traffic,—nearly 50 tons passing in for every 3 tons coming back,—and the fact that the great coal imports arrive mainly during the vintage, enormously complicate the question of supplying wagons, in spite of electrification of the traffic, *e.g.* through the Giovi tunnel and a funicular line for the transport of coal from Savona to S. Giuseppe. Cf. the Turin-Modane and the Milan-Sondrio lines.

Naples is somewhat in the same position, except that its hinter- **Naples.** land and the basis of its modern progress are strictly national, not international. As a fine natural harbour, on the edge of a very fertile plain, with a dense, poor, and clever population, it had many natural advantages ; and these were increased by the recent creation of a free zone round it. Thus, with a large local market, easy conditions of export and import, and practically complete exemption from taxation, the city is now the second largest in Italy, with a total population (including the suburbs) of 1,000,000. The artificial impulse has, however, been rather prejudicial to the old industries, and over-production is widespread, especially in the textile industries ; and at the same time the development of factories has completely destroyed a useful source of supplementary earnings from home industries, such as wood-carving and lace-making. One great advantage is that, like Genoa, the port has practically no rival, Leghorn being 200 miles north, Messina at least 150 miles south, Bari more than 100 miles east, and Brindisi 50 miles farther still.

With a dense and largely vegetarian population Italy must have an **Labour.** abundance of cheap labour ; and this is generally of a high standard, with centuries of inherited skill, especially in the handling of stone— from mosaic work and marble-cutting to road-making and bridge-building. There is also abundance of water-power ; and most of the actual water is of unusual purity, and therefore invaluable in textile industries. Further, the local raw materials are of great excellence—silk and marble, coral and sulphur, hemp and rice. The chief drawbacks are the widespread presence of malaria and the poverty which limits the people to two meals, of poor food, per day, forces them to live in over-crowded houses, and drives them abroad or into various forms of gambling and dishonesty. On the other hand, the spread of education and commerce, and the discipline and unifying influence of conscription, are raising the standard of comfort and removing the old jealousies between province and province.

Industrial development has been easier in the north than the **Indus-** south. Apart from the better climate, the more certain rainfall, the **tries.** greater fertility and water-power, the north has been favoured racially and historically. The Round-heads represent centuries of economic and political conditions favourable to the development of individualism without anarchy ; they have been inoculated with Northern ideas, though the total influx of Teutons probably never reached 100,000 persons ; and they have been largely under Austrian control. All these conditions combined to develop a burgher population, with business-like habits; for every 15 illiterates in Piedmont there are about 50 in Naples and 55 in Sicily; and the criminal statistics show very similar contrasts.

Textiles.   In the western parts of the continental area, where the extremes are greatest,—Turin having recorded a temperature of 7° F.,—animal products are more suitable than vegetable products; Piedmont specialises more in woollens, *e.g.* at Biella and Varillo, Turin and Pinerolo, while Lombardy specialises more in silks, *e.g.* at Como and Bergamo, Brescia and Milan. In the eastern part of the plain, as on the Ligurian coast, animal products are still worked, *e.g.* the wool and silk of Schio and Vicenza; but the smaller range of humidity encourages the working of vegetable products, *e.g.* the spinning of cotton at Pordinone and Chiavari, and the spinning and weaving of flax at Bologna and Ravenna.

Iron.   The greatest development has, however, taken place on strictly mechanical lines; and in this respect the peninsula has been, if anything, more favourably situated than the north. Italy is almost as poor in iron as in coal (lignite), but the deposits at Cogne and Nurras could be greatly developed; and there are really important steel-works at Terni, with power from the falls on the Nera, at Savona and Naples, and at Portoferraio ("Iron-harbour"), and on the opposite coast at Piombino. Where both ore and fuel have to be imported, *e.g.* at Savona, work is generally confined to later processes, *e.g.* the conversion of imported pig-iron into steel and the rolling of rails, etc.; and in the neighbourhood of great harbours there is a good deal of shipbuilding, *e.g.* at Sestri and Castellamare. Other forms of transport plant are also important, *e.g.* the motor-works of the Fabrica Italiana Automobile Torino (F.I.A.T.) at Turin.

Sicily.   Of the dependent islands Sicily is much the most important. It is almost entirely agricultural. A great increase in population has entirely killed its old importance as an exporter of grain; but the climate and the water-storing properties of its limestone are very favourable to the growth of oranges and lemons, which cover the coastlands along almost the whole of the east and north coasts from Catania to Palermo.

Sardinia.   The wild granitic highlands of Sardinia are rich in metals; but the rugged and inaccessible character of the island, and its bad climate, have been adverse to its prosperity. It is an island of dwarfs—man and beast. The small area, with its small food-supply and its bad climate, were always adverse to good physique in man or beast; the best of both were constantly leaving the country, man as well as beast being for sale ("Sardi venales") in earlier times; and constant in-breeding of the resultant inferior types has emphasised such typical "Mediterranean" traits as extreme length of head and shortness of stature.

The coastal part of the new territory is practically the old Küstenland, and its importance centres on Trieste, Pola, and Fiume. Pola is a fine naval station, and is well supported by the Italian possession of the Zara enclave and the islands of Lagosta and the well-named Pelagosa ("Open-Sea Island"); but Trieste has not a tithe of the commercial value to Italy that it had to Austria, and it is unfortunate that the possession of Fiume should give Italy a practical monopoly of the direct Mediterranean outlets of the various trans-Alpine routes from Central Europe.

The "Küstenland" ("Coast Land") includes a physically Italian area in the valley of the Isonzo, which drops on to the marshy lowland at Gorz,—the Karst terraces, sparsely peopled by Slavs and with a typical discontinuous river in the Rieka,—and the real coast-lands of the Istrian peninsula, densely peopled by Italians. Sheep-rearing on the heights and salt-working along the coast, *e.g.* at Pirano, are typical occupations; and the tunny-fishermen have access to excellent little ports, such as Porto Quieto and Paruzo (cf. Rovigno, with its busy tobacco industry). But, apart from Trieste and Pola, the area has neither commercial nor industrial importance, though there are a number of popular watering-places dotted along those parts of the coast least exposed to the bora, *e.g.* Capo d'Istria and Abbazia. In the new hinterland Italy has the important railway junction of Tarvis and the rich mercury mines of Idria. Cf. p. 97.

Trieste has one great advantage in being the natural terminus of the most easterly Alpine railway; but, as a port, it has only a narrow foothold on a strip of lowland below a steep scarp. Here, it is between the strong southerly gales from the Adriatic Low-Pressure centre (cf. p. 55) and the stormy bora, which at times makes the harbour inaccessible even for large steamers. In spite of fairly good railway facilities, therefore, traffic from the interior tends to gravitate down the Elbe or down the Danube; and only the most determined support from Vienna, especially in providing direct railway communication with Central Europe *via* Salzburg, enabled Trieste to become an important centre of American trade. Even this it had to share with Fiume, which was similarly supported from Budapest; indeed, Fiume ("River") is almost entirely an artificial creation—where the "little river," Fiumare, enters the stormy Quarnero Gulf from the last ridge of the Croatian "karst," the one with a typical fishing industry (sardine and tunny) and the other with an equally typical Pilgrims' Church, hung with thank-offerings from rescued mariners and approached by a "ladder" of 400 steps. As the capital of the new province of Carnaro, Fiume will completely dominate the tiny port of Baros, which—with the Delta—has been given to Jugo-Slavia. Jugo-Slav interests are to some extent safeguarded by the lease—for a nominal rent of one gold lira *per annum*

—of the Thaon de Revel docks ; but the lease is only for 50 years, and the coastal railway is entirely within Italian territory.

Pola.

Pola is marked out by site and character for a naval station, while its intensely unhealthy climate is adverse to the growth of a commercial centre. It is on an almost landlocked bay, with an entrance less than 800 yards wide and defended by islands ; so it became one of the chief naval stations of the Roman Empire, and still has the finest remains of a Roman amphitheatre in Europe. Its only characteristic trade is in the glass-sand which was originally worked by the Venetians, who built (in the sixteenth century) the still surviving town walls.

CHAPTER XII

THE SCANDINAVIAN PENINSULA

THE race-home of the old Vikings is a lonely peninsula which **Scandi-** presents the most marked contrasts to the central peninsula of the **navia v.** Mediterranean basin. Like Italy, it is largely mountainous, it has **Italy.** a considerable proportion of useless land, and it has been hard to govern from a single centre, especially in days of bad communication ; but the distribution of relief is profoundly different, and the different distribution of relief and the different latitude produce a difference of climate which admits of very few common crops. This, again, implies that the useless area in Scandinavia is useless from cold, not from malaria, and that the political difficulty is connected, not with a relative excess of length, but with the presence of a central mass of barren highland stretching over about half of the total area.

More important than all these differences historically were the **Patri-** differences of approach into the area. The early Goths of the **archal v.** Germanic steppe, as they moved westward under the pressure of **larist.** later nomads from the east, found the steppe narrowing with nearness to the Atlantic, until it practically disappears at the foot of the Schleswig peninsula. On the morainic lake-studded plain, with its fertile Baltic and Carpathian margins, these pastoral Goths had been tempted into agriculture, and had had an apprenticeship to boating ; and, as these conditions were bound to weaken patriarchal ties, it was a foregone conclusion that Scania would get energetic individuals—*via* the Danish islands—from the semi-patriarchal population of the Brandenburg plain. And the most typical features of the peninsula should throw light on the process by which it converted this semi-patriarchal inflow into a sternly particularist outflow.

The outflow from the peninsula, especially from the 12,000 **Oceanic** miles of the Norwegian coast, has been one of the greatest political **Develop-** phenomena ; and its causes are still largely operative. For we **ment,** shall find here a population driven by a barren and inaccessible hinterland to concentrate on a lonely, but relatively fertile, coastland ; and, though this was safe enough to leave them in perfect freedom, and isolated enough to develop in them a marked individuality, the teeming fishing-ground in front decided the lines on which that development should run, and made their history oceanic rather than continental.

Skerry Guard. The most characteristic feature of the whole area is the "skerry-guard" which fringes the coast almost continuously from the mouth of the Tornea round to the Varanger fiord.

It is not fully developed in the Gulf of Bothnia, and is entirely absent from the recent formation of Scania, where it is re-placed to windward by a line of sand-dunes ; but it is developed to a unique degree between Stavanger and the North Cape, and it provides the whole coast, except in Scania, with an almost continu-ous series of navigable sounds, which are at once the scene of a busy and safe commerce and a first line of defence against foreign attack. It is significant that all the artificial harbours of the area are on the Scanian coast, *e.g.* Helsingborg and Malmö.

Portion of the coast of Norway 70 miles by 40, showing over 400 islands.

East *v.* West "Fence." The eastern "fence" presents some marked contrasts to the western. Both are usually rugged ; but, while the eastern islands are always low and often fertile enough to be well wooded, the western ones are always high and barren. Again, the Swedish islands increase in size towards the south, *i.e.* towards the mouths of the great "continental" rivers, especially the Vistula and the Niemen, and so formed naturally stepping-stones across the Baltic, *e.g.* Born-holm and Gotland ; but the Norwegian islands increase in size towards the north, *i.e.* away from European influence, Hindö (Lofo-tens) having an area as large as Warwickshire and rising to 4000 feet. Under these circumstances it was quite natural—in the days before the opening of Archangel, and before the Reformation had destroyed the North European demand for fish and tallow (for candles)—that Visby should be the metropolis of the Baltic and the focus of all trade between Bruges and Novgorod. It was equally natural for the Swedes to have trans-Baltic interests and even possessions.

Coast-land— East *v.* West. The contrast between the eastern and western "fences" is repeated on the coasts behind them. For the hinterland is a block of very old rock—too old for coal—which was tilted down to the south-east when the old continent of Arctis sank under what is now the North Atlantic. The western edge of this fractured block was, therefore, elevated and exposed to storm and wave, while the eastern edge sank gradually into the sheltered Baltic. While the Swedish coast is normally a "bay" coast, therefore, the Norwegian coast is a "fiord" coast; and while the former is tideless—though the current out succeeded in the seventeenth century in silting up the famous old fishing-ports of Skanör and Falsterbo—the tide in some of the narrow sounds on the west is so strong as to be dangerous, *e.g.* the Maelström in the Lofotens. At the same time the actual height of the tidal wave is not great, and even in the larger fiords it is partly masked by the huge outflow of fresh water on the surface—at least in summer.

The human life of Norway, then, centres about a skerry-fenced **Fiord Life.** fiord system, the great national waterway running northward and southward inside the skerries, and being fed by the provincial waterways that run eastward and westward up and down the fiords. The calm water of these wonderful fishing-grounds is practically never frozen, for the submarine sill at the mouth is too high to allow the deep current of cold Arctic water to penetrate, while there is nothing to stop the warm air and drift from the Atlantic. The typical fiord is so narrow that the whole mouth can be easily netted,—though nets were not used before the sixteenth century,—and so steep that "you have to lie on your back to see the sky"; but at the head of the fiord, where the glacier "took the water," and at similar places along the sides, there are wedges of lowland which have been for centuries the source of all home-grown food. As the various natural divisions of these available patches were too small to be further subdivided, they were transmitted entire to one son, the others moving off; and, as the parents neither needed their children's help on the small farms or in catching the fish at their door, nor were even able to support them at home, the other sons moved off early, finding immediate sustenance by fishing, but looking to a farm-plot elsewhere for the future. To this day the same phenomena persist. Though the pastoral and agricultural land does not exceed 4 p.c. of the total area, it employs about 30 p.c. of the population.

These were the real *Vik-ing*, the "Sons of the Calm Water," **Vikings.** and they settled first on the fertile patches along the fiord—for the fishing was everywhere equally good, the dark-blue water of the fiords being usefully "clouded" by the milky water from the glaciers— where there was most forest; and then from behind the natural breakwater, with its teeming waters and poverty-stricken hinterland, a nursery at once of seamen and of beggars, the Vikings poured out to be the Sea-kings of the stormy ocean. For they were heart and soul individualists. Young married couples, having no society but themselves, and having no "patriarchal" obligations, had chosen each other freely; there was no public life or policy; man and woman being equal, personal responsibility was pushed to the extreme; they "paddled their own canoes" literally and metaphorically.

And it is to this source that we trace the innate individualism
of the Saxons and the Franks, the Frisians and the English, the
political and religious "Protestants" of Northern Europe. Norway
still has the largest mercantile marine in the world for her population, with a large preponderance of "tramp" vessels, carrying specifically for foreign countries. On the other hand, this individualism left
great opportunities, which led to great inequalities of wealth ; and,
once a particular family had become united enough and strong
enough to build a Viking ship—on a model the essential lines of
which are still followed by the Norwegian shipwrights—and seize
an island for their own, they probably enslaved a population of

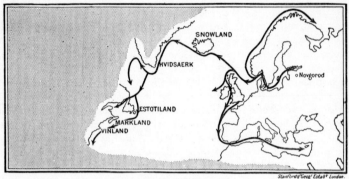

Viking raiding-routes.

aboriginal refugees on the island, and they certainly doubled their
chances of making a successful raid.

Waterside Centres. The history of Italy illustrates the advantage in early days of sites
on the shore of an inland sea, and in this respect Sweden had an
obvious advantage over Norway ; but even in Norway the essential
slope of the land is down towards the south-east, and human
activities gravitated naturally towards the safer waters of the
Skager Rak—the wide Öslo (Christiana) fiord coming to be known
as " *the* Vik "—even from Trondhjem. At all times, therefore, but
specially when the Baltic was " the Great Sea," the coastal strip in
both countries has been the vital part ; the length of the coast and
the shape of the country have evolved foci at opposite points of the
compass ; and all towns of any size are to-day on sea or lake or
navigable river.

Chief Foci. In each case the most important foci mark the opposite ends of
a natural depression across the country ; but in Norway the Glommen valley runs north and south, while the lake-studded floor of the
old strait which once joined the Skager Rak to the Baltic—as its continuation joined the Gulf of Finland *via* Lake Onega and Lake
Ladoga to the White Sea—runs east and west. In Norway, there-

fore, we have essentially a North Gate in Trondhjem, and a South
Gate in Öslo, while in Sweden we have an East Gate in Stockholm,
and a West Gate in Göteborg.   And the inflow of Christian intruders from Denmark naturally drove the heathen along the line of
least resistance, so that the last heathen capitals were at Trondhjem
and Upsala.   It was because the last heathen capital had been there
that Trondhjem was made the first Christian capital; and it is still
the religious capital of Norway, with a population almost exactly the
same as that of Canterbury, from which it received its original
ecclesiastical organisation.

The whole Öslo fiord, like the Trondhjem fiord, is scarcely typical; **Öslo.**
but the very conditions that make them lack grandeur and inaccessi-
bility, because parts of
the great depression,
have increased their
economic value.   To-
day Öslo does not stand
on the site of two earlier
capitals, for the site of
these was moved suc-
cessively farther and
farther up the fiord—
from near Laurvik to
near Tönsberg, and
from Tönsberg to the
still safer Öslo; and this
name has now been

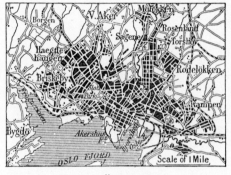

The site of Öslo (Christiania).

given to the whole Metropolitan centre.   Like the other wood-built
cities, it suffered greatly from fires, and was destroyed by fire a
generation before the great fire of London; and Christian IV.,
who rebuilt it, gave the new city his name.   It is now Öslo again.

Half-way by sea between Trondhjem and Öslo the Hanseatic **Bergen.**
commerce needed a depôt, and Bergen was chosen.   It is characteristically not at the mouth, still less at the head, of an important
fiord; but it occupies a central site between the great Sogne and
the Hardanger and Bukker (Stavanger) fiords.   This seemed to the
Hanseatic merchants the pivot of the North Sea trade.

The same conditions obtain in Sweden.   Göteborg represents **Göteborg**
the work, if not the actual site, of all the places that have controlled **and Stock-**
traffic round the Skaw and up and down the Gota valley; and **holm.**
Stockholm represents all the famous centres—generally religious or
royal capitals—on or near the seaward end of Lake Mälar.   Of
these, Björkö was an island depôt in the Baltic; Sigtuna occupied a
safer position (A.D. 1000) inland on the lake; Upsala was up a river
flowing into the lake.   Stockholm itself is not an island in the sea,
nor on the shore of the lake, nor yet on the banks of the river.   It

is on a group of islands between lake and sea, where the skerry-guard is widest (45 m.), *i.e.* at the precise point where the Viking stronghold of the lake emerged from the great forest to meet the Viking battlefield and trading-ground of the sea.

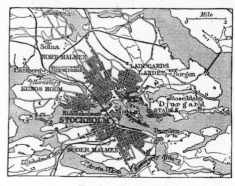

The site of Stockholm.

Malmö.   Malmö, unlike Bergen, was more than a half-way site by sea between the two great foci. It represented the old mart and fishing-port of Scania, which got silted up after its town had been burnt to the ground by the Hanseats; and it inherited the trade of Lund ("Beech" town), which held the same relation to the beech-forest of Scania as Stockholm held to the coniferous forest of Svealand. As both conquest and Christianity came from the south, Lund became the first Danish capital and the site of the first bishopric; and it is still one of the chief university centres of Sweden.

Continental Development.   The coast-lands are as different as the actual coast-lines. The Swedish belt gives easy land-transport and typical "land" occupations, and its climate is typically continental, especially in winter. It made, therefore, a good base for a military and agricultural people; but it did not justify them in trying to hold trans-Baltic territory, of which the vital points, *e.g.* Stralsund, Riga, Revel, were isolated by ice in winter.

Relief.   The cause of the great difference in climate between the east and the west coasts of the peninsula lies in the character of the relief. From north to south down the peninsula there runs a huge, broad backbone, with an average height equal to that of Ben Nevis, and peaks of nearly twice that height, *e.g.* the Galdhopig (8500 ft.) and Glitretind (8400 ft.) of the Jotunheim ("Giants' Home"). This naturally gives peculiar facilities for holding snow, especially in the higher and wetter southern section, where the Jostedalsbrae is little more than 50 miles from the ocean and overhangs the broad gully of the Sogne fiord; but even in the northern section the Svartisan glacier has an area of 400 square miles, and the Jökel glacier actually drops icebergs into the Sörö Sound.

Mountain Backbone.   Where the backbone of the relief forms the political frontier, *i.e.* as far south as the northern frontier of Svealand, the steep single scarp of the plateau is so near the sea that the Swedish frontier below the 7000 feet of Kebnekaisse comes within 6 miles of the

Ofoten fiord; and this nearness to the sea, and the number of
peaks along the coast south of Sulitälma (6160 ft.) cause the
whole formation to look from below, *i.e.* from the Norwegian coast,
like a boat upside down.   Hence its name of Kiolen ("The Keel")
given by the Norwegian fishermen; but eastward it falls in terraces.

Where the backbone ceases to be the political frontier, it is cut **Political**
by the Trondhjem-Christiania depression, which extends seaward **Frontier.**
as the Kattegat,—thus giving Norway historically a more intimate
connection with Denmark than she ever had with Sweden; and
this cuts off the long Kiolen from the bulky mass of the Dovre-field
("Steep-mountain") and Jotunheim, themselves separated by the
lake-filled Romsdal and Gudbrandsdal gullies. . This line of least
resistance is in Norway the "Heart of the kingdom," as the lake-
studded depression in Svealand is the heart of Sweden; and it was,
therefore, essential that, when the political frontier left the physical
divide, Norway should have the whole basin of the Glommen as
a natural unit, and that the political frontier should run approximately along the Glommen-Vener divide.   In the very thinly-peopled
north, on the contrary, where there was no chance of disturbing
natural associations and activities, the great need was simply for an
easily recognised and indisputable line, which was provided by such
great rivers as the Tana (180 miles) and the Tornea (227 miles).
Throughout, however, the frontier is really more a belt than a line,
and that too a belt of desert; and where it is actually habitable, it
is occupied by alien peoples, nomad Lapps, called "Finns" by the
Norwegians in the north, and real Finns in the south, who further
emphasise the political divide.

West of the great plateau backbone the climate must obviously **Nor-**
be marine, and its typical phenomenon is precipitation, rain and **wegian**
snow falling on at least two hundred days in the year.   It is **Rainfall.**
specially heavy in winter and towards the south-west, *i.e.* where the
highest and steepest relief is combined with low latitude and nearness to warm Atlantic influences.   For instance, in the Stavanger
and Hardanger areas there is an average fall of over 80 inches;
but inland in the same latitudes it falls on only half as many days,
and half of the total fall is in the form of snow.   In the Lofoten
islands the total reaches 60 inches; but farther north there is a
sudden decrease, though there is still a large percentage of cloud.

On, and east of, the plateau the climate is normally continental, **Nor-**
and its typical phenomenon is a wide range of temperature.   Even **wegian**
in Norway, therefore, there is a strong contrast between the west, **Tempera-**
with its mild rainy winters and its cool rainy summers, and the **ture.**
interior and east, with their warm summers and cold winters.   It
is most significant that the highest mean annual temperature
(45° F.) and the highest mean winter temperature (35° F.) are both
in the south-west, and that mid-winter there is in February, while

the highest summer temperature (62° F.) is in the south-east, and mid-summer comes in July.   Contrariwise, the lowest mean annual temperature (26° F.) is in the interior, *i.e.* the south-east of Finmark, —with an average 7° lower than farther north, but on the sea-coast at Vardö,—and the same area

Annual rainfall map of the Baltic region.

has the lowest winter temperature (– 60° F.).   The winter there is very long, 243 days having a mean temperature below freezing-point, and the normal for December to February being 4° F. ; so, while the mean temperature in the south-east is below freezing-point on 120 days in the year, the extreme south-west is practically free from frost.   It is equally significant that the snow-line on the Jotunheim (*c.* 4000 ft.) should be nearly 1000 feet lower than on the less exposed Dovrefield, and that in the lee of both, 250 miles from the sea in the south-west, Rörös should have a winter temperature of 13° F.   Indeed, on the lower levels of the valley near Rörös it drops 2° or 3° lower still ; and the gravitation of the cold heavy air causes the winter wind in the Skager Rak to blow normally from N.E.

Swedish Temperature.   The general conditions of Central and Eastern Norway are repeated and emphasised in Sweden within common latitudes ; but the Baltic exercises some climatic influence, and the Kiolen system is not broad enough or high enough to deprive Northern Sweden entirely of Atlantic influences.   Even Sweden, therefore, has not a purely continental climate ; but latitude is as important as relief, and continental influences are stronger than marine.   For instance, there is steady latitudinal variation throughout the 1000 miles of extension from north to south ; the mean annual temperature on the northern frontier is *c.* 27° F., and on the southern (Lund) is 45°, while Haparanda has *c.* 32°, Umea 35°, Hernösand, on the northern limit of orchard-fruit, 38°, Stockholm 42°.   Mid-summer comes in July (51° to 62° F. according to latitude), but mid-winter comes in February (3° to 30° F.) ; spring begins in the north-east in May, but in the south-west in March, while summer begins at mid-June in the one and mid-May in the other, and autumn begins at mid-August in the one and October in the other.   The lakes in the north-east freeze in October, and remain frozen for two hundred days ; those in the south-west do not freeze till December, and are frozen for only one hundred days.   Those close up to the foot of the Kiolen have a shorter winter than those farther east, *i.e.* farther away from the " föhn " effects of the cross-plateau winds.

The same conditions are reflected in the rainfall.   The average annual fall is about 20 inches, the amount increasing towards the south and towards the west, the south-west having fully 35 inches (Göteborg).   The maximum comes in summer except in the marine south-west, where it is typically in autumn, and the minimum in spring.   In the lee of Öland there is an exceptionally small fall, Kalmar having less than 15 inches ; but the rest of Scania may be compared with the Metropolitan district, each having, *e.g.* fifty days of snow in the year. **Swedish Rainfall.**

Sweden, again, like Norway, has two centres of minimum cold. The one is in the far north, within a few miles of the Finmark centre, and has about the same temperature (under 4° F. in January) ; the other is across the international frontier from Rörös, and has about the same temperature as the latter (under 9° F. in January).   The corresponding reaction in summer is also approximately the same in the two countries, length of day compensating for shortness of season.   The sun is actually visible at "midnight" at the North Cape from May 12 to July 29, and is not visible at "midday" from November 18 to January 23, while at Trondhjem there is no darkness from May 23 to July 20 ; and this means as much to the navigation of the Skerry waters as it means to the cultivators of the Swedish lowlands to have the sun visible at mid-summer for twenty-three hours every day at Haparanda, and for nineteen hours at Gefle. **Midnight Sun.**

The character and position of the main watershed account for the number and the volume of the rivers, and the slope of the plateau determines their general direction towards the south-east ; but, as the plateau sinks to the Baltic from the Kiolen in terraces, the course of the chief Swedish rivers is broken by at least three falls or sets of rapids, between which there is generally a stretch of quiet navigable water.   In both countries the rivers flow normally in U-shaped glacier-cut valleys, in which morainic dams have collected ; but, while these are seldom more than 400 feet above the sea in the shorter Norwegian rivers, they are at least twice as high in Sweden.   For instance, Lake Mjosen is about 400 feet above the sea, while in Sweden all the similar lakes are about 1000 feet.   In each case, however, they occur typically where archean and newer strata meet, and are typically long and narrow, sometimes occurring in a series, *e.g.* on the Skellefte and the Lulea, the series in the latter being 50 miles long with an average width of 1¾ miles.   In each case, too, there are naturally some **River System.**

magnificent waterfalls, *e.g.* the Harsprang; but the Norwegian falls are nearer the sea, and have the steadier volume.

Swedish Rivers.   Relatively the Swedish rivers are much the more important, and have the marked advantage of flowing independently of one another, but more or less parallel with one another, to separate mouths in the Baltic. Thus, there are 60 important rivers emptying into the Baltic between Tornea and Gefle. A dozen of these have an average length of fully 200 miles, with a total fall of 1500 feet so distributed that the current is normally enough for " free " floating without being enough to cause bad " jams," the average pace being about two miles an hour, and the total length of water being about 16,000 miles.

Forest.   The unique value of the rivers is due to the fact that the typical climatic control of the peninsula takes the form of forest-growth, about 52 p.c. of the total area in Sweden and about 23 p.c. in Norway being forested. In both countries the moistness of the sub-soil, the absence of wind in the resting season, the sufficiency of heat in the growing season, are very favourable to tree-growth; but these conditions are found mainly to the east of the water-parting, where too the short summer makes the annual " rings " so close that the wood is hard and durable, while the long winter makes it exceptionally tenacious. That is to say, even in Norway, though the seaward scarp is often forested down to the water's edge, all the best forest is towards the south-east, *e.g.* in the Osterdal part of the Glommen valley and the Gudbrandsdal part of the Laagen valley. The poorness of the coastal and fiord timber is due partly to the unfertile character of the archean rock and partly to the exposure to wind; but even the poorest is suitable for " pulp " industries, for which the fiords supply unfailing " power."

Water-Supply.   The conditions in Sweden are rather different. Owing to the smaller precipitation the timber-line is higher, and the water-supply less constant; but a large proportion of the big rivers, especially the Tornea, Lulea, Angerman, and Ljusne, have their main streams flowing through areas of very fine timber. Indeed, the Ljusne has 90 p.c. of its main stream through good forest, which helps to account for the large timber trade of Soderhamn; and the Angerman floats an average of perhaps 4,000,000 logs per annum.

Floods.   The best forest is found between 60° and 64° N., *i.e.* Upsala and Umea; and the special export from the sandy débris of the crystalline rock is naturally of pine and fir, the exporting centres being naturally to the south of the area, *e.g.* Gefle and Drammen. The total value of the timber exported from the peninsula exceeded £10,000,000 a year before the war; but 70 p.c. of it came from Sweden, which is nearly half as large again as Norway (17 : 12), and has more than twice as much forest and less than half as much desert. Sweden also has the best facilities for transport. For the

south-easterly lie of her numerous river-valleys gives her a double
flood every year—one from the very early thawing of the snow in
the valley itself, and the other from the mountains a month or two
later.   Consequently, except in occasional years of unusually
prolonged spring-warmth, when the two floods become continuous,
logs can be floated from the farthest corners of the country to the
Baltic in a single season; and, though occasionally the rivers lack
water, there is no large area of forest in any part of Sweden which
cannot be worked from want of water.   In any case, the lakes never
lack water; and, though towing and warping involve time and
expense, these are generally compensated by the facilities the lakes
give for storing the logs and regulating the head of water.

The high timber-line in Sweden incidentally involves a large **Alp**
area of real alp pasture on the higher levels and a still larger area of **Pasture.**
useful agricultural land on the lower levels.   Till about 1880
Sweden produced bread-stuffs in excess of her own needs, but she
now imports £10,000,000 worth of wheat a year, mainly because
of the competition of the great grain-lands of the New World and
because of the drain of her farm labour into the town industries.
This has increased the relative importance of grass-land, but has
tended towards making even pastoral industries mechanical; and,
even where there is a seasonable migration to an alp or upland *saeter*,
you may find mechanical-milkers and cream-separators at work, as
well as all kinds of machinery for transmitting the precious mountain
hay down to the lowlands where the cattle are stalled in winter.

Even agriculture reflects the same tendency, *e.g.* in the sup- **Agricul-**
planting of grain by sugar-beet, especially towards the south.   Thus, **ture.**
in Sweden, 60 p.c. of the total area in Scania is cultivated, while in
central Svealand the proportion is only 30 p.c., and in the extreme
north not 3 p.c.   Not half the cultivated area is now under grain,—
mainly oats and rye, except in the extreme north, where only barley
can ripen; and even this generalisation disguises the truth.   For
Scania, with only 2½ p.c. of the total area, raises 25 p.c. of the total
grain-crop, oats (35 p.c.) and wheat (33 p.c.) being more important
than barley (20 p.c.) and rye (18 p.c.).

The old crystalline rock contains some rich deposits of metal, **Minerals.**
especially along the northern side of the Skager Rak-Svealand
depression; but it is very unevenly distributed, the grey gneiss of
the north and east being mainly associated only with such unimportant minerals as garnets and graphite, and the red gneiss of
Gotland being devoid of mineral wealth.   The special deposits are
where the crystalline rock is very fine-grained or is associated with
limestone, as in the Kopparberg ("Copper Hill") province.   There
between the different types of rock are rich beds, or layers, of
metal, *e.g.* the manganese of Dannemora, the zinc of Ammeberg,
the cobalt of Tunaberg.   Still more important are the copper of

Falun, worked since the fourteenth century, the silver-lead of Sala, worked since the sixteenth century, and the iron of Grangesberg. Similar deposits of iron of immense extent are found in the fine-grained gneiss of Gällivare and (poorer in metal) in Finmark (Langfiord) and Varanger (Pasvikelven), as similar deposits of silver-lead and copper are found respectively at Kongsberg and Rörös. Cf. the zinc of Grua.

NORWAY

Population.
Though Norway is quite as large as the British Isles, its population is only 2,800,000 (1929); and the reasons for the discrepancy are obvious. In the first place, fully two-thirds of the country is barren, and an additional 21 p.c. is forested; and the normal occupations are farming and fishing. The densest population is found in three places—round the Skager Rak, in the Laagen-Glommen basin, and round the Bukken fiord. The two former naturally have their focus in Öslo (260,000), which fairly represents all the activities of the country, the industrial element being very largely associated with a potential water-power of 12,000,000 h.p.

Water-Power.
The great utility of the water-power of Norway is based on three considerations. The country is wonderfully rich in lakes which, owing to the depth and narrowness of the glacier-cut valleys, have often very narrow outlets; a typical outlet of this kind in the sub-merged part of the country has made Horten the natural head-quarters of the Norwegian Navy. Then, in almost every case these lakes combine the advantages of being near enough to the sea for the power to be easily delivered at a good harbour, and being situated in firm rock on which to build dams, etc., or through which to cut tunnels or channels. Lastly, the waterfalls are much more valuable than, e.g., the Alpine falls, because of the heavier precipitation, the greater accumulation of snow during the longer winter season, and the more rapid melting of the snow and ice during the longer summer day.

Industries.
The population, then, round the Skager Rak is becoming distinctively industrial. On the west coast the special development, from Drammen to Christiansund, is in the manufacture of paper and pulp, in electro-chemical industries (manures) and electric smelting, e.g. at Skien—also famous for its saltpetre—Ulefoss, Tinnfoss, and Arendal; on the east coast the flour-milling of Moss and the condensing of milk at Sarpsborg are more typical. Again, while ice is a typical export in the west, e.g. from Porsgrund and Kragerö, granite "setts" and matches are typical in the east, e.g. from Frederikshald and Frederikstad.

Nordic Type.
Inland, especially between Öslo and Hamar, the population is mainly engaged in farming; and butter has become a typical export from Trondhjem and Christiansund. It is most character-

istic that the population in the relatively fertile thoroughfare of the Glommen basin should be very fair and very tall Teutonic "Long-heads." Indeed, that basin is noted as the home of the purest type of Teuton, and the reason is not far to seek. The excessive glaciation of the area, which accounts for the poverty of the native flora and fauna, led to its being peopled late ; and the hard climate and barrenness must always have been adverse to a dense popula-tion. On the other hand, the natural "line of least resistance" was that of most fertility, so that the Teutonic intruders had little difficulty in ousting the natives, and no inducement to go beyond the limits of the fertile farm-land. But geographical isolation always tends to emphasise types, especially where a sparse popula-tion leads to a good deal of "in-breeding" ; so that all the con-ditions were favourable to the development of a highly individualised people of a very pure Teutonic type.

The displaced natives seem to have found refuge in what is **Stavan-**
now the third centre of population, *i.e.* on the lowlands round the **ger.**
broad Bukken fiord ; and to-day we find the population round Stavanger and Haugesund distinctly shorter, darker, and broader-headed than in the Glommen basin. The coast-line is unusually low and sandy for Norway, and so had much less attraction for the Hanseats than at Bergen ; but the place has now obvious advantages for trade with the countries round the North Sea, and both Stavanger and Haugesund are acquiring an important export of tinned provisions. This is mainly in "sardines" (sprats), and accounts for the large imports of tin-plate and olive-oil, Stavanger alone having imported some 10,000 tons of tin-plate in one year and 1200 or 1300 tons of olive-oil. Stavanger has also a growing dairy industry (mainly butter), for which the peat-bogs between Stavanger and Egersund provide a useful fuel.

Quite generally, the population is distributed in the proportion of **Wood and**
$\frac{8}{12}$ on the coast-lands and $\frac{3}{12}$ on the lowlands of the Glommen basin ; **Fish.**
and nearly 10 p.c. of the total value of Norwegian exports is repre-sented, in normal times, by "fish" (32 p.c.) and "wood" products. Both fishing and forest industries are favourable to the development of fine types of Man ; fishermen and foresters are essentially brave and enduring, lovers of freedom and space, individualistic and conservative. In each case, too, the conditions of life involve essentially that equality of power and of sex which is the only basis of true democracy and the only standard of real civilisation.

The absence of the fishermen from their homes, referred to on **Seasonal**
p. 12, is due to the site and the seasonal movement of the **Fisheries.**
fisheries. For instance, the cod-fishing has two particular centres, off the Lofoten Islands and off Finmark ; and the former is naturally the earlier (March to April), Vardö not being reached much before the end of May. So, the herring-fishing is most important south of Bergen

in spring (cf. the Haugesund and Stavanger " sardines "), but north of Namsos in autumn ; they come inshore in spring to spawn, they avoid shore water while the fiords are pouring out volumes of cold fresh water, and the subsequent inflow of warm salt water brings them inshore again in search of food.

Movements of People.
There are also, of course, the distant fisheries, *e.g.* the Arctic whaling of Tromsö and Hammerfest and the Antarctic whaling from Aalesund and Tönsberg, while both Laurvik and Haugesund are interested in whaling off the African coast ; and, on the other hand, the salmon-fishing is quite local, and the mackerel-fishing almost so, *i.e.* confined to the extreme south.   Incidentally, the industry has a rather adverse influence on the population statistics.   It accounts for the high mortality amongst men[1] and so for the pre-ponderance of women, and for the willingness to emigrate; and these two results practically counteract the very high birth-rate and the very low death-rate of the country.   Though Aalesund actually sends out the largest number of " boats," Bergen is still the great centre of the industry ; it has associated trades in barrels, salt, ice, etc., and—like Molde and Trondhjem—has a Leper Hospital. Only the " down " market remains in the far north—at Hammerfest ; but the fish-eating birds which supply the down, are themselves largely migratory, those from Finmark moving south into Finland and those of Norrland moving down the Glommen valley to the Skager Rak.

Wood Products.
The principal timber-exporting towns are naturally on the Skager Rak, *e.g.* Öslo and Drammen, with Frederikstad and Frederik-shald, Porsgrund and Arendal; but some is exported north-wards, mainly *via* Trondhjem.   But the timber itself is now less important than the wood-pulp, mechanical and chemical (cellulose), and the paper, for printing and packing.   The mechanical pulp is naturally centred on the best water-supplies, and the cellulose on those with easiest access to sulphur pyrites ; but the old centres, *e.g.* Drammen, are finding it more and more difficult to procure the wood locally, especially as the small dimensions required for the cellulose industry are very adverse to the natural reproduction of the forest—so much so that the State has had to undertake whole-sale re-afforestation.   At present much the largest export of cellulose is from Trondhjem, which also monopolises the export of sulphur pyrites from the hinterland between Mendal and Rörös, while the chief export of pulp is from Namsos, which is still farther from the old centre of production on the Öslo fiord.

Houses.
Obviously, in a country where precipitation is so heavy and so largely in the form of snow, as in all similar forest areas, it is natural for the houses to be built of wood and essential to have high-pitched roofs with overhanging eaves to throw off snow easily.

[1] The proportion *born* is—106 boys : 100 girls.

Obviously, too, in such a country inland communications are **Communi-cations.** very difficult. The lakes certainly are very useful, whether frozen or unfrozen; but the obstacles to railways are so great that roads and posting have become of prime importance, the skydsgut or "post-boy" being often a woman. Under the circumstances, Norway had the least mileage of rail in Europe up to 1910—even now the total is only *c.* 2400 miles—and the railways are mainly international, there being no less than four main routes into Sweden. In the far north there is the "iron line" from Narvik, the most northerly line in the world, and built specially to give the Swedish iron mines access to open water all the year round. The development of Central Sweden has led to the construction of a direct route from Trondhjem *via* the Storlien Pass to the Baltic port of Sundsvall; and, of course, Öslo has also direct connection with both Svealand north of Lake Vener and Gotland south of it.

The ice-free ocean, inexhaustible water-power, Spitzbergen coal, **Textiles.** and the marine climate, will some day make Norway one of the great textile-producers of the world; and the separation from Sweden has given an impulse in this direction. But in the meantime the textile industry has scarcely emerged from the domestic stage except in relation to shipping, *e.g.* the making of rope and sails. The two great products are pulp and paper, responsible for about 28 p.c. of the total export values.

SWEDEN

Human activities have a wider scope in Sweden than in Norway **Occupa-tions.** at present, and are much less connected with coastal features, partly because so much of the coast is ice-bound in winter. Both the area and the population are 40 p.c. larger than in Norway, while there is 220 p.c. more forest and 300 p.c. more farming land. Farming and forestry are, therefore, of supreme importance; and, while the birth-rate remains as high as in Norway, the death-rate is the lowest in Europe. Mining and textile industries are growing in importance, and it is roughly correct to describe Norrland as the land of timber and iron, while Svealand and Gotland form the land of farming and textiles.

This union of the two southern divisions of the country is **Political Divisions.** justified by the general fertility and natural facilities for communication, which are so obvious that the joint area was always difficult to split into separate political areas; and it was these conditions that made it so easy for the Swedes of Svealand and the Goths of Gotland to merge in a single people as early as the thirteenth century.

Gotland offered most advantages in early days, as might be **Gotland.** guessed from the ease with which the Danes conquered and converted the people in the ninth century. It has a long coast, well supplied with little harbours which could accommodate all kinds of shipping up to the Age of Nelson. The low latitude and the low relief combined with the peninsular form to give an exceptionally good climate; and the young rock which surrounds the old core of Svealand, gave a rich soil. So the whole peninsula came to take its name from the most favoured portion (Scania) of this favoured area. With its pine-clad core of Småland, its oak-forested lowlands in the north, and its beech-forested lowlands in the south, it still sums up most of the life of Sweden; and it includes the most important pastoral and arable areas of the country, butter and bacon being typical exports. Svalör is a very important centre.

Svealand.   Svealand was less prosperous in olden days owing to its more difficult relief, its slightly inferior climate, and its greater isolation, paganism lingering on till the middle of the twelfth century, *i.e.* 300 years after it had died out in Gotland; but it was essentially stronger, partly because of the virile character of the Dalarne Highlanders—who served Gustavas Vasa so well that they left practically no one behind them to perpetuate the strain. The Dalarne hinterland and the lake-studded foreground, which is of such recent formation that Arctic fauna still survive in the lakes, now combine all phases of Sweden's modern development—pasture and tillage, mining and manufactures, intellectual and administrative; Stockholm and Upsala, Falun and Dannemora, are typical centres.

Economic Divisions.   These old political divisions are now practically obliterated, in favour of the economic division made above—a land of mining and forestry to the north of a line from the mouth of the Dal to that of the Klar, and a land of farms and factories to the south of that line. At the same time the very fact that the old divisions have been so elastic, suggests that the area has a natural unity, which has made the people wonderfully homogeneous. This unity was no doubt based on the isolation of the area by tundra and mountains, by sea and speech, from foreign interference; and it was encouraged by the geographical compactness of the area. In such an area it is quite characteristic that land should be owned by both peer and peasant, and that the Constitution should show both autocratic and democratic features; for the people have common interests, common language, and common creed. About 85 p.c. of all the arable land is tilled by persons who own it—which partly accounts for the relatively dense rural population (38 per square mile in Svealand and 57 in Gotland); and the nobility do not own 1 p.c. of the estates or more than 25 p.c. of the area.

Forest.   More than half the country is forested; and, as in Norway, there are very important industries subordinate to the actual lumbering. The mass of the forest—*i.e.* all north of " Lakeland "—is coniferous, with pine and fir as the main stock and birch very common

on the higher levels; and its exploitation is bound up with the
question of water-power, for nearly all the timber ports, *e.g.* Umea and
Hernösand, Söderhamn and Gefle, are also engaged in the manufacture of pulp and other bye-products.   Indeed, timber and wood-
pulp and paper are normally responsible for more than half of the
total exports in value.   It is typical that northern ports, including
Skelleftea and Sundsvall, should specialise in the pulp and cellulose,
while southern ports, such as Vestervik and Kalmar, specialise in
joinery.   The largest industry is that in sawn wood (deals, battens,
etc.), which is mainly confined to the north; but this is bound to
become relatively less important, because a timber forest requires
eighty to ninety years for re-afforestation, whereas a pulp forest can be
re-afforested in thirty to thirty-five years.   At present there are only
about 200 pulp and paper mills, while there are over 800 joinery
factories and probably 1200 sawing and planing mills.   Heavy
penalties are inflicted for excessive felling and for failure to re-plant.
And so Sweden remains the largest timber exporter in the world.

There are two main iron-fields in Sweden, the "Lapland" and **Iron.**
the Central or Grangesberg; and Lulea (Svarton) and Oxelösund
are the special iron-ports, the former ice-bound for months (six or
seven) every year and the latter sometimes, as in 1910, not frozen at
all.   As the Central field is very conveniently placed for home use,
while the cost of freight debars the Lapland ore from a similar
destination, special regulations have been made about the export
trade.   Thus the amount that may be exported from the Grangesberg field is restricted to 13,250,000 tons per annum, while that
from the Lapland field may reach to 133,750,000 tons, of which,
however, 103,100,000 must come from the Luossavara-Kiruna mines,
i.e. those least accessible from Sweden and nearest (100 miles)
to the Norwegian port of Narvik.   Even though 30,650,000 tons
a year are now allowed to the Gällivara mines, they are about
130 miles from the Baltic and therefore relatively accessible for
consumption in Sweden.   These restrictions hold good till 1932.
The Kiruna field, fortunately for foreigners, produces unusually rich
ore, containing often 70 p.c. of iron; but, as it contains 1 to 2 p.c.
of phosphorus, it is less useful where smelters on the basic method
are relatively few, as, *e.g.*, in Britain, than in, *e.g.*, Germany.

The water-power of the country is being utilised in connection **Water-**
with both the iron and the wood industries.   The total amount **Power.**
available is estimated at fully 8,000,000 horse-power; but it is
not available anywhere for more than nine months of the year, and
not more than 25 p.c. is available anywhere at low water.   Of the
total, however, probably 75 p.c. is in Northern Sweden, *i.e.* where it
is of most use, at least to the iron and wood industries.   The falls
are not usually high, averaging less than 50 feet; but the volume of
water is generally very great for a considerable part of the year.

For instance, the Krangede Fall on the Indals is estimated at 60,000 h.p., and the Harsprang ("Hare's Leap"—a typical name in a country where the hare is the most important animal found in all parts of the area) is estimated at 46,000 h.p. Nearly all the rivers, too, as we have seen, are dammed by morainic lakes which act as water-heads. The famous Porjus Fall on the Lulea occupies such a site at the outlet of Lake Lulevattnet, and is being utilised for the new electric railway to the Gallivara mines. It is the number of such lakes that makes yachting the typical summer sport in Sweden ; indeed, lakes cover 10 p.c. of the total area of Sweden. They are known as " the eyes of the Earth," and the crystalline rock supplies them with such quantities of mica in solution that—like the eyes of the people—they are typically blue. Cf. p. 91.

Industries. It is the presence of the large lakes in the more strictly peninsular part of the country that has helped to make the climate there more favourable for both agriculture and textile industries ; and the facilities for transport are correspondingly great and associated with water-power, *e.g.* on the Motala and the Trollhätta Falls, the latter alone already supplying 160,000 h.p. The great industrial centres of the country are, therefore, found closely in touch with the river-and-canal route (180 miles) *via* Lake Vener and Lake Vetter between Göteborg and Stockholm ; and the most advantageous position is one that is at approximately equal distances from iron, wood, and navigable water. Norrköping, at the head of the 35-mile Bravik fiord, fulfils these conditions best, and has become the chief industrial centre, specialising—like its neighbour, Linköping—in textiles. It is also a hardware centre ; and, like the other centres which manufacture steel and machinery, *e.g.* Dannemora and Eskilstuna, it uses charcoal as fuel, greatly to the improvement of the smelted product. Jönköping, with local supplies of magnetic iron and sulphur, and easy access to the pith and potash of the Smäland pine forests, is another important centre, with textile, iron, and match industries ; but the climate is more favourable to the textiles on the west of the Smäland heights, *e.g.* at Boras.

Along the windy coasts of the mainland and on the adjacent islands wind-power is used as well as water-power, *e.g.* in the cement and beet-sugar industries of Öland and Gotland ; but the most typical industry round this southern part of the coast is granite-quarrying, *e.g.* at Stromstadt and Halmstad, Karlskrona and Oscarhamn. The least typical industry here is the coal-mining of Helsingborg, which is very conveniently situated with regard to the cross-Sound ferries from Malmö and Trelleborg.

Communications. Malmö and Göteborg are the two great railway termini for foreign trade, the latter being served by no less than seven separate lines, including an important private line which taps the great collection of wood-pulp factories to the west of Lake Vener. The cheapness of land and of iron and timber, and the climatic interruption of sea-traffic, have given such an impetus to railway-construction that Sweden has now the largest mileage in Europe proportionately to her population. The relative length of the typical lakes gives special importance to terminal points, such as Jönköping and Örebro; and strategic considerations help to keep the State lines generally well inland. Thus, the relative deficiency of railway accommodation in Eastern Svealand is partly due to the pre-war possession of the Äland islands by Russia. At that time the primary bases of the Russian Navy were at Kronstadt (nearly 400 miles) and Libau (over 200), and the secondary bases were at Sveaborg and Revel; but—in spite of the Äland Treaty—Russia had made several attempts within a few years to garrison the natural harbour of Fogeltjarden, which is within 100 miles of Stockholm. In olden days this promontory of Sweden was strong both by position and in virtue of its Viking strain along the coast and its Dalecarlian Highlanders in the hinterland; but both strains have died out—largely by the decimation of war—and the primary naval base of Sweden is now at Karlskrona, equally distant from Libau and Danzig and with the island of Öland to mask all movement of vessels between the primary base and the dockyard of Oscarhamn.

The essential importance of this lies in the fact that Sweden, unlike Norway, is a typical Baltic Power, with Baltic products and Baltic needs. **Sweden "Baltic."** For instance, timber is specifically a Baltic product; the demand for it is growing; and Sweden has better facilities than her neighbours for supplying the demand. Again, dairy products are very closely connected with the Baltic; and Sweden is rich in peat, which makes quite a good fuel for dairy purposes. She can easily import cheap machinery and cheap textiles from Germany and bread-stuffs from Poland; but she lacks coal and capital, and her population grows slowly. She is already making good the lack of coal by the use of her water-power. Over 2000 power-stations are at work, four of them of more than 40,000 h.p., and some 1,600,000 h.p. is in actual use for transport, lighting, and running carbide, steel, zinc, and nitrate works. The mass of the plants are along the Dal and 25 the Gota; and as scarcely half of the minimum power used is derived from water, and only one-third of the minimum estimate (3,500,000 h.p.) is as yet developed, it is probable that the recent decrease in the relative importance of agriculture will be accentuated. Even now more than half the population is engaged in manufactures and commerce.

CHAPTER XIII

THE Balkan peninsula had obviously special advantages for intercourse with the early civilisations of Egypt and Mesopotamia (cf. p. 9), and this intercourse followed lines the permanence of which is implied in the route of the Baghdad Railway and in the proposal to divert the Suez mails from Brindisi to Salonika or Athens.

Rear-guard of Europe. The fundamental control in this was the impassable barriers to pressure from the south which were imposed by the parallel belts of the Mediterranean and the Sahara. All movement was naturally east and west, and converged either from Nile or from Euphrates on the Balkan peninsula. This area consequently became the natural gateway of Europe, with one thoroughfare joining Asia and Europe and another joining the Black Sea and the Mediterranean; that is to say, it contained a land-route which lay N.W.–S.E., and which is now followed by the Orient Express, and it controlled a sea-route which lay N.E.–S.W., and which gives the only easy access to Russia by sea in winter. The peninsula thus became the rear-guard of Europe against the hordes of Asia; and this accounts largely both for the extraordinary mixture of race and language, of creed and political interest, in the peninsula, and for the legitimate concern of other Europeans in the great land-and-sea junction of Constantinople.

The Bosphorus.

Sea Frontier. In earlier days its sea-surroundings had three great advantages —a quiet sea, a highly articulated coast, and an island front.

Except in the purely continental part of the area, *i.e.* on the Black
Sea, the coast is for the most part wonderfully indented, although
the sea itself is neither very stormy nor subject to high tides;
even dangerous promontories, such as that of Malia, made useful
"beacons"; and the indentations are of all sizes—small and
large—thus supplying both a number of good harbours and the
maximum of encouragement to early navigation.   The latter was
further encouraged by the number of islands, tempting even timid
sailors from point to point, especially across the southern opening of
the Ægean and along the western shore of Anatolia; and this influence
is still reflected in the distribution of the typical Greek population,
which is essentially coastal, especially on the parts of the coast that
have most commerce, *e.g.* along the north of the Sea of Marmora.

The character of the coast is due to the fact that the land has **Character**
been partly submerged.   The symmetry and continuity of the **of Coast.**
island-lines perpetuate the original feature-lines of the mountain
ranges; and it was the pressure of the sunken block of coast that
excited—on the side away from the young uplift (cf. p. 22)—the
volcanic activity of Milos and Santorin, and that is still responsible
for such hot springs as those at the Pass of Thermopylae ("Hot-
Gates") and for the occurrence of earthquakes[1] in Greece on one
day out of every four.

The Cyclades "bridge" was specially important in early times, **Island**
because it extended the east-and-west Corinthian Gulf route to and **Front.**
from Asia Minor, as the Morava valley now extends the north-and-
south Ægean route to and from the Suez Canal; and it made the
Ægean practically a lake.   Thus, ancient Delos, like modern Syra,
gave a fine harbour in a central position on the through route
between Athens or Corinth, and Miletus or Smyrna.   Many of the
islands, too, are honeycombed with coves and caves—an ideal site
for refugees, smugglers, and banditti.   It was certain, therefore,
that, if the mainland came under the control of an alien power of
Steppe-men, the bolder spirits amongst the coastal Ship-men would
migrate to the islands; and there, with nothing to lose and all to
gain, they would develop such a net of piracy as would drive the
mainlanders off the sea altogether and even shake their hold on the
coast-land.   And it is significant that to-day we find the best type
of the Greek race on these islands.

In proportion as the mainlanders retired from the coast, deserted **Harbours.**
farms would become nurseries of malaria; and, on the contrary,
a fine port in a barren area would be profoundly attractive to the
islanders.   Such a port, if at a critical central site, would become
exceedingly important; and such a site was occupied by Athens
and by Corinth, for both could control the two divisions of ancient
Greece—continental and peninsular.   In modern times, however,

---

[1] The action of earthquakes has greatly widened the old pass at Thermopylae.

the great increase in the size of ships has entirely altered the relative importance of the old harbours; and artificial improvement has only been justified economically where the position was otherwise favourable for commerce, *e.g.* at Varna and Burgas, Gallipoli and Volo, Patras and Mesolonggi. And, considering the relatively small area, these artificial harbours cannot compete with the three great ports of Athens, Constantinople, and Salonika.

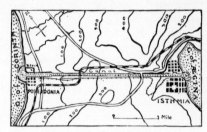

Isthmus of Corinth Ship Canal.

Athens *v.* Corinth. The harbour of Athens, between the island of Salamis and the Piræus peninsula, is larger, deeper, and safer than that of Corinth; and, though the latter controls what is nominally a shorter and safer route to the Suez Canal than that *via* Brindisi, the Corinthian Canal is too narrow and too much troubled with currents to attract much commerce, quite apart from the obstacle of heavy dues. Indeed, ancient Corinth, with its "tramway" for the transport of ships across the isthmus, was really better off than modern Corinth; and it was probably fortunate that lack of labour and fear of impiety deterred Periander from carrying out his idea of cutting a canal. Athens had, however, the real, if not obvious, advantage of having a poorer hinterland; the relative barrenness was due to a deficiency of rain—kept off by the harbourless and mountainous bulwark of Eubœa—which implied a greater freedom from disease, and the lack of land-products forced the people into sea commerce. It was mainly this early intercourse with outside peoples, with its valuable exchange of ideas as well as of material things, that gave the inquisitive and acquisitive Athenians such pre-eminence in ancient Greece.

The Golden Horn. The site of Constantinople seems to have been never properly appreciated until it came under the control of an emperor whose mother—Helena of York—came of a fishing race; but from that date (A.D. 330) onward the place itself has been more important than the people who have held it, as might be suggested by the fact that the crescent moon is the crest of the city, not of its rulers. When the people of Rome had ceased to rule the Roman world, and the Roman empire was now on its defence, especially from the east and north-east, the right capital for an emperor who wished to cultivate new relations with the Christian Church, was the safest site in that part of the area most exposed to attack. Such a site was provided by the peninsula which divides the Golden Horn from the Sea of Marmora, and which was itself cut off from the mainland by an almost continuous line of lake and swamp. This

site, with its perennial streams and its seven hills,—on one of which
the mosque of St. Sophia occupies a position very similar to that
of St. Peter's Cathedral in Rome—was a natural fortress, difficult
to approach either by the narrow fortified [1] isthmus of lake and
swamp, or by the narrow fortified straits of the Bosphorus (20 miles)
and the Dardanelles (40 miles), and impossible of investment
except by an enemy equally strong by land and by sea. It was
thus an ideal site for a people on their defence, and well earned
its name of Stamboul (" Into the City ").

Salonika has a worse harbour than the other two, but a richer **Salonika**
hinterland and easier access to that hinterland ; indeed, it controls

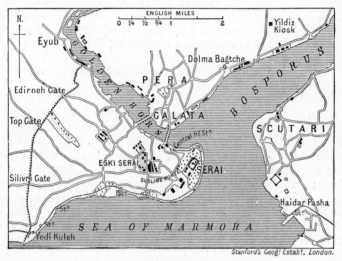

Golden Horn.

the shortest, if not the safest, route from Central Europe to the
Suez Canal. The fertility of the district soon attracted outsiders,
especially the Levantine Jews, so that the city—unlike Athens—
was developed from the outside, not from within ; and the actual site
is sheltered by the Chalkis peninsula, defended by the lakes and
swamps of the Chalkis isthmus, and away from the malarial estuary
of the Vardar. Commercially, the city is not only in the centre
of the European coast of the Ægean, but also occupies a position
somewhat like that of Venice, where an east-and-west land-route
meets a north-and-south sea-route.

There are three important lines of approach to the peninsula **Approach**
by land—the Morava valley, the steppe, the Skutari peninsula. **by Land.**
The strictly land frontier (nearly 850 miles) is very much longer

---

[1] The landward wall in the fifth century was 200 feet thick and 100 feet high.

than that of Italy or Spain ; and, even at its shortest, it is an unsatisfactory one in some ways, for it is generally taken as running along the line of the Kulpa-Save-Danube—in other words, a "primitive" river-frontier. It is precisely these underlying conditions that account for the international importance of Belgrade and for the delicate relations of Bulgaria and Rumania with their common command of the great international waterway of the Lower Danube. The narrow gorge of the Morava, running almost due north-and-south for over 100 miles, has further vitiated this frontier ; in olden days it was a scene of constant political movement northward, as it is now of constant economic movement southward. It was the breadth of the continental frontier that made it relatively easy for an essentially continental power such as Macedonia to control the whole peninsula, and for essentially continental peoples such as the Slavs to confine the coast-loving Greeks to the purely peninsular area south of 41° N. This implies the absence of the Slavs generally from most of the coast, a fact which has somewhat relieved the strain of "the Dalmatian problem."

Yellow Men. These Slavs penetrated at the north-east corner from across the Russian steppe as well as from the north-west by the Morava valley ; and the importance of the steppe route, in the distribution of people over the peninsula, lay in the fact that it was followed also by the Bulgars, *i.e.* by Yellow men, who conquered the White Slavs. The south-east corner gave access to another Yellow type in the Turks ; but the latter approached the area over the semi-desert steppe of the Anatolian plateau, not over the rich steppe of the loess lowlands. This Turkish inflow accentuated the political and ethnic difficulties of the inter-continental position by a religious complication, so that the peninsula became a transition zone between the Crescent and the Cross, thus giving an opportunity for the development of an indigenous Greek Church. In an area where there has been such a mixture of race and language and economic interest, religion is liable to become a very disturbing and dominating element ; and, in this connection, it is significant that their Greek Church exercises a directly unifying influence over the scattered Greek population.

Nucleus of Relief. The character of the relief has emphasised almost every weakness due to site. The essential nucleus is a V-shaped archean block, pivoting on Belgrade and extending its limbs to the Bosphorus and the Negroponte Channel. This tough old block was an immovable obstacle to the Alpine folding, and diverted the folds in two directions, the one continuing the normal east-and-west lie of the system, in the Balkan range, while the other was crushed up against the western face of the block in a N.W.–S.E. direction.

Western Zone. This western, or Illyrian, zone may be divided into three typical sections—Dalmatian, Albanian, and Ionian—all of which consist essentially of parallel ranges of folded limestone (and similar rock). In Dalmatia these parallel folds lie N.W.–S.E., in Albania almost N.–S., and in Ionian Greece again N.W.–S.E. ; and the change in Albania, which is mainly due to a change in the character of the rock, has greatly affected the relation of the interior to the Adriatic.

Dalmatia gives an ideal illustration of the way in which the sea **Dalmatia.** invades a mountainous land when it is submerged with its feature-lines parallel to the invading sea. By every subordinate transverse valley it invades the main longitudinal valley on the inner side of the coast range, forming what are called L or T gulfs; and where

Orographic structure of the Balkan Peninsula.

the folding has been very regular and intense, this gives peculiar facilities for access to and from the sea. Of course, the coast itself is generally steep and regular; but it is protected by the long islands that lie parallel to it, and these unsubmerged portions of the original coastal range are separated from one another by parallel channels that tap the main inner channel at right angles. The strategic strength of such a coast is illustrated by the history of such cities as Spalato and Ragusa, "the City of Freedom"; and the geographic control is illustrated by the fact that here alone on the face of the earth has a Slav population become a typical fishing population.

In the Albanian section the coast-line is so flat and inhospitable, **Albania.** and the coast-land is so malarial, that the geographic control has been exactly the opposite of that in Dalmatia. Not only are the

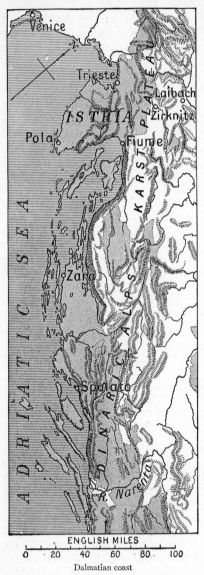

parallel ranges very numerous and very close together, especially to the west, accentuating the difficulty of access to and from the sea; but the succession of island and channel down the Dalmatian coast is here repeated as a succession of basin and saddle. The land is, therefore, pitted with tiny montane basins and lonely glens, each shut in by a typical Demir Kapu ("Iron Gate"), which have made it a typical home of separate communities with varied race and creed and economic or political interest. Progress has been almost impossible, especially in the least accessible areas, some of which even now have not been thoroughly explored; and government has been peculiarly difficult. Matters have been further complicated by the "Karst" character of the limestone, for the long, deep, narrow grooves of the cavernous limestone are normally either flooded or stone-dry, the rivers thus being equally useless for navigation and irrigation. Where the surface has sagged over a subterranean cavern, there are typical sink-holes or dolinas; where it has actually tumbled in, the larger depression, or polye, may reveal a section of an underground river.

ENGLISH MILES

0   20   40   60   80   100

Dalmatian coast

Many of these underground rivers have no visible outlet, nor are any portions of their course itself visible except where it crosses a polye. The few rivers which do remain continuously visible, because they run along geological faults, as the Drin and the upper Vistritza and the Viosa, choke up their mouths with débris from the softer rock.

With approach to the centre of maximum depression or total submergence, the channels between the islands and the encroachments on the land increase in size ; but the parallel lines can still be distinctly traced, not only in the Pindus range, but also, *e.g.*, the outer line of uplift in the Glossa promontory and the islands of Corfu and Leucas, Cephalonia and Zacynthos, and inner lines of depression in the valleys of the Arta and Aspropotamus, the Ruphia and the Iri. The sandstone promontory of Malia, like the crystalline promontory of Matapan, suggests—what is actually the case—that the system is continued through Cerigo and Crete to Carpathos and Rhodes, and that it has the typical Alpine feature of a crystalline axis flanked by sedimentary rock (cf. p. 29). *Ionian Coast.*

The eastern section of the system in Greece, while still young and folded, has come so much under the influence of the old crystalline block that it presents some marked differences. In the first place, its up-and-down folds often run east and west, not north and south as in the Salambria and Hellada valleys, the Othrys and Parnassus ranges. Again, its soil is less fertile, even in the plains of Thessaly and Boeotia ; and this greatly influenced the fate of the Cyclades, which—excepting Naxos—are the barren rocky peaks of the once continuous mountain-system that linked the peninsulas of Argolis and Attica to the Ionian peninsulas of Asia Minor. And, lastly, where this east-and-west lie has been invaded by the north-and-south lie of the Illyrian folds a very complicated interlacing has taken place, giving rise to a number of small intermont basins, such as played such an important part in the history of the early City States of Classical Greece. The knot of Pindus dominates the transition area, with rivers draining in all directions,—Vistritza and Viosa, Arta and Salambria,—thus facilitating access between Thessaly and Albania, Epirus and Macedon. The Salambria basin gives easy access by rail over the plain of Thessaly by the grain-market of Larissa or the old battle-field Phersala (Pharsalos) to the port of Volo. *Eastern Zone.*

The V-shaped archean block is a mass of mountain-crowned plateau which has been carved with deep valleys by the great rivers of the area. These rivers are naturally found mainly in the area of greatest precipitation, *i.e.* the west ; but the position of the block naturally sends most of them into the Ægean. We should expect, therefore, to find the most important either along the frontiers of the old block and its Alpine folds, as the Drin and Morava, or towards the centre of the V, as the Vardar and the Struma. This general tilt to the Ægean laid the richer lowlands of the area open to Asia ; but the particular features of the highlands cut one valley *River-System.*

very markedly from another, as Thrace is isolated from Macedonia by the Rhodope mass. The complication of a double lie in the mountain structure developed a complicated double water-parting in the river-system, the pivot of which lies where the great obtuse angle of the Illyrian folds converges on the acute angle of the Balkans and the Rhodope, *i.e.*—in pre-war days—precisely where Servian, Bulgarian, and Turkish frontiers met. Such a reflection of geographical features in the political map suggests that the given distribution of power might be made satisfactory; but the complicated relief, by giving each important natural area its own speech and creed and political interest in antagonism to all the others, was in this case profoundly adverse.

Bulgarian Knot. There are three knots of great peaks round which the rival interests are mainly focused. The Bulgarian knot of Muss-Alla (9600), Rilo, and Vitosha commands the Sofia basin; and it has rivers draining in all directions—Struma and Isker, Nishava and Maritza—so that it is really the strategic, and may become the commercial, centre of the peninsula. The transverse valleys are too narrow and too steep for any natural traffic N.E.–S.W. except actually at Sofia, and the same place stands on the line of least resistance N.W.–S.E. used as the Orient Express route. Sofia, therefore, is the objective of the projected Bucharest-Salonika railway, as Trajan's Gate was the old landmark between Illyrium and the Orient; the two foci command the apex of the Balkan-Rhodope angle.

"Servian" Knot. The Servian knot of Shar Dagh (8850), Shlieb, and the Kopaonik commands the Prizren basin; and it too has rivers draining in all directions—the Ibar and the Vardar, the Drin and the Southern Morava. But the westward drainage becomes involved in the Karst limestone, and only the Kopaonik was within the frontier of pre-war Servia; so that it was a centre of intrigue rather than political strength, and its slight commercial importance centred on the junction of Uskub. The monasteries of Studenitza and Ipek were, in fact, regarded as storm-centres for this area of "Old" Servia, which the Turks called Kossovo, the Austrians called Novi-Bazar, and the Germans called Amselfeld. It touched Montenegro, Bosnia, Servia, Bulgaria, Albania, and what we call Macedonia; it drains to the Adriatic, the Black Sea, and the Ægean; it is mainly peopled by Albanians, Servians, and Bulgarians; and till lately it was owned by the Turks, but administered by Austria. The multiplication of names almost suggests how critical a position the area has always held.

Balkan Range. The normal east-and-west trend of the Balkans does not materially interfere with the typical north-and-south lie of the main lines of communication, partly because so many rivers flow northwards to separate confluences with the Danube that there are really more obstacles to movement east and west over the Bulgarian plateau than to movement north and south across the range. Though typically Alpine, with a crystalline axis flanked by younger sedimentary rock, they nowhere reach 8000 feet; they are richly-wooded rounded hills, rocky only towards the base; and they are crossed by at least thirty practicable carriage roads. On the other hand, the important passes are all at a considerable height, the Shipka being nearly 4500 feet; and west of that the range is high enough to hold a good deal of snow up to the middle of summer. The two chief passes are at the two ends of the Great Balkans, the Shipka and the Upper Isker; and the former has been greatly over-rated, owing to the magnitude of Suleiman's operations in 1876. As a matter of fact, it has a fairly easy approach both from the south by the Tunja valley, and from the north by the Yantra valley.

The range made Bulgaria physically almost an ideal Buffer State between Russia and Turkey, but it does encourage movement southward rather than northward. The reason for this is that its "Russian" foreground is a porous limestone plateau largely covered with loess (cf. p. 24), while its "Turkish" foreground is an alluvial valley; and the rivers which descend to the Danube have—in the normally dry climate—ploughed such narrow steep-sided valleys in the loess that they accentuate the difficulty of movement east and west due to their flowing independently of one another to separate confluences with the Danube. Most of the important towns in Bulgaria are more or less hidden at the bottom of these cañons, and are placed so as to guard the approaches to the passes—Plevna and Shumla, Sofia and Philippopolis, Tirnova and Kazanlik. *Balkan Fore-grounds.*

The main water-parting of the peninsula is so high and so near the Adriatic—within 5 miles in Montenegro—that the westward rivers would be useless for navigation, even if they did not flow through Karst limestone; and, as it is, even those which flow north-ward or southward before crossing the coast range have not even important roads up their valleys. But the secondary water-parting between Shar Dagh and Muss-Alla is exceedingly important, not only because it throws off rivers northward and southward, but also because—though in the heart of the area—it has a minimum elevation, between the Morava and the Vardar, of only 1300 feet. This fact gives much commercial importance to Uskub (Skoplie). *Double Water-parting.*

The height and position of the main water-parting put the peninsula climatically into relations with the Black Sea rather than the Mediterranean; and the nearness to the vast mass of Asia so accentuates this that, except along the Dalmatian coast, it has a much more continental climate than Italy. This is shown in many ways. For instance, a very large proportion of the area has a winter temperature under 32° F. for at least two months, and a summer temperature of over 64° F. for at least two months; and in *Climate.*

each case the extreme is accentuated from south to north and from west to east, the regular winds from the steppes being very cold in winter and very hot in summer.

Relief Effects.   Athens gets these winds dry and bracing after crossing the mountains of Eubœa, while Constantinople gets them raw and noxious off the Black Sea, one result being that olives cannot be grown there.   The Pelion-Ossa ranges protect the plain of Thessaly, as Eubœa protects the plain of Attica; but such relief effects are only local, the climate being generally "regional," and its continental tendency being due to distance from the Atlantic, the height of the noon-day sun in such a latitude, and the influence of Asia on the prevailing winds.

Rainfall.   Again, much the heaviest rainfall occurs in the west and north-west, thanks mainly to the low-pressure system over the Adriatic in winter (cf. p. 55), and there is a typical autumn and winter rainfall round the Ionian and Ægean coasts; but most of the area has a summer rainfall, drawn in off the Black Sea by the low-pressure centre which forms over the Lower Danube basin in early summer.

Regional Contrasts.   Two economic features of the climate are specially important. The continental exposure to the cold N.E. winds in winter, while very favourable to agriculture, involves a heavy snowfall and great liability to sudden frost; for instance, in 1902 a sudden frost on December 6 froze up 38 steamers—for the whole winter—between Braila and Sulina, and over 120 grain-barges between Braila and Ruschuk.   On the other hand, the marine exposure to the south-west involves autumn rains after summer drought; and this brings a scourge of malaria both to the lowland areas and to such montane basins as that of Monastir.   Quite roughly it may be said that the north-west has a Riviera climate, that the east has an Asiatic winter, and that the south has an African summer, bananas ripening in the open air round the Kalamata Gulf.

Soil and Vegetation.   Over the old block and within reach of its influence in eastern Greece the soil is relatively poor, while amongst the Alpine folds it is naturally rich; but the dry exposed uplands are everywhere barren, while the mountains in the summer-rain area are covered with dense forests, largely of oak and beech.   Where these forests —with their acorns and mast—are near to rich lowlands which can produce large crops of maize, as in Jugo-Slavia and Walachia, pig-rearing is a typical industry, supplemented in Jugo-Slavia by the growing of plums.   On the higher and drier Bulgarian plateau the typical crop is wheat, and the uncultivated parts of the steppe are grazed by sheep and cattle, while Roumelia, *i.e.* lowland Bulgaria, in the lee of the Balkans, cultivates the silk-mulberry on the Maritza plain and roses in the Tunja valley, especially at Kazanlik, *i.e.* near the mouth of the Shipka ("Wild Rose") Pass.   In the

summer-drought area typically Mediterranean crops are grown,
opium and tobacco in Turkey and olives and currants in Greece.

As the inter-continental site has produced great variety of race, **Popula-**
with more or less corresponding variety of speech and creed, so the **tion :**
complicated relief has increased the racial, religious, and linguistic **Yellow.**
difficulties.   No other equal area in Europe is so incoherent, so
full of intrigue, so rich in
opportunities for the interference of outsiders, whether
well-intentioned or otherwise ;
and it is not easy to localise
individual interests.   Even
before 1914 the purely
Turkish population, the descendants partly of the
Ottoman invaders of the
14th and 15th centuries, and
partly of more recent colonists
brought from Asia, was large
and compact only where most
"at home," *i.e.* on the north-

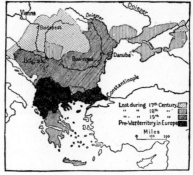

The Pre-War shrinking of Turkey in Europe.

east of the Bulgarian steppe and in the south-east of Thrace ;
and, though the latter had the great advantage of proximity to
Asia Minor, the conditions of life are less congenial, and the
population was small and diminishing.   Even the Slavonised
Yellow men of Bulgaria, amongst whom the Turkish Yellow men
were relatively numerous, and who were found in large numbers
in Turkey, especially on the Ægean hinterland, were at least twice
as numerous as the Turks.

The Slav population, mainly descended from Carpathian **Popula-**
immigrants of the seventh century, numbers at least 10,000,000 ; **tion :**
but its pre-War influence was small, partly because of its internal **White.**
disunity, and partly because of European fear of the expansion of
Slav power.   The internal divisions were based on the natural gravitation of the Adriatic provinces towards Roman creed and Latin
civilisation, and the natural survival of Greek creed and Byzantine
civilisation in the mountainous interior and the Euxine-Ægean
provinces.   The adherence of Montenegro to the Greek influence
reflected the position of the peninsular water-parting (cf. p. 133).
The Albanians, who are descended from the primitive Illyrians, and
the Greeks are the oldest inhabitants of the area, the Albanians
being mainly confined to the western interior, while the Greeks are
massed on the coasts and islands.   Cf. p. 165.

What we insist on calling Macedonia is quite a typical area, **Mace-**
though that name is practically unknown on the spot, and though **donia.**
the area is really two areas, the highland basin of Monastir and

the lowland valley of Salonika.   It was typical of this dual area that in it before the War there was no *Macedonian* race or speech or creed; there was not even any single dominant race or dominant speech or dominant creed at all in it.   The population consisted of Turks, who ruled, Greeks, who traded, and Bulgars, who tilled, in about equal proportions.   All these types were bilingual or trilingual, and changed their speech temporarily with their politics.   And Greek, Bulgarian, Servian, and Rumanian churches seemed to be all equally busy making converts and building schools as a basis for claiming a share of the land if, and when, it was some day divided.   The consequent internal dissensions were both the main cause of the Turkish rule continuing and the only excuse for foreign interference, with its absurd subdivisions of influence.   The shepherds and wood-cutters of the highlands had nothing in common with the lowland tillers of the soil; the river-valleys that link the two, were isolated by malarial "fans" from the fertile coast-lands; and the coast-land, with its linking railway, was "unlinked" by the successive spheres of foreign influence—British round Drama, French round Seres, Russian round Salonika, Italian round Monastir, and Austrian round Uskub.

Language and Creed.   This confusion of political and economic, social and religious, elements is still characteristic of the whole peninsula.   There are a dozen local tongues, of which five have more than local distribution—Turkish, Bulgarian, Servian, Rumanian, and Greek; a Greek man may belong to the Bulgarian Church, and speak Turkish. Indeed, the latter is so soft and musical that, except for French in Rumania and German in Servia, it was more or less the *lingua franca* of the area; and it was actually ousting the harsh and consonantal Bulgarian tongue from the Bulgarian theatre.   There are half a dozen creeds, of which the Greek, Bulgarian, Moslem, and Mosaic have widespread political importance, and which greatly complicate the calendar.   Thus there are four "years" in Turkey—a Moslem civil year, a Moslem religious year, a Greek year, a West European year, some counting by lunar months, and others by solar months; Turkish time is kept for natives, and East European time for foreigners, trains being run by the latter, though the local time-tables are printed in the former!

BULGARIA

Frontiers and Relief.   The Treaty of Neuilly gives Bulgaria "freedom of transit, with guaranteed facilities," to the ports of Kavala and Dede-Agatch [1]; but she has lost all of her old coastline on the Ægean as well as four important "enclaves" on her western frontier.   She still includes, however, three distinct areas — plateau, plain, and mountain basin; and considering her "Buffer State" origin, her

[1] Now called Alexandroupolis. Cf. Vodena, now Edessa.

frontiers are remarkably natural.   The plateau (*c.* 200 miles × 60), lying parallel with the Danube, has an inhospitable water frontier, for the sea-coast is dangerous and stormy, and the right bank of the Timok-Danube is a steep scarp, the great fortress of Silistria occupying a typical piece of steep-faced crag.   East of the Silistrian frontier the Dobruja is so nearly desert that one may see camel transport ; and south of the Timok the Stara-Planina has its most used pass (St. Nicholas) at a height of over 4500 feet.   The Roumelia plain has somewhat more artificial frontiers, but even here there is a large proportion of natural barrier.   The Stranja Balkans (or Istranja Dagh) in the south-east are very difficult country, and the Rhodope Balkans (or Despoto Dagh) are so compact and so inaccessible from the south that Roumelia can get access to the Ægean only *via* the Maritza valley.   Indeed, the old block is so much more *Dagh* (real "mountain") than *Balkan*[1] ("forested alp") that it remains a country apart ; the sedimentary flanks of the crystalline crest are covered with forests, in which bears and numerous packs of wolves are found ; and their human inhabitants include such interesting relics as the Pomaks, or Moslem Bulgarians, whose log-built huts are typically Mongol in character.

The precise line of frontier, with its double row of huts and posts, is very involved, partly because of the intricate relief and partly because of the interference of outside Powers in such treaties as those of San Stefano and Berlin.   But the difficulty and impermanence of the actual line have been compensated by the unity and conservatism of the people.   The mass of these are Bulgarians, *i.e.* Slavonised Yellow men ; and the Slavonic veneer is specially prominent in their political attitude and relations.   For instance, it was Russia that—with or without an eye to the Bosphorus—won for them their freedom, and trained their army ; their language has been strongly affected by Russia, and they still use the Russian characters in writing.   Again, in consequence of a political demand for religious independence, the National Church was declared in 1870 to be outside the Orthodox Communion.   And the results of the Serbo-Bulgarian war, with the subsequent interference of Austria (1913), left the people as hostile to Austria and Servia on purely political grounds as they are really to Russia by temperament and inheritance.

The climate over each of the three great divisions is more severe than in similar latitudes elsewhere in Europe, but varies with the relief.   On the exposed plateau of Bulgaria proper the extremes, both seasonal and diurnal, are great, and the changes of temperature are very sudden ; the greatest extremes and the most sudden changes are in winter, when − 24° F. may be registered.   The natural vegetation here is mainly of a steppe character, bulbous and

International Relations

Climate.

---

[1] Balkan means literally "stony hills," but is always associated with wood and pasture.

umbelliferous ; and the summer rains allow large quantities of grain to be grown, especially wheat for export and maize for home consumption. The average value of the grain crop for the last five pre-war years was *c.* £14,000,000. The sheltered Roumelian plain is much warmer than the Bulgarian plateau, and has more or less Mediterranean vegetation, roses and tobacco being special crops, while even rice is grown round Philippopolis. The mountain-basins of Samakov and Sofia in the Isker valley, and Radomir and Kustendil in the Struma valley, are more equable than the plateau and less equable than the plain, the temperature seldom exceeding 86° F. or falling below 0° F. ; but the vegetation in the northern basins is sub-Alpine, while in the southern, especially the Kustendil basin, it is distinctly richer. Extremes decrease along the sea-coast, but the Black Sea influence is otherwise " Euxine " (used euphemistically for " Axine," *i.e.* inhospitable) ; and the violence of the winds may be gauged from the relative safety of the two ports. Though access to the food-supplies of the plateau made Varna a fairly good Franco-British depot in the Crimean War, it is a very poor harbour, shallow and dangerous during N.E. storms. Burgas, though only a roadstead, is quite safe because sheltered by the Emineh Balkans, and is never ice-bound. The fact that Varna is occasionally ice-bound, like the average annual temperature (52° F.) and like the calm dry autumn, shows that the climate is predominantly continental.

The Bulgars. The curious mixture of Slav and Mongol in the Bulgarians proper, who are found mainly in the north and the west, is leading to a very interesting development of the country. They have assimilated many Slav traits and customs, but put virility into all of them. Their oval faces, straight noses, and stocky frames are as typical as their patience, perseverance, and devotion to the spade. They are stolid and democratic individualists, who have learnt to stand alone, and whose steppe qualities are as obvious on the moral side as on the material, *e.g.* their sheepskin cloaks, bagpipes, rawhide boots, love of meat and cheese and butter, and the nomad habit of wearing all their wealth in a portable form on their persons. They are so much the best type in the whole peninsula that they will probably outlast all their rivals. Their Slav aptitude for combination, and the Mongol tenacity with which they pursue national aims, appear specially in their attitude to agriculture and transport. Agriculture till 1878 was very greatly hampered by the insecurity under Turkish rule, the ignorance of the cultivators, want of capital, of communication, and even of population—for the passage of Turkish armies through the country in the wars with Austria, Poland, and Russia led to constant emigration ; but co-operation and education are revolutionising the industry, and the Government makes great efforts to concentrate all the trade of the

country on their own seaports of Varna and Burgas.   Except at
Ruschuk and Somovit till recently no railways tapped the Danube,
even the ports of Lom Palanka and Nikopoli and the fortresses
of Vidin and Silistria being neglected.   And it is partly this that
accounts for the chief textile centres being essentially *inside* the
long "hosreshoe" of railway from Varna *via* Shumla (Shumen) and
Plevna (Plyeven) to Sofia and from Sofia *via* Philippopolis (Plovdiv)
and Eski-Zagra to Burgas.   For instance, the great woollen centres
are Gabrovo and Sliven ; and all Government employées must wear
the—really admirable—native "homespuns."

The pastoral industry, as in Rumania, is making great progress, **Pasture.**
but in the direction of meat rather than dairy products, though a
large amount of sheeps'-milk cheese is made.   The presence of real
"Balkans," *i.e.* rounded hills well forested and with large areas of
pasture, not only protects Bulgaria from severe summer drought,
but also accounts for the fine grain and flavour of the meat.   The
mutton is equal to the best Welsh type, and the beef to the very
best that comes from either Chicago or the Plate ; and both labour
and stock are abundant and cheap, while the facilities for transport
to Varna and Burgas are so good that produce can be delivered in
London within ten days.

The typical industry in Roumelia is rose-growing, though it is **Roses.**
mainly confined to the Tunja valley, *i.e.* the sheltered gully between
the Balkans and the Karaja Dagh.   Here nearly 200 villages, at an
average height of 1300 feet, are devoted to the work, cultivating
more than 18,000 acres of roses ; these yield *c.* 25,000 lb. per acre,
200 lb. of roses being equivalent to 1 oz. of attar.   Most of the
stills are at Karlovo and Kazanlik, at the mouth of the Shipka
("Wild Rose") Pass.

There are innumerable distilleries and flour-mills in the grain **Indus-**
areas, saw-mills on the Rhodope and Balkan torrents, and tanneries **tries.**
between the forest and the steppe ; but the country in the meantime
is essentially non-industrial, one result of this being the entire
absence of large towns.   Only Sofia (210,000) has more than
90,000 inhabitants ; and it has, in addition to its enormous political,
strategic, and commercial importance, easy access to the only
coal (lignite) worked in the country—at Pernik.   It shares, therefore,
practically all the little industries of the area—tanning, like Plevna
and Shumla; manufacturing the local tobacco, like Philippopolis and
Ruschuk; weaving, like Sliven and Samokov, Gabrovo and Karlovo.
The climate is much more suited to the working of wool and silk
than of cotton ; but cotton is spun as well as woven at Varna, and
—like the silk—can even be produced in the country, *e.g.* round
Haskovo.   The same area also produces various oil-seeds, *e.g.* anise
and sesame, while colza is produced along the Danube, *e.g.* round
Ruschuk (Ruse) and Sistova (Svishtchov).

JUGO-SLAVIA

Political Difficulties.

The present kingdom of Jugo-Slavia includes the old kingdoms of Servia and Montenegro, the provinces of Bosnia, Herzegovina, Dalmatia, Croatia, and Slavonia, and various smaller parts of pre-war Bulgaria, Austria, and Hungary, especially part of the Banat of Temesvar. Indeed, before the war its people were living under six different governments, and their representatives sat in fourteen different legislative assemblies. Jugo-Slavia, therefore, not only faces unfriendly nations in almost every direction, but actually includes thousands even of Jugo-Slavs who fought against Servia, as well as nearly half a million Germans and nearly half a million Magyars. And it will probably be found that it was a fundamental blunder to annex such a large part of Hungary or the purely Bulgarian "enclaves."

Religion.

Even where what may be called "racial" difficulties are relatively small, as in the south-west and the north-west, there are very serious religious difficulties, e.g. in the non-Christian populations; for many of the annexed Albanians are, like many of the Croats, Moslems, and the rest, like the rest of the Croats and the Slovenes, are Roman. Nor is this all; for a main cause of old troubles is still present, though the Corfu Pact nominally guarantees the strict equality of the Greek, Roman, and Moslem faiths, and of the Roman and Cyrillic scripts. In the old days the southern Slavs were not only divided from their northern relations by the German-Magyar wedge, but also—like the northern Slavs—made incoherent and impotent by internal differences, political and religious. The Slovenes (or Wends) were politically Austrians, and their natural gravitation to the Adriatic had kept them Roman in creed. The Croats, with similar gravitation to the Adriatic, were also Roman in creed; but politically they were Hungarians. The Slavonians were also Hungarian, but their land gravitates eastward, and their creed is Greek. All three were mainly "Servian" by race, and all were politically attracted to Servia; but they were, and are, content to make "patriotism" depend on creed, and mark the differences in every possible way, e.g. by costume, by script and "fount" of type, etc., thus gravely threatening the stability of the Jugo-Slav State. Economically, too, they are foredoomed victims of the middlemen in virtue of their perfectly useless languages—useless, that is, for World markets. But there was this great difference that, while Austria—after 1866—*forced* her Slav subjects to maintain their own Slovene speech, Hungary *guaranteed* theirs to the Croats and Slavonians, thus sacrificing the opportunity for consolidating the Hungarian kingdom which would have been given by the spread of the Magyar language.

Both the political and the religious difficulties will probably **The**
focus on the position of the capital. Though the annexed Banat **Capital.**
territory has removed the fundamental defect of Belgrade as a
capital—its position on the frontier—the city is still marginal ; and
to this there are political as well as strategic objections. Servia is
the largest of the political units in the Serbo-Croat-Slovene State,
and was the real and proper nucleus of the state ; but the deliberate
attempt of the Austrian and Bulgar armies—for three years—to
exterminate the Serbs was so far successful that they succeeded
in starving to death or assassinating 1,300,000 (!). Thus to-day
more than half the population of the whole kingdom, representing
far more than half the area, is opposed to the dominance of Servia,
and objects to having the capital at Belgrade.

Another serious problem is access to the sea.   The western **Access to**
flank of the State is a belt of limestone—largely of Karst character— **the Sea.**
lying between Shar Dagh and the Karawanken ; and the densest
population is in that part of the belt across which Austria-Hungary
had its direct access to the sea, and in the hinterland of this saddle
are now the most fertile areas of Jugo-Slavia. The character of
the Dinaric ranges makes it almost impossible to get direct access,
e.g. from Spalato, to the core of the country ; Trieste is almost
useless except to the extreme north-western corner ; and Salonika,
also not Jugo-Slav, has a very thinly peopled hinterland. The Drin
valley is the natural line of movement to and from the Kossovo
plain, but is not Jugo-Slav even now. If the Great Powers—at
the instigation, and in the supposed interests, of the Germanic
kingdoms—had not prevented Servia from getting access to the
Adriatic here, there would have been no geographical basis for
the international friction which the Pan-Germans thought favourable
to their plans, and which ended in the Second Balkan War ; and
the excuse at the time was that " it was impossible to build a
railway along it "—though the Austrian (rack and pinion) line to
Sarajevo ran through much more difficult country in the Narenta
basin, and though the Romans built a road up the Drin valley over
which for centuries iron-ore was carried in ox-wagons ! There
remains only Fiume, where the Adriatic lies nearest to the Danube
system, and where the Karst belt is both low and narrow. Of course,
it is not Jugo-Slav, though the urban centre of Fiume-Sušak is
predominantly Jugo-Slav, but the artificial harbour of Baroš—wholly
Jugo-Slav—is becoming important.

The country may be divided into three main Natural Regions : **Natural**
(1) the long strip of Adriatic coast-lands, with the typically Medi- **Regions.**
terranean alternation of mild, wet winter, and hot, dry summer,
that is so favourable to fruit ; (2) the triangular Save-Morava
uplands, with the typically continental alternation of cold, hard
winter, and warm, damp summer, that is so favourable to deciduous

forest; and (3) the bleak belt of limestone highlands between the other two, with relatively easy access landward, where it is more or less immaterial, and very difficult access seaward, where it is vital. The continental basin expands northwards, with some change of relief, on to the "Voïvodina" lowlands, and contracts southwards, with some change of climate, into the Monastir-Vardar basin. The former, especially from the Banat and Bačka alluvium, gives the Jugo-Slavs not only an important bridge-head (cf. the historical importance of Peterwardein), but also a granary from which to make good the deficiency of grain in Servia; in the latter the Vardar basin has little economic value, but its commercial importance and its political difficulties are more or less focussed at Uskub (Skoplje), which was the Roman capital of Dardania. It still controls the routes which guided the Roman choice—between the Shar Dagh and Kara Dagh into Kossovo, *i.e.* the route of the Novi-Bazar railway, and round the Shar Dagh *via* Kalkandale to Durazzo (Dyrrachium); but now the route east of the Kara Dagh *via* Vranja and that south *via* Koprulu ("The Bridge") are more important than the Adriatic connection, and of course the roads are of no importance compared with the railway. Quite roughly, these natural divisions correspond to the political units—Dalmatia; Carniola, Bosnia, Herzegovina, Montenegro; Servia and Croatia-Slavonia.

Dalmatia.   Dalmatia presents a typical instance of a country too long for its width (cf. p. 85); it is over 200 miles long, while its width varies from 1 to 35 miles. From very early times, therefore, it was a land of isolated city-states, and its civilisation was always urban; and during the war it was a cause of great trouble to Italy. For, longitudinally, coast and islands are a single unit; but latitudinally, the islands make two groups. To the north, parallel lines of hilly and *overlapping* islands, lying roughly north and south, protect a maze of waterways from storm and from observation from the sea, thus making one of the finest tactical naval bases in the world. South of Spalato (Split) the islands are fewer and farther apart, and more east and west, and so shelter the waterways east of them from neither storm nor observation. The bora, too, leaves the Dalmatian waters unruffled, but rages against the Italian coast; the sea current works up the east coast and down the west, carrying Po mud—or mines, invisible in the muddy water. And every time the Austrians attacked at sunrise, the Italian ships were thrown up into brilliant light, while the Austrians were invisible against the shadowed coast. So Italy wanted the Dalmatian coast. The configuration was exaggerated by the detailed relief of the area, and even political unity has by no means eliminated further causes of incoherence in the deep racial jealousies of Slav and Italian and the still more bitter *odium theologicum* between the

Orthodox and the Latinski Slavs. Of the 5000 square miles only
a narrow strip along and off the coast is of any real value, and even
this strip is peculiarly incoherent, the healthiest and most fertile
areas being definitely insular, *e.g.* on the islands of Brazza and
Curzola, Lissa and Lessina. The rest of the area is more or less
typical Karst, and has been described as a huge "petrified sponge";
and, as the Dinaric Alps reach a height of over 6000 feet, and
follow closely the infinite indentations of the coast, access inland
is as difficult as the procuring of water. Thus, fully 200 villages
inland have no natural water-supply ; and, though Spalato was the
second port in Austria, it had not even a railway into Bosnia (!).
There are now three lines running inland from the Dalmatian coast
—one linking Sebenico (Šibenik) and Spalato with Yagreb *via* the
Unna valley, a second linking them with Brod *via* the rich iron-field
of Ljubija near Prijedor, and a third being the extension from Gravosa
of the old Ragusa (Dubrovnik)-Serajevo line to the Save *via* the
Bosna valley (serving the Vareš iron-field) and to Zaječar and the
Danube below the Ivon Gates *via* Užica and the Western Morava
valley.

No doubt, the destruction of the forests in olden days by the Its Popu-
Venetian shipbuilders and by pirates greatly increased the mischief, lation.
by tending to increase marsh—and so malaria—in the valleys of
the chief surface streams, especially the Cetina and the Narenta ;
and re-afforesting is made peculiarly difficult by the shallow soil,
the Karst character of the rock, and the unchecked ravages of
ubiquitous goats. On the other hand, the fact that movement of
water is largely underground minimises loss by evaporation, etc.,
and leads to a great concentration of volume and power where it
issues from the seaward face of the lowest terrace (cf. the Ombla—
from Trebinje—near Gravosa). This is one of the few assets of
the area, and it is being used specially in the manufacture of
cement and calcium carbide, *e.g.* at the falls of the Kerka behind
Sebenico and at the falls of the Cetina behind Almissa. These
are, however, quite modern developments, and have as yet done
little to check the enormous emigration, one-tenth of the total
population sometimes having emigrated in a single year. This
phenomenon, like the excess of male births, is quite characteristic
of a people who are primarily fishermen ; and the wages of the
seamen and the savings sent home by the emigrants go some way
towards redeeming the poverty of the land.

The chief asset of the area, however, is its climate. Though Its
the biting bora may blow at any time of the year—for it is little Climate
more than an exaggeration of the normal gravitation of air from
the snow-clad mountains—it is rather north-*easterly* than northerly,
and the normal circulation of air over the Adriatic Sea is cyclonic
(cf. p. 55). This not only accounts for the unique development of

seafaring habits in a typically Slav population, but also—by the
high humidity implied—for the relatively large proportion of
blondes;[1] and the influence on vegetation is equally marked.
Though the arid heights, with their heather and juniper and
thyme (cf. the important honey trade), support nothing but goats,
in the coastal valleys almost every kind of "Mediterranean" fruit
flourishes, especially the wild cherry (*marasca*) and the vine; and
the typical industry—after fishing—is the making of wine and
liqueur ("maraschino"), specially round Spalato, the chief commercial centre (cf. Zara).   North of Lissa the fishing is more for
sardine and tunny, south of it for coral and sponge, the extraordinarily clear water being a great advantage in the latter case;
while in the extreme south the transit sea-borne trade of Herzegovina
via Metrovič and of Montenegro *via* Cattaro employs a good many
hands.   With a mid-winter temperature of over 45° F. and a great
wealth of archæological interest (mainly Roman), the coast attracts
many visitors, especially to Spalato ("The Palace" of Diocletian).

Bosnia-Herzegovina.   Bosnia-Herzegovina, though a political unit under Austria, is
geographically two distinct areas; as they say locally, "Bosnia begins
in forest, and Herzegovina in rock."   Bosnia is generally Balkan
in physique and Danubian in climate, while Herzegovina—which
actually penetrates through Dalmatia to a 14-mile strip of harbourless
coast on the Adriatic—is specifically Dalmatian in both physique
and climate; Bosnia is a definite section of the continental Save
basin, while Herzegovina is as definitely the coastal basin of the
Narenta.   To the north-east of the Dinaric Alps, which reach a
height of 7500 feet, the forested highland is carved by deep alluvial
valleys—notably those of the Verbas and the Bosna—deploying on
to the Posavina, or Valley of the Save, between the similar transverse
streams of the Unna and the Drina.   These valleys are invaluable
for transport, *e.g.* to Sarajevo from Brod *via* Doboi and Zeptsche, or
from Novi *via* Banjaluka and Jajce.   Sarajevo has also direct rail
communication to the Novi-Bazar plains and *via* Mostar and the
Narenta (Narevta) valley—by rack and pinion—to Metrovič and the
Adriatic.   From the north of Mostar, where it cuts through a narrow
gorge, the crest of which is 7200 feet above the sea, the Narenta works
its way down the parallel terraces of grey Karst limestone, dividing
Herzegovina roughly into two areas, forested on the Bosnian and
barren on the Montenegrin side; and it is the only river which flows
above ground throughout its whole course, though the underground
courses of the others can generally be traced by the lines of poljes.

Its Products.   The forested Danubian slopes, with their typical summer rains,
are noted for maize, pigs, and plums, the distilling of plum-brandy
being a characteristic industry in the Posavina (*e.g.* at Bijeljina).

---

[1] Somewhat the same result is found in Servia itself in the heart of the Shumadia
("Forest"), where there is shade as well as humidity.

The winter rains of the Adriatic slope are more favourable to tobacco and the vine, Mostar having a famous School of Viticulture. Bosnia is certainly rich in minerals, precious metals having been worked from Roman times, and the coal and the iron-fields (*e.g.* at Zenica and Ljubija) and the salt pits of Dolnja Tuzla are now being properly worked; but the political history of the area has been adverse to its prosperity, and the Serbo-Croat population—though centuries of experience have developed in them great aptitude in metal-working (cf. the chased and inlaid metal ware of Sarajevo)— is predominantly agricultural. As the administrative, commercial, and, above all, military centre, Serajevo is much the most important town; and its population, aided by the old encouragement of "immigration" from Austria and Hungary, has increased very rapidly. Mostar, the rival "capital," is quite small; and the climatic differences between the two are almost equally marked. At Mostar temperature ranges from 41° F. to 76° F.; at Sarajevo from 27° F. to 65° F. In connection with this area Spalato and Ragusa (for long an independent republic) now have some possibilities, the one in connection with the Bay of Salona, which was a terminus for the old Roman roads, and the other in connection with the Bay of Gravosa (Gruž). In both cases progress depends on the new railway facilities; but Ragusa owed its greater safety in olden days to the very fact that the Herzegovina is largely barren "karst."

The old Carniola ("Frontier") area is an intermediate zone **Slovenia.** between very different types of relief and very different racial elements. The north is Alpine, while the south is typical Karst; and the two are divided by the three sugar-loaf peaks of the Triglav, the highest point in the Julian Alps (*c.* 9400 feet). This Alpine outpost not only, like the somewhat similarly placed Grintouz, has a magnificent view, but also is the natural rampart between the Slav (Slovene) and the German and Italian elements, the Slav including 95 p.c. of the whole population. In the Alpine basin of the Upper Save, with its heavy rainfall, timber and flax are typical products, and there is a "Home" lace industry; but the population is very scanty. The Karst, though rather more densely populated, is a barren and depressing area, exposed to the bora. The excessive faulting in parallel fractures has accentuated the natural porosity of the rocks by a series of terraces, the topmost of which are "stone dry"; and the seismic movements along the fractures help to break in the roofs of the numerous caves dissolved in the limestone by the underground streams, thus dotting the surface with sink-holes, etc. (cf. p. 132). Other typical phenomena associated with Karst structure are grottos and caves, *e.g.* at Adelsberg (Italian) and Planina,—intermittent lakes and discontinuous rivers, such as Lake Zirknitz and the Laibach,—and earthquakes, such as that at Laibach in 1895. The Laibach is a typical river, its first surface section being known as the Poik, which disappears underground to traverse the Adelsberg grotto, reappears as the Ung near Planina, only to disappear almost immediately, reappearing again at Oberlaibach. Railway communication, however, is not so difficult over the Karst as across the Julian Alps or the Karawanken, so that Laibach— always a suitable site for a capital, as commanding the relation of the Karst saddle to the great bend on the Save—is an important junction. Trbovlje produces annually 1,000,000 tons of coal (just good enough for railway use) and Misica has lead mines. The Kanker-Save confluence makes Krainburg ("Frontier Town") a great road centre; but the only town of any real importance is Laibach (Ljubljana).

The Karst. The map measures 300 miles by 150. Karst region, white; Adriatic drainage, black; Danube drainage, stippled.

Montenegro. Montenegro owed its name to the dark forests that in the fourteenth century covered the heights in which those Serbs found refuge who would not submit to the Turks. Like so many units within this peninsula, it has only indifferent roadsteads on its coastline—Antivari and Dulcigno; and it owed to Russia this coast and its most fertile lowlands, in the Moracha valley north of Podgoritsa ("Mountain-Foot"), and adherence to the Greek Church increased the influence of Russia. But in 1914 Austria held the harbour of Cattaro, which gives best access to Cetinje, only ten miles inland, and the marriage of Princess Helena to the King of Italy did much to weaken the Russian influence.

Economic Geography. The bleak and now disforested mountains rise to a height of 8000 feet in an area not twice the size of Lancashire, and give the country a very intricate river-system, characterised by profound gorges, innumerable caves, and subterranean channels. The latter are specially common in the Karst area, which covers nearly all the northern half of the country, but, of course, are absent from the schist formation of the Brda highland, where the floors of the Tara and Lim valleys are fairly fertile. The lowlands along the coast and in the Moracha and Zeta valleys are still more fertile, and—with a typical Mediterranean climate—specialise in fruit-growing. Apart, then, from the sheep and goats of the highlands and the fish of Lake Scutari, the country is very poorly supplied with food-products; and, as the difficult communication inland is accentuated in winter by the heavy snowfall, life is very hard.

People. In dress and bearing the men are typical mountaineers, pledged

to freedom and descended from warrior ancestors for 500 years
back. Their national dress includes all their weapons, so that
they are walking arsenals, and the whole force can be mobilised
at a few minutes' notice. But, in these days of peace, with no
possible lines of development, industrial or otherwise, they have
become little better than picturesque loafers, and their women have
become mere drudges and pack animals, while the value of imports
is three or four times that of exports (*e.g.* sumach and smoked mutton),
and emigration is inevitable. For this the acquisition of a coast gave
encouragement; but the survival of the little area as a separate kingdom was essentially due to its isolated position and its intricate relief.

In this area we have one of the delicate problems which the **The**
Jugo-Slavs have to solve. For the change in the direction of the **Scutari**
Adriatic coastline is reflected in a change of direction in the **Problem.**
feature-lines of the hinterland. The Drin valley, therefore, as we
have seen (p. 143), is the natural western outlet of Servia; and, in
default of that, they should at least own the Boyana, which is an outlet, not only of Lake Scutari, but also of the Drin itself. But half the
lake, with the town of Scutari, is in Albania; and the frontier runs
along the river for only half the distance to the lake, and on the
northern bank. The river is navigable by small sea-going boats
for twelve miles, but is really spoilt by the inflow from the Drin.

Croatia-Slavonia is a particularly interesting area, though it does **Croatia-**
not correspond with the medieval Croatia and Slavonia, the latter **Slavonia.**
including the whole " Mesopotamian " area, while the former reached
farther south than the Unna-Save. The two names represent the
original tribe (the Croats) and their race (Slav), and the tribe
belonged to the *Northern* Slavs; but they passed through various
stages of political relations—a period of Italian or Byzantine
influence, two centuries as a Croat kingdom, five centuries
under the direct control of Hungary, two more centuries under the
Turks, a century under the Austrians, a few years of French rule,
—and then, after some vicissitudes and a National Revival, under
Hungary again. The existence of two distinct dialects would
suggest the division of the area into two parts, Adriatic and Continental; but the natural physical divisions are almost as varied as
the political relations have been. For a long time Croatia was
divided from Slavonia by the famous Military Frontier; for still
longer the line of the Kulpa-Save has been regarded as the frontier
between the Balkan peninsula and the continent of Europe;
longitudinally, the west is highland, and the east is lowland;
latitudinally, there is a sequence of Karst saddle, fluvial plain,
Alpine " bergland," and again fluvial plain.

The Karst area rises in the Kapella to over 5000 feet; it has a **Its Physi-**
dangerous and capricious climate, subject to violent Bora gales, **cal Char-**
accompanied by terrific snow-storms; and it is almost waterless, *e.g.* **acter.**

the seven streams of the Lika all plunging underground together near Gospič. The Alpine bergland (*c.* 3000 feet), on the contrary, is well enough watered to be densely forested, largely with oak and beech ; and the foothills supply the excellent alp pastures known as Zagorjc ("Hillside-land"), while their lower Syrmian continuation in the Fruska Gora (*c.* 1770 feet) is covered with vineyards, *e.g.* near Karlowitz. The lowlands vary, mainly with exposure, from poor steppe to rich prairie or fen and swamp, those along the Drave being very fertile, while those along the winding Save are so marshy and liable to such floods in spring and autumn that they are often impassable on the Bosnian border except at Brod, and on the Servian border except at Mitrovič.

Its River System. These floods are, of course, partly due to the meandering of the river, which is almost as sinuous as the Theiss ; but, like the similar floods along the latter river, they are mainly due to the constriction of the Danube and the obstacles in its bed east of Belgrade. The Drave is much less troublesome, as its banks are higher. Indeed, it is the high right bank of the Drave that compels the Danube to change its course accordingly ; and this helped to make the valley the natural route for invaders from the east, whether Huns or Slavs or Turks. The river is actually navigable for rafts downwards from Villach ; the Mur confluence makes Legrad always accessible for ordinary boats ; and steamers can reach Barcs, if not Zakany. The Save, though at least as long as the Drave (450 miles), is much less useful, for much of its actual mileage is wasted on the windings that expose it so greatly to flood, and its channels and sand-banks are constantly changing. The confluence of the Kulpa enables steamers to reach Sissek, and small boats can use the winding Kulpa for 60 miles—up to Karolyvaros (Karlstadt), *i.e.* within 50 miles of the Adriatic ; and this has an obvious connection with the presence of early ("Neanderthal") Man, *e.g.* in the Krapina valley (cf. p. 45).

Economic And Political Import- ance. The area is subject to earthquakes along the lines of Alpine fracture, *e.g.* at Zagreb, where hot springs also make their way out by the fracture, and to violent gales and sandstorms outside, *i.e.* east of, the shelter of the Bergland ; and it is in various ways very backward, especially industrially. But a very large proportion of both the population and the area is devoted to agriculture, especially between Zagreb and Warasdin, the great output of maize and the forests of oak and beech—the oak mainly between Zagreb and Sissek—accounting for the importance of the pig-breeding industry. But the typical product is the plum (cf. p. 146), and the favourite occupation is horse-breeding. The latter seems to be a direct result of the importance of the area as containing the old Military Frontier. For strategic reasons the country was covered with good roads (2000 miles), even across the Karst, *e.g.* inland from Fiume and from Zengg. It was largely the road-system that made Sissek more important than Zagreb (Agram) in olden days.

The Military Frontier, though extended later into Transylvania, was originally organised against the Turks; and therefore its terminus was at Zengg, and its chief bases were along the Austrian frontier—at Karlstadt and Warasdin, with an advanced base near Sissek. Its defence perpetuated, if it did not actually evoke, the zadrugas, or communal houses, of the Frontier Slavs—with a common central hall, off which private houses opened, so that the whole population (perhaps up to 300) could be collected with maximum ease; and, as the loft of the hall was always fully stored with food, and the whole block of buildings was surrounded by a palisade, it formed a natural fortress capable of sustaining even a prolonged siege, and of resisting with great success a sudden raid. The western route across the area is still the most important, though its real terminus is now Fiume, not Buccari or Novi or Zengg, and its focus is now Zagreb, not Warasdin; but the more important route strategically has been that *via* Semlin and Peterwardein or Eszek. For Semlin was a great focus of Hungarian foreign trade, while Peterwardein controlled the last bridge across the Danube in Hungary, and was farther from the frontier.

The "Military Frontier."

If one refers now to a map of the Austro-Hungarian Empire in 1913, it throws a good deal of light on the political problems before the Jugo-Slavs.

"A Succession" State.

More than half the population of that empire consisted of Slavs; and there was, and is, a broad belt of Slavic speech right across the northern half of the Balkan peninsula. Inside this belt, before the war, the peoples were very feeble economically, but politically, their numbers and their position made

Old Austria-Hungary, showing countries and provinces.
Austria, white; Hungary, stippled.

them really formidable. In fact, both inside and outside of the empire the Jugo-Slavs were so distributed as to cause the maximum inconvenience to Austria and to her German master. Inside the empire the mass of the Jugo-Slavs lived in the corner across which both Austria and Hungary had the only direct outlet to the sea; and outside of it the nucleus of the whole Jugo-Slav power was astride the great "Berlin-Baghdad" route to the Levant and Anatolia.

Old Servia.   Servia was not much more than half the size of Bulgaria, and was greatly handicapped by want of access to the sea, the only compensations being that it sat astride the Orient Express route, that a considerable proportion (over 400 miles) of its frontier was navigable river—Drina, Save, Danube, Timok,—and that its shape has such a relation to that of the whole peninsula that it has a certain equality of interest in all directions. But, of course, its position astride the Orient-Express route was the real cause of the outbreak of the war, as the blocking of access *via* the Drin Valley to the Adriatic forced the Serbs to look to Salonika for a sea-outlet, and thus—as was obviously the intention of the culprits—so greatly accentuated international rivalries in the area as to bring about the Balkan Wars.

Access.   Its physical setting in the Western Balkans, the Rhodope block, the Alpine region of Zlatibor, is very rough and formidable. Even

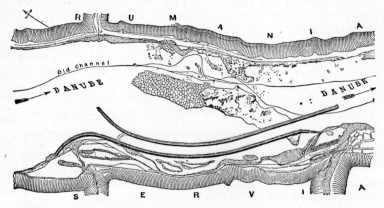

The Kazan or Klisura Canal, near Orsova.

the apparently easy line of access by the upper valley of the Morava is really a 50-mile gorge, in some places 3000 feet deep and so narrow that both road and railway are hewn out of the solid rock. This is complicated by the relief, which is largely a chaos of mountain ends—Dinaric, Carpathian, Rhodope, Albanian—falling into two main blocks, east and west of the Morava gorge, so that movement north or south parallel to the gorge is almost impossible. These conditions minimise the danger of the through-route in time of war without minimising its advantages in time of peace ; but of course they are as adverse to commercial development as they are favourable to guerilla warfare.

Relief.   The high land towards the north-west is a waste of desolate limestone, while the low land beyond—between the Drina and the Save—is typical fen (the Machva) ; and the liability to flood which is implied in this, and which is largely due to the windings of the

Save, has a real strategic value as far east as Belgrade. There the Danube is a mile and a half wide, and the only bridge is across the Save; and the city stands on a 400-foot platform which, from south-west round to south-east, drops northwards to swampy lowlands. But in the interior there are two side-entrances to the main valley, the Ibar valley from the west, and the Nishava valley from the east. The Ibar valley is relatively unimportant, as there is little prospect of trade or danger from that quarter; but, of course, the Nishava valley carries the Orient-Express route to Constantinople, and leads directly into Bulgaria.

The permanence of the geographic control here is remarkable. **Geographic Control.** Pompey considered the key to the peninsula to be the confluence of the Ibar with the Servian Morava; and, of course, the southern valley of the Ibar basin is the famous Kossovo Polye (cf. p. 132). The medieval tsars of Servia considered the key to be at Krushevatz, commanding the confluence of the Servian and Bulgarian Moravas. The two great historic lines of invasion—from the south and the east, *i.e.* by the Vardar route and Leskovatz and the Nishava route and Pirot—converge on the old routes from Durazzo and Belgrade at the railway junction of Nish. And the only satisfactory site for a capital was that occupied by the old capital of Kraguyevatz, in the heart of the Shumadia ("Forest"), on the flank of the great road north of all its various side-entrances and cross-routes, and within easy reach of the navigable part of the Morava, *i.e.* north of Chupriya.

The worst possible site for a capital was that of Belgrade. A **Belgrade.** spur of the Avala plateau at the confluence of the Save and the Danube, commanding the crossing of great N.–S. and E.–W. routes, on the frontier of the kingdom, was a good site for a Beograd ("White Castle"); and it is now an excellent site for a great rail and river junction, as it was a great collecting and distributing centre in the palmy days of river-trade on the Save and the Drave, the Danube and the Theiss, all of which pivot cn the Morava-Danube confluence. But for a capital it is

Site of Belgrade.

still too near the frontier, *i.e.* liable to surprise and politically exposed to intrigue. And so, though it is more important as a route-centre than any other place in the peninsula, it is also more significant than any other as a storm-centre.

The chaos of forested heights—with their plethora of wild life, **Economic Geography.** *e.g.* bears and boars, wolves and lynxes—is threaded by innumerable long, deep, torrent-cut gorges, such as that on the Morava, along the floor of which there is often a rich strip of flat land, especially on the Tertiary formation of the Shumadia ; and the northward slope of the country makes the latter also less exposed than the southern watershed to the bitter N. and N.E. winds. The lower Morava basin, therefore, produces very large crops of maize (for home use) and wheat (for export), and vines and plum-trees grow luxuriantly with very little care, while the beech and oak forests fatten enormous herds of swine. Indeed, it is said that, since the days of Prince Milosh, the Pig-driver, the foreign policy of Servia has always turned on pigs ; and the Austrian sanitary precautions against swine-fever—from imported pigs—used certainly to vary curiously with the political tension.

Serbs.   As the only country in Europe except Switzerland that had no sea-coast, Servia was bound to have delicate and difficult relations with its neighbours, because command of the great road might have made it a great nation. But it has failed to use the opportunity, mainly because its population is so essentially Slav. Fully 90 p.c. are Serbs, typical Slavs, with great gifts for co-operation and an utter lack of initiative. They live in villages, not towns ; and the villages are largely communal, as the political instinct is patriarchal. All sons are equal ; there are no rich and no paupers ; there is no nobility or even middle class ; and so both natural leaders and natural ambitions are absent. It is a nation of self-contained, non-progressive tillers of the soil, whose women are taught that it is more important to till their parents' land than to find a home for themselves. Such a people have no chance against such thrifty and industrious rivals as the Bulgarians, or against such intellectual and adaptable rivals as the Rumanians, whilst the overwhelming influence of Austria made even contraband gravitate north, and imposed German as the commercial language. Historically, too, these Serbs are the descendants of the vanquished at the battle of Kossovo (A.D. 1389), who were prepared to accept the dominion of the Turk when the virile amongst them retreated into the dark forests of Montenegro.

Industries.   It is not surprising, then, that they have entirely failed to develop their land. For instance, it is rich in minerals, especially amongst the old rock of the Pek basin. The Romans worked gold and silver, iron and lead ; and the merchant princes of Ragusa made fortunes out of the Servian mines. But to-day beyond the mining—mainly by foreigners, especially Belgians—of a little lead in the north-west (*e.g.* at Krupem), coal at Senje (with a light railway to Cuprija), some iron and the very rich copper mines at Maidan-Pek (" Pek Mines ") and Bor, the mineral wealth is still neglected. The same is true of other industries. There is home-weaving of the local flax and the very abundant supplies of wool—for Servia has more sheep for her population than any other country in Europe ; plum-brandy is distilled, and prunes are dried ; honey and bees-wax are collected ; a little wine is made ; and beet-sugar is refined. In such a climate maize is easily grown, because it is more tolerant than other grains of rough, hilly, badly prepared land ; but really both the country and the people are more suited to the raising of animals than to agriculture, and the farmer's object is essentially to provide a minimum of necessaries and comforts as a basis for a maximum of idleness and amusement.

ALBANIA

The most significant fact about the Thraco-Illyrian highlanders **Pre-historic Type.** of Skypanie, or Albania, is that they seem to be incapable of being assimilated. They were holding this land 1000 years before any Slavs ever crossed the Danube, and held it against Goth and Hun and Avar. Romans and Byzantines, Serbs and Bulgars, Venetian and Sicilian kings of the House of Anjou, all tried to assimilate them, and all failed. Here is a sound basis for any claim to political independence, even though the total area is certainly under 20,000 square miles, and the total population below 1,000,000, and the capital (Tirana) only a glorified village. Even the configuration suggests the same tendency. For the change in the direction of the coast is associated with a change of physical history, the sunk coast of Dalmatia giving place to the raised coast of Albania ; and the consequent " deltas," while very fertile, are so malarial that they are very thinly peopled, and thus form a " barrier of desolation " between the interior and the Adriatic.

The famous *Via Egnatia* ran up the Skumbi valley and round **Access Inland.** the northern ends of the great lakes—Okhrida, Prespa, and Ostrovo —to Thessalonica ; and this ancient thoroughfare seems to have proved a line of relative civilisation between northern and southern Albania, which centre respectively round the Drin and the Viosa. As we have seen, the shallow sea and malarial coast-lands—aided by the bora in spring—more or less isolate even the lower part of the coast from San Giovanni to Helora ; and the Akrokeraunian scarp is quite impassable. But a few river-mouths, especially in the lee of islands and peninsulas, are used, *e.g.* Durazzo, Avlona, and Hagioi Saranta ; and the hinterland of these, especially Durazzo, gives access to important routes. For instance, the Viosa basin taps Yanina and the Metsovo Pass, as both the Drin and the Boyana—which now acts partly as a distributary of the Drin *via* Scutari (Skodra)—give access round Shar Dagh, and as both the Skumbi *via* Elbasan and the Semeni *via* Berat give access to the lake-plateau and Monastir.

These adverse conditions combine with the Karst limestone and **Isolation.** the heavy snowfall (*Albania,* *i.e.* apparently " Snowy Land ") to make the interior of Albania very difficult of access ; and this is reflected in the character of the people, and is emphasised by their difficult language—which is older than Classical Greek—and their complex social institutions. Indeed, some parts of northern Albania, *e.g.* the foothills of Shlieb, are to this day unexplored. Of course, conditions are further complicated by the fact that the physical and climatic divide from Shar Dagh to Pindus is neither an ethnic nor a political divide, Albania proper overlapping into Kossovo and Macedonia.

Relief.   West of the physical divide the land may be subdivided into three sections—northern, central, and southern. The northern area is profoundly intricate, especially round the Prokletia ("Accursed") Mountains, which are often snow-covered till August; and it is in this area that the least-known districts of all Europe are found, even round relatively large—Jugo-Slav—towns such as Diakova and Ipek. The central area is much less difficult and more fertile, especially in the Semeni valley, where the Berat district grows very good tobacco, and, like the similar Koritsa district, contains a large number of Vlachs; but the southern area again becomes exceedingly rough and intricate. In creed, the north is mainly Roman, the south is Greek, and the rest (two-thirds) is Moslem.

Products.   The natural products of the area are surprisingly important, considering its backward state politically and economically. Not only are there valuable forests of valonia-oak [1] and beech, *e.g.* round the beautiful lake of Skutari (half the size of Middlesex, and very rich in "sardines"), but almost the entire "bread" supply of the Dalmatian coast and islands comes from Albania! The mineral wealth, too, is unquestionably great; but, as communication nearly everywhere is confined to bridle paths, there can be no development of either mining or industry. Indeed, even the famous old industry in arms, especially yataghans, though it still survives at Skutari (or Skodra), is languishing owing to the import of modern revolvers; and the possibility of developing the country by trade is very doubtful, though the light railways and motor roads built during the war— especially between Valona and Tepelani and Koritsa—are very useful.

People.   The people call themselves *Shkupetar* (probably "Rock-Dwellers"), and it is certainly their rocky environment that has preserved them through the centuries in practical independence. For they are the most ancient existing race in Europe, the Ghegs of the north being apparently the descendants of the earliest "Aryan" immigrants, who may be called Illyrians, while the Tosks (or Tuscans) of the south seem to have a similar relation to the prehistoric Epirots or Pelasgians. The number of Slavonic place-names confirms the historic accounts of Slav, Bulgarian, and Walachian intrusion or conquest; but the Ghegs and Tosks proper have maintained themselves in practical purity, as in practical

---

[1] Valonia takes its name from the old port of *Avlona* or *Valona*.

autonomy, west of a line that may be drawn roughly from north to
south generally parallel with longitude 21° E.   Inside, *i.e.* west of,
this line they remain scarcely touched by outside influence except
along the *Via Egnatia*, where, too, the population is strongly
"intrusive," especially Jugo-Slav and Vlach (Walach); and amongst
their primitive virtues is absolute fidelity.

Even the fierce and lawless Ghegs, steeped in ignorance and **The**
superstition, are "faithful unto death"; and, as they are magnificent **Ghegs.**
soldiers, they had special value in the eyes of their Turkish rulers,
and for ages they supplied the Sultan's bodyguard.   But they were
Moslems and subjects of Turkey voluntarily, and only because that
was the easiest way of getting the right to carry arms—for the purpose
of "vendetta," which is often a matter of race; as a rule, they paid
no taxes, and were not subject to conscription.   So deadly are these
blood-feuds still that competent observers believe that only 25 p.c.
of the purely Highland population die natural deaths.

The Tosks, though still feudal Highlanders, are not quite so **The**
primitive, for they have come under the influence of the Greeks **Tosks.**
and of the essentially peaceful Walachians of the Zygos-Pindus
area, once known as "Great Walachia."   They are, therefore, less
pastoral and more agricultural, less exclusive and more talkative,
just as they wear kilts,[1] while the Ghegs wear trews; and, if only
they were educated, they would take a place appropriate to their
essential character.   Already their fidelity and versatility make
them much sought after as dragomans and kavasses.   But want of
education is a terrible drawback, and the existing conditions only
accentuate racial troubles.

Nearness to Italy *via* the less inhospitable Adriatic coast has **Religion.**
linked the non-Moslem portions of the Ghegs to the Roman
Church; but the more inhospitable Akrokeraunian coast of the
Ægean has thrown the non-Moslem portion of the Tosks to the
Greek Church.   The result is that even in times of peace the
Christian part of this "race born to arms" has no religious bond,
as it has no common sentiment or authority or economic life.

GREECE [2]

Within the course of a single century (530-430 B.C.) Athens, a **Ancient**
little city of 100,000 free men, produced twelve names of the very **Greece.**
first rank in the world's annals of genius.   A century later she
meant little more to the world intellectually than she does to-day.
And the loss was not only in intellectual power, but also in physique
as related to the power of bearing heavy armour (cf. p. 160).   What

---

[1] Called "Greek," but the Greeks probably copied them from the Tosks.

[2] Greece proper is treated first, and then Macedonia separately.

light, if any, can geography throw on the pathetic problem? Probably this—that the geographic factors which were behind the early rise of Greece were also behind its early decay. The mild winter was not bracing enough for northern intruders, while the dry summers gave dangerous power to the actinic rays of sunshine under an unclouded sky; the seasonal work implied seasonal idleness—devoted to democratic discussion, heroic games, perennial war; and so various causes were working together for ill, and the constant war meant decimation of the finest human type—the suicide of which involved " The Passing of a Great Race."

World Relation.   Greece gives, then, some exceedingly interesting aspects of Historical Geography, as accounting for the special development of a particular people in a particular place. Its world-relation is best expressed climatically, as in latitudes of warm-temperate summer-drought, where northern intruders—Pelasgi, Achaeans, Dorians—would first be stimulated, and then over-stimulated, by the high percentage of ultra-violet rays in the sunlight. With accumulated energy from the steppe, and yet less power of, or need for, work in the more southern latitudes, these early intruders would combine energy with leisure, which is the geographical basis of all art. But from 400 B.C. to A.D. 600 these were latitudes of progressive desiccation, during which hunger and actinic stimulus gave rise to many epoch-making migrations in Europe, *e.g.* of Goths and Huns and Vandals, and during which in Greece the river-system dwindled to a series of intermittent torrents and stagnant pools—a mosquito paradise.

Regional Relation.   The regional relation of the area is best expressed in politico-economic terms, as within easy reach of the Levant, Egypt, and Magna Graecia; and, as the convergence of so many subordinate seas—Adriatic and Ionian, Black and Ægean—on the Mediterranean made this a great trade-centre, intercourse, both peaceful and otherwise, with land-neighbours was a natural sequel, *e.g.* in the expeditions to Egypt (456 B.C.) and Sicily (415 B.C.). And there is abundant evidence[1] that from the disastrous Egyptian expeditions—on which the amount of sickness amongst the troops was characteristically proportionate to the extent of the disaster—the Greeks brought malaria into Europe.

Relief.   The physique of the area accentuated the geographic control exercised by the focal position on the activities of the inhabitants. The symmetry of the feature-lines, which is so marked that it seems to have even influenced Greek theories of art, is due to the whole group of peninsulas and islands being a partly submerged section of a single mountain loop of the main Alpine chain; and this involves a great multiplication of small geographic divisions within the one Hellenic unit. It also implies that the inhabitants must be both mariners and mountaineers, and that the pressure of population on

---

[1] Admirably collected and criticised in *Malaria*, by Jones, Ross, and Ellett.

such small areas of relatively infertile mountain must soon have crushed out an ill-fed surplus from their tiny homes.   Again, as we have already seen (p. 133), the complex interlacing of the structural lines in the interior gave rise to lonely montane basins which formed isolated political units, so that it is said that "there is no Greek History, only the history of separate Greek States." All these conditions favour individualism—in commerce and in politics, as well as in philosophy and art.

The mountainous relief is further connected with the peninsular **Peninsu-** forms, which are nearly always unfavourable to unity, because their **lar Forms.** mountainous back-bone throws off the human interests in opposite directions ; and both parts of old Greece have a rough mountainous centre—the butt of Pindus and the Arcadian highland—which is essentially infertile, and which was in early days inaccessible and impregnable.   The valleys that radiate from these two centres are cut off from one another by mountainous spurs on all sides except towards the sea, so that communication between valley and valley came to be carried on by sea, the great nursery of Democracy.

Professor Myers has pointed out how these conditions, as found **Crete.** in Crete, influenced the invention of writing.   The varied relief, with its consequent variety of climate and products—corn and fruit, supplemented by alp pasture and bay fishing—made the land self-contained ; the great height (Mt. Ida = 8000 feet) in such a small area (c. Argyleshire) caused such heavy falls of rain and snow that few springs ran dry in summer ; but the supreme difficulty of oral communication between valley and valley except by sea led to a great development of navigation and—as soon as the island came under a single political influence, e.g. that of Cnossus—to the development of a system of writing by which communication could be carried between different parts of the land.

This is only one specific illustration of the general process. **Site and** Obviously, the smallness of the area and its isolation by mountain **Size.** and sea on the margin of civilisation favoured early growth ; with the spread of civilisation westward, Greece, as a central focus, collected ideas as well as merchandise ; but eventually the physical limitations must have cramped progress at home—especially when the outlook was no longer on to the greatest sea in the known world, but on to what was almost a backwater on one of a dozen ocean routes, as they must have favoured the distribution of civilisation abroad by outflow from the over-populated focus.

As the summer drought comes on, the winter rain lies about in **Climate.** marsh beloved of the mosquito, and many of the rivers become a series of pools, e.g. the Ilissus ; and, as the winter rain comes on, the dry loose soil is rushed down into the streams in such quantities and with such violence as constantly to dam up the beds and divert the whole stream.   And all this, once the malaria parasite had been introduced into the country, was terribly favourable to its propagation, though previously the even temperature had been equally favourable to the " Eurafrican " natives, and though the excess of food-supply had caused a quick increase of population at first amongst the "Eurasians" who intruded from the north.

People. These natives, like all Eurafricans, preserved the long head of the arboreal primate ; like all inhabitants of very sunny areas, they were dark ; and, like all underfed representatives of over-populated areas, they were short. They were, therefore, likely to be easily dominated by the vigour, and strength, and unity of the tall, fair intruders from the north, whose round heads—as evidenced by the statues of Greek gods and heroes—say unmistakably "Steppe." But it was precisely on the intruders that the burden of war fell, and decimated their numbers, *e.g.* at Corcyra, Thebes, and Platoea ; the nerve, too, of the survivors was gradually destroyed by the over-stimulation of light, as their physique was by malaria ; and the race died out. In the fifth century B.C. Athens alone had 35,000 citizens capable of bearing heavy armour ; 500 years later, according to Plutarch, "all Greece could scarcely furnish 3000 !" For malaria was fatal to these fair Northerners except in the healthier windy islands and on the dry Attic plains, and it was precisely here that the clear sky and dry air gave the sunlight most influence on their nerve. So the men who fought the Persians and built the Parthenon left no one behind them. The modern Greek is usually round-headed, but it is thanks to a large infusion of "modern" Slav blood.

Vegetation. The economic vegetation is varied in character, but limited in amount. The bare mountain sides can feed only sheep and goats, so that the typical food of the old Eurasians—milk and butter, cheese and meat—can never have been abundant, nor is it quite appropriate to the climate. And the variety of crops must always have been a "Mediterranean" variety, more or less limited to plants with long or bulbous roots, *e.g.* olive and vine, narcissus and asphodel,—with aromatic qualities, *e.g.* lavender and myrtle,— or with a power of ripening quickly, *e.g.* barley and wheat. But in days before the great draining schemes, especially in Bœotia (Lake Copais) and Thessaly, the area suitable for grain was very small ; and, the home land being therefore mainly devoted to wine and oil, corn had to be imported. This involved both home manufactures to pay for the imported corn, and command of the sea to guarantee safe passage of commodities out and in.

The Olive. Of course, the summer drought has always been most favourable to the olive ; and olive-oil is an admirable food in such a climate— with great nourishment in small bulk, easily assimilated, and so sustaining that there is no need for heavy or constant meals. But the tree grows so slowly, and needs so little care, that it does not encourage dense population—to which also the lack of milk is very adverse; the crop is picked so roughly (cane-beaten) by the more ignorant peasants, *e.g.* in Corfu and Zante, that the fruit-buds for the following year are terribly damaged—hence the fable that "the climate (!) allows a crop only every second year"; and such rash destruction of the groves as was prompted by the demand for currants and raisins in France (for wine-making) at the beginning of the phylloxera scare (1877) can never be made good during the lifetime of the destroyers. As olive-oil is "bread and butter" in Greece, this has increased the tendency to emigration, to which islanders are always prone, especially when badly governed at home.

Another result of substituting the vine for the olive has been **Currants** gross over-production of currants and sultanas, especially currants, which come mainly from the west of the Morea, while the sultanas come—like the excellent local tobacco—mainly from the more continental east.   And this over-production is all the more regrettable because the currant industry is very precarious, as the berries are sun-dried, and the drying period coincides with the beginning of the winter rains.   The development of grain-growing and cotton-growing in the north-east is, therefore, of great importance; and the lack of labour is minimised by the fact that the level plains of Thessaly and Bœotia are not only very fertile, but also admirably adapted to the use of machinery.

Capital for this purpose is scarce, but population—which, like **Popula-** the forest, has always preferred the windward west—is beginning **tion.** to gravitate towards the grain-lands.   In the west the density per square mile was *c.* 145, while in the east it was only *c.* 114; but the Population Exchanges with Bulgaria and Turkey, and an inflow of *c.* 60,000 refugees from Russia, have changed this.   Politically, the result is a racial unity (94 p.c. Greek) which has solved automatically the Macedonian problem with its constant threat to the peace of Europe; but the economic result is less happy.   The emigrants numbered *c.* 400,000 Turks (*c.* 320,000 being "rurals," mainly from Macedonia and Thessaly) and *c.* 70,000 Bulgars (*c.* 65,000 being "rurals," from Macedonia and Western Thrace). The immigrant Greeks, however, numbered over 1,150,000; more than half were "urbans," including a very large number of widows and girls from Anatolia; and there was little chance of their finding permanent work except in the half-dozen industrial centres of Greece, *i.e.* in Eastern Greece.   The results of this inflow on the population of these centres will be found in the Note on p. 165.

The economic minerals in early days were of little importance, **Minerals.** for the most abundant are silver-lead and marble; and these are more or less monopolised by Attica in the Laurium mines and Pentelikon quarries.   In modern times the emery of Naxos, the sulphur and volcanic cement of Santorin, the chrome of Phersala, and the magnesite of Eubœa have some importance; and the

M

iron-ores of Attica, Eubœa, and Seriphos would be much more valuable if there was easy access to fuel. But in early days the easy access to copper (the "Cyprian" metal), and the ease with which it was melted, encouraged the use of bronze; and this again was adverse to the success of the Eurafrican when he came to blows with the iron-using Eurasian.

Athens. Four historic sites have special geographic interest—Athens, Navarino, Lepanto, and Thes-Salonika (cf. p. 129). Athens, the "Edinburgh of the East," is a typical "double-city," with its Acropolis, its link of Long Walls, and its Piræus. The height (512 feet) of its rock-castle and the distance from the sea (6 miles) combined with the rough surface and poor soil of Attica to ensure safety. The advanced eastward site, with its command of the neighbouring port, ensured an outlet, and made it easy to conquer and then control the islands of the Ægean, *e.g.* Naxos, as it is easy

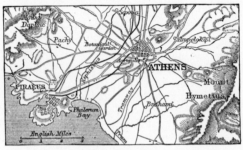

Athens and Piræus.

for them, *e.g.* Syra, to supply the modern Athenian with spring vegetables; and the barren hinterland made it an imperious necessity to command the rich coast-lands of Macedonia and Asia Minor through the possession of Thasos and Samos, as it was to command the spring shoals of tunny from the Euxine by the possession of the "volcanic lighthouse" of Lemnos. Safety and sea-power were the beginning and the end of her prosperity.

Lepanto. Lepanto is the ancient Naupaktos, on the famous "Narrows" (1 mile) of the Gulf of Corinth. A great naval-station first of Athens, then of the Venetians, and then of the Turks, it could watch from a safe distance inland the relations between Greece and Magna Graecia, *i.e.* the Strait of Otranto. It was, therefore, a foregone conclusion that, in a combined attack by Spain and Venice, the Papal States and Austria, on the Turks, the allied fleet must converge on the most critical point in the line of least resistance against the foe, *i.e.* these "Narrows."

Navarino. Navarino is the ancient Sphakteria, of little use as a harbour because of its poor and difficult hinterland, but a magnificent naval-station because of its protecting island of Sphagia (Sphakteria). Two of the allies in the famous battle came from the west, and their first aim was to cut off the Turko-Egyptian fleet from its base of supplies in Northern Africa. It was, therefore, again a foregone conclusion that the English, French, and Russian fleets would converge on Cape Matapan; and the nearest refuge for the Turko-Egyptian fleet was in Navarino Bay.

Of course, Macedonia also is of immense historic interest, and the name may reasonably be given to all the new lands acquired by Greece in the Balkan peninsula, for they did form the core of Alexander's empire. But the Greeks have no claim, ethnic or other, to the rest of the old Balkan Macedonia. Unfortunately, these lower and middle portions of the Vistritza and Vardar, Struma and Mesta basins have been the worst governed area in the whole peninsula; and, though even in 1914 the Greek type was dominant on the coast-land, the Bulgars were equally dominant in the hinterland—as *proved* by the prevalent, typically Bulgar, "post-fixing" of the definite article—and the Struma valley is the natural link between Sofia and the sea. No doubt, it is true that the Bulgar farmer could not develop the coast-land, any more than the Greek trader could plough the hinterland; but that is no good reason for cutting Bulgaria off completely from the sea. *[Macedonia—Political.]*

This does not mean that the coast-land is less agricultural than the hinterland, or that the eastern basins are more open than the western. Just the opposite is true: the coast-land is much the more fertile, and the Vistritza and Vardar basins have more lowland than those of the Struma and the Mesta. Indeed, the latter are typically torrential, with profound gorges and malarial estuaries and flood-plains; and the Struma not only expands into lakes which absolutely block normal east-and-west traffic, Lake Takhyno being 20 miles long by 5 miles wide, but is so torrential along the central part of its 225 miles course that there is no continuous road along its banks at all. But the soil is often very fertile, growing opium and oil-seeds, cotton and rice, and tobacco. The tobacco of the hinterland, *e.g.* Seres and Drama, is as good as that of Xanthi, while that of the coast-lands round Kavala Bay is the finest cigarette tobacco in the world. The Vardar basin is also very fertile, and specialises in silk and tobacco, the "Uskub" tobacco being quite as good as that from Seres and Drama. Other important products are cotton and opium; but the latter suffers from the greater exposure to north and north-east winds in spring, when there is no snow to protect the plants. The cotton favoured the rise of some textile centres along the steep face of the Kara Tash, *e.g.* Karaferia and Vodena; and on the "Kampania" marsh, between which and the Kara Tash scarp the Monastir railway runs *via* the Vitritza valley, there is a typical cultivation of red pepper, *[Macedonia—Economic.]*

mainly round Vodena.   At the other end of the belt, Dede-Agatch, though inferior to Kavala (in the shelter of Thasos) as a harbour, is the only direct outlet of Thrace to the Ægean.   The progress of the area, however, has been greatly impeded by its political difficulties (cf. p. 138), which are largely due to the predominance by character, if not by numbers, of the Bulgarians amongst a polyglot and heterogeneous collection of mutually antagonistic Greeks and Turks, Serbs and Albanians.

TURKEY

Position.   Turkey has now little more than a foothold in Europe—in the quadrant of "Thrace" that lies roughly between the Straits and the Istranja Dagh and between the Black Sea and the "navigable" part of the Maritza, *i.e.* roughly within the Turkish frontiers of 1914. From the coast north-east of Midia a line has been drawn for about 60 miles westward—bending north of Kirk Kilisse—and then southward for half as far again, roughly parallel with the Maritza, to Ibrije Burnu ; and the whole area between this line and the actual frontier is made a "Demilitarised Zone."   Similar lines run north-east—(1) from the Saros Gulf to the Sea of Marmora, and from the latter, between the Chatalja Lines and Constantinople, to the Black Sea, and (2) from near Eski Stamboul to the Sea of Marmora, and from near Kurtal to the Black Sea ; and the whole area between each of these pairs is again a "Demilitarised Zone."   Along the whole of this European coast there is not one harbour of any importance except the Golden Horn ; Enos is of very little use even during high water on the Maritza, and Rodosto is too near Constantinople to have any effective hinterland.

Thrace.   On the Bulgarian and Greek sides of the frontier there is a similar "Demilitarised Zone," extending even 20 miles up the Arda valley ; and so practically the larger and the best part of Thrace is, or should be, effectively neutralised.   Taken as a unit, it is the most prosperous part of the area.   Pivoting on the Rhodope, with its specifically Moslem population, it gets some political and commercial stability from its nearness to Constantinople, and is cut off from the infectious unrest of the Vardar basin by the very difficult belt of country immediately west of the Mesta. It is essentially agricultural, with a very rich soil and a climate very favourable to the mulberry, large gardens of which—interspersed with vineyards—cover the hilly "peninsula" between the Maritza and the Arda, especially round Adrianople and Mustapha Pasha (Bulgar), and the hills west of the Maritza-Ergene confluence, especially round Soufli and Dimotika (Greek).   On the well-watered lowlands, rice, cotton, opium, and madder ("Turkey-red") are also grown, but silk is the great product of the basins.   The railway runs on the Bulgar bank of the river, but Turkey owns the important station of Karagach on that bank.

Where the confluences of the Tunja and the Arda make the **Adrian-** Maritza navigable for small boats in winter and spring, is obviously **ople.** the most important site in the vilayet; but Adrianople has only the shadow of its old importance. In the days when traffic between Europe and the Levant and even Egypt went by land rather than by sea, it was a real commercial metropolis; but the annexation of Eastern Roumelia by Bulgaria, the consequent diversion of traffic *via* Burgas, the critical position so near the new frontier, the growth of other towns in the vilayet such as Soufli and Kirk Kilisse (" Forty Churches "), and their consequent wish to trade direct with Constantinople and Salonika and even with the outside world *via* Dede-Agatch, have all combined to undermine the influence and importance of the old capital. It remains a relic of the past, thoroughly Oriental in appearance, with its wooden houses and crooked lanes, and in its distribution of people in separate quarters, Turkish, Greek, and Bulgarian; but its old importance may be gauged from the choice of it as a residence alike by Hadrian and by the Turkish sultans during the century before the fall of Constantinople.

The demilitarisation of the Straits and their coast-lands—which **The** extends, not only to the Turkish islands of Marmora, Imbros, and **Straits.** Tenedos, but also to the Greek islands of Lemnos and Samothrace —seems to depend on very slender safeguards, especially as all pre-war "rights" seem to have been surrendered, *e.g.* the right to have a British man-of-war always stationed at Constantinople. The neutral strip does not exceed 10 miles in width behind either Constantinople or Gallipoli, and the narrow straits in front of them could easily be rendered impassable if mine-fields were guarded by heavy artillery, which is nowadays as mobile as fixed defences are relatively weak. And in the event of Turkey being concerned in any war, the provisions for neutrality would be merely waste paper. Too much attention is paid to the city and too little to the waterway. Constantinople is less important commercially than the Straits, and their commercial importance depends largely on the economic development of South Russia.

NOTE ON GREEK POPULATION

The immigrants form a serious problem for the moment, owing to the poverty of Greece; but, as they include not only many agricultural peasants, for whom there are room and work in Thessaly and Macedonia, but also many skilled artisans, *e.g.* silk-weavers and carpet-makers, they ought presently to be as real an asset to peace as they will be—and already are—a serious loss to Turkey. There is already a thriving carpet industry, *e.g.* round Athens.

CHAPTER XIV

THE IBERIAN PENINSULA

Site. THE site of the Iberian peninsula may be described as practically both inter-continental and inter-oceanic, and a comparison with the Balkan peninsula brings out the relative importance of each influence. Like the Balkan peninsula, the Iberian links Europe to a neighbouring continent, and turns its back on the central peninsula of Italy; but the Pyrenees minimise the value of the link, and while the south-eastward trend of the Balkan lands laid them open to all the influences of early civilisation from Egypt and Asia, the south-westward trend of Iberia faced a pathless desert or a pathless ocean. While the Straits of Gibraltar were for all those centuries, like the Pyrenees, practically a terminus, the Hellespont, like the Danube valley, was a thoroughfare.

African Trend. The physical barrier of the Pyrenees (cf. p. 26) was so marked and complete that it became naturally a linguistic and cultural, as well as a political, frontier; and this threw Iberia, by the line of less resistance round the Nevada and across the Straits of Gibraltar, into the lap of Africa. The peninsula has, therefore, been much exposed to the inflow of African influence, peaceful or otherwise, and even to domination from or through that part of Africa which shares in the sub-tropical summer-drought of the Mediterranean basin. The whole area may be called intermediate, in flora, fauna, and population, between the continent of Europe and the continent of Africa; but there is no transition area, racial or cultural, between Spain and France, except perhaps in Provençal Catalonia. The name Cartagena still speaks of the old domination of Carthage; it was as the opponent of Carthage that Rome entered the peninsula; and it was with Roman Christianity that the Saracens fought. The modern Spanish possessions in and round Marocco, which have a total area equal to that of Great Britain—though the largest of them (Rio de Oro) is only a convict-land—illustrate the same point; indeed, both Ceuta and Melilla stand on the sites of old Roman fortresses. And we shall find that, while the Balkan peninsula is European in physique and has been Asiatic in influence, the Iberian is African in physique as well as in influence.

This fact underlies the failure of Iberian trans-oceanic adventures. **Non-Oceanic.** For the absorbing aim of expelling the Moors concentrated all the vitality of the Castilian Christians on a military development, to the neglect alike of the industries which had been introduced by the Moors, and of the natural advantages of their inter-oceanic position ; so that by the time that the final expulsion of the Moors left the Castilians free for colonial development over a newly-opened ocean, political influence was focused in the parts of the country least accessible from the great harbour of Cadiz and least capable of dense population, and the nation had lost any "habit of the sea" which they had ever possessed. Like the old Romans, therefore, they were little better than marines, though they put their whole strength into war ; and their over-sea exploits were only a "flash in the pan."

As in Africa, the proportion of coast to surface is very small, **Poor** which is equally adverse to commerce and to climate ; and both its **Coast.** immediate and its intermediate relations are bad, for an old block that has been isolated by the foundering of a neighbouring sea-floor has naturally neither an inviting coast-line nor a foreground of islands. The Azores, Madeira, and the Canaries are obviously not "Iberian" islands at all ; and before the fifteenth century, when the Azores became a province of Portugal, they "led nowhere." The Balearic islands did lead Aragon to Sardinia and Sicily, and still preserve the pure Catalan speech ; but, except for the strategic importance of Port Mahon, they have had little or no influence on Spain itself.

As in Africa, again, the relative shortness of coast-line is **Lack of** accompanied by an absolute lack of good harbours. The long **Harbours.** straight coast in the north, where the old block is buttressed by young folded mountains that run parallel to the foundered shore, is naturally steep and rocky everywhere ; and, though there are naturally numerous small indentations between the spurs of the range, the ocean and river currents, as in Africa, silt up possible harbours, *e.g.* at Bilbao, Santander, and Gijon, with appalling rapidity, and involve constant dredging.

Where the feature-lines of this northern coast run out across the **Western** western margin, the sea-filled valleys between the folded ridges **Ports.** widen and deepen out into well-sheltered bays or gulfs, the spurs from each ridge giving constant protection even from western gales. High tides, too, keep these "rias" well scoured of silt ; but the absence of glaciation has deprived them of the typical features and commercial advantages of fiords, with their broad floors and deep inner waters. Of course, in olden days nearly all these rias made admirable harbours for the small ships then in use ; and a few of them, *e.g.* Vigo and Pontevedra, Corunna and Ferrol, can accommodate even the largest of modern vessels. In those days, too, the north coast, along which the eastward current is so troublesome, was relatively unimportant. But the chief trade of the country to-day does not go through the best natural harbours, which are too far from the coal- and iron-fields; and it is significant that only in Galicia is there a typical fishing population—engaged specially in the sardine-fishing.

Lisbon.

Along the rest of the west coast there is only one harbour of any real value, that of Lisbon.   Here, on the western side of the Tagus estuary, in the lee of the sierra be-

The lower Tagus, showing the
Mar da Palha.

hind Torres Vedras, just within the "bottle-neck" through which the great river has to force its way, is a large and very beautiful harbour, safe from all gales except those coming from due west (cf. p. 57) and commanding at least three of the world's greatest trade-routes.   Elsewhere the exposure to Atlantic gales, moving sandbanks[1] on the old submerged lowlands, and —possibly—the influence (on the compasses of passing ships) of the magnetic iron-ore in the archean rock, combine to render navigation very precarious (cf. the wrecks of the *Serpent, Roumania, Trinacria,* etc.); and, as access inland is almost as bad as access to the coast, movement is more or less limited to the shipping of port wine at Leixoes and Oporto and the collecting of salt in the lagoons of Aveiro and Setubal.

Southern Ports.

The south coast may be divided into two parts.   From Cape St. Vincent—the *Sacrum promontorium*, or Sagres, of Prince Henry the Navigator, where the meseta runs out into the ocean—to Cape Trafalgar, as between Cape Roca and St. Vincent, the Atlantic gales blow over the low coast of a Tertiary basin; and the result is a typical sand-dune coast broken by lagoons such as that to which "Lagos" owes its name, and by river-mouths such as that of the Rio Tinto, on which stand the "copper" port of Huelva and Columbus's old haven of Palos.   These dunes give place round the Guadalquivir estuary to almost unbroken marsh (the Marismas), profoundly unsuitable for the site of a harbour, though Magellan actually started on his great voyage from the old Roman and Arab port of San Lucar.   Where the terminal ridges of the Sierra Nevada are truncated on the verge of the ocean, very good harbours such as those of Cadiz and Gibraltar are found; but, as the coast begins to run parallel to, instead of across, the young folded ridges, it becomes naturally steep and regular.   Between two spurs, as at Cartagena, a magnificent basin may be found within an island-

[1] It is such shifting sands that spoil the harbour of Figueira at the mouth of the Mondego.

guarded strait ; but difficulty of access inland makes it more
suitable for a naval station than for a commercial harbour.

The east coast suffers from the essential inclination of the **Eastern**
peninsula towards the Atlantic, and from the climatic control of the **Coast.**
stormy "Lion Gulf." In the lee of the Nevada before they run
out into the sea in the lofty Cape de la Náo, Alicante has been
made a safe harbour, and provided—with difficulty—with railway
communication inland ; and the easy access inland by the Llobregat
valley has justified similar development at Barcelona—the Gothic
capital of Septimania, the Frankish capital of Aquitania, the twelfth-
century capital of Aragon, and eventually the commercial capital of
modern Spain. Elsewhere, especially on the low Tertiary coast-lands
of Valencia, the stormy winds give a typical sand-dune coast, with
complete or incomplete storm-beaches, as in the so-called Lake of
Albufera (*Al Baheirah*, "the Small Sea ") and the lagoon of Mar
Menor ("the Smaller Sea ").

It would seem probable, then, that the Iberian coast has been **Coast v.**
generally rather a barrier to access than a base for outlet ; and that **Core.**
the combination of minimum of coast with maximum of core has
discounted the advantageous position between ocean and sea, while
the small outlook of the sea-face and the inheritance of Mediterranean
provincialism paralysed the large outlook of the ocean-face and the
development of world relations. Portugal, at the junction of the
great east-and-west sea-route with the still greater north-and-south
ocean-route, became the focus for trade between the camel-men
of the tropical Orient and the ship-men of the Narrow Seas ;
and to shut the Tagus
against the ocean
carriers, *e.g.* the Dutch,
was at once typical
and suicidal.

About three- **Surface.**
quarters of the sur-
face is occupied by
a high, compact,
abrupt - faced " me-
seta," the old axial
core of which runs
from north to south.
When the foundering
of the crustal seg-
ment gave rise to the

Physical structure of the Iberian Peninsula.

•••••• CENTRAL WATERSHED   ᴀᴀᴀᴀᴀᴀESCARPMENTS.   ▨ IBERIAN PLATEAU (Meseta)

western basin of the Mediterranean, this meseta was ribbed with
parallel ridges of sierra, and young folded ranges were thrown up on
the northern and southern flanks, the Cantabro-Pyrenean and the
Nevada systems ; and it now lies between the Cantabrian Mountains

and its own upturned edge, the Sierra Morena—both with heights over 7000 feet—and is divided into two parts by the central ridge of sierra, which runs from Cape Roca, *via* the Estrella, Gata, Gredos, and Guadarrama mountains, to the peak of Moncayo (*Mons calvus*, "the Bald Mountain"). The northern part (averaging 2700 feet) contains the provinces of Leon and Old Castile, while the slightly lower southern part contains Estremadura and New Castile.

Isolation. The complementary gorges (cf. p. 2) on the inner sides of the young folded ranges, *i.e.* the Ebro and Guadalquivir-Segura valleys, only emphasise the obstacle of the ranges themselves to access to the table-land from France or Africa; and thus the essential isolation of the interior and its monotonous "table" relief had every opportunity of blending its various inhabitants into a homogeneous people, in an area too large for premature expansion (such as ruined Greece) and too small for them to be incoherent. Thus consciousness of unity made them too individualistic for foreign intruders to have any chance of survival except by approximation to the type appropriate to the environment. How this favoured intruders from Arabia, we may presently notice.

Access. The parallel belts of sierra in the Pyrenees and Nevada allowed easy access only round the ends of the range, *e.g.* *via* Tolosa and Gerona, Seville and Murcia. Military history, therefore, centred in A.D. 778, in 1367, in 1813, etc., round the Pass of Roncesvalles, which gives the most central access to the meseta; railway construction has been almost entirely coastal; and the connection between the two is seen in the famous historic sieges of such modern railway-junctions as San Sebastian and Gerona (the scene of twenty-five sieges!), Barcelona and Bilbao. Indeed, it was the enormous importance of the western end of the Pyrenees that enabled Aragon or Navarre, when holding it, to hold also, or at least to dominate, the whole northern flank of the range.

Compactness. The essential compactness of the interior confirms its isolation, and tends again towards a homogeneous population. A "circle" touching all the four coasts *via* Lisbon, Gibraltar, Valencia, and Bilbao has a diameter of at least 500 miles; and the climatic effect of this may be illustrated by the fact that Madrid has 120 days in the year perfectly cloudless. Of course, the abrupt scarp is partly responsible for this; and its abruptness may be gauged from the fact that the main line from Seville to Madrid *via* the famous Despeña-Perros ("Dogs' Gate") Pass rises 2000 feet in 35 miles on the Morena scarp. And it is the relatively heavy rain against the scarp that has attracted such a large population to the piedmont lowlands.

Eastern Lowlands. The inclination of the table-land down towards the Atlantic had very important historic results, because it not only cut off the lowlands of the Ebro valley, Valencia, and Andalusia from the Castiles, but also made movement along the Mediterranean coast relatively easy. Germanic hordes, therefore, moved easily down that coast, the Goths leaving their name in Catalonia (originally Gatalonia) and the Vandals in Andalusia (Vandalusia); and the Moors moved up the same route with equal ease. Indeed, it was to this that the old port of Tarraco owed its ruin. For it stood, as the modern Tarragona stands, on the mouth of a small river (the Francoli); and during the years when it was laid waste successively by Goths and Vandals and Moors, the port got so much silted up that it was subsequently deserted. Incidentally, of course, the few routes which did give relatively easy access to the plateau, became of very great importance, *e.g.* the Jalon valley between Zaragoza and Guadalajara and the Jucar valley between Valencia and La Mancha. Similar conditions account for the importance of the Pancorbo Pass —now threaded by the railway between Vitoria and Burgos—in the extreme north, and of the Despeña-Perros Pass in the extreme south —by which the Moors were eventually driven out of Castile.

The westward trend had special importance in the west. In the **Western** first place it gave rise to such a natural extension of Leon into **Lowlands.** Galicia, *e.g.* by the Sil valley, that in the great struggle the forested hills of Galicia became united to Leon while the unforested western lowlands were still under the Moors; and, as the passes across the Cantabrians had previously taken Leon and Castile to the "Asturias" coast, there was easy communication by sea between all this forested highland—with its typically "European" climate and products— producing a unity which persisted even after the Moors had been expelled from Portugal.

For Iberia, though isolated enough to make a homogeneous **Political** people, is—like Scandinavia—large enough for more than one **Division.** kingdom; and the Portuguese unit is so much cut off from the interior by the influence of the old north-and-south axis (cf. p. 163) that she is still scarcely affected by her political neighbour, while her obvious seaward and southward trend encouraged independence. Not one river that is common to the two countries is really navigable above the line of rapids which mark—in about longitude 7° W.— the old core, *i.e.* practically the International frontier, though at times the Tagus can actually be navigated up to the site of Trajan's old bridge at Al-Cantara ("The Bridge"). This is by no means the only difficulty. The two most important rivers, the Tagus and Guadiana, approach the frontier from the Spanish side through very barren steppe—part of it deliberately "wasted" by King Alfonso I. to make the natural steppe a still more impassable frontier-belt between his kingdom of Asturias and the Saracens.

Again, in passing through the actual frontier-belt of the old core, **Frontier** all the chief rivers—Minho, Douro, Tagus, and Guadiana—plunge **Peoples.** down off the steppe-plateau through profound gorges, such as probably gave its name to the Tagus ("The Gash"). Indeed, the frontier section of each valley shows an almost incredible difference between the people living on the opposite sides, *e.g.* in the middle Douro basin between Zamora and Braganza, along the Tagus west of Al-Cantara, along the Guadiana south of Badajoz. All these physical conditions, and the historic influence of the very gradual reconquest of the country from the Moors, tended towards the institution of separate political units, *e.g.* Aragon and Portugal, of which Portugal had the best natural chance of continued separate existence.

Iberia v. Scandinavia. Comparison with Scandinavia is inevitably suggested; for both are peninsulas between inland sea and ocean, with a relief and area which justify the existence of two political units with marked unity of human type. But Spain, of course, shared the access to the Atlantic in the early days of ocean development; and the Mediterranean ranks now as an oceanic route. It was the Mediterranean, again, that gave Spain, as the Baltic gave Sweden, the momentum of an earlier start (cf. Venice and Rome); and yet it was the Mediterranean which gave Lisbon advantage over Corunna as the natural meeting-place of Hansa and Orient trade, while the Atlantic gave Lisbon the advantage over Cadiz in distance from the African base and nearness to the Crusading nations. What this last advantage involved, may be summed up in the statement that Prince Henry the Navigator was the grandson of John of Gaunt, when the Duke of Lancaster, as Hereford, controlled the Bristol Channel.

Historic Advantages. Both Spain and Portugal had special advantages in those early days. As we have seen, they are both within latitudes from which Trade winds blow in summer, and to which Anti-Trades blow in winter; and both had their densest population on the fertile lands below the scarp of the meseta, *i.e.* practically on the coast-lands. But America brought both within grasp of sudden and excessive wealth —always dangerous, but especially when won, as in their case, with little or no effort; and this wealth was largely in precious metals. On the one hand, the old Moorish industries were despised and dropped; on the other, the precious metals were so much over-rated that their export was prohibited, which was a death-blow to any industrial progress.

Portuguese. Portugal, with the smaller area, the fewer people, the poorer resources, could make less of her opportunity; and so she over-strained herself, and overdrained herself of population. She thus lost the best and most vigorous of her young men, and then tried to make up the deficiency by recruiting males from the type of population at once most suitable for her great home industry of agriculture and most easily procured, the African negroes. The result is seen in the physical ugliness of her people, in their moral slimness, and in the intellectual laziness that is so typical of gross mongrels—*i.e.*

the children of parents representing quite different stages of civilisation—especially in the presence of a Negro strain.

The political relation of the meseta to the surrounding lowlands is, however, not confined to the division of the whole into two kingdoms; and the fact that the political frontier on the coast-land runs along the Minho and the Guadiana suggests that the relation is primitive and fundamental. The main water-parting runs roughly from the source of the Ebro—below the famous Reinosa Pass, which now carries the railway from Valladolid to Santander—*via* the source of the Tagus to the source of the Guadalquivir—on the La Mancha saddle between the Nevada and New Castile—and then along the Alpujarras (*Al Busherat*, "The Grass-Place") and the Nevada crest to Gibraltar; it thus marks roughly a natural frontier between the Castilian plateau and the lowlands of Aragon and Valencia, between Murcia and Andalusia, as for a long time parts of it marked a political frontier between Christian and Saracen. **Water-Parting.**

The central watershed runs from Cape Roca *via* the Gredos and Guadarrama to Moncayo; it is a very typical granite sierra or saw-toothed ridge, with an average height of well over 5000 feet; and not only do the saw-toothed notches in the separate ridge-sections make very poor passes, but the hilly parameras, or plateau-basins, between the sections are often dotted with heights even greater than those of the ridges. Thus, the Almanzor, in the "gap" between the Gredos and the Guadarrama, reaches nearly 9000 feet. No railway crosses either the Gata or the Gredos, though the intervening gap does carry the line from Plasencia to Salamanca; and the lines from Madrid to Avila and Segovia involved an immense amount of tunnelling. The whole plateau of Old Castile was, therefore, focused at Valladolid, and found its easiest outlets northwards across the Reinosa Pass and the equally famous Pajares Pass —which now carries the Oviëdo-Gijon railway—and eastwards down the Ebro valley. Even here the central watershed is practically continued in the Pyrenean spur which faces Moncayo across the Ebro gorge, cutting off Navarre and the upper basin of the Aragon river from Aragon and the upper basin of the Segre river. **Water-shed.**

These two rivers, the Aragon and the Segre, illustrate both the essential tilt of the whole peninsula towards the west and the exaggerated isolation of each valley by the parallel ridges of sierra on each side. Indeed, the Catalan wall of Aragon contains in the name of its chief height, Monserrat (*Mons serratus*, "the Saw-toothed Mountain"), lasting evidence of the impression made, on intruders from Alpine Italy, by the typical notched crest of these Iberian ridges. Again, the central sierra, being the highest, has the deepest complementary depression flanking it; and, therefore, it offered the most suitable site for a capital, not only by reason of its central position, but also by reason of the relatively easy access along the **Sierra Control.**

Tagus-Jalon depression—now followed by the main line from Lisbon to Barcelona.

Historic Capitals. The best site actually chosen was that of Aranjuez (the Roman *Ara-Jovis*, "Altar of Jupiter"), where the Tagus plunges down to the 1200-foot contour, in the very heart of the country. The site of Toledo, also a Roman centre (Toletum), is equally central (25 miles from Aranjuez), and its river-girt crag is stronger strategically. Madrid has only the advantages of being nearer Old Castile, and of avoiding the steep climb up (from Toledo) out of the Tagus valley. The morbid egotism of Philip II. found in the gloomy valleys of the Guadarrama a disused graveyard for the site of his Escorial (*Scoriae*, "Rubbish-heap").

Use of Rivers. The value of this river-system for navigation is practically negligible, except for the Tagus and the Guadalquivir, though the other chief rivers can actually be navigated, *e.g.* the Guadiana up to Mertola (42 miles); but their value for irrigation is almost incalculable. In Murcia and Valencia unirrigated land has a value never more than one-twelfth of that of irrigated land in the same neighbourhood; and it is said that the whole cost of the Imperial Canal (Tudela to Zaragoza) was defrayed by the increased harvest of a single year.

Guadalquivir. The Guadalquivir owes its special importance and so its name (*Wadi al Kebir*, "The Great River") mainly to the great contrasts of relief in its basin, which includes the Veleta ("Watch-Tower") glacier at a height of over 9300 feet in latitude 37° N. From this section of the Nevada it is fed, by the Genil and Guadiana-menor, with unfailing supplies of melted snow and ice in summer; in winter all its upper basin is rain-fed by the S.W. winds; and it drops on to the Andalusian lowland more than 200 miles from the sea. It was, therefore, the "Great River" commercially, though 200 miles shorter than the Tagus (565 miles) and with a basin 17,000 square miles less than that of the Ebro (38,600). It is, however, not continuously navigable from Andujar; for a spur of the Sierra Morena is responsible for the Montoro rapids, and the bed of the river has been so much choked with silt that boats cannot be regularly used above Cordova. Indeed, only extensive dredging enables large ships to reach Seville, at the limit of tide, 70 miles up river. On the other hand, the volume is more or less constant, though floods occasionally raise it as much as 8 feet; and it is concurrence of flood—due to and accompanied by strong S.W. gales—with high tides that causes the wide submersion of the estuarine lowlands, the Marismas. These, though providing fine cattle-pasture, are very unhealthy, an additional deterrent to the rise of any important town on the mouth of the river.

Climate. The climate, like the racial traits and the normal occupations, may be roughly classified as Cis-Cantabrian and Trans-Cantabrian;

and the difference is illustrated by the two ends of the Pyrenees (cf. p. 27). The Atlantic end has an evenly distributed rainfall, giving a typically marine succession of cool summer and mild winter, with European products, and so the Galician, Asturian, and Basque occupations are fishing and forestry, mining and cattle-rearing, while the Mediterranean end has only winter rain and "African" products, *e.g.* cork and esparto. South of the Cantabrians, then, the climate is extremely continental, with great range and quick changes of temperature, as the daily or seasonal low-pressure centre succeeds the high-pressure. Unfortunately, when the low-pressure centre over the heated plateau in summer is active, it has a serious rival in the still stronger centre over the Sahara, so that there is a minimum of inflow ; and, when the high-pressure centre over the chilled plateau in winter has once settled down, it is such an effective obstacle that then, too, there is a minimum of inflow.

Obviously, then, there must be great deficiency of rain except **Drought.** round the edges of the plateau ; and even on these, except to the north-west, there is no excess. Of course, as the mass of the precipitation falls in winter, the snow-fall is relatively heavy ; but not enough falls to guarantee any water-supply for more than half the year, and the rivers usually dwindle away to mere "wadis" in summer. These conditions imply great extremes of temperature, especially of heat : and it is the activity of the dry air in the hot season that is responsible for the vast areas on the table-land and even in the Ebro basin that are absolutely treeless, there being no means of replacing any moisture

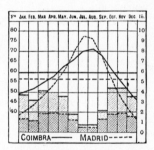

Mean monthly temperature and rainfall of Coimbra and Madrid.

transpired by leaves and carried away by the wind—a condition fatal to tree-growth. There is also an enormous amount of dust, which accounts for the prevalence of haze (caligo) in the dry season and of mist in the wet season. It also increases the radiation, especially off the reddish soil of the Ebro and Granada steppes. The total result is that Iberia, like Australia, with one of the most insular positions, has one of the most continental climates ; skating is quite common in Madrid in both December and January, while the Solano may give the city a summer temperature of 109° F. in the shade ; and temperature diminishes regularly with distance from the sea in winter and from the interior in summer. Cf. p. 207.

From the detailed examination of the climatic phenomena it **Climatic** has been suggested that the whole area might be roughly divided **Belts :** into four belts, of which the Atlantic belt stands apart. Indeed, **Atlantic.** in some parts of it the rainfall is excessive, reaching normally about 4 feet at Bilbao and 6½ feet at Santiago, perched up on an exposed shoulder of the Galician highland. Both places have an average January temperature not below 45° F. and an average July temperature not above 70° F. This Atlantic belt extends down through Portugal into the north of the province of Estremadura. Oporto and Coimbra both have an average annual temperature just under 60° F., with a range of 20° F. at Oporto between January and July and one of 21° F. at Coimbra. There are thick fogs on the lowlands and along the coast, and extraordinary variations in rainfall. Most rain falls in winter, when 16 feet has been recorded; Oporto has nearly double the rainfall of Coimbra (34 inches); and the Estrella and the Traz-os-Montes heights are covered with snow for several months in winter.

Meseta Belt.

This Atlantic belt impinges on to the "Meseta" belt, the transition being very obvious even inside the Portuguese frontier; and the "Meseta" belt includes the greater part of the Ebro basin. This is the belt of greatest extremes and most sudden changes of temperature, changes of even 50° F. within a few hours not being uncommon. At Leon the mean temperature varies from 37° F. in January to 73° F. in July, and at Madrid, from 39° F. to 76° F., the former having 19 inches of rain and the latter having 15, of which only half an inch falls in July. From the greater part of the area trees are entirely absent; and the vegetation otherwise, though of Mediterranean type, is peculiarly specialised, many of the species not being found elsewhere. The north-western part of this belt, especially round Palencia and in other parts of the Pisuerga basin, is the great wheat-growing area of the peninsula; and still nearer to the Atlantic belt, *e.g.* in the Minho basin, rye is grown. The south-eastern part is the great esparto-growing area; and the intermediate area is typical steppe, largely saltish and producing the stimulating aromatic herbage which developed the famous cattle of the Guadarrama and the merino sheep of the Toledo highlands—the sheep migrating in April to the higher and in September to the lower lands, *i.e.* towards the north-east in summer and the south-west in winter.

Roman Conquest.

It is significant that the Romans conquered the country *via* the wide and tame Douro basin, not *via* the narrow and savage Tagus basin; and their route can still be traced by such names as Zaragoza ("Caesar Augusta"), Pamplona ("Pompeiopolis"), Leon (the depot of the faithful VIIth *Legion*), and Badajoz ("Pax Augusta"). This took them, between the wheat-fields of the plateau and the cattle-pastures of the coast-lands, to Estremadura (*Extrema Dueri*, "The Farthest Points beyond the Douro"); and their Emeriti, or discharged veterans, then found a peaceful home in *Merida*.

The natural hinterland of the eastern coast north of Cape Palos forms a "Mediterranean belt," with relatively small range of **Mediter-** temperature and a high average, the annual mean being 61° F. at **ranean** Barcelona and 64° F. at Alicante; and there is a typical winter **Belt.** rainfall of 23 inches at Barcelona, dwindling to 14 in the south. It was this specifically Mediterranean climate that made the crescent of lowland between Lerida and Zaragoza such a suitable base for the Romans in their conquest of the peninsula, and it is this area that contains the famous huertas (*hortus*, "a garden"). Practically all the native plants here, whatever their Botanical family, have the fleshy and leathery foliage of summer-drought environment; and the typical cultivated plants are fruits—nuts and olives, mainly to the north, oranges and lemons, mainly to the south, and vine and mulberry, mainly in the centre. Everywhere the basis of prosperity is irrigation, though vine and olive are largely "dry" crops; and much of the water, as it gushes from the base of the limestone scarp, is led over artificial terraces on its way down to the floor of the valley. And, as the increase of population demands increased food, *e.g.* garlic and onions, chick-peas and lentils, artesian wells are being dug to supplement the natural supply. This is true of nearly all the Trans-Cantabrian area, so that now 80 p.c. of the whole is registered as productive, and over 10 p.c. is under irrigation.

The rest of the country forms an African belt, with a curious **African** intermixture of luxuriance and desert. In Portugal south of the **Belt.** Tagus the mean annual humidity in many places is as low as 30 and in others as high as 80; and the great heat of summer and the winter floods make the climate very trying. In the exposed parts, *e.g.* at Cintra, tree-ferns are as typical as cacti are in the sheltered parts. But rice is a typical product even on the Valencia coast, and dates actually ripen at Elche, while the Sierra Morena ("Sombre") is said to take its name from the forests of olives along its southern face, especially near Cordova. It would seem, there-fore, that the more typically "African" climate is only found within the area exposed to the leveche (cf. p. 59). That is to say, fertility on the Murcian and Almerian lowlands is in oases, while in Malaga and Granada it is typically tropical. In this southern belt cane-sugar is a typical product, and the rice yield is the highest in the world.

As with most irrigation areas, the conspicuous feature in the **Variety of** economic geography is the variety of products; and of those which **Products.** enter into commerce, the most typical are the olive-oil of Andalusia (Seville and Cordova) and Catalonia (Lerida and Tortosa), the oranges of Seville and Denia, the raisins of Valencia and Denia, the almonds of Alicante and Denia, the cork of Catalonia and Alemtejo ("Beyond the Tagus"), the wine of Oporto and Jerez. Most English imports of oil—as well as large quantities of the fruit pickled and preserved—come from Spain, but the sub-tropical

N

climate yields an inferior oil (cf. p. 95); the other fruits are excellent, and the cork is the best in the world for champagne bottles.

Wine.   Most wine is grown in the Ebro basin, and much is exported to France; but it is inferior to that of the Douro and the Guadalete basins.   In the south the rains of the late winter and early spring are followed by a very dry summer and autumn which, in the marine exposure of Jerez, produce a wine peculiarly rich in organic ethers, the best sherry almost rivalling cognac in this respect.   The port vines are grown specially on the northern slope—which is the broader as well as the sunnier—of the deep Douro valley, in the lee of the Sierra de Marao (4665 feet); and here they get the "roasting" in summer which develops their "resinous" qualities (cf. p. 208).   The high-pressure centre off the Portuguese coast in summer, however, usually results in August rains, and these just save the Oporto wines from the natural results of "roasting" as seen in those of Tarragona from similar latitudes on the east coast.   In this relatively advanced area, too, where a number of British firms —including the Cockburns, Crofts, and Grahams—actually own "quintas," every legal protection is enforced against deterioration of product, *e.g.* protection against planting vines on low (under 165 feet) alluvial soils, which produce large quantities of wine, but poor quality.   The real "port" area, therefore, now lies practically between the Tua-Douro confluence and the western frontier of Traz-os-Montes and between the latitudes of Villa Real and Lamego.

Popula-tion.   The uniformity of relief and climate, which thus becomes apparent in the vegetation, is reflected also in the population, and has evidently been emphasised by the isolation and compactness of the area.   The pre-Roman "irreconcilables" retreated up the Ebro valley into and across the Cantabrians; and after the Roman empire was broken up, the movement of Barbari down the east of the peninsula from the north, and subsequently of Arabs up the east from the south, tended to concentrate refugees towards the same north-western corner, with its Atlantic climate.   Here, then, the Mediterranean natives were isolated, in an "Atlantic highland," where less precarious food-supply developed stature, and where other conditions—possibly, the mountain environment—broadened the head.   Here, at any rate, they became typical Highlanders (using the bagpipe); and those nearest the ocean margin developed into a typical fishing race, holding their women in honour and supplying nurses to all the richest families in Spain.

"Cas-tilian" Core.   The safest part of this rugged highland was the central section between the sea and the watershed, west of the great Peñas de Europa (8700 feet), and here the Kingdom of Asturias remained independent even after retreat from its old capital of Astorga.   The new capital of Oviedo commands the one great route, *via* the Pajares

Pass, from Leon to the port of Gijon.   The Kingdom of Leon
occupied the continental face of the same highland, and had less
chance of expansion than its eastern neighbour, Castile.   The
latter had easy access by the Pisuerga valley to Valladolid and
Madrid, by the Ebro valley to Navarre and Aragon, and by the
Reinosa Pass to Santander and the ocean ; and it probably owed its
name as much to the natural rock-castles of its environment as to
the actual castles built by the Christians.

Within the Atlantic belt of climate, Basques, Galicians, Asturians, **Portu-**
and Portuguese, all have the same folklore ; and Galician is simply **guese**
a dialect of Portuguese.   But the geological change from the fertile **Fringe.**
Devonian rock of Asturias to the barren Cambrian rock of Galicia
doomed the non-fishing population of Galicia to a life of constant
poverty and hardship.   And, while the famous nurses of Spain
come from the fishing Galicians, the non-fishing population has
made " Gallego " a term of general contempt (" Knock-about ")
throughout Castile.

All round the plateau, however, population is now increasing at **Minerals.**
the expense of the interior, especially where the scarp is richest in
mineral wealth (cf. p. 49) and in water-power.   Fine iron is
abundant along the sea-face of both the Cantabrians and the
Nevada ; and, though at present it is only worked properly in the
neighbourhood of coal, *i.e.* in the north, the better quality in the
south is already attracting attention.   Other minerals are abundant,
especially copper and lead, each 50 per cent more valuable than the
iron.   Indeed, owing to the variety of rock, Spain has a great variety
of mineral wealth, including copper and lead, mercury and silver, and
rock-salt.   And, where the most important minerals are lacking, *e.g.*
Barcelona, with neither coal nor iron, there commerce is easiest.

On the other hand, want of fuel or water-power, constitutional **The**
or climatic lethargy, poor transport, and other drawbacks are very **Arabs.**
adverse to progress ; and the country has never recovered from the
expulsion of the Arabs.   For the Arab was peculiarly useful to
Spain.   As a native of desert and barren steppe, he knew the value
of water both for pedigree stock and for plants with cooling
astringent juices.   He irrigated the lowlands into "gardens," by
means specially of the Jenil and Guadalaviar, the Segura and
Sangonera, thus incidentally minimising the chances of malaria ; he
introduced the orange and the mulberry ; he drew wine and oil
from what the Christians had called desert ; he gave Spain her
famous mules and merino sheep.   He also changed the old Roman
games into chivalric contests, in which mounted lancers showed
coolness and dexterity rather than brute strength and ferocity ; and
to his religious influence Spain owes—perhaps, the Inquisition—
certainly that sense of brotherhood which makes the Spanish
peasant the most democratic in Europe.

Social Relations. Even the unsatisfactory relations between employers and employed are a legacy from the Arabs. For Arab cultivators lived on, despised and ignored, amongst their conquerors for generations before their final expulsion from the country ; and during this time the attitude of indifference and irresponsibility became so ingrained in the employers that it has remained as their permanent attitude towards their employees. And the results would have been worse than they actually are if so many factors had not otherwise made for unity—the compactness and isolation of the area, the uniformity of relief and climate, the common religion and common language, and the artificial centralisation. These have been strong enough to minimise the natural antagonism between the arid and sparsely peopled, but united, Castilian plateau and the fertile and densely peopled, but disconnected, units of the coast-land.

SPAIN

Population. No other country that is at all comparable with Spain in natural advantages, is so sparsely populated. The population on the Meseta, *i.e.* in Leon and Old Castile, New Castile and Estremadura, scarcely exceeds 70 persons to the square mile ; in Aragon it is less, and in Navarre it is not much better (82). Indeed, the average for the whole is only about 50 p.c. above that of Connaught, the poorest part of Ireland. And this seems to be wholly due to war at home and to drain of population to America. There is evidence that the population 2000 years ago was three times what it is now ; and things would be much worse than they are but for the provinces which have been, and still often are, considered the most backward, Vizcaya (540), Guipuzcoa (400), and Pontevedra (335); Barcelona has 480. Even in the specifically Moorish provinces the only one with an average appreciably over 200 is Valencia (240). Area, however, must be considered as well as density ; and the total result is that natural antagonisms, *e.g.* of mobile herdsman and sedentary gardener, are accentuated between the meseta and its outlying neighbours, Galicia having more people than either of the Castiles, while Andalusia has as many as both of them put together.

Primitive Conditions. Though war and emigration have been the great influences in the past, there are now other influences at work. Communications and education, especially the former, have improved immensely. It is not very long since (1909) there were 5000 villages in the land which could not be reached by wheeled traffic ; and where, 1000 years ago, Arabs were teaching geography from *globes* in free schools to children of both sexes, 45 p.c. of the population were said to be unable to read and write. Pack-mules and ox-carts were still quite common ; and the recent development of railways had done a minimum of good because, for strategic reasons, the Spanish gauge is different from (wider than) the French. Even now, heavy taxation unfairly distributed is still very adverse to farming, in which the implements are still often of a very primitive kind, while the stock has deteriorated terribly. Here, too, the national pastime of bull-fighting adds to the difficulty. For, except on the "deltaic" islands of the Guadalquivir, the bulls not only are given the best land, but also need a very large area *per caput*—to prevent them from fighting one another. Still another adverse influence is the competition of what is almost the "forced labour" of the convent industrial schools, *e.g.* in laundry work, with the labour of non-clerical adults.

For various reasons these adverse influences have had least **Cantabrian** effect in the northern provinces. As compared with the rest of **Provinces.** Spain, these provinces are specifically mountainous and forested; coal and iron are abundant in the Cantabrian section, and can easily be imported in Catalonia; both the Basques and the Catalans are naturally enterprising, as the people of Navarre and Galicia are naturally industrious; and the climate is favourable to the development of textile industries, while the position favours access to and from the great markets of Western Europe.

The Cantabrian provinces specialise in mining. Of course, **Western:** the staple industry in Galicia is still fishing, mainly for sardines; but the reckless methods employed, *e.g.* the (illegal) use of dynamite on dark nights, and other causes, *e.g.* change of temperature[1] in the coastal waters, are making the fish scarcer and scarcer. Vigo is the chief centre, and still has a large export industry, and heavy catches are made off Marin (the port of Pontevedra) and Villagarcia; but it is significant that the two ports of Vigo and Corunna account for nearly half the emigrants from Spain. On the other hand, the mineral wealth of Galicia is being developed, the tin being in special demand (*e.g.* for Welsh tin-plate, Vigo alone exporting yearly some *thousands of tons* of tinned sardines); and the growth of the Asturias coal-mining makes a regular demand for pit-props, *e.g.* from Villagarcia and Corcubion. The fertility of the Minho valley, especially between Orense and Lugo, "the hub of Galicia"—which it certainly was in Moore's retreat—is extraordinary, the sides being devoted to vine and olive and the plain to maize.

Asturias was never completely subjugated even by the Romans, **Central:** and half the "Transmontane" mountaineers still reveal, in physique and language, their purity of race and independence; but their historic struggle for independence was fatal to commercial enterprise, and this largely accounts for the slow development of the area in modern times, though it contains the best coal-field in Spain. The field is in the basin of the Nalon (or Pruvia), and has

[1] The sardine is a delicate fish, and avoids water approaching 68° F.

made Oviedo the most important coal-producing province in the country. The high humidity causes such heavy falls of snow in winter that transport inland is much impeded, but there are good ports at Gijon (*via* Musel) and Aviles. The climate favours textile industries, *e.g.* at Aviles, as the coal favours glass-working, *e.g.* at Gijon. The city of Oviedo, besides commanding the Royal Road to Madrid *via* the Pajares Pass—which cost so much that Charles V. asked whether it was paved with silver—is the centre of a thriving agricultural district, raising a considerable amount of beet-sugar.

Eastern : Though the provinces of Oviedo and Lugo have larger iron reserves, that of Santander is specifically concerned with the mining of iron and zinc ; and the town of Santander, a large smelting centre, is growing faster than any other town in Spain. The mountain pastures support an important dairy industry, and sugar-beet gives a good yield. In Vizcaya, on the other hand, farming is rather neglected ; but Bilbao has very important shipbuilding and other industries along the Nervion river. Much of the local ore is shipped from cantilever piers dotted along the rugged coast. Iron ore is also worked—with lead and zinc—in Guipuzcoa, but here again agriculture becomes important, both the apples and the chestnuts being famous. Irun commands the frontier bridge across the Bidassoa, and Pasages is a rising port, San Sebastian—in spite of its old strategic importance—having now become little more than a summer resort.

Pyrenean Provinces. The Pyrenean provinces, like the Cantabrian, illustrate the adverse influence of extreme isolation, for the two seaward areas of Navarre and Catalonia are far ahead of the central Aragon ; but, while the sea influence in Navarre is specifically climatic, in Catalonia it is more economic. Indeed, as the Cantabrian area tends to mining, so the Pyrenean tends to be industrial, especially outside the Ebro basin proper. In the upper part of the basin the mountainous land of Navarre is rich in forest and park-land, and therefore its special product is live-stock of all kinds, especially coarse-woolled sheep ; and its apple orchards are famous. The position of Pamplona, on the flank of the Ebro and commanding the Roncesvalles Pass, made it a very

The harbour of San Sebastian.

important fortress ; Tudela is at the head of the Imperial Canal. The lower part of the Ebro basin is less favourable. There are great extremes of heat and cold, and nearly all the rain falls in frequent thunderstorms ; much of the parched chalky soil is saturated with salt, and many streams are brackish ; and the only hope is in irrigation. Even Zaragoza itself, a typical "oasis" city, with a range of temperature often varying 50° F. within a single month, is important now only as a railway-junction.

Catalonia, with a central watershed in the Sierra Llena, is in a **Catalonia.** much better position. The climate is still rather extreme and subject to sudden changes of temperature, and the amount of dust in the air favours mist and fog; but it is quite favourable to agriculture, and gives a great variety of crops, especially wine and nuts. The people are frugal and industrious as well as enterprising and energetic; and careful cultivation and irrigation have made the agricultural part of the province more or less able to support the manufacturing and industrial part.

The old province is now divided into four new provinces— **Gerona.** Gerona, Lerida, Barcelona, and Tarragona. As a frontier province, Gerona has had rather a chequered history. The town of Gerona itself has been besieged twenty-five times—though only taken four times—and the fortress of Figueras is still considered the key to the frontier either by Port Bon and the Col de Perthus or round Cape Creus and by Rosas Bay. Unfortunately, the best agricultural land is the Ter plain between Gerona and Figueras, so that agriculture is backward; but the province is well forested, the cork being specially good, and there are profitable sea fisheries. A great many sheep are reared, and the wool is manufactured locally, especially at Gerona; cotton and linen industries are also scattered over a number of little towns; Port Bon is one of the most important commercial outlets of Spain; and the Trans-Pyrenean railway to Aix will greatly aid commercial development.

Except for a few tracts of lowland, mainly along the Llobregat, **Barcelona.** the Barcelona province consists of forested mountains, generally rich in minerals (lignite, lead, zinc, salt); and, as both the Llobregat and the Ter supply considerable amounts of power, and as the import of coal and raw materials by sea is very easy, the province has become the chief centre of Spanish industry and commerce, and population is strongly drawn to it, Barcelona (770,000) rivalling even Madrid in size. All the typical industries of Spain are found here, including woollen, cotton, and silk textiles, worked iron, fancy leather, art furniture, etc.; and the easy access inland round Monserrat by the Llobregat valley has carried the textiles up-stream to water-power. Barcelona city is thus a real industrial metropolis, specialising in textiles; and its relations with its hinterland are very ancient. It seems to have taken its name from the Carthaginian general, Hamilcar Barca, who preferred the hill-girt open beach, with its access to the Llobregat, to any site on the troublesome river-mouths of Catalonia; and, though the union of Castile and Aragon, and the contemporaneous discovery of America, transferred the balance of power elsewhere for a time, Barcelona has long ago regained the prominent place—by providing a fine artificial harbour—though the people, who are largely Provençal in type and origin, still " owe the Castilian a grudge."

Lerida. Lerida is the most backward of the Catalan provinces, again largely for historic reasons. The town itself, on a height overlooking the Segre and the famous Llaños de Urgel, is the key of both Catalonia and Aragon ; and, as such, it has been a constant scene of warfare since the time of the Punic Wars. The Llaños themselves are redeemed from their natural barrenness by irrigation, but the rest of the province is very mountainous ; and the abundant water-power is neglected, except for saw-mills. A very large number of sheep are raised, and leather and woollen industries are carried on in Lerida town.

Tarragona. Tarragona, though mountainous, is very fertile, and produces quantities of wine and oil, the wine specially round Tarragona itself and the oil largely from round Tortosa. Almonds are also a typical product, especially round the junction of Reus. The typical Catalan people have, however, developed more or less all the natural resources, *e.g.* silver and lead, marble and china-clay ; and manufactures include leather and all kinds of textiles. The old city of Tarragona occupies a typical cone-hill (550 feet) overlooking the sea ; the new one, which has been provided with a good artificial harbour, is famous for its underground wine-cellars, one of the typical exports being the " Grand Chartreuse " liqueur.

Levante Provinces. The Levante provinces have a strip of very fertile lowland running along the coast, the site of the famous huertas or *vegas*, so that they are predominantly agricultural. Behind the lowland the relief rises in terraces to a height which accounts for the very large number of sheep and goats, especially sheep, raised in Castellon and Valencia, and which guarantees a large amount of water for irrigation—though the Turia feeds so many huertas that, except in flood-time, it is a very scanty stream when it reaches the sea ; and in front of them the low level and the exposure to the " Levant " wind have raised a series of sand-dunes, which in places completely block the movement of river-water seaward, and are very favourable to salt industries, *e.g.* at Torrevieja. These conditions are also very favourable for irrigation, and the Turia and the Jucar are invaluable for this purpose ; indeed, all the typical crops are irrigated, *e.g.* the rice of the Valencia vegas, the dates of Elche— which often exports over 20,000 tons of dates in a year—the oranges of Castellon and Valencia, the raisins of Valencia and Denia, the almonds of Alicante, the onions of Gandia.

Valencia. Rice and cane-sugar are important " home " crops, but the special work is the raising of sub-tropical fruit for export ; and for this the warm, dry, equable climate is as favourable as it is for the rearing of bees and silkworms and for the curing of " Valencia " raisins and tobacco (at Alcoy). Some of the soil is naturally very fertile, especially along the Segura ; but the prosperity of the area is based on the Moorish irrigation-works, and in appearance and industries (*e.g.* weaving of esparto) the land is typically Moorish. Both Valencia and Alicante are typically Moorish towns, with white flat-roofed houses ; and Alicante, with a citadel perched on a hill 400 feet above the sea, has its houses arranged in the typical crescent and approached through avenues of palm-trees. Valencia, as a central harbour, *e.g.* attracting the iron export of Teruel and the almond-trade of Palma (de Mallorca), has become the third city in the country, with a population of over 270,000.

The Segura valley, especially at the confluence with the **Murcia.** Sangonera, continues the typical Moorish horticulture into the province of Murcia ; indeed, both Lorca, the old key to Murcia in the Moorish wars, and the city of Murcia have typical huertas, specialising in oranges and silk, and both suffer greatly from occasional floods.[1] But the line of the Nevada-Balearic uplift makes the area specifically a mining one, and the large export of esparto is a significant comment on the climate generally. Iron, copper, silver-lead, sulphur, and saltpetre are all abundant, especially round Cartagena. The mines near the city are very productive, and have materially helped to revive its old prosperity. This was based on its importance as a naval station, with the largest harbour in Spain except that of Vigo ; and, therefore, the city not only suffered greatly from the results of the Spanish-American war, but also lost some of its commerce in the meantime to the neighbouring "iron" port of Porman. The relatively greater development of "iron" ports, *e.g.* Garrucha and Aguilas, is a feature of this southern coast, and is connected with the use of cables for bringing down the ore from the sierra ; for instance, Aguilas ships as much iron-ore to Great Britain alone as Cartagena ships altogether. Even where other ores, *e.g.* silver-lead and zinc, are of importance, as at Mazarron, the chief progress is in the shipping of iron.

The Murcian province of Albacete is the pivot of S.E. Spain. **Anda-** It contains a part of La Mancha, and is drained *via* the town of **lusia.** Albacete (famous for saffron) to the Jucar basin, *via* Hellin to that of the Segura, and *via* Alcaraz to the Guadalquivir. Westward from this point, roughly marked by the La Sagra (de Segura) boss, the "Andalusian" area combines the characteristic features of all the other areas already referred to. The lowland in many places resembles that of the Ebro basin in its saltish soil and brackish lakes, though the area of rich land is much greater ; the coast-lands repeat the horticulture of the Levante ; the mountains rival the Cantabrians in their mineral wealth. Its physique and climate,

---

[1] During the War of the Spanish Succession, Murcia was even defended by the intentional flooding of the huerta.

however, set it apart.   Its scenery is unique in the peninsula ; the winter climate of Seville is almost ideal ; its "Great River"—the Roman *Boetis*, which gave the area its old name of Boetica —and its isolation combined to "force" an early civilisation ; that civilisation produced such world-famous monuments as the Alcazar of Seville, the Mosque of Cordova, and the Alhambra of Granada ; but it implied an alien domination which accounted for the mixture of race and the differentiation from the Castilians in earlier times, and accounts for the backward state of the area in agriculture and industries in modern times.

Almeria.   Each province of the area tends to have stretches of lowland and mountain—in different proportions.   For instance, Almeria has a great ridge of sierra (8000 feet) rich in iron and silver-lead, and fertile gorges and coast-lands that produce all kinds of sub-tropical fruit, especially almonds and the white "keeping" grape. Thus Adra exports almonds from the coast-land and lead from the Berja highland ; the town of Almeria often exports 2,000,000 barrels of grapes a year and quantities of almonds, and its export of iron-ore (and manganese) is increasing very rapidly.   A quantity of iron-ore also goes by the line from Baza to Lorca for export *via* Aguilas.

Granada.   Granada presents still greater contrasts.   It faces to the Guadalquivir, and its strip of harbourless coast is so much isolated by the loftiest part of the Nevada—including the Mulahacen and Veleta peaks—that there has been little encouragement to develop such roadsteads as that of Motril ; and the only railway connection with the coast at all is *via* Loja (the old key to Granada in the Moorish wars) and Malaga, or *via* Guadix and Almeria.   This in turn has retarded mining, though the sierra is rich in iron and other minerals, *e.g.* alabaster.   At the same time these adverse relief features give the province a unique river-system, including the Genil and Guadiana-menor, the chief feeders of the Andalusian plain.   As the soil is exceedingly fertile, the area was practically self-contained ; and, as the Guadalféo gives access by the chief valley of the Alpujarras to Motril, it made an impregnable refuge for the Moors for many centuries.

The loss of Cuba has led to a revival of the old Moorish industry of sugar-growing, and it is quite typical of the climate that both beet- and cane-sugar can be raised, *e.g.* at Loja and Granada. The latter, which *may* take its name from the pomegranate (granada), occupies a magnificent site 2200 feet above the sea, on the "peninsula" between the Genil and its Darro tributary, in a vega of almost incredible fertility ; and its hinterland has been for ages famous for its fine wool.

Malaga.   The greater proportion of lowland in the south of Malaga has caused the latter province to develop seaward ; and this has been further encouraged in two ways.   The famous Peñarrubia gorge cut by the Guadalhorce has greatly facilitated railway access to the coast—at the city of Malaga; and the quantities of silt, rich in organic matter, brought down by the Nevada torrents on to the coastal sill in the lee of the Gibraltar peninsula, has led to an important fishing industry. These two conditions have attracted foreign capital in a unique degree; so that while the city stands next to Seville for the export of olive-oil, and has also a large export of wine and fruit (raisins and almonds), there has been a great development of industries on the spot, *e.g.* textile, metallic, ceramic, etc. The hinterland is characteristically rich in iron, especially near Marbella, and in lead; and even textile industries flourish, *e.g.* at Antequera, also famous for its beet-sugar industry. Cane-sugar is cultivated on the coast; and, as the spread of viticulture in Argentina is checking the export of typical "sherry" wines and so leading to a contraction of the area under vines in the Malaga province, the sugar industry will probably continue to increase in importance. The very mild and equable climate makes canary-seed another typical product.

The province of Cadiz has a magnificent bay in a most com- **Cadiz.** manding position on one of the greatest trade-routes in the world; but various causes are adverse to its prosperity. The only mineral wealth of importance is the salt evaporated along the coast, *e.g.* at Cadiz and San Lucar; and the special product inland, the sherry of Jerez, is one for which the demand is decreasing, though it happens to be one of the most wholesome wines in the world. Further, the Spanish-American War dealt a great blow to the Naval Station— which is on the island of San Fernando (Isla de Leon)—as to those at Cartagena and Ferrol; and the continuation of the direct line from Ronda[1] to San Roque (for Gibraltar) and Algeciras, and the popularity of the latter as a winter resort, have taken away from Cadiz much of its old importance as the terminus of the trans-

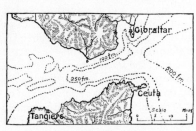
The Strait of Gibraltar.

continental railway-route. At the same time, the facilities for ocean traffic at Gibraltar have far outstripped those at Cadiz, though even the inner harbour at the latter has now been dredged to a depth of 25–30 feet.

Site, relief, and climate **Gibraltar.** combine to give Gibraltar almost unique advantages— strategic and economic. The old importance of the site, as separat- ing Cadiz from Cartagena and Brest from Toulon, is a fair index of its modern importance, as linking the Indian Ocean to the Atlantic

[1] Ronda has the finest bull-ring in Spain and a most famous breed of horses.

and the Old World to the New.   Many of the native inhabitants are of *Genoese* descent; about 3500 steamers call at the port every year, and half of them coal there.   The site is a link site in other respects; for some of its flora and fauna are not found elsewhere in Europe, *e.g.* the Barbary apes, and its caves have yielded mammal remains of the greatest interest, including a human skull at the lowest stage of evolution above the " Missing-link " of Java.

"The Rock."   From the sandy coasts of old sea-floor, which makes the neutral ground—with its unclimbable iron fence—a natural frontier belt, the Rock rises almost sheer to a height of 1200 feet, and then runs—with a typical sierra crest—for a couple of miles due south to O'Hara's Tower (1400 feet), only to drop by precipitous terraces to the Europa Flats, which at Europa Point drop again precipitately into ocean depths.   From the crest of the sierra, with an elaborate system of range-finding, the great guns command the Straits (12 miles wide) strategically, as the Signal Station (1255 feet) commands them commercially.   Between the La Luna heights (2600 feet) in the west and the Rock itself the Bay of Algeciras gives safe access to an enclosed harbour in which a whole fleet can anchor secure from torpedo attack, with facilities for coaling every vessel and docking seven or eight of them.   Again, the caves—so typical of limestone—which, like similar ones at Ronda, have produced such valuable remains, seem to have suggested the tunnelling operations that have such an important relation to the defence.   Indeed, the precipitous eastern flank of the sierra is scarcely approachable except by tunnels, *e.g.* above Catalan Bay.

The Town.   From this abrupt eastern flank the sierra sinks more gradually westward, so that the natural site for the town was facing the open Atlantic; and this, with the north-and-south direction of the sierra (cf. p. 162), accounts both for the mild, even climate, and for the relatively heavy rainfall.   The average temperature is only 65° F., with a mean maximum only 12° F. higher ; and the average rainfall is about 34 inches, but varies from about half that up to nearly twice it.   This guarantees enough to supply the whole community, from carefully constructed underground tanks, with pure water for drinking and cooking purposes in spite of the small area (3 m. × ½ m.). This smallness and historic isolation from, if not actual hostility to, Spain made the place dependent on Marocco for supplies ; and it seems to have been the threat of a sultan to withhold supplies, unless full freedom of trade were granted to his ships, that converted Gibraltar into a free port as early as 1705.   It is curious, therefore, that it is very largely the political difficulties which centre on Marocco nowadays, that prevent Gibraltar from reaping the full advantage of its economic position.

Morena Provinces.   The Sierra Morena bears somewhat the same relation to the Andalusian plain on the north as the Sierra Nevada does on the south ; and along its face and spurs mineral wealth of various kinds is abundant. In the province of Huelva it is specially copper, the Rio Tinto mines having been worked for 2000 years, and the Tharsis mines almost as long; but iron and manganese are becoming steadily more and more important. At the other end, in the province of Jaen, Linares has produced silver-lead also for 2000 years ; and the hinterland of Jaen is as famous for wool as the foreground of Palos is for fishing (sardine and tunny). In the intermediate area, *i.e.* the province of Cordova, the Sierra Morena is rich in both copper and silver-lead ; it produces fine wool and very large quantities of olive-oil ; and in recent years the Belmez coal-field has had an annual output of fully 500,000 tons of good coal— 30 p.c. of it being anthracite—actually on the direct line of rail north into the Guadiana basin.

The focus of all Andalusia is the province of Seville. Though **Andalusia.** there is a large export of minerals (mainly iron and copper ores) from the port of Seville, the province is essentially agricultural, the most important local minerals being the marble and chalk of Moron, and the china-clay of Lebrija and Osuna. Except along the hilly frontier of Cadiz and Malaga and north-west of the Guadalquivir, where the spurs of the Sierra Morena reach Lora, the province is very flat and exceedingly fertile. There is a large production of wheat and barley, and of wine (Manzanilla and Amontillado) ; but oranges (both sweet and bitter) and olives are the special crops, and the yield of oil is very large—four times that of Cordova in weight and with four times as large an area under olives. Still more typical is the stock-farming, horses and cattle, sheep and goats, all being of fine quality ; and this accounts for the typical "animal" industries of the province, *e.g.* the famous historic shoe-making industry of Ecija (noted also for its woollens) and the fancy leather of Seville itself and Utrera. The latter is one of the centres where fighting bulls are bred, between the "Mesopotamian" marsh-lands of the Guadalquivir and the Nevada moorlands.

Seville itself, the fourth city in Spain, has always been one of the **City of** great tidal ports of the country ; and the river has been dredged **Seville.** and canalised to admit vessels drawing 25 feet of water. It is also a great industrial centre, specially famous for its cigar and porcelain works ; the patron saints of the city are said to have been potters, and the gipsy suburb of Tirana has manufactured porcelain for many hundreds of years. The low level (30 feet) and the consequent windings of the river have exposed the city to constant floods, and that perhaps accounts for the Romans preferring the site of Carmona for their great stronghold. Crowds of visitors flock to Seville at Easter, when the orange-trees are in flower, the bulls "spring-ripe" for fighting, and the religious services almost unique for colour ; but its real beauty is best seen at Christmas, when the oranges are ripe, and the violets and carnations in flower, and the white lines of the typical Moorish houses are not glaring.

The Castiles. The ancient kingdom of Castile includes a typical piece of the Cantabrians in the province of Santander (cf. p. 167), and an exceptionally fertile piece of the Ebro valley in the province of Logroño—where the Rioja plain raises quantities of good wine, especially round Logroño[1] itself; but the mass of it consists of the most characteristic part of the meseta. On every side of this except towards Leon and Murcia there is a natural frontier of mountain, *e.g.* the Demanda, the Cuenca, and the Morena sierras, giving rise respectively to the Douro, the Tagus, and the Guadiana; and the Guadarrama system divides Old Castile, *i.e.* the part freed first from Moorish rule, from New Castile. The latter, as the more cut off from oceanic influence, has the severer climate, though even in Old Castile the extremes of heat and cold are very great. In both, however, the plateau itself is so fertile that, after rain, quite a luxuriant vegetation springs up; and where a heavy sub-soil is capped by a very porous and friable material, *i.e.* a very bad conductor, percolation is so rapid and evaporation so slow that the land is extraordinarily productive, as in Palencia and Toledo. Elsewhere the land is useless except for sheep, and even these have to emigrate in winter to the lower levels of Estremadura. The typical scenery is like that of La Mancha (" The Droughty Land "), described in *Don Quixote*.

Burgos. Old Castile, as the upper basin of the Douro, pivots on the Sierra de la Demanda, between the provinces of Burgos and Soria. The latter is a land of austere mountains, so barren and poor that the population does not reach 40 per square mile! Burgos, though less rugged, is scarcely more fertile, except in the Ebro basin; but it has two advantages. Its large area gives great facilities for sheep-rearing, though the town of Burgos is no longer famous for its cloth and woollens—for which a normal winter, with perhaps 20° of frost, still makes demand; and the Pancorbo Pass controls all the natural movement between Madrid and Paris to such an extent that it is called "The Iron Gate of Castile." It also offers an obvious way of escape from the poverty-stricken Arlanzon basin, and there is constant emigration to the more prosperous centres in the Basque Provinces and Catalonia. The strategic importance of the town of Burgos, where the Arlanzon suddenly turns south-westward, was increased by its situation on a hill protected by the broad and swift river.

Palencia. The province of Palencia presents a great contrast to its neighbour. Not only is the rainfall heavier, accounting for the forest and park-land below the Cantabrians, but the heavy sub-soil

---

[1] Logroño is a typical hill-town, overlooking the Ebro plain from a height of about 1200 feet.

of the Pisuerga basin yields large crops, *e.g.* of wheat and flax; and, as the northern park-land makes famous pasture, the province has important old industries in flour-milling and leather-working, in linens and woollens, especially rugs. The campos of Palencia extend into the province of Valladolid; and, as there are increased facilities for irrigation, especially along the Pisuerga, the province shares—in spite of its low rainfall (12½ inches at Valladolid itself)—with Palencia in the title of "The granary of Spain." Stock-rearing is also important, but the old woollen and linen industries cannot compete with more favoured centres. The political importance of Valladolid city, once the capital of Spain, was based on the same control of great cross-routes as has made it in modern times an important railway-junction; but Medina (del Campo), though off the line of the Douro, is now more important in this respect.

The two southern provinces of Old Castile, Avila and Segovia, **Avila and** though drained to the Douro, are essentially mountain rather than **Segovia.** plateau areas; and the relatively heavy rainfall, which also accounts for the extent of forest on the Gredos and Guadarrama slopes, gives great facilities for irrigation, *i.e.* in the superb gardens of the Royal Palace at La Granja. Avila is as famous for its merino wool as Segovia is for its grain, and in both the rugged granite sierras contain valuable minerals. Segovia is the more interesting town, mainly because of Trajan's magnificent aqueduct, built of the Guadarrama granite; but Avila occupies the more important position, commanding the gap between the Gredos and the Guadarrama and so the main line from Madrid to Corunna.

The eastern provinces of New Castile, Guadalajara and Cuenca, **Guadalajara.** are much poverty-stricken. Both suffer from drought and from great extremes of temperature, so that their population is very thin —only slightly above or below 45 per square mile—and the rearing of stock (mainly sheep and goats) is their typical industry. There is some floating of pine-timber down the Tagus, but most of the area is literally *Guadalajara*, "Valley of Stones."

The western provinces are rather more favoured. For instance, **Madrid.** in Madrid the presence of considerable tracts of clay and the precipitation on the Guadarrama heights encourage the growth of timber, such as is characteristic of the Royal domains of the Escorial and Aranjuez; there are valuable quarries in the sierra itself; and quantities of live-stock are reared. Above all its central position made it the site of the national capital, and so all the great railways converge on it. The city of Madrid is almost the mathematical centre of the country; and, as such, it has a certain amount of commercial and industrial importance, *e.g.* in the manufacture of tobacco and leather. But it has an unpleasant climate. Its height, its distance from the sea, and its lack of shelter make it liable to very sudden and extreme changes, the daily range of

temperature sometimes exceeding 50° F. In winter icy air—
"which will kill a man without blowing out a candle"—gravitates
from the Guadarrama heights ; and these again in summer take all
the moisture out of the normal N.W. wind, leaving the city a prey
to fiery dust-laden gales from the barren plateau or to a brazen sky
that sometimes allows a shade temperature of over 108° F.

Toledo.   The " oasis " of Aranjuez, at the Tagus-Jurana confluence in
the sheltered valley, was therefore really a better site for a capital ;
and the tongue of land along the Tagus on which the Royal park—
with its famous elms and sycamores—extends, ought to be politically,
as it naturally is, part of the " valley " province of Toledo. The
" valley " lands are well watered from the Toledo Mountains, which
were densely forested till recently ; and the Alberche, besides its
value for irrigation, gives a direct line of approach to or from
Madrid which can be tapped from Salamanca at Talavera, now
famous only for its pigs—descendants, doubtless, of those that fed the
hungry army in 1809.   The valley pastures feed dairy cattle, draught
oxen, and fighting bulls ; but the prosperity of the area has been
hindered by war, for the valley is the most important "line of least
resistance " in Central Spain, as may be judged from the fact that
to-day it carries both the main line southwards to Cadiz and the
main line westwards to Lisbon. The site of Toledo city, on its
granite boss, guarded by the Tagus on all sides except the north,
recalls—on a grim and larger scale—that of Durham. Its archbishop is " primate of all the Spains," and it was the scene of
innumerable Synods between the fifth century and the sixteenth.

Ciudad Real.   What the Tagus is to the province of Toledo, the Guadiana is
to Ciudad Real ; but the latter includes a considerable part of the
La Mancha steppe, with its severe droughts and plagues of locusts.
To the west and south, however, the land is much more fertile,
and the climate encourages considerable forests of oak and beech,
in which large herds of pigs are reared.   Alcazar and Valdepenas
are important railway-junctions, and the line from Valdepenas to
the great mercury mines at Almaden passes through a valuable
little coal-field at Puertollano.

Leon.   The old kingdom of Leon had very marked frontiers on all
sides except the east, and its natural drainage by the Esla and the
Tormes gave it supreme control of the Middle Douro.   The
modern province of Leon represents the strongest part of the old
kingdom, strongly guarded by its mountainous frontier on the
north and west, and pivoting on the Montañas de Leon, through
which there is easy communication between the Minho and the
Esla basins only at Manzanal—on the main route from Astorga to
Corunna and Vigo. Sir John Moore could easily have checked
Soult here, but wished to entangle him in the Galician glens ; and
Moore's life was sacrificed only because his men could not resist

the wine-cellars of Ponferrada.   In the north-west of the province
the Vierzo is semi-Atlantic in climate, and has rich wooded pastures
on its hills and rich grain-lands and vineyards in its valleys.   In
this part, too, the people, while less Castilian, have few Moorish
traits.   Indeed, the Maragatos are even said to be a remnant of the
old Celtiberian natives.

The province of Salamanca is also strongly placed—against the **Sala-**
Gata heights ; but there is relatively easy access into Portugal both **manca**
by the Douro valley and *via* Ciudad Rodrigo and Fuentes d'Onoro
and into the Tagus basin by Beja and the Alagon.   These conditions imply both the rainfall which accounts for the wealth of
forest and pasture, famous for its live-stock, and the nodality which
made the capital the site of a great university, of a most critical
battle, and of one of the most important railway-junctions in Spain.
Indeed, it was only the scourge of war that arrested the natural
development of the area ; and, on the other hand, it was bad
transport along the actual valley of the Douro that kept the
intervening province of Zamora free from war, and now condemns
it to poverty—through neglect of its forests and its mines.

The feature-lines of Estremadura have a very marked east-and-   **Estrema-**
west trend, the middle courses of both Tagus and Guadiana—   **dura.**
separated by the Guadalupe sierra—lying parallel to the Gata-Gredos
barrier in the north and the Morena barrier in the south.   The
heights, especially near the ocean, are so well forested, with beech
and oak and chestnut, that the area is very famous for its pigs ;
but the lowlands are drought-stricken, viper-haunted steppe, liable
to locusts and seasonal floods, so that almost the only important
industry is sheep-farming.   Historic disadvantages have also handicapped the people.   Their natural outlet has been usually through a
foreign, if not an actively hostile, country ; and landward they were
far from, and much cut off from, the important centres of national
life, while the success of Cortes and Pizarro encouraged the best
of their fellow-countrymen to copy their example, and so robbed
Estremadura of her finest citizens.

The province of Caceres has fared rather better than that of **Caceres**
Badajoz.   It is rather more fertile, especially on the Arroyo plain ; **and**
and, as the Tagus valley is more difficult than that of the Guadiana, **Badajos.**
the southern route was the more troubled by war (cf. Badajoz and
Albuera).   On the other hand, though Badajoz is rather the less
healthy, especially along its great river, it had—until the construction
of the Tagus-valley line from Lisbon to Madrid—more commercial
opportunity ; and this compensated to some extent for lack of
industrial development, and has made most of its modern centres
more or less important railway-junctions, *e.g.* Merida and Zafra.
The precise historic outlet of the Caceres basin was by the *Via
Lata* which ran from Gades to Rome, and which is carried across

the Tagus at Al-Cantara by "The Bridge"—*20 yards* higher than the Forth Bridge, with central arches wider than the dome of St. Paul's, 1800 years old, and still bearing Trajan's hexameter:

Pontem perpetui mansurum in saecula mundi.

PORTUGAL

Relation to Atlantic. Within a well-defined frontier-belt of sparse population along river-gorge and mountain-crest, Portugal forms a more or less natural unit, profoundly influenced by the Atlantic climatically, but curiously independent of it otherwise. Traz-os-Montes was the only one of the six old provinces which did not touch the Atlantic, and yet access to the ocean is very poor. All the estuaries of the larger rivers are used; but the Minho and the Guadiana are frontier rivers, while the Vougo and the Sado empty into lagoons. There are valuable salt-pans, and in the north the salt has encouraged for ages a busy glass industry, *e.g.* at Figueira and Leiria; but even the mouth of the Mondego is little used, and the ship-canal from Aveira to the ocean has probably never paid even the cost of its construction a century ago.

Relief. The relief of the country is varied, though it nowhere reaches a height of 7000 feet; and it may be roughly described as mountainous to the north of the Tagus and lowland to the south, though there are valuable vegas (or veigas) on the Minho flood-plain and crinas (plateau-basins) in Traz-os-Montes, while in the south Algarve is almost entirely mountainous. The Estrella sierra is the natural divide both physically and climatically, and so ethnically. Exposure to the Atlantic gives the country the richest flora in Europe, and numbers of plants have been imported—from the New World and elsewhere, *e.g.* the agave; but the Estrella flora is Alpine, while that of Alemtejo is almost Saharan, and that of Algarve is tropical, while that of Traz-os-Montes is almost Mediterranean (cf. the olive and silk industry of Braganza). The onion is as typical of the north, *e.g.* Ovar, as the carob is of the south.

Population. About six-sevenths of the total population is found north of the Estrella, the density round the Paiz do Vinho, *i.e.* the port wine country, exceeding 400 to the square mile; and the type there is largely "Galician," with Roman and Suevic and Visigoth elements, while to the south it is largely Arab and Berber and Negro and markedly shorter in stature. Everywhere, however, there has been a great mixture of blood; and this perhaps accounts for the relatively high standard of character and intelligence amongst the half-breeds in Portuguese areas abroad, *e.g.* Brazil. And perhaps no other country in Europe could have produced a "Mozarabic" type—Portuguese by birth, Christian by creed, Berber by speech, and Arab by custom. On the other hand, no other country in the world, with equal advantages, has 40 p.c. of its area uncultivated; and even in Oporto 70 p.c. of the population is illiterate.

Southern Portugal has three typical features, the lowlands of **Southern Provinces.** Estremadura, the upland plains of Alemtejo, and the mountains of Algarve. The Sierra de Monchique, which runs out into the ocean as Cape St. Vincent, gives Algarve a relatively heavy rainfall and rich copper-bearing beds (cf. Tharsis); cork and almonds are typical exports from Faro, and copper from Villa Real de San Antonio, and the osier-work (baskets) of Loule is very famous. But communication inland is difficult, the coast is inhospitable except for the refuge of Lagos—famous in war rather than peace, and the hinterland is unhealthy. This is the essential drawback of Alemtejo to-day, at all events south of Beja; but historically it has suffered from the fact that its most fertile areas are along the Spanish frontier, really fine olive-oil coming from round the frontier fortress of Elvas, only a dozen miles from Badajoz. The mineral wealth is considerable, especially copper between Aljustrel and Beja and gold between Beja and Evora; but it is little developed, mainly owing to lack of transport.

The unhealthy marsh-lands of Estremadura are specially devoted **Lisbon.** to the raising of bulls, while the drier parts raise good wheat. Lisbon, on its terraced hillside, had its approach from landward guarded of old by the fortresses of Abrantes and Santarem, and from seaward by the fortress of Cascaes, now one of the summer resorts of the Portuguese Riviera (south of Cape Roca), where the people of Lisbon take refuge from their mild but oppressive atmosphere with its very high average humidity. There is an important sardine fishery off the coast, which has its headquarters at Setubal.

Northern Portugal pivots on the province of Beira, astride of **Northern Provinces** the Estrella; and, as the Mondego flows right round the eastern end of the sierra, the ancient stronghold of Guarda has become the most important railway-junction in Portugal except, possibly, that of Abrantes. Sheep-farming is important to the south-east, *e.g.* near Castello Branco, where there are busy woollen industries; better access to the sea encourages mining to the north-west, *e.g.* at Vizéu (tin and wolfram [1]). In the extreme north the wide cultivation of maize and the presence of forests account for the importance of pig-rearing, *e.g.* at Lamego, famous for "Lisbon" hams. But the most typical industry is the salt-making along the low sandy shore, *e.g.* at Aveiro. To the south the inroads of the sand, *e.g.* at Leiria, have been stopped by wide planting of pine-trees on the lines followed on the French Landes; and land is being reclaimed for cattle-pasture and rice-growing—a typical industry between Bussaco and Aveiro and between Coimbra and Figueira. But historically

[1] Both minerals are found widely distributed in the province, *e.g.* at Guarda and Castello Branco.

the blown sand was another line of defence in front of the granite ridge of Cintra, for the sand extends practically as far south as Peniche, and from there to Cape Roca—*i.e.* the foreground of Vimiera and Torres Vedras—is a line of sheer and lofty cliffs.

Oporto. The balance of commercial power, however, is on the Douro, Oporto holding to Lisbon somewhat the same relation as Barcelona holds to Madrid. The river itself is crowded with small steamers, —though large boats cannot even reach Oporto, but have to use the artificial harbour at Leixoes; and the hardy and industrious peasantry are the best part of the Portuguese population, live-stock and fish, maize and olives, and—above all—wine being the typical products. Textile industries are found in the older centres, *e.g.* Braga (cotton) and Braganza (silk)—though Oporto itself is the great textile centre—while mining is developing new centres as Moncorvo (coal and iron).

Economic Outlook. The general outlook for Portugal at present, however, is not very bright. Beds of coal and lignite are worked at Cape Mondego and Coimbra, and the country is certainly rich in copper and iron, tin and wolfram; but it is essentially an agricultural area, two-fifths of the population being engaged in agriculture, and yet—except in occasional years—it cannot feed its own people. This is largely due to the extraordinary amount of land which, though reasonably good, is left uncultivated from lack of transport; and one result is persistent emigration (*e.g.* to Brazil), especially from the Oporto district. In the meantime, Portugal "monopolises" only two products, the natural forest output of cork (half the world's supply) and the wolfram, which is collected by country people; and, as long as the colonies are such a financial burden on the Mother country, the essential need for improved transport is not likely to be met except where foreign capital is interested, *e.g.* in the wine area of the north and the copper area of the south.

CHAPTER XV

FRANCE

ALL things considered, France has the most favourable position **Position.** of all the great Powers in the world; and the early history of her expansion over-seas reflects alike the imperial value of being in the centre of all the land on the face of the earth, the climatic value of being half-way between pole and equator, the economic value of being the land gateway between continent and ocean.

The regional relations of the country are of special interest in **Regional** political geography, partly because her influence has been so much **Relations.** stronger landward than seaward; and this difference was only accentuated by the Revolution. For in earlier days the Navy had been essentially an aristocratic service; and the utter decimation of the aristocrats cut off the supply of officers with hereditary instinct for the sea, so that Nelson had to fight a type of officer essentially different from—and inferior to—the type with which his predecessors, *e.g.* Hawke, had had to deal.

The most conspicuous characteristic of the frontier features is **Varied** their variety; and, as this is equally true of seaward and landward **Frontier.** features, any attempt to classify all the coastal features together, *e.g.* as "Marginal Lowlands," only conveys an absolutely false idea of physical uniformity, and divorces the interesting differences between the coastal people, *e.g.* Breton and Gascon, from their legitimate geographical base. Further, this variety of coast is seen both in detail and in outlook; for instance, there are ports on the English Channel which are naturally only cracks in a steep chalk scarp, *e.g.* Boulogne and Dieppe, while others stand on dune-fringed alluvium, *e.g.* Calais and Dunkirk, and still others are bays between granite promontories or cut out of other ancient rock, as Cherbourg. Cf. Brest.

The triple outlook of the coasts has been of profound signi- **Coastal** ficance in the story of French maritime relations. French routes **Outlook.** to the west and north-west are better now than any others in Europe except the British, as in the early days of trans-Atlantic expansion they were better than any others except the Iberian; and the French routes to the south and south-east are better

than those of any other "Atlantic" Power. On this the historic
influence of the French in Canada and India, and the possession
by France of such islands as St. Pierre and Réunion, are obvious
comments.   More than half the frontier is sea-coast, and the
fronting waters include such natural nurseries of fine seamanship
as the stormy Bay of Biscay and the Gulf of "(Roaring) Lions,"—
really, of course, *Liguria*—while the paucity of good natural harbours
was at once an impulse to seamanship and a check on commerce.

Strategic Ports.   Further, one early result of spanning Europe from north to
south on the Atlantic seaboard was the tendency for the best
natural harbours to be more or less monopolised for strategic
purposes; for, obviously, the best strategic positions were those
which would otherwise have had most facilities for commerce.
Thus, the fine advanced sites of Brest and Toulon, with their
incidental advantages of Viking and Phœnician blood in the
local populations, were sacrificed to strategic needs; and the first
inferior harbours to be "improved" were those on the Narrow
Seas, *i.e.* "inside" the Cotentin peninsula, which commanded the
two ends of the sea-approach on Paris—Cherbourg and Dunkirk.
Cherbourg—only 70 miles south of the Isle of Wight—betrays by
its name (Caesaris Burgum, "Cæsar's Castle") its strategic importance in very early times; and it was the strength of the position
between dune and marsh or floodable "carse" that attracted Crom-
well's attention to Dunkirk ("the Church amongst the Dunes").

Port Dues.   In days of small ships—when, too, roads were bad, and piracy
favoured an up-river site—France had a number of useful little
harbours, some of which are still very useful for local harbours, *e.g.*
Caen on the Orme and Dieppe on the Arques; and, with the
development of internal wealth and external commerce, the French
were rich enough to develop estuaries, such as those of the Seine
and the Loire, and cracks in the chalk scarp or gaps in the sand-
dunes, as at Boulogne and Calais. The inevitable result, however,
is that port dues at such places, when calculated simply on the
actual cost of rendering the particular place capable of giving harbour
facilities, must be very high, when compared with those at natural
harbours such as Rotterdam and Hamburg.

Sea Fishing.   The variety of coastal features referred to above is likely to
prove of great value in the modern development of fishing, with its
double relation to food supply and naval power; for the parts of
the coast that are naturally least useful for commerce, are often
most useful for the propagation of fish. For instance, the short
south coast is divided by Cape Couronne into two approximately
equal (*c.* 200 miles), but very distinct, parts. The rocky eastern
half is broken by beautiful bays, such as those of Hyères and Nice,
and by deep gulfs which make admirable harbours, especially
those of Marseilles and Toulon; but the west is a line of dune-

fringed lagoon, *e.g.* Vendres and Leucate, the outcome of centuries of struggle between the silt-laden floods of Pyrenean and Cevennes torrents and the westward gales and drift of Rhone mud. Where the coast is high and rocky, the continental shelf is narrow, and *vice versa*; and, where currents meet or part, there plankton accumulates, and fish follow it. Cette is the chief fishing port here only because its commercial importance, as the outlet of the Canal du Midi, causes it to be kept free from sand; and it is mainly the importance of the salt industry that handicaps the fishing industry in the more typically lagoon ports.

Precisely similar conditions obtain on the Atlantic except that **Ocean** the salt industry there is relatively unimportant — because it **Fishing.** cannot compete with the natural advantage of " summer-drought " possessed by the Mediterranean coast—and that the Atlantic coast is not only double the length of the Mediterranean coast, but has also typically oceanic advantages, *e.g.* of tide and oxygen. The Landes district has a characteristic lagoon coast; but the strength of the rivers is small, and that of the west wind is very great. Only the largest river, the Leyre, has been able to make any real struggle, and its estuary is the Arcachon basin, off which the surface temperature of the water varies 20° F. (52° F.–72° F.). Between the great oyster-market of Marennes and Sables d'Olonne river mud is abundant, and the islands of Oléron and Ré provide shelter from western gales; and, as the outport of La Pallice is monopolising commerce, the old landward harbour of Rochelle is specialising in fishing. Farther north, where the east-and-west folds of the old mountains dip seaward as rias, the coast becomes bolder, though still there is some island-shelter, *e.g.* Belle Ile sheltering the Morbihan Gulf; and, though there are important fishing-stations both on the mainland and on the islands, *e.g.* Lorient and Croisic, the native people are deep-sea men rather than alongshore fishermen. Of course, the special products of this west coast are sardines and tunny. From Camant to Sables d'Olonne the sardine is supreme, and the fishing has been the cause of much trouble at Douarnenez and Concarneau.

But the north coast is the most important in the fishing industry, **Channel** mainly because it does not confine itself to any one or two kinds of **Ports.** fish, or any one or two fishing-grounds, boats from Dunkirk and Gravelines being as common off Iceland as boats from Fécamp and Granville are off Newfoundland. The "sea-meadows" off Brittany and the "Calvados" bay are famous—or notorious—alike for their currents and for their rich mud, while the eastward ports have easy access to the North Sea. The western ports, *e.g.* Morlaix and St Brieuc—if not St. Malo—are somewhat " out of the way," while other industries make great demands on available labour in the Calvados ports; and, on the other hand, the better railway service

has given special advantages to cross-channel ports, especially the
"cracks in the chalk." Boulogne and Dieppe, the two greatest
fish markets in France, have direct services of their own to Paris;
and Fécamp, which shares with Boulogne in control of the distant
fisheries, has very easy access to the Havre and Rouen connections.
The total value of the industry—which directly employs 130,000
men afloat and *c.* 60,000 persons on shore—approaches that of
England and Wales; and of this Boulogne is credited with nearly
one-fifth, while Boulogne and Fécamp are said to be responsible for
one-tenth of all the herrings landed in European ports.

**Land
Frontiers.** The land frontiers are largely of a mountainous character; but
the various sections are so distinctly marked off by strips of lowland
or, at least, by a river gorge, that the mountain obstacle nowhere
imprisons, though it forms a very real protection. Further, traffic
is concentrated on these river gaps, and the obvious danger-zones
are defined by them. Thereby the danger is lessened, and the fact
that different gaps face different nations again minimises risk of
invasion; but, unfortunately, the two most important gaps face the
least friendly nation.

**Burgundy
v. Lor-
raine
Gates.** In days when the Danube was more important than the Rhine,
and the Rhone than the Seine, the Burgundy Gate was also more
important than the Lorraine Gate, partly because it joined Danube
and Rhone, and partly because it was essentially central. In those
days, too, its narrowness (18 miles) made it very easy to defend; and,
in any case, it was rather a route for French expansion, *e.g.* Richelieu's
seizure of Alsace, than a dangerous inlet into France. It is significant,
however, that the main line of railway from Dijon to Lyons keeps to
the west bank[1] of the Saone, and only crosses the waterway south
of Lyons. The Lorraine Gate now is much the more important of
the two, mainly owing to the modern importance of Rhine and Seine,
but partly to its greater breadth. It carries the Orient-Express route
eastward, and is marked by such memorable sites as those of Sedan
and Metz, both on rivers which—unlike the Doubs—lead outwards,
not inwards.

**Frontier
Lines.** The precise frontier line is very varied in feature, and its political
importance is not in all parts obviously related to its physique. For
instance, the "permanent" neutrality of Belgium and Switzerland—
which is not likely to be violated by France—minimises the importance of the physical frontier. In the case of Belgium it is a purely
arbitrary line (cf. p. 250), which immensely increases its economic
value; in the case of Switzerland, the arbitrary link between the
Jura and the Alps has a high economic importance, especially as it
crosses such a natural meeting-place of peoples as a large navigable
lake. And the Jura (cf. p. 34) are sufficiently high and wide and
continuous to make an excellent natural barrier between peoples.

[1] The main lines to Paris along both Somme and Seine do the same.

The Pyrenees and Alps are an absolute protection without **Pyrenees** absolutely prohibiting peaceful intercourse; and the latter is as **and Alps.** much encouraged with Italy by the Alpine tunnels as it is discouraged with Spain by the change of railway gauge. While the sierra character of the Pyrenees, however, afforded minimum temptation to French aggression into Spain, the convergence of the Alpine valleys on the concave side offered maximum temptation to aggression into Italy (cf. p. 84), especially as the French language —like the Kingdom of Burgundy—had crept down the Little St. Bernard Pass as far as the great road-junction of Aosta (cf. p. 30), thus laying the foundation of a natural political bond between Savoy and Piedmont.

The 200 miles between the Belgian and Swiss frontiers are the **Lorraine** vital part, and here both physical features and political or military **Frontier.** distributions are of profound significance. The racial differences are strongest approximately along the water-parting between rivers flowing into the North Sea and rivers flowing into the English Channel or the Mediterranean; but the geographical features between the basins of Rhine and Seine offer no real barrier, scarcely even an obstacle, although Lorraine had been for ages before 1871 roughly divided between French-speaking and German-speaking people. And the difference of attitude on the part of the two nations towards the fundamental problems may be judged more fairly from deeds than from words. It is, therefore, of profound moment that the French side of the frontier is held on a system which is of real use only for defence, while the German system is one which is meaningless or ridiculous except for aggression. [*These two sections are retained verbatim from the* 1913 *edition.*]

The French have fortified the whole line—at some distance **Military** from the actual frontier—which should guard them against any very **Organisa-** sudden surprise, but the scattered garrisons are obviously incapable **tion.** of making any concerted attack; the Germans have concentrated an estimated 1,000,000 men at two foci—Metz, 30 miles south of the Belgian frontier, and Strassburg, half-way between Metz and the Swiss frontier. Each of these is a great railway-junction inside a huge ring of fortifications, capable of easily holding half a million men apiece, and with extraordinary facilities for transporting troops between the two foci. Strassburg itself is not very threatening, however valuable it was in olden days as a base for the French in crossing the Rhine; and the nearness of Metz to Paris and the trivial obstacle of the Argonne are so obvious that surprise might have been thought impossible. But the cause of perennial unrest on this frontier is the fear of surprise *through violation of neutral territory*, Belgian and Swiss. And historians who remember the fate of Silesia or the events preceding the battle of Pirna, may justifiably wonder what products known to Economic Geography

could possibly be served by the "heavy" railways to Malmedy—
a mile and a half from the Belgian frontier—and to Pfirt, not very
much farther from the Swiss frontier (cf. pp. 273, 285).

Relief.   The relief of the country is fundamentally simple, the various
natural regions being so grouped and related as to form a very
complete, compact, and comprehensible unit.   There is a highland
core of old crust-block girdled almost continuously by lowland of
varying width ; and this is flanked southward by the young folded
mountains of the Alps and the Pyrenees and northward by the
old plateaus of Brittany and the Ardennes.   Traffic round this core,
therefore, must always have been physically easy, though it might
be interrupted by political accidents, *e.g.* the possession of Guienne
and Gascony by England ; and, if such foreign intrusion were
maintained for any considerable time, it must have given special
importance to the Paris basin, as the natural link between all the
parts of the country that were not held by foreigners.   On the
other hand, once the foreign control was withdrawn, physical conditions would distinctly favour the obliteration of racial differences,
e.g. between Iberian and Kelt or Kelt and Teuton ; and the
supremacy already acquired by the central Paris basin would make
it very difficult for outlying areas to combine against the centre, *i.e.*
for provincial vassals to threaten their king.   It was quite characteristic, however, that determined opposition to the central authority
should come from the Counts of Toulouse,—individualists and
"aliens" in politics and creed—and equally significant that its
punishment in the vile Albigensian "Crusade" should mark a
great step in the unification of France.

Nucleus.   The nucleus of the area is the peneplain of the Central Plateau,
or Massif, a rugged block of old crystalline rock, flanked by younger
sedimentary formations and broken towards the centre by recent
volcanic action.   This peneplain slopes down more or less gently—
by way of the intermediate levels of Limousin and Marche—to the
west and north-west from a height of nearly 5600 feet in the
Cevennes, so that it drains naturally to the Garonne and the Loire ;
and, as its upturned margins in the Cevennes, Lyonnais, and
Beaujolais "mountains" form a steep riverless scarp to the Rhone
valley, *i.e.* the funnel by which civilisation entered the country, it
became—like the similarly unattractive and inaccessible recesses of
Brittany and Savoy—a refuge for the conquered natives, with their
typical round heads, short stature, and dark complexion.   In each
case, too, the unattractive and inaccessible area was likely to
perpetuate social and religious individualism long after the unity
and solidarity of the rest of the country had been firmly established.

**Volcanic
Centre.**   The volcanic action has left its traces in such hot springs as
those of Vichy and Chaudes Aigues ("Hot Waters") as well as
in the typical puys of Auvergne ; and it is in these puys that we

find the culminating peaks of the massif, those of Cantal (*c.* 6100 feet) and Dore (*c.* 6200). To leeward of the main heights any depressed areas are likely to suffer from drought and dust; and the great importance of the Limagne plain in early days was largely due to the intense fertility of the wind-borne volcanic dust. It is equally significant that the name of its capital, Clermont (*Clarus Mons*, "Clear Mountain") should be taken from the neighbouring Puy de Dôme—that the local cathedral, in which Peter the Hermit preached the first Crusading sermon, should be built of lava—and that the permanence of the local control should be illustrated by

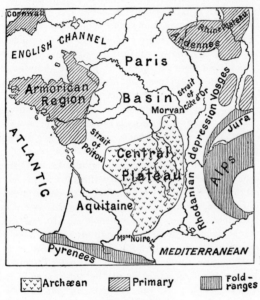

Structure of France.

such typical "agricultural" industries to-day as biscuit-baking and fruit-preserving. Even the wind-borne dust is still prominent—in causing mist and fog.

The nearness to the Atlantic, the considerable height within such a small area, and the details of relief, have combined to give the massif special significance in the hydrography of France; but, owing to the local distribution of rainfall (over 70 inches in the highest and most exposed parts) and to differences of rock-formation, the fate of the northward rivers has been very different from that of the westward rivers. The impervious crystalline rock of the north-ward slope, with its quick "run-off" of rain and even of surface-soil, has developed more or less parallel streams flowing independently

Crystal-line Water-shed.

of one another from areas of maximum rainfall, *e.g.* Loire and Allier, and separated by a marked ridge, *e.g.* the Forez mountains. The pace and volume of these rivers, and their heavy burden of silt, have—aided by the physical history of the area—enabled them to cut down their valleys in the areas of lighter rainfall—to leeward of the summit—into almost cañon form; and population was attracted to these valleys in very early times owing to their value as trade-routes as well as owing to the fertility of their wind-borne soil. Roanne is a town as old as Clermont, and Le Puy has a name as significant.

Karst Lime- stone. The westward rivers have also eroded cañon valleys, especially the Tarn; but the conditions of flow are quite different, for the massif is flanked here by limestone which is not only porous, but even easily soluble. Here, then, we have typical "Karst" phenomena. The originally continuous plateau has been carved —by rivers that rise close to the Loire and the Allier, *e.g.* the Lot and the Tarn—into a series of limestone promontories called Causses (*calx*, "lime"). The surface of each block is a weird wilderness pitted with sink-holes, some of which reach a depth of 700 feet, while below it is honeycombed with caves — rich in stalactites and even in the relics of early Cave-dwellers — and tunnelled by a network of rivers. In the course of about 30 miles the Tarn receives thirty subterranean tributaries and not one on the surface; and sheep and mules are the typical products of the Aveyron valley, the Roquefort cheese being made of ewes' milk.

Hydro- graphic Centre. This old block, from its extreme northward extension in the granite plateau of Morvan to its extreme southward extension in the Montagne Noir, completely dominates the river-system of France, isolating the Saone-Rhone basin and feeding—generally with flood-water—the three other great basins. Except the Loire, all these basins are approximately of the same size (*c.* = Ireland); and, as the water-parting is well towards the east of the country, all of them except the Rhone have more or less equal exposure to wet winds off the Atlantic. But the varying volume of the Loire and the rapids on the Garonne ("The Rough") force traffic on to lateral canals—the Loire needing also to be protected by levées; and, therefore, their adverse physique and régime have again increased the relative importance of the favourable physique and régime of the Seine ("The Tranquil").

Loire v. Garonne. There is a further distinction between them. For the physical relation of the Loire and the Garonne to the massif, and their climatic relation to the area of summer-drought in the south-east, cause them to draw the great proportion of their water-supply from the massif, *i.e.* their great tributaries are concentrated in the one case on the left bank and in the other case on the right bank; and the valleys of these tributaries lead up into those areas of hard

old rock which are so typically connected with populations individualistic alike in creed and politics. · And the Loire, though
fed by several large tributaries from the Norman Heights, *e.g.* the
Loir, the Sarthe, and the Mayenne, enters again near its mouth
an area of old rock and individualistic population in Brittany and
the Vendean Bocage.   As the clay flats of the Sologne within the
great bend at Orleans became naturally a vast expanse of forested
marsh, traffic from the Paris basin was forced to keep to the right

Stanford's Geog! Estab!, London.

Peripheral distribution of French towns.

bank between Orleans and Tours, and special importance was given
to the Gap of Poitou, as the only link between the two great Tertiary
basins of Bordeaux and Paris.   Poitiers and the Vienne have,
therefore, strategical importance precisely similar to that of Aldershot
and the Kennet between the Hampshire and London basins in
England.

The Seine and the Garonne basins have, as great Tertiary basins, **Seine *v*.**
much in common ; and, except in régime, even the rivers show **Garonne.**
curious similarity.   In each case the basal channel, which controls
the direction and outflow of the whole basin, is on the extreme left—

the Ariège-Garonne and the Yonne-Seine; and, as all the great tributaries enter from the right and across the general line of advance, their flood-water is particularly troublesome. Thus, it is the Marne that is most blamed—in Paris—for floods which are mainly due to the inflow from the Yonne on the one side and the banking-back of the whole current by the Links of Seine on the other side; and it is in passing the Causses that the right bank of the Garonne is provided with a lateral canal—from Toulouse to Agen.

Two Areas. A line drawn from Agen *via* Angoulême and Troyes to Sedan divides the whole country into two well-marked areas—the western being generally low and level, while the eastern is generally high and hilly. In each case there is an obvious exception, for the Rhone valley is, like the Breton highland, a separate unit; but Brittany is too much isolated to affect the political unity of the western lowlands, while the lowness of the Côte-d'Or and Carcassonne Gaps—respectively 1000 and 625 feet—would have prevented the isolation of the Rhone valley even if it had not been the natural gateway of civilisation into France.

Climate. The climate is essentially temperate, partly because of latitude and general level, but chiefly because the position of the main water-parting gives free access to Atlantic winds almost everywhere; and the one exception—in the lee of the eastern Pyrenees—would be essentially "Mediterranean" even if there were no physical obstacle in the shape of the Pyrenees. Even as it is, the average rainfall of Perpignan (23 inches) is greater than that of Paris. The climatic contrasts of the country are, therefore, as in England, mainly due to differences of exposure, the north-west quadrant corresponding closely to our south-west quadrant, while the north-east quadrant corresponds to our south-east quadrant (cf. p. 238); rainfall varies mainly with height and Atlantic aspect, about two-thirds of the area having some rain at all seasons (most of it in autumn), while temperature varies mainly with height and latitude, the isotherm of 70° F. in July following the line from Agen *via* Angoulême to Troyes.

Climatic Regions. From a comparison of the various influences, five types may be distinguished. The lofty central massif (1) has cold winters and hot summers, with a mean annual temperature of 52° F. and a maximum annual rainfall of over 5 feet, most of which falls in summer; but, while under such circumstances the Millevache granite gives good pasture for cattle as well as sheep—the latter exceeding 200 per square mile—the Causses limestone can support only sheep. Brittany (2), with the same average temperature and rainfall—though most of the rain falls in "winter"—has a mild winter and a cool summer; and, while the massif has discontinuous heavy rains, Brittany has frequent fine rains—of great value in dairy farming. The Bordeaux basin (3), with the same mild winter as Brittany, has a higher summer temperature, accompanied by a higher average temperature (nearly 54° F.) ; and the summer temperature would be still higher but for the regular cool N.W. winds (cf. p. 56).   The fact that these winds owe much of their value to their coming from a high-pressure centre, accounts for the relatively low [1] rainfall (28 inches). The greatest extremes of mean temperature are between the Paris

Annual rainfall of France and Spain.

basin and the summer-drought basin, the mean of the former being only 50° F., while that of Languedoc and Provence is above 57° F. ; but in each case there is a marked modification with distance from sea and ocean.   The Paris basin proper (4), with a rainfall slightly less than that of the London basin, has a slightly colder winter and slightly hotter summer ; and the extremes increase up to the Vosges foothills, where the winter mean is only 48° F., while the summer is

[1] The Pyrenees rainfall behind Biarritz, however, sometimes exceeds 70 inches.

hot enough to be distinctly rainy. The purely Mediterranean area
(5) is so much exposed to Atlantic influences that its typical Mediterranean winter is made exception-
ally mild ; but, with movement northward into the lee of the massif, there
is a marked change—up to the Vosges
foothills. Indeed, the mean temperature of the Saone basin is only
52° F. ; the winters are still wet—
because all regular winds have to
follow the narrow valley northward
or southward—but they are also cold,
because easterly winds work through
the Burgundy Gate ; and the same conditions reversed account for
the heat of the summer.

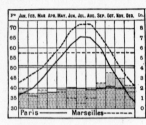

Rain and temperature lines.

Physique v. Climate. When the chief physical features of the country, with their
variety of relief and of structural character, are related to this variety
of climatic types, we seem to have almost an epitome of each of the
great areas of Europe which have been associated with marked individuality of human type—Nordic, Alpine, and Mediterranean. But
the fertile Nordic plain works southward right up to the young Alpine
folds, while the barren plateau belt works northward right up to the
Narrow Seas, leaving valley gaps between itself and the Alpine uplift. Movement into the area being normally dependent on ease of
access and such attractions as obvious fertility, and success in intrusion being reasonably limited to vigorous peoples, fair, long-headed
foresters from the Nordic plain flooded the fertile lowlands from
Belgium to Bordeaux, and dark, long-headed fruit-growers from the
Mediterranean coast occupied the " summer-drought " portion of the
fertile Rhone valley, while the Alpine Roundheads were isolated in
areas that were specifically unattractive—to primitive man—and
inaccessible or easily defensible.

Ancient Cores. Savoy can claim to be all three. The massif, if more favoured
with fertile patches, is equally defensible and inaccessible, especially from the south-east, *i.e.* the point nearest to the long-headed
intruders. Brittany, in actual physique less defensible and more
accessible, if not also more attractive, was so much more remote
that intruders never penetrated it until they came by sea ; on the
landward side it was, like its rock, quite impervious—even to the
insinuating French tongue, and to this day " Cornish " is spoken
in Cornouaille. When isolated under these adverse conditions,
the stocky-framed Alpine peoples often degenerated, especially in
the somatic quality most dependent on food-supply, *i.e.* stature ; for
these " islands of (agricultural) misery " exercised a control similar
to that exercised by real islands in dwarfing fauna, and their typical
peoples now are notorious for shortness of stature and badness of

teeth.   Where very different conditions are found in close proximity
—as where the granitic Morvan plateau overhangs the rich Tertiary
soil of Burgundy, or where the granitic rock of the upper valley
of the Aveyron merges in the limestone plain of the lower valley
—the contrasts are still most glaring; and, again, the 666-foot
contour is significant (cf. p. 45).   The plains certainly got the fertile
rock-sweepings from the hills, and possibly the hills got the feebler
human-sweepings from the plains.[1]

On these plains, then, we should expect to find the most **Roman** important of the old provinces and great fiefs of France; but all **Settle-** subsequent subdivision was somewhat coloured by the original **ment.** Roman settlement, with its conscious emphasis on strategic points and its unconscious response to climatic control.   For the Roman hold on the country was essentially based on a thorough occupation of the area of summer-drought, with the climatic phenomena of which they were entirely familiar.   This took them at least as far north as Vienne, the old capital of the Allobroges, and at least as far west as Toulouse, afterwards the capital of the Visigoths.   In each case command of a climatic divide, with its supplementary products on opposite sides, made the site naturally a commercial and political centre, so that for some time—while " Gaul " included both Britain and Spain—Vienne was made the capital of "all Gaul."   This limited area, as Gallia Narbonensis, roughly marked out Provence (the first *Pro-vincia*, " Advanced Conquest ") and Languedoc, the one roughly east and the other west of the Rhone.

It was characteristic that the Romans reached the area, not by **Romans** sea like the Phœnicians and the Greeks, but by land *via* Augusta **and Land** Taurinorum (Turin) and Tarraco (Tarragona).   By the Durance **Approach.** valley they " arrived at " the rocky headland of Avignon (*Advenio*, " I arrive ") on the " Roman " bank of the Rhone, thus giving that place a connection with Rome which was significantly revived by the Popes in the fourteenth century; round the Pyrenees they arrived at Narbo Martius on the " Roman " side of the Aude.   In the advance from each centre important posts were kept inside the best possible river-front, as Valence between Rhone and Isère and Carcassonne in the great bend of the Aude; and, as the Spanish connection was at first much more important than the Italian, the first colony was established at Narbonne—a fine strategic site, protected by lagoon and sea and river on every side except the west—and the place was made the capital of Mediterranean Gaul, with highroads to Toulouse and Avignon.   With the political separation of France from Spain, and the political union of " Atlantic " France and " Mediterranean " France, Narbonne, like Orange and Vienne, lost its importance; Avignon and Valance, though still commanding Alpine routes, could

---

[1] The development of water-power is completely changing the economic value of
hills, and France more than doubled her water-power plant during the war.

not compete landward with Lyons or seaward with Marseilles; and the Gard-valley route on to the massif made Nîmes more important than the old "Gallic" capital of Arles at the head of the Rhone delta.

Gallia Lugdun-ensis.   Gallia Lugdunensis, as its name implies, pivoted on Lyons, but included also all the land between the Seine and the Loire; and the relatively narrow "neck" of the province was held from three stations—Lyons, Autun, and Sens.   Lyons, on its river-girt peninsula, in the centre of the great north-and-south route of the Saone-Rhone depression, had good connection with Rome by the Upper Rhone, and commanded the best short route up into the Loire valley (just north-west of St. Étienne).   Augustodunum held the Côte-d'Or Gap between rivers draining to the Atlantic and the Mediterranean, occupying a river-girt hill on a tributary of the Loire; and the choice of the site—to the exclusion of the old capital of the Aedui at Châlons on the elbow of the Saone—like the building of a temple on it to "Janus of the Two-Faces," was entirely justified.   The amount of traffic through the gap may be gauged by the corruption that the original name has suffered, or by the survival to this day of such a significant industry as the making of horse-cloths.   The capital of the Senones had only temporary importance; for the confluence of the Vanne with the Yonne, where the latter leaves the plateau, was bound to yield place to other confluences farther down the Seine, as the North Sea and the English Channel became more important than the Alpine passes and the Mediterranean.

Loire Flank.   With the "neck" of the province thus held, the two great rivers were made the key to the rest, and at first the Loire was thought the more important.   Two sites were of paramount importance, the political capital of the Turones and the strategic point at which the broad,[1] shoaly, rapid Loire swerved nearest to the Seine.   The latter was well protected by the forested Sologne marsh on the south and by the marshy "Fontainebleau" forest on the east, while it was within easy reach of the rich grain-lands of Beauce.   Tours, on the Cher-Loire peninsula, was in an equally defensible site and in an equally fertile area; but its essential value—from the days of Martel onwards—was as the key to the Poitou Gap.   The poor navigation on the Loire, the relative decline of agriculture, the practical absence of coal, and external causes such as the centralisation of the circular lowlands on Paris and the opening of the Suez Canal, have all combined to decrease the relative importance of the Middle Loire valley.   But it was to Tours that the seat of Government was moved from Paris in 1871.

Seine Flank.   On the Seine, as on the Loire, only two centres seem to have been very important, the old capital of the Parisii and Rotomagus

---

[1] The bridge at Orleans ("Aurelian's Camp") has nine arches.

(Rouen). The development of the latter has depended largely on "modern" advantages, *e.g.* (1) the fact that the great north-east bend—which attracted the attention of the Romans through being at once the most pronounced feature on the river and at a safe distance from the sea—put it into close relations with Dieppe; (2) objection to—or original impossibility of—bridging the river any farther north; (3) the suitability of the site and the climate for the import and the working of textile fibres. The position of Paris, on the contrary, has always been one of supreme importance. About half-way in the course of the Seine across its fertile basin, at its confluence with its chief tributary, the Marne, islands in the river were first a refuge and then a means of bridging the river. Forested marsh and "Barbarians" on the northern bank caused the first expansion to be on to the southern "Roman" bank, thus giving "Versailles" its initial relation to Orleans and Blois; no place farther south could rival it, because the critical point is obviously where the three great waterways—Yonne and Seine and Marne—unite; no place farther north could rival it, because there were fatal strategic objections to being involved amongst the intricate "Links of Seine," where one bank or one part of a "link" is always commanding or being commanded by another. The network of waterways led to a network of roads, and the latter to a network of railways, until Paris became "a river, road, and railway star"; and these conditions reacted on one another until, five years ago, Paris could claim a larger trade as a port than any seaboard harbour, and ranked next to Marseilles and Le Havre even for foreign commerce.

Belgica and Aquitania were simply the flanks of the other two provinces, but were organised on the same principles. In Belgica, which was practically all the land between the Jura Mountains and the Dover Strait, the two foci were at opposite ends—Visontio (Besançon) and the old capital of the Remi. The river-girt rock in the loop of the Doubs was, in those days, unquestionably the "Gate-post," though modern artillery and political control have deprived it of its old importance,—its military rôle having been moved outwards to Belfort, while its political rôle has been moved inwards to Dijon, which faces the Burgundy Gate, but is in the rear of the Saone and has its back against the Côte d'Or, and so commands all the best passes to Yonne and Seine, to Marne and Meuse. The adoption of Reims as the other focus, no doubt, had the advantage—seldom ignored by the Romans—of keeping up old associations in the minds of conquered people, as at Paris and Tours; but it was justified otherwise, though the justification was not obvious at first. For the town stands between the Champagne clays and the Argonne chalk, *i.e.* between wine and wool, and between Aisne and Marne, *i.e.* between the latitudes of Sedan and

Metz; and, from the time when the Holy Roman Empire fronted directly on to the Meuse and the Saone, Reims challenged the foe from a safe proximity to the frontier, much as Scone challenged the Highland frontier beyond Dunkeld.

Aquitania.   Aquitania, which was all the rest of the Gallic area, stood four-square—the Pictones dwelling round the rocky hill of Poitiers, one branch of the Biturges round the modern Bourges, another branch round Burdigala (Bordeaux), and the Arverni on the plateau; and the real foci were the lowland Bordeaux and the highland Augustonemetum (Clermont), the home of Vercingetorix. The Allier valley is still the best natural route across the Auvergne plateau, though the presence of coal and iron has made the Loire valley more important economically; and Bordeaux is still much the most important place on the lowland. Without a rival along miles of dune-fringed coast, protected by Landes and lagoons seaward and by the river landward, the effective meeting-place of five great river-valleys, and at the lowest point on the largest river at which it could be bridged, the city had every opportunity of monopolising the commerce of the whole basin, and of specialising in shipping the products of the mild Médoc peninsula to the Severn ports of England. In modern times it has come to control typical South American imports, such as rubber.

Brittany.   Seaward of 1° W. and 47° N. there is a land of ancient rock and even rainfall which enable the Bretons to raise, especially on the more fertile northern coast-lands, market-garden and dairy products that are much in demand in the neighbouring English market, especially early cauliflowers and potatoes from Cherbourg and St. Malo. The old rock extends into Anjou and Maine, where it is worked at Angers and other places in the Mayenne basin for such a typically Cambrian product as slate; but the area is specifically Breton—in history, politics, and creed. Storms and strong tides, fog-haunted islands and crumbling coasts—worked for such a typically Cornish product as china-clay, *e.g.* at Quimper —have isolated it seaward except to intruders of the Viking type; impervious rock, heavy rains, and salt winds have encouraged bogs inland and discouraged forest on the exposed parts, while remoteness from Paris has emphasised the isolation due also to unattractiveness. Internally, parallel belts of rugged upland and water-logged lowland divide it up into such isolated strips that even now three or four dialects can be distinguished. Along each coast facilities for fishing and for access inland raised little towns such as Quimper and Vannes, Morlaix and St. Brieuc; but, of course, Brest is the great centre. It has been hampered—almost as much as Lorient—by the restrictions of a naval station, but during the war it was made into a finely equipped modern harbour. Except for Fougères, with its boot industry, the only inland centre of importance is Rennes, where the relatively modern east-and-west route between the Noire and d'Arrée heights crosses the old north-and-south route of the Vilaine valley between Redon and Dinan, the Vilaine being navigable for the whole distance over which its valley forms the route, *i.e.* for the 90 miles from its sudden south-ward bend at Rennes. The town has a typical "confluence" site ; it is built of granite, and is a very important butter market—for London *via* St. Malo (cf. p. 192).

The less fertile archean rock of southern Brittany extends **Vendée.** southward into Vendée, where it rises in the forested terraces of the Bocage ("The Woodland") to the Gatine Hills, and sinks seaward beneath the "Breton" salt marshes—now largely drained and reclaimed. Protected by the scarp of the Gatine and by the marshes, amid a labyrinth of heaths and woods, the Vendéans had every opportunity of developing the political and religious individualism appropriate to—perhaps a product of—this hard and rugged rock, of resisting invasion by land or sea, and of affording an unbreakable line of communication between Nantes and La Rochelle. In modern times, owing to the existence of a small coal-field on the edge of the old rock, industries have been developed in La Roche, as under similar circumstances at Laval and Segre ; but the chief industrial centre is Nantes.

The group of islands in the river, which have caused the **Nantes.** transfer of so much commerce to the outport of St. Nazaire because they break the scouring power of the Loire, had an admirable strategic and commercial position in days of small vessels ; and the oceanic influence is so strong climatically that the town is a very busy textile centre. Standing between the coast and the archean rock, it has also a typical industry in the tinning of iron-plate and the making of tin boxes—both for sardines ("Le Croisic") and for the preserving of vegetables ; but the most important industry is the smelting and working of iron, *e.g.* at Nantes, St. Nazaire, and Trignac. Coal is easily imported, and there is a small coal-field and a considerable iron-field north-east of Nantes, the iron extending as far north as Redon and as far east as Angers.

Eastward and southward from the edge of the old rock, right up **Wheat** to the foot of the Ardennes and the Vosges, of the massif and **and Wine** the Pyrenees, stretch the great wheat and wine lands of France. **Lands.** Throughout the area the presence of early-summer rains and late-summer heat on the lowlands is favourable alike to the quantity and the quality of the wheat, though the proportion of gluten—like the capacity for effervescence in the grape—seems to have some obscure connection with low winter-temperatures, and therefore increases towards the north-east ; and the warm, dry slopes that flank the lowlands, form ideal sites for raising "wine," varying in character from the claret of the marine climate to the champagne of the continental. The dividing line is found in the "waist" of limestone and chalk lowland—pinched in between the granitic heights of Vendée and Marche—which gave wealth and military importance to the Counts of Poitou. To the north the sparkling wines of Saumur are inferior—except in rare years—because the marine influence is too much felt just before vintage, while to the south—only 250 miles to leeward (N.E.) of the Cantabrian crest (8700 feet)—the juice of the Cognac grape is unrivalled in the world.

Charente. No doubt the care and skill of the Charente people have been developed by generations of experience; but equal care and skill, on similar soil with similar vines elsewhere, do not yield the same result. For, though the rainfall is not heavy, the Atlantic influence so "filters" the sun's rays that the carbides of hydrogen are not oxidised, and the grape juice is matured in perfection—neither vinegary nor resinous. It is due to the organic ethers thus preserved that real brandy is "a Water of Life" in emergencies. The development of the industry was, no doubt, much aided by the river itself, which is navigable up to Angoulême, and which—by the relation of its upper course to the upper course of the Vienne—made Angoulême, on its river-girt height, important as a military post and Rochefort as a naval port. It was the clearness of the Charente stream and easy access to the decomposed granites of Limousin that gave Angoulême its fine-paper industry; and it was the partial monopoly of Rochefort for naval purposes that led to the development of Tonnay, farther up the river, as a brandy-shipping port. The old strategic value of the marsh-girt hill at Rochefort has, however, been discounted by the winding channel and shifting bar of the Charente estuary; and, on the other hand, the deepening of the La Pallice harbour must direct old-established currents of trade to Rochelle both from Bordeaux—where the difficulty of river-navigation causes delay, and from St. Nazaire—where delay is caused by frequent fogs.

Aquitaine. All Poitou was within the frontiers of Aquitaine, but the typical part of Aquitaine was the great Tertiary basin of Guienne and Gascony. This suggests at once a division into a rich agricultural belt in the north and a poor pastoral belt in the south, the one ending seaward in the Médoc peninsula and landward in the tobacco-fields that stretch from Perigueux (famous for its patés and its truffles) to Montauban, and including the prune orchards of Agen and Cahors (also famous for truffles), while the other ends seaward in the Landes and landward in the valley of Toulouse, famous for its draught-oxen. But the old poverty and the debatable position between France and Spain which made the "Gascon," like his Béarn kinsmen, an adventurer, are alike things of the past. About four-fifths of the total area of dunes (250,000 acres) has been made productive, and now forms the largest continuous forest in

France. Inside the natural dunes is a wall of artificial dunes, planted with sand-binding grass; and then to leeward of the double fence the maritime pine flourishes, forming an absolute protection to the interior, *e.g.* the Graves vineyards—though the growth of the trees on the windward side is rather stunted—and yielding a fine supply of turpentine and timber (*e.g.* pit-props and telegraph-poles). The great fan of calcareous clay from the Pyrenees, which once favoured an independent Armagnac, is now famous for its "brandy"; and tourists have brought prosperity to Bayonne and Dax, Tarbes and Pau. The generic name for all the torrents that built up the fan is *Gave*; but the one on which Lourdes and Pau stand is known specially as The Gave. Toulouse, as the landward focus of Aquitaine, held the balance between Gascony and Guienne, and became a great wheat and wine (and tobacco) market; and its position between the Albi and Rodez coal-fields and the iron and manganese of the Pyrenees is reflected in its foundries and metal industries. Its position on the right bank of the river gave it originally the protection of the marsh which accumulated within the concave curve.

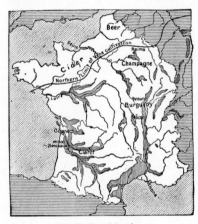

Distribution of the vine.

The wheat and tobacco of the upper basin of the Garonne give place to wine and maize in the lower basin, the area supplying a large proportion of the wine—only 2 or 3 per cent of the whole—which can be classed above *vin ordinaire*. Soil and situation are of prime importance, the Garonne wines being better than the Dordogne wines. The Médoc is slightly more marine in climate than Graves and Sauternes; and the Haut-Médoc clarets are grown on the slopes of Margaux, Lafite, Latour, etc., while the Graves wines are grown on the flat sandy lands ("Landes"), and Sauternes are grown landward of the Graves. These southern vineyards are equally famous for red wines and white, and the best of each, *e.g.* Haut-Brion and Yquem, are equal to the "first growths" of the north; but the latter are all red. The Dordogne wines, *e.g.* St. Emilion, are "hill" wines of cheaper varieties; and for 1,000,000 gallons of "classified" there are 4,000,000 of "bourgeois" and 100,000,000 of *vin ordinaire*.

Like the Tertiary basin of Bordeaux, that of Paris is flanked—though much more continuously—by rings of chalk and limestone,

"The
Garden of
France." both covering a much larger area in the basin of the Seine than in
that of the Loire.   But between the two great northward bends of
the Loire, near Orleans and Angers—shut in by the dry limestone hills
of Maine and Berry—the Cretaceous and Tertiary elements are so
well mixed, and have been so much enriched for centuries by river-
floods, that the area has come to be called "the Garden of France."
To leeward of the ancient rock, which reaches in the forested
Monts des Avaloirs of north-west Maine the highest point in all
north-western France (c. 1400 feet), as to leeward of similar rock
in Cornwall and Wales, the "garden" begins as a fruit-garden, the
valley of the Mayenne being famous for its apples and its cider.
The corresponding valley of the Indre in Berry is almost as famous
for its chestnuts.   In each basin, below the hard ancient rock, there
are bare limestone hills, which make admirable sheep-pastures;
indeed, parts of Berry carry 20 sheep to the acre, and Châteauroux
has an old, but still busy, cloth industry.   All the rest of the area
in question is very fertile, especially in the "Champagne" between
the Cher and the Indre, and it formed the great bread and wine
land of Medieval France.   As it also gave one of the most
important lines of movement, and as the most important part of the
route—between Orleans and Tours—was exceedingly picturesque,
e.g. the riverside cliffs between Blois and Tours, it came under
close settlement in very early times, though large patches of forest
still survive.   It seems mainly due to these conditions that it is so
markedly "old-fashioned" in many ways, e.g. in its typical "old"
textiles (linen and wool)—linen specially at Le Mans and woollen
at Châteauroux—and in the survival of antiquated methods of
farming, so that the yield of the various crops is relatively low.

Anjou.   The survival of these industries in modern times has been
helped by the distribution of patches of coal near the edge of the
old rock, e.g. between Angers and Cholet and near La Flêche.   Le
Mans—with a typical bell-foundry industry, dependent originally on
the tin and copper of the old rock—has more importance than La
Flêche only because, as the head of navigation on the Sarthe, it was
the capital of the old province of Maine; Angers makes linen and
woollen fabrics like the *challies* which take their name from Cholet,
but is better known for its slate-quarries and market-gardens.   Its
economic development was, however, retarded by its political and
strategic importance as the capital of the Counts of Anjou—which
exposed it to serious danger from invasion up the Loir, as well
as in later times from Huguenots and Vendéans.   So far as one
may press a connection between the hard old rock and militant
individualism in creed or politics, it would be significant that Angers
is within reach of slate-quarries and that a typical industry at
Saumur, as at Nantes, is the making of tin-plate.   Saumur—an
island town at the confluence of the Thonet with the Loire—had

been an isle of refuge for centuries before it became the metropolis
of French Protestantism; indeed, its name is probably a corruption
of *Salvus Murus* ("Safe Wall"), and the sides of both river-valleys
are honeycombed with caves.

The Seine portion of this "Paris" basin may itself be divided **Seine**
into two areas by the line north of which climatic or economic **Basin.**
reasons make the cultivation of the vine unprofitable.   This line is
marked very clearly by the water-parting between sea-ward and
Seine-ward streams, *e.g.* between Somme and Oise; and south of it
there is the same succession of Tertiary basin, chalk scarp, and
limestone scarp, from west to east of the Seine basin, as there is
from east to west of the Thames basin, making it naturally an area
of wheat and wine, pasture and stone-quarries—the freestone being
specially important just north of Paris itself and just south of
Fontainebleau (cf. the "Bath" stone of Caen and Bayeux).   The
chalk downs are naturally as favourable to sheep[1] as the heavy
"bottoms" are to cattle, and the ovine population is very large;
but the distribution of both sheep and cattle is practically determined
by economic considerations, *e.g.* the demand for milk and mutton in
the densely peopled "Isle of France."   Both are, therefore, largely
stall-fed, and so the mass of the sheep are found, not where the
pasture is really most favourable, but where there are most agricultural bye-products (*e.g.* trefoil, lucerne, etc.), *i.e.* in the famous
wheat-lands of Beauce and Brie.   The best cattle area is in the
heavier rainfall to windward of the sheep—in Perche.

As in the Thames basin, the steep scarp of the chalk uplands **"Cham-**
faces away from the centre of the basin; and this has important **pagne"**
results, strategic and economic.   Those near Paris, like somewhat **Lands.**
similar positions near London, offer special facilities for defending
the metropolitan area from attack from the continental side; those
farther away, especially in Champagne, supply the two great requirements of the vine in the northern hemisphere: (1) a slope of 30°
to 45° between the actual terraces on which the vines are mostly
planted, and (2) a south-eastern aspect, so as to catch the maximum
of sunshine in the late autumn.   Laon—itself on a limestone hill
—and Soissons (Augusta Suessionum), Reims and Epernay, control
gaps in the inner chalk ring, the Aisne gap being the most important,
while Sedan and Verdun, Chalons (sur-Marne) and Troyes control
gaps in the limestone ring, the Seine gap giving an important
commercial connection *via* the Langres plateau with Dijon, while
the Marne gap leads to the "Toul Gate" of Lorraine.   Here, as
beyond the Cotswolds, we have an industrial area—specialising in
hardware to the north, where Longwy and Briey have rich deposits
of iron, and in textiles to the south, where Epinal and St. Die have

---

[1] These are of "English" breeds in the north of France, and of merino type in
the south.

water-power from the forested Vosges. Between the two areas, which are linked together naturally by the navigable Moselle, Nancy has the additional advantage of rich beds of rock-salt, and has developed very important industries, in iron and textiles, chemicals and glass (cf. the Dombasle chemicals and Baccarat plate-glass).

Moselle Iron-field. The industrial development in this district has been very marked in recent years, partly in connection with better use of water-power, but mainly in connection with the mining and smelting of iron, the output of Meurthe-et-Moselle in 1911 being two-thirds of the total for France ; and the latter involves some difficult problems. For the only ore used till lately was of a silicious type found on the Luxemburg frontier, *e.g.* at Longwy and Villerupt, or round Nancy itself; and, as a matter of fact, the geological expert who reported on the proposed frontier-line before the Treaty of Frankfurt, included "the totality of the ferruginous basin" in German Lorraine. But later large quantities of more calcareous ore were found in the marshy area round Briey and Hornècourt, *i.e.* immediately in front of Metz. Like the rest of the Lorraine ore, it is rather "rich" in phosphorus; but it is also rich in metal (40 p.c.), and the amount of lime (up to 16 p.c.) makes it easy to work and to fuse. The two great difficulties are fuel and transport. Neither France nor Belgium can spare much coal, and the supply from the German mines has been always very precarious, both for purely political reasons and because of the control of the German Colliery Syndicate by the German Metallurgical Syndicate. For strategical reasons, too, the means of communication on the French line of approach to Metz are naturally limited. These are the conditions underlying the regular exchange of fuel and metal between the Tyne ports and French Lorraine.

The war has, of course, made considerable changes. Altogether Lorraine contains 42 p.c. of the iron-ore reserves of Europe, Sweden coming next with only 12 p.c. ; and that puts France in this respect into much the same position in the Old World as the United States hold in the New World. These "minette" ores of Lorraine do not average more than 38 p.c. of metal, while the U.S.A. ores average 50 p.c. ; but the change of ownership means not only that Germany has lost over two-thirds of her pre-war supplies, but also that France has acquired all the admirably equipped furnaces and mills. Thus France, which was of first-rate importance in the pre-war metal market only for antimony and aluminium, is now of still greater importance for iron.

The Coke Problem. This is far from being the only great gain even in the matter of minerals ; for she added to her deficient supply all the large Seille salt-field, the valuable oil-wells of Pechelbronn, and the Wittelsheim potash deposits—the greatest known in the world except those at Stassfurt. Not only so ; but she also added 1,900,000 to her population, including such a large body of skilled textile workers

that she increased her total "cotton capacity" by 27 p.c. for
spinning, 36 p.c. for weaving, and 100 p.c. for dyeing and bleaching and printing.   Moreover, as this Alsace industry is based
mainly on water-power, the annual 17 or 18 million tons of the
Saar coal mines—given to France in compensation for the German
destruction of French mines—can be devoted entirely to the
Lorraine iron-works.   But even in 1913 the Saar mines could
supply only 15 p.c. of the coke needed, and the French mines only
12 p.c., while 69 p.c. came from Westphalia.   For this the French
had to pay 13 francs per ton more than the Germans paid, and
12 francs more than we did; at the pit-head their own coal cost
40 p.c. more than ours, and 20 p.c. more than the German coal.
This meant an extra burden of 16 francs per ton for pig-iron.   The
fundamental facts remain unaltered to-day except that now Germany's
need of iron-ore is as great as the French need of coke; and the
problem ought not to be insoluble in a country with 7000 miles
of inland waterways, largely concentrated in its north-eastern
quadrant.   The Lorraine mines produced 3,000,000 tons in 1925.

Alsace-Lorraine is essentially a double area, with the crest of Alsace-
the Vosges as the natural division.   Lorraine falls in more or less Lorraine.
gentle terraces westward, while Alsace falls abruptly eastward, and
the average temperature to leeward (*e.g.* Strasbourg) is slightly
higher than to windward (*e.g.* Metz), while the average rainfall is
slightly lower—this being reflected in the greater area of forest on
the Lorraine slopes of the Vosges and the greater area of vineyards
in Alsace.   The Saar valley, with some coal of its own (at Forbach)
and easy access by water to the Saarbrücken coal-fields, has specialised
in glass and earthenware, *e.g.* at Saargemünd (cf. the Hagenau
earthenware); and it also benefits from the Marne-and-Rhine Canal,
which crosses the river at Saarburg,—the permanence of the control
exercised here by the Zabern Pass being reflected in the series of
historic battles fought round the old site of Pfalzburg (pfalz—Latin
palatium).   Between the Saar and the Moselle the barren plateau,
which includes the valley of the Seille, contains the valuable salt-
bed of Château Salins (cf. the chemical industry of St. Avold);
the soil and climate in the Moselle valley itself have greatly
encouraged intensive agriculture; and the Saar coal-field is known
to extend some distance into Lorraine.   The subdivisions of Alsace
are very different.   The western part includes the mass of the
Vosges, with an important "alp" dairy industry (cheese); the
east is a typical part of the Rhine valley-plain, largely forested;
and the Ill valley, which separates forested plain from forested
heights, is rich in water-power, it has a relatively high humidity
favourable to textile work, and it has always enjoyed certain commercial advantages from its position between France, Germany,
and Switzerland, and from its easy access to the Rhine.   Mulhouse

and Colmar are textile centres on the Rhine-and-Rhone Canal at the foot of the Burgundy Gate and in the potash district.

Stras-bourg and Metz.   Strasbourg ("The Castle by the Road"—from Paris to Vienna) has a very typical site, and has had a very typical history. It is not on the "turbulent" Rhine, but a few miles up the Ill, at its confluence with the Breusch, and only 2 or 3 miles west of the Rhine; and, as this strong military position happens also to be just opposite the Zabern Pass across the Vosges, the French were able to bind the city to France by the Rhine-and-Marne Canal to the Seine as well as by the Rhine-and-Doubs Canal to the Rhone. The Romans had used the same position for the collection of tribute—at *Argentoratum*, thus laying the foundation of the banking interest in the Middle Rhine basin; during the latter Middle Ages it was one of the most influential cities in the empire; and to-day, with improved access to the Rhine, it is a really important industrial and commercial centre, with a busy trade in agricultural products (including the famous *pâtés de foie gras*). Metz, too, was a Roman centre, and was provided by the Romans with the system of military roads (radiating to Trèves, Verdun, Rheims, Toul, Langres, and Strasbourg) to which it owed much of its subsequent importance, under its bishops and as a free imperial city. Its site, like that of Strasbourg, is on a fertile carse—between the Seille and the Moselle; and, as a fortress, down to 1870 it had never been taken in battle, —hence its title of *La Pucelle*. But, while Metz has been purely military, Strasbourg has had also economic importance; and this is likely to increase, especially during the time (7 years) that it holds the Baden port of Kehl.

Canal *v.* Rail   Obviously, canals have not the strategic disadvantages of railways; and this consideration underlies the relative importance of the two in north-eastern France, and must be kept in mind in comparing relative cost of transport. The State maintains all the waterways free of toll, but admits that the total net cost of water transport is higher than that of rail transport. At the same time, encouraged by relief and rainfall, it has spent infinitely more on canals in the two great centres in the north and north-east than on any others; and the result may be seen in the percentage of "first-class" navigation on the rivers. Even in 1913 the percentage of "first-class" depth (6½ feet) was exceedingly high :—

Northern :			North-Eastern :		
Lys,	45 out of	45 miles	Saone,	234 out of	234 miles
Scarpe,	41 ,,	41 ,,	Marne,	114 ,,	114 ,,
Scheldt,	39 ,,	39 ,,	Aisne,	37 ,,	37 ,,
Aa,	18 ,,	18 ,,	South-Western :		
Western :			Garonne,	96 out of	289 miles
Loire,	35 out of	452 miles	Dordogne,	26 ,,	167 ,,
Vilaine,	31 ,,	91 ,,	Adour,	21 ,,	72 ,,
			Charente,	16 ,,	108 ,,

It is not possible, however, to press the figures—for two reasons. On the one hand, France is so largely self-supporting that her internal trade cannot fairly be compared either with her external trade or with the internal trade of a country like our own ; and, on the other hand, relief and structure account for some of the glaring contrasts. For instance, precipitation on the central massif is "held up" for weeks in winter as snow and ice, and does not escape to the Loire until it receives the warmth that is brought by *rain*-bearing winds, so that the river practically gets two floods at once. Contrariwise, in months of maximum plant-energy and maximum evaporation, the fissured limestone above Orleans "masks" a flood altogether ; and in August the river is sometimes a series of practically stagnant and actually discontinuous pools.

The Channel lands, eastward of the old rock, while having **Channel** marked unity of climate, may be roughly divided into an eastern **Lands.** area of agriculture and industries and a western area of pasture and commerce ; but there are obvious exceptions — economic and otherwise, and they are increasing. For instance, Normandy is as famous for its apples and cider as for its cattle and horses, its butter and "Camembert" cheese ; Bayeux and Alençon have been famous for lace for centuries, while recently the Orne basin has been one of the chief French sources of iron-ore. On the other hand, the amount of waste-products in the east, *e.g.* from beet-sugar and oil-crushing works, has enabled the demand for milk for the dense population to be supplied by stall-fed cattle ; and the commercial centres on the Seine, *e.g.* Rouen and Elbeuf, have had every opportunity for maintaining—in a climate favourable to all textile work—old woollen industries (cf. Lisieux and Falaise) or developing new cotton industries (cf. Louviers and Évreux), both based on easy import of coal and raw materials. Similar, but slightly inferior, facilities on the Somme have made Amiens also an important textile centre, its modern development being based on its old wool industry—the principle of "pile"-weaving (for carpets) being applied to both silk (velvets) and cotton (fustians, *i.e.* corduroy) ; but the city has always had political importance, commanding the great bend on the Somme half-way between Paris and Calais. It was this, added to its safety—protected on islands in the river and by the surrounding peat-bogs—that made it a suitable capital for Picardy, as it was the inferiority of the Somme that prevented it being superseded by Abbeville seaward or by any town landward.

Rouen was in a very different position. No doubt the island- **Rouen.** centred site in its amphitheatre of hills, 70 miles from the mouth of the river, made it a place of great importance by sea and land in early days ; but the deepening of the Seine up to Paris and the deep draught of modern vessels have ruined it as a harbour, though it must always—apparently—be the seaward focus of the great railway and canal systems of the whole Paris basin, and therefore attracts such a stream of colliers that it returns a very heavy tonnage for vessels entering the port.

Le Havre. The Lower-Seine Department is a sort of neutral ground, with the arable land of the Caux and the pastures of Bray, the industries of Rouen and the commerce of Le Havre, "*the* Harbour" of the whole Seine basin. But even here modern development has depended on the river, because the river means Paris. Purely seaside places such as St. Valery and Dieppe may have packet-

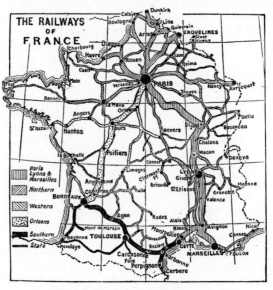

The width of the lines indicates their relative importance.

stations and export flints,[1] but their prosperity comes from being —like Trouville—bathing-resorts for Paris. As nearness to the ocean became important, Harfleur was bound to give place to Le Havre ; and the value of the trade from the coal-field—in this only reflecting the overwhelming superiority of the right-bank over the left-bank tributaries of the Seine—was so enormously greater than that from the west that Harfleur had no chance from landward, nor had it the same chance as Havre seaward for "anticipating" trade on its way to Antwerp and other ports farther east.

Influence of Paris. But everything here was controlled by Paris. Mackinder has pointed out how the influence of Paris effectually prevented the rise of any other really large city in the basin, but directly encouraged

[1] About 350,000 tons a year were exported from Caen before the War.

the growth of good-sized towns at "equal" distances in all directions, *e.g.* Havre and Rouen, Amiens and Reims, Troyes and Orleans. Nothing is more typical of the modern aspect of this than the importance of Paris as a railway-junction, on the one hand, and, on the other hand, the concentration of the *cotton* industry on the Lower Seine. In early days, no doubt, the variety of minor natural regions, *e.g.* the chalk hills of Artois or the fluvial basin of Picardy, favoured the existence of several small political units; but the variety of relief over the whole area is too small, and the unity of climatic control is too marked, to have allowed these units to survive. In such a geographic environment, Roman ideas of centralisation could only flourish profoundly, and so exaggerate the natural tendency of it, as focused at Paris. The history even of small towns, such as the Beauce grain-market of Chartres and Fontainebleau on its famous "glass"-sands (worked also at Nemours), yields convincing evidence of the overwhelming influence of Paris; and, farther afield still, Crécy and Agincourt flank essentially "the Paris road," while the whole 18 miles of navigation on the little Aa from St. Omer to the sea below Gravelines has long been "first-class."

The damp climate of the eastern Channel lands, with its even **Lille Coal-** rainfall, is more favourable to roots and "grasses" than to fruit and **field.** grain, though the hardier cereals flourish; mangolds and potatoes, flax and colza, are largely grown, but sugar-beet is the great product. This is partly because of the large demand for sugar in the more "Teutonic" parts of France, but mainly because of the relation of the coal-field to the treatment of the roots whether for sugar or for alcohol; and it is important that the waste-product guarantees the milk-supply of the area, and that the large number of dairy cattle guarantees abundance of manure for the beet-fields. The coal-field lies partly in the Pas de Calais, north of Arras, *e.g.* at Lens and Liévin, Béthune and Brouay, and partly in the Nord, especially north-west of Valenciennes and south-east of Douai, *e.g.* at Anzin and Aniche. Sugar-beet is largely grown in both departments, but still more largely where land is slightly less valuable—in the department of the Aisne.

The textile industries are based on a favourable climate, **Textile** abundance of coal, hereditary skill that is as typical of French **Indus-** Flanders as of Belgian Flanders, and excellence of local raw **tries.** materials (wool and flax), though the mass is now imported, *e.g.* both wool and linseed coming from the Argentine. There is great division of labour, *e.g.* Calais and Arras, like Douai and Valenciennes, specialising in lace,—Cambrai and St. Quentin in table-linen,—Fourmies and Croix, Roubaix and Tourcoing, in woollens. Lille is the great centre, with a population of just over 200,000 and with all the typical industries, especially cotton (cf. St. Quentin) and linen (cf. Armentières), and metallurgical (cf. Vimen) and chemical (cf. Chauny); and Dunkirk—about 50 miles from Lille—is the great outlet, being now only below Marseilles and Havre amongst the real seaports of France, with a harbour able to accommodate ships up to 20,000 tons (cf. p. 205).

Burgundy. Once over the Langres plateau—by one of the limestone valleys, *e.g. via* Chaumont and Langres or Auxerre and Avalon—the Côte d'Or scarp has the south-eastern exposure so favourable to the vine; and here, where the sheltered Saone basin gets "baked" in summer, the famous Burgundy wines are produced, especially between Dijon and Châlons, *e.g.* at Beaune. The Beaujolais wines, *e.g.* from Mâcon and Villefranche, are of the same type. Here, too, the oolitic limestone contains—on the side away from the frontier—both coal and iron round Le Creusot (cf. the Langres cutlery). The coal was worked here long before the iron, and even drew for a time the famous Sèvres works from Paris; but a century ago the place changed its name from Charbonnière to Le Creusot, and now has the largest iron industry in France, including both ordnance and locomotives. In the Jura oolite there is no coal, but the industries there are mainly of "Swiss" character, *e.g.* the watches and clocks of Besançon and Montbéliard and the mathematical instruments of Morez and St. Claude, though heavier work is done along navigable water, *e.g.* at Dôle.

Lyons Gorge. The essential conditions of the Saone basin are more or less repeated between the narrowing of the valley just below Lyons and its opening out again just above Montélimar; for the lowland strip is flanked westward by the mineral-bearing scarp of the massif, rich in coal and iron round St. Étienne, and eastward by the Savoy Alps, with their abundance of water-power. The latter, especially along the Mont Cenis railway in the Arc valley, is being largely used in the manufacture of aluminium; but it is also available for the textile industries of Grenoble and Chambéry (cf. Briançon and Annecy), though kid gloves are a more characteristic product of these hill towns. The typical textile is, of course, silk, the Rhone valley supplying France with about one-tenth of the silk which is used in the country, and the water being of a quality admirably suited to the dyeing of silk. Hitherto Lyons, the great centre—with a total product valued in 1913 at about £16,000,000, mainly pure silk tissues and gauzes—has depended on the coal of St. Étienne, itself a large producer of silk ribbons and trimmings; but now a great deal of electricity is being transmitted to Lyons by overhead wire from Alpine waterfalls. Indeed, one of the chief features of modern development in the area is the utilisation of water-power, especially in the Savoy and Dauphiné Alps—both locally, *e.g.* in mines and quarries or chemical and metal industries, and for transmission; and France uses now more water-power than any other European country.

The whole land from the Maritime Alps to the Poitevin marsh once was called Provence, and all its people spoke what was essentially the *langue d'oc.* This implied, and actually involved, a unity of political sentiment and a unity of religious development which were based on a rich variety of influences—Greek and Roman, Spanish and Saracen — unified in passing through the funnel by which they entered the area, as the Mohawk-Hudson valley unified the medley of races that rushed into the United States in the early days of colonisation. The heart of the old Provence, in its widest sense, like the perfection of the *langue d'oc,* was in the limited area of this funnel to which we still give the unofficial names of Languedoc and Provence; and to a historic unity of political and religious influences they add a climatic unity —of summer - drought — which gives them a further unity of economic interest. The total result is that naturally the region is extraordinarily self-contained; it produces nearly everything that is characteristic of France, and scarcely any industry is limited to any one part of the region, the only vital distinction being that Languedoc is a lowland backed by highland, while Provence is a highland backed by lowland. This means that, as we have seen, the best harbours must be in Provence, so that such an industry as shipbuilding may be confined to, *e.g.,* Marseilles and Toulon (La Seyne); and that the narrow coast-land of the Riviera beneath the overhanging scarp of the highland must be well protected climatically, *e.g.* from the mistral, so that typical invalid resorts, *e.g.* Hyères and Cannes, Nice and Mentone, may also be confined largely to Provence.

Old Provence.

The whole coast-line produces salt, *e.g.* at Hyères, on the Étang de Berre, in the Pyrenean lagoons; and, where the salt-works are very conveniently placed for transport, as along the main branch of the Rhone in the Camargue below Arles, there are very important chemical-works, producing *e.g.* carbonate of soda for the soap-works or caustic soda for the aluminium-works. Bauxite actually takes its name from the Baux hills above Arles; and the bauxite and aluminium industry is making enormous strides, not only amongst the lignite mines of the Bouches-du-Rhône between Aix and Marseilles, but also on the Alpine torrents between Draguignan and St. Raphael. Metallurgical progress in Languedoc is less rapid, mainly because the mineral-bearing scarp there is inland, and so transport is dearer; but there is an important coal-field between Alais and Bessèges, where the Gard basin yields both iron and zinc, and the Eastern Pyrenees are a very valuable source of iron-ore. Languedoc has also,—with great facilities for transport westward (by the Canal du Midi) as well as

Provence and Languedoc.

northward,—a large area of lowland, so that its agricultural output is larger than that of Provence. The two together are essentially a " land of wine and oil "—the wine mainly in the west and the oil in the east, the one merging southward in the market-gardening of Roussillon while the other merges southward in the flower-growing of the Var; and both are famous for their poultry[1] and for their fruit—grape and olive, peach and apricot, mulberry and almond.

Provençal Olives. The connection of the olive with the flower-growing, as that of the market-gardening with the wine-making, is by no means accidental. Both the olives and the flowers need a light and fertile soil, with shelter from the cold north winds and exposure to the southern sea ; but the character of the soil otherwise, the latitude, the altitude, even the distribution of rainfall, are relatively of no moment. For instance, the northward limit of the olive has no connection with latitude, little with altitude—up to 2500 feet or more, and not much with seasonal rainfall, for it flourishes outside the limits of normal " Mediterranean " rainfall ; but it must be protected against N., N.W., and N.E. winds. The centre of the olive trade of all France is the centre of the flower trade—Grasse, though the actual market has been moved to Nice; and it is most characteristic that the Parma violets—which " open the season "—are raised under the shade of olives and "citrons," that the most important single product is orange-blossom, that the delicate perfume of the roses (the next in importance) is due to the pollen carried by the bees to the rose-beds from the orange-groves, and that the olive — which " ends the season "—should be the basis, with the vine, of the whole scent industry. For no animal fat seems to be as " pure " as a vegetable fat, and no scent can be trusted to remain " true " unless the alcohol used is of grape-origin. When true essence of violets is quoted in Grasse at 100 guineas an ounce, it becomes obvious why such an enormously more costly product as attar of roses is seldom made in the Var valley, but only in countries where the value of human life is more or less at a minimum (cf. p. 143).

Languedoc Wine. The wine industry in Languedoc is more related to soil than to climate directly, and is more noted for quantity than quality, whereas exactly the opposite is true of the olive-oil of Provence. As a rule, more than one-third (*c.* 400,000,000 gallons) of the total wine-crop of France comes from Hérault and Aude, the former producing twice as much as the latter ; and, while the typical Provençal culture is on a sheltered terrace, that of Lower Languedoc is on an open plain of pebbles and clay mixed with the " lagoon " sand. The effect upon the distribution of population is most marked, especially between Montpellier and Béziers. The density approaches 300 per square mile ; and landward of the Étang de Thau, 95 p.c.

---

[1] The poultry of the Bresse, *e.g.* round Bourg, are said to be the best in France.

of it is "continuous," only the odd 5 persons in every 100 living
"scattered."

In both provinces there are important textile industries, mainly **Textiles.**
silk—Montpellier having an Institute of Sericulture—but also
woollen, the sheep of the reclaimed plains of Crau and Camargue
producing a very fine quality of wool. Relatively more attention is
paid to wool in the west, *e.g.* at Nîmes and Béziers, with their easy
access to the sheep-pastures of the Pyrenees and Cévennes as well as
of the Crau and Camargue,[1] and to silk in the east, *e.g.* at Avignon
and Montélimar. There is also division of labour between various
centres; for instance, while St. Étienne and St. Chamond specialise
in ribbons and trimmings, and Lyons is at once the great market
and the maker of " broad goods," Avignon and the " Alpine " towns
specialise in " light goods." Gloves are a typical product on both
sides of the valley, *e.g.* at Annonay and at Romans.

The two great foci of the whole Rhone valley, Lyons and Mar- **Mar-**
seilles, are, therefore, no longer rivals. Both owe their specific **seilles.**
industries, in silk and oil, to natural products of the Rhone valley,
the mulberry and the olive; but the industries of both have long
ago outgrown the home supplies of raw material, and Marseilles has
thus become a large importer of raw silk for Lyons and of oil-seeds
and copra for its own soap, candle, and allied industries. Other
imported raw materials, *e.g.* hides and sugar, are the basis of important industries in and near Marseilles; and the great port controls
the export of all the typical products of its hinterland except the
wine, which is attracted to Cette by the Bordeaux canal.

The essential prosperity of these industries in modern times has **Central**
depended on the coal-fields that skirt the old rock of the massif, but **Plateau.**
these are not confined to the eastern scarp. Those at Creusot and
Blanzy, St. Étienne and Bessèges, are specially rich and accessible;
but others are found on almost every side and along the line of
recent disturbance. The largest fields are where this line of disturbance emerges from the massif northwards and southwards, and in
each case the field is eastward of the line, *e.g.* between Commentry
and Moulins, Aubin and Decazeville; and there are small lateral
fields, *e.g.* that of Ahun, which supplies the carpet-factories of Aubus-
son, and that of Beaune, which supplies—*via* the Allier—the rubber-
works of Clermont (Ferrand). There are, therefore, busy industries
on several parts of the plateau outside the St. Étienne district, *e.g.*
textiles at Moulins and Roanne, hardware at Montluçon and Camaux,
and—on the more exposed aspects, where the granite is more quickly
decomposed—porcelain, *e.g.* at Limoges and Nevers. The quality
of the stone on the outskirts of the massif is reflected, *e.g.*, in the
lithographic industry of Issoudun, the cutlery of Moulins and Chatelle-

---

[1] A large number of the sheep are migratory—moving in summer up to the
Cévennes.

rault, as the vegetation and fauna are reflected in, *e.g.*, the woollens of Châteauroux and the gloves of Tulle.

Industrial "Indivi-dualism." Except for the motor industry at Clermont—a typical modern industry for an old transport centre that has easy access to a rubber-port—these are mainly old industries of an area with a fertile agricultural valley and rich pastures on the rainy volcanic land below its highest peaks. The more modern industries sprang up on the richer coal-fields in the low fertile valley to the east. But both valleys were old lines of movement, and drained the surplus population from a relatively barren area to greater opportunities, seasonal or otherwise, elsewhere. Such opportunities were more and more of an industrial kind; and the whole basis of French industries is individuality. The manual skill and the natural taste of the people enable them to specialise in the production of artistic and highly finished products, the high price and the "personal" individuality of which keep them more or less outside competition, and so give them a constant, if somewhat limited, market. When the distribution of the coal-fields is related to the sources from which the typical industries have drawn their supplies of extra labour, the inference seems irresistible that this individuality has a direct relation to the area of archean core and to the influence of the old *langue d'oc.*

Agricul-tural "In-dividual-ism." The agricultural individualist has been even more important, especially from the domestic point of view. Nearly 95 p.c. of France is "productive," and of this more than 45 p.c. is actually cultivated, in farms averaging *c.* 30 acres and worked—with more industry than science—by the owner. He naturally thinks first of his own needs, with the result that in 1913 France was almost self-supplied with a necessary minimum of food, especially bread and sugar, and had a very well-balanced system of farming. While raising more wheat—half of it in the Paris basin—than any other European country except Russia, she did not neglect oats and rye, fruit and vegetables (for stock as well as people), sugar and stock (for food and other purposes). The devastation of the war has involved the temporary import of food, *e.g.* wheat and sugar—a vast proportion of the beet lands, as of the wool (81 p.c.) and flax (93 p.c.) spindles, being in the devastated area—and the foreign wine-market has shrunk greatly, *e.g.* in U.S.A.; but the farming is becoming more scientific, without losing its pivot in the peasant farmer. It is he that, in the last 100 years, has made the French, as a nation, at once intensely non-military, and yet willing to make any sacrifice to keep their sacred soil safe from the foreign invader.

CHAPTER XVI

BRITISH ISLES

MATHEMATICALLY, the British Isles are in the centre of all the land **World-** on the face of the earth; climatically, they occupy one of the most **Relation.** temperate areas; commercially, they are on the edge of the busiest ocean; geologically, they are on the shelf of the most advanced continent.   But their world-relation is perhaps best expressed historically; for their history represents a continuous series of adaptations to a progressively widening environment.   At the beginning of historic times they were on, or even just outside of, the margin of civilisation, while to-day they are in the centre of it; and thus they were the last important unit to be included in, and the first to be excluded from, the Roman Empire, while they are now the nodal objective of all the transcontinental railways that thread the vast Eurasian plain, and of all the Great-Circle routes that form the shortest links between the areas of densest population on the opposite sides of the North Atlantic.

In this development the controlling influence has been the **Ocean** ocean, and herein lay a unique opportunity.   For the ocean is **Influence.** the one great physical unit on the face of the earth; it implies the nearest approach to climatic unity; and so it made possible the political unit of the British Empire.   As it is also the ocean that has brought about the economic unity of the earth, and yet the mass of economic products are from the land, a site essentially between ocean and continent offered special facilities for its people to control the commerce of the world and to further the Brotherhood of Man.   In an unprejudiced survey it is scarcely possible to deny that England, in spite of all her faults, has been the mother of Modern Civilisation; nor is it a mere accident that practically the whole world measures longitude from Greenwich.

The most important consideration in the regional relation of the **Insu-** islands is probably the physical character of the Narrow Seas, and **larity.** then the insular freedom from extremes of climate; and the latter— so far as it can be regarded as independent of the former—has been historically the less important.   Indeed, it is scarcely possible to exaggerate the political importance of an island unit in early historic times; for the same conditions which guarantee strategic strength against external aggression, greatly favour both internal unity and that consciousness of race which is the basis of true patriotism, while insular inbreeding always tends to develop a plastic organism likely to present wide variations (cf. insular dialects), and therefore to make quick progress in civilisation. In the case of England, too, traffic on the mainland of Europe was so hampered by forest and marsh that in very early days it was driven on to the rivers or coastwise; that is to say, even the continental traffic was conducted by a medium in which an island race could most easily share (cf. p. 262).

The Narrow Seas. The most important feature of the Narrow Seas historically was their narrowness. England is closely akin in structure and relief to the neighbouring continental lands, and was likely to produce a similar type of people; but insularity was bound to cause some differentiation, and the one racial danger would have come from isolation. From this she was saved by the narrowness of the protecting seas, for she was always near enough to feel the full influence of her neighbours without becoming dependent on them. This was true in almost every side of her national life. Economically, English farmers could keep sheep—and so lay the foundations of the industrial development of the country—in days when war made sheep-farming almost impossible on the continent. Again, epidemics have—even in recent years—reached the opposite coasts, but have not crossed the sea; or, if they have crossed it, it has only been in a relatively feeble form. So, when the sea could not quite stop invasion, it delayed it considerably—in days when ships were too small for any large army to be suddenly transported across it; and it thus led to a useful variety of inflow and influence, distributed from different foci, *e.g.* Scandinavian from the north, Saxon and Danish from the east, Roman and Norman from the south.

Sea v. Land Front. The progressive narrowing, eastward and southward, on Dover narrowed the strategic front in such a way as to give maximum facilities for naval concentration; and it is this that has justified enormous expense in quite modern times on the construction of a great naval and commercial harbour on one of the worst natural sites for a harbour along the whole coast. The progressive widening to the Atlantic gave every encouragement for expansion over-seas, resulting in an extraordinary inflow of wealth and development of power; and much of the wealth from the wide ocean was spent across the Narrow Seas—in costly wars which kept the balance of power in Europe—while the rest of it fed home industries which had almost a monopoly of the world-market as long as our possible European rivals were hopelessly handicapped by the constant war. The greatest market for English wool in earlier days was within a few miles of Waterloo!

The narrowness of the British seas is due to causes which

practically also involved shallowness, and the latter has in turn **Shallow** involved several great advantages. For instance, it is the shallow- **Seas.** ness that protects our coasts from the influence of the deep, icy currents from the Arctic Ocean ; it is the main cause of the great fishing industries, on which our whole naval power has risen ; above all, it is responsible for the high tides which visit our estuaries. And these high tides were as useful for their motive power in the days of sailing-ships as they are now in carrying huge steamers far inland.

The actual coast-line is of a character which enables almost **Coast-** maximum use to be made of these conditions. It is so long and **line.** so much broken that there is no place in the whole country much more than 70 miles from tidal water ; it is so varied, in relation both to the land behind it and the sea in front of it, that it has encouraged useful — supplementary or complementary— variety of human activity ; and it is so developed as to give a maximum of good harbours *vis-à-vis*, as the Clyde and the Forth, the Mersey and the Humber, the Severn and the Thames. More-over, where a lowland has been submerged under a shallow en-croachment of the ocean,

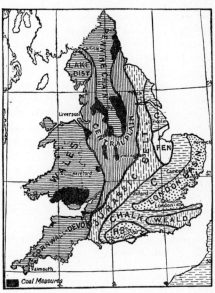

Natural divisions of England.

there must have been originally a complete river-system ; and its remnants are apt to be symmetrical, as the Thames is to the Rhine and Scheldt, the Humber to the Elbe and Weser, and the Solent to the Seine. It is not merely the particular feature that is repro-duced ; the whole area is strictly comparable, *e.g.* the Paris basin with the Hampshire basin or the polders of Holland with the "Holland" fen of Lincolnshire (cf. p. 211).

Isolated, then, from Europe by a shallow and narrow waterway, **Island** the British Isles were able to maintain their political independence ; **Group.** their safety not only kept them free from fear of invasion, and so from any need for military tyranny, but also so minimised the cost and amount of men and material needed for home defence as to leave a maximum of both for trade and empire over-seas. The definite frontier and small area compelled their people to recognise limitations, to realise themselves, to develop a national type, and that a plastic insular type.   The fact that their unit was a group of islands, not merely a single island, greatly encouraged individuality, independence, initiative ; and these were strengthened by the fact that the natural divisions of relief favoured the existence of three separate kingdoms in the largest island.   The culminating advantage was that the kingdom nearest to Europe was large enough and of the right physique to make eventually a homogeneous, firmly knit, strong leader, while the incoherent units of featureless plain in Ireland and intricate heights in Wales were in the background.

Surface v. Coast.   The character of the surface has an intimate relation to the variety of coast-line.   From a belt of hard old rock in the west, overlooking the Atlantic from a considerable height and carved by glaciation and exposure to the Atlantic into a bold and angular coast, largely of fiord type, Great Britain slopes down to an expanse of soft young rock in the east, which disappears gradually under a shallow and narrow sea.   Through this eastern coast, with its smooth and rounded outline, many rivers from the western heights carry out immense quantities of silt, with the accompanying organisms that make welcome food for fish.   And where there is no lack of fish food, there food-fish are not likely to be lacking.

Fish.   In these Narrow Seas the nature of the "ground" is equally favourable to the habits of the fish and the operations of fishing ; the nature of the water—especially its temperature and saltness, its shallowness and the action of the tides—is as favourable as that of the air above it, to a variety of fish life, *e.g.* migratory cold-loving cod and herring and delicate sedentary sole and plaice ; and their latitude coincides with the natural limits of most of the valuable food-fishes—cod and haddock not being important in European waters south of 50° N., soles and turbot being more or less confined to 50°–55° N., and mackerel being negligible north of 50° N.   The latter was peculiarly important in early days owing both to its normal distribution south of 50° N. and to its rapidity of movement. "Fast fish, fast boat," they say ; and it must never be forgotten that Drake and his Sea-Dogs came from the mackerel ports !

Physique.   In structure and relief the islands show great variety without undue complexity, the variety being emphasised by the small area ; they epitomise the geology of the world, and yet continue the simple feature-lines of Europe.   They thus present a variety of scenery and resources under conditions favourable to human activity, but have a structural unity which almost justifies their forming politically a united kingdom ; while the fact that they continue the feature-lines of Europe, facilitated the inflow of intruders and their movement across the whole group in the normal direction of those feature-lines, *i.e.* from north-east to south-west.

The nucleus of the whole area, if not actually the oldest part, **"Silur-** is the rim of slaty "Silurian" rock which is the base of most of the **ian"** land—in all the four kingdoms—that shuts in the Irish Sea. This **Nucleus.** is, historically, the real British area; its physical features, *e.g.* the Cambrian and Cumbrian Mountains, have Cymric names; its people are still typically Mediterranean—long-headed, but short and dark; its "native" languages show how its soft oceanic climate and relatively low relief favoured a uniform Mediterranean type of people at the expense of the more vigorous Roundheads who intruded from the "Alpine" grass-lands of the continent, but— like similar Roundheads elsewhere (cf. p. 80)—died out, leaving no traces except in their vigorous Keltic languages and in the round skulls of the pre-Christian burial barrows. As these languages are in no sense "native" either to the people or the place, and—like the minor Slav tongues of Eastern Europe (cf. p. 394)—are useless for purposes of world-commerce, it seems as futile to encourage them artificially on so-called patriotic grounds as it is certain that they will die out naturally on economic grounds.

This hard old rock is practically bounded northwards by a line **"Silur-** from Armagh to Dunbar and eastwards by one from the Bass Rock **ian"** to the Wrekin. It is typically slaty, as in the peaks of Skiddaw **Features.** and Saddleback and the Mourne Mountains, and is actually quarried for slate in Wales and Cumberland; it is mined, especially for lead, *e.g.* in the Lead Hills and the Isle of Man; its impervious strata, considerable height, and windward position combine to give it grand or beautiful "lake" scenery, *e.g.* in Cumberland and Wicklow —though in the latter except for Wicklow Head, which is slate, the rock is mainly igneous; the scenery is finest where there have been volcanic upheavals, as in Scafell and Helvellyn, Snowdon and Cader Idris; and the volcanic action, which was probably due to the amount of water embedded in the sedimentary "Silurian" rock, seems to have played some part in the damming of the glacial valleys, as in the case of Derwentwater and Windermere.

Almost all round this slaty nucleus, and penetrating through it **Carboni-** in some places to the Irish Sea, there is a belt of rock of carboni- **ferous** ferous age. It is mainly millstone grit (sandstone) and limestone; **Rock.** and, though south of the Bristol Channel and west of the Irish Sea there is little or no coal in it, the corresponding area in Great Britain has been the basis of all our modern industries and com- merce. Particular significance, therefore, must be attached to the fact that—before the development of the coal—it was one of the most backward parts of the country, as illustrated *e.g.* by the support given by its people against Constitutional Government in the Civil War; and, where it is entirely devoid of coal, it must be expected to be somewhat backward even now.

Red Sand-stone.   The actual coal-fields are closely associated with a ring of red sandstone, which is specially developed in three places—(1) on both sides of the Severn, almost from its source to its mouth; (2) on both sides of the Pennines from the Tyne round (southward) to the Eden, St. Bees' Head being a mass of New Red Sandstone; and (3) in the depression of Lowland Scotland north of the (Armagh)-Girvan-Dunbar line. This red sandstone, whether "Old" or "New," and whether coal-bearing or not, is very fertile; thus the Old Red is equally fertile whether associated with coal in the Clyde-and-Forth plain or dissociated from it in Strathmore, and the New Red is

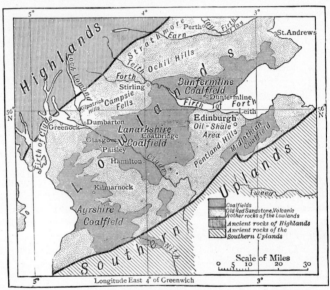

The midland valley of Scotland.

equally fertile whether associated with coal round the South Welsh and the South Pennine Mountains or dissociated from it in the Vale of York or the Vale of Taunton. Moreover, as its special value is for the production of milk (cf. Devon and Cheshire), our dense populations sprang up in places which were—or ought to have been—within easy reach of abundant supplies of good milk.

Coal-Measures.   The coal-measures themselves are largely sandstone-flags and fire-clay, and industrial development has been greatly facilitated by their relation to deposits of salt and iron. The richest coal-mines are found where the coal-measures are ranged round millstone grit, as in South Wales and the South Pennine counties; at important points in the line of the New Red Sandstone, e.g. Droitwich and Stafford, but especially along the Tees (Port Clarence and Middlesborough) and the Weaver and Wheelock (Northwich and Middlewich), there are most valuable salt-beds ; and the richest iron-fields are, or have been, found where the upper part of the so-called New Red Sandstone is represented by ridges of limestone, the source of flux for smelting purposes.

Roughly parallel with the eastern edge of the New Red Sand- **"Young"** stone from the Tees to the Exe run alternate belts of plain and **Rock.** ridge, of varied formation, but all "young"—lias, limestone, and chalk. The lias is rich in alum, *e.g.* near Whitby ; and its marlstone portions are equally rich in iron, *e.g.* in Lincolnshire and Northampton- shire ; the limestone contains, *e.g.* in the Bath "freestone," a building stone of great beauty, easily quarried and cut, and yet hardening on exposure to weather ; the chalk encloses, and holds in basins, the clays and more recent deposits which have been the basis of English agriculture. In this connection it is important that all these young ridges present a steep scarp to the north-west, *i.e.* the quarter from which they get much of their summer rain (cf. p. 56), but slope down gradually on the south-east to the Tertiary deposits.

But, as the sandstone ring merges south-eastward in softer and **Ancient** richer rock, so it merges north-westward, *i.e.* north of a line lying **Rock.** roughly between Londonderry and Montrose, in older and harder rock. This is not only the oldest and hardest, but also the highest and most northerly, formation in the whole country ; and, except for the Old Red Sandstone round the Moray Firth, it has little wealth other than its granite, and that has value only within easy access of water-carriage. This north-western oceanic quadrant, therefore, is also likely to remain backward, except so far as its water-power may be developed ; and in any case it must always present a marked contrast, with its moors and mountains, to the corn and cattle lands, the woods and orchards, of the south-eastern continental quadrant, which—in the days when "Agriculture was King"—was the gateway of civilisation for the whole country.

As the area north and west of the Exe-Tees line consists of very **Western** old and hard rock, it has weathered very slowly ; and, therefore—in **Heights.** spite of its age—it remains as the highest part of the country, broken by small areas of lowland which have been fertilised largely at the expense of the highlands above and around them. Its natural advantages would, at first sight, seem to be limited to easy access to the sea, abundance of water, and mineral wealth, especially in coal ; but these are conditions which have become progressively more and more favourable to density of population.

The ridged land south and east of the Exe-Tees line owes its **Eastern** low level to the fact that it consists of rock so young and soft that **Lowlands.** it has not been able to resist the various weathering agencies, even though these have been less violent than on the western margin of the country. This would have pushed the water-parting of the

country westward, even if the hard old rock had not had the higher
elevation originally ; and so the longer rivers must have flowed eastward towards the continent, and the larger amount of alluvium must
have been distributed over what was naturally the more fertile rock.
The more resistant parts of this, however, have survived as ridges of
limestone and chalk between the expanses of clay and other newer
material ; and they have a more or less uniform steepness of scarp
towards the north-west and a more or less uniform height.   The
Cotswold scarp has the same relation to the Avon as the Lincoln
Heights have to the Trent ; and it is the ends of the main limestone
and main chalk uplands that, in the Cleveland moors and Yorkshire
wolds, have carried the coast-line out eastward between the Humber
and the Tees.   The Trent and the Ouse meet so far inland, not

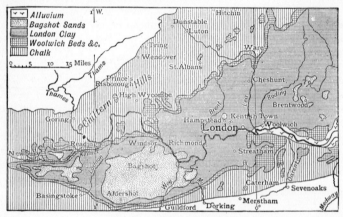

Structural map of the London basin.

because the Trent is controlled by the Lincoln Heights, but because
both are following—the one southward and the other northward—
the New Red Sandstone plain ; and evidence of the eastward
extension of the coast-line through the break in the main chalk
upland, between the East Anglian Heights and the Lincoln wolds,
is found in the silting up of the old harbours of Boston and King's
Lynn.

Tertiary Basins.   The glaciation which provided *e.g.* the boulder clay of the heavy
wheat-soils in East Anglia and the lime which lightened and enriched
that clay, was not extended south of the Thames ; and in this
southern unglaciated area the chalk uplands have a normal west-and-
east lie, not south-west and north-east.   And from the pivot of the
Wiltshire upfold the two chief downfolds have been filled up with
Tertiary materials to form the London and Hampshire basins.   The
acute-angled fan of " London clay " that spreads out eastwards from

Newbury represents the Tertiary estuary of the Thames ; the obtuse-angled fan of "Bognor clay" that spreads out southwards from Andover represents a similar formation of equal agricultural value.

The climate is of the most favourable "Atlantic" type (cf. p. 53), **Climate** but the "insular" freedom from extremes is not due to insularity *per se.* In the first place [see diagram on p. 238], the low-pressure systems which reach the islands about every ten days, on an average, the whole year through—though the interval is actually less in winter and greater in summer—follow frequently one of two tracks ; one is the "bay of warmth" which marks the beginning of the continental shelf, *i.e.* north-west of the Outer Hebrides, and the other is the English Channel. Obviously, when the Icelandic centre is dominant, *i.e.* in winter—when, too, the high pressure over Europe deflects warm winds northward (cf. p. 55)—this must mean very heavy rain in the British Isles, especially on the higher western parts. But as winds in a low-pressure system occupy in turn every point of the compass, rain can be brought by any wind ; the east coast may get purely cyclonic rains from an east wind. Indeed, the surest sign of rain over the Thames basin is the S.E. wind that marks the advanced "shoulder" of a low-pressure system that is working up channel.

High-pressure systems, on the other hand, do not "follow a **High-** track" at all ; they do not even "travel" as a rule, but only spread. **pressure** In summer high-pressure influences may spread, at all events to the **Systems.** south of the islands, from the Azores centre ; and then the air is refreshingly cool, both because it comes off the ocean and because it comes from a high-pressure centre. In winter high-pressure influences may spread, at all events to the south-eastern quadrant of Great Britain, from the cold block on the continent ; and, if very cold heavy air sinks down then into northward-looking valleys, *e.g.* even the Clyde valley, it may lie there for weeks—skating having continued occasionally even in Glasgow for three consecutive months.

Again, in the "continental" quadrant of England, which by **Contin-** structure and soil has been made predominantly agricultural, there **ental** is a typical "continental" acceleration of maxima and minima **Quadrant.** (cf. p. 55) ; and this involves, amongst other things, a relatively heavy rainfall on the limestone and chalk uplands in *July,* *i.e.* the month immediately preceding normal harvest.

The freedom from extremes is specially a matter of temperature ; **Tempera-** and in this connection elevation is an important factor. For **ture.** distance from the Atlantic and proximity to Europe cause temperatures in summer to decrease from south-east to north-west, *i.e.* from the lowest elevation to the highest ; and the actual temperature in July over the north-west of Scotland averages under 54° F., when that in the Home Counties is over 63° F. The height, however, is not great enough to materially affect the isotherms, which are "sun-lines" in summer and "sea-lines" in winter; in summer, therefore, they run normally east and west, the

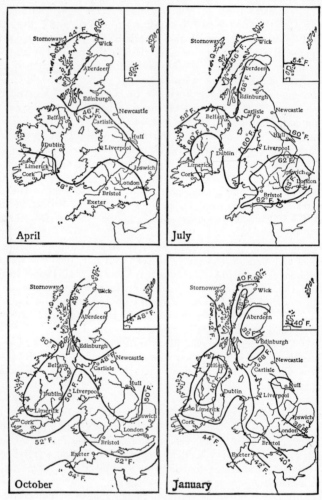

Seasonal isotherms.

temperature falling northwards, while in winter they run normally north and south, the temperature falling eastwards.

Climatic Regions. Extremes are greatest, therefore, in the south-east quadrant; and this implies several advantages to agriculture, including a hard winter and a hot summer, with a low but well-distributed rainfall.

In these respects the north-eastern quadrant is in most agreement
with the south-eastern, but it has a slightly higher rainfall and a
slightly smaller range of temperature (20° F. *v.* 23° F.). As this
area includes a considerable amount of low and fertile land, *e.g.*
the Old Red Sandstone of Strathmore, agriculture is again predominant. Similar conditions are also found on the limestone plain
of East-Central Ireland ; and it is significant that Ireland sometimes
has a higher return per acre on her grain crops than either England
or Scotland. A statistical return a few years ago was—

> Wheat—Scotland, 37 bushels ; Ireland, 31 ; England, 30.
> Barley—Ireland, 39 ; Scotland, 36 ; England, 33.
> Oats—Ireland, 43 ; England, 41 ; Scotland, 37.

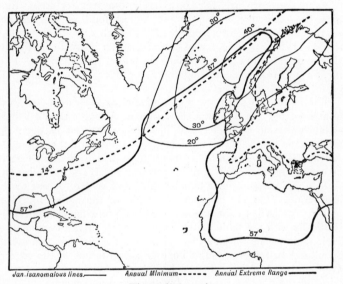

Jan. isanomalous lines.———   Annual Minimum- - - - -   Annual Extreme Range———

Winter gulf o' warmth.

The western parts both of Great Britain and of Ireland are **Cattle-**
those most free from extremes of temperature—largely because they **Rearing.**
are less free from extremes of rainfall ; and it is in this combination
that the secret lies of their predominance in cattle-rearing, which has
hitherto depended on the growth of lush grass for a maximum proportion of the year and the minimum need for housing the beasts
during the rest of the year. In Ireland—outside the area mentioned
—the range of temperature scarcely exceeds 16° F., while in the
north-west of Great Britain it is 18° F. ; but both level and latitude
are greatly in favour of Ireland, North-Western Scotland being
negligible as a cattle-rearing area. The south-western quadrant of
England, however, is the most favoured area. With a range of

19° F. it has quite a warm winter, heavy rainfall, and a most fertile soil, largely red sandstone. Along the whole of the British west coast, too, the high relative humidity is exceedingly favourable to textile industries, although the northern half of the country is too narrow to have a low humidity even in the east.

Chief Industries. The chief industries of the country may be ranged under five heads—commerce, manufactures, farming, mining, and fishing; and in each case geographical conditions have concentrated activity at certain foci. The bases of the commerce and manufactures are, of course, the fishing and mining. The former, apart from its value as supplying food, is the only school for a navy, mercantile or otherwise; and it is the mineral wealth that has led to such congestion of population—adverse to, and largely drawn away from, rural industries—that the country must import food as well as raw materials for manufacturing purposes. In each case, too, the chief foci present interesting points of contrast, which justify their separate existence, and throw light on their historical development. It is only on the causes underlying these contrasts that emphasis will here be laid.

Ten Great Ports. For instance, for the small area of 120,000 square miles there are at least ten great commercial harbours, *i.e.* more than all those —comparable in character and importance—found between the mouth of the Guadalquivir and that of the Elbe; and they represent what may be called parallel belts of hinterland from south-east to north-west, decreasing in fertility and ease of access from the Old World and increasing in mineral wealth and ease of access to the New World. On the continental margin of the agricultural area the two clay basins contain the two oldest ports, largely concerned historically with the trade of the opposite parts of the continent, of which their basins once formed part. On the inner margin of the agricultural belt the two most important river-basins of the country have found outlets at Bristol and Hull, both related to the sandstone plain and the limestone upland, but the ocean-port much older than the seaport. The coal-fields "behind" the agricultural belt have their great outlets at their extreme ends, but here the seaport is much older than the ocean-port; indeed, Cardiff is only a creation of the last fifty years. Windward of the coal-fields are the two great textile harbours of Liverpool and Manchester, both commanding the Cheshire Gate to and from the centre of the slate-girt Irish Sea. Isolated on the northern margin of the same sea, at once farther away from privateering in days before the Industrial Revolution and nearer to America in later days, Glasgow and Belfast owe their existence on the banks of natural "creeks" to the experience in dealing with a sand-choked creek in the Cheshire Gate, though in the latter case the Dee was actually replaced by the Mersey.

The outlets of the two clay basins agree in their natural **Tower** advantages of nearness to the continent, fertile hinterland, and **Hill.**

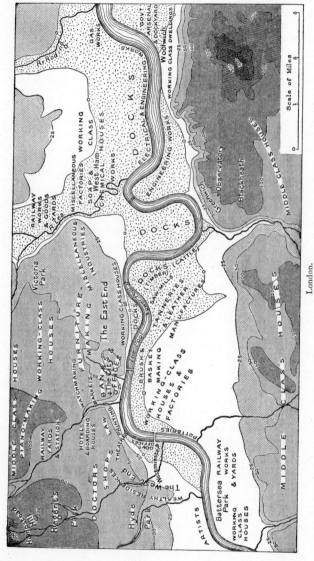

London.

The dotted area alongside the river is that which, in the absence of artificial embanking, is marshy ground, liable to be flooded at high tide. The two bridges marked are London and Westminster bridges; the two tunnels, Blackwall and Rotherhithe; the two crosses mark St. Paul's Cathedral and Westminster Abbey. (The first-named of each two is the more easterly.) The sailor could have found a port farther east, but not with hard rock on both banks of the river, *i.e.* not where merchants could find a good crossing-place.

double tide; but, especially in relation to the "double" character of the tide, they present marked contrasts. Tower Hill was the spot on which—in prehistoric times of land travel—all tracks converged to get round the estuarine marshes which made the river itself unapproachable, and so made it an appropriate and impassable barrier between glacial and non-glacial England; and it was the permanence of this "control," on a smaller scale, that made the river above Tower Hill a boundary between so many counties. Even at Tower Hill the ford was so often inaccessible that a village —for detained traders—sprang up on the shoulder of the hill, guarded by a fort on the summit; and the ford was soon replaced by a ferry, as the ferry was subsequently replaced by a bridge, on which all roads converged.

"Roads" v. Waterways. When waterways supplanted landways, this focus of roads became an objective of navigation; and the consequent power of distribution was only increased when again traffic became land-traffic, but carried on by canal and rail. The smallness of the area made the whole of it more or less the railway-hinterland of London, so that London grew at the expense of other ports, especially Bristol; but the development of the provincial ports, with their local advantages, is now taking the provincial trade away from London. At the same time, London never had any local competition, for the marshy nature of the alluvium on the shores of the estuary practically forbade the existence of any towns, though useful forts could be built where the chalk approached the river on both sides, e.g. at Tilbury and Gravesend, and great castles could be pile-reared amongst the treacherous swamps, as at Sheerness and Queenborough.

Transhipment and Market. The mere accident that whole fleets collected in the Downs during easterly or north-easterly gales, helped to make London a great port of transhipment, thus increasing its "nodal" value; and the consequent growth of population made it an enormous market— with an immediate demand now from 7,000,000 people—which encouraged the growth of transit outports, such as Harwich and Dover, but effectually prevented their becoming centres of population (cf. p. 222). It was under such circumstances that London developed into the greatest port in the world, which it has been for the last 200 years; and much modern criticism of the port implies some ignorance of its geographical conditions.

The Thames. Quite apart from the absurdity of comparing its hinterland with that of its great rivals, e.g. Antwerp, Rotterdam, and Hamburg (cf. p. 273), there is practically no comparison between the Thames and the rival rivers. London has much the best channel of the four. Not one of the others has anything like a 30-foot minimum low-water channel up to its lowest docks, as London has approximately up to Tilbury; still less has any one of them a maximum high-water channel of 50 feet. This 20-foot range, which gives the largest vessels a chance of reaching the Royal Albert Dock, is due to the meeting of two tides—one twelve hours behind the other—which complement each other in flowing up the Thames; but the same two tides counteract one another eastward—where crest meets trough instead of crest meeting crest—giving Rotterdam a tidal range of only 5 feet, and incidentally causing the Rhine to deposit a delta. The Scheldt, and still more the Elbe, are certainly more favoured than the Rhine in this respect; but the Elbe is much troubled by ice.

The Thames has, however, two great drawbacks, one historical *Historic* and the other natural. The latter is that the tide—being double *London.* in the sense that two tides go up the river at the same time—is too strong; the former· is concerned mainly with the predominance of the city in very early times. For London was a great market 1000 years before railways were thought of, and all that time she was a great port; and so her river-front had come to be occupied by wharves, etc., and the land behind it had been covered with warehouses, etc., with the obvious result that the centre of the port was practically closed to the intrusion of railways. Further, as ships increased in number and in size, they could not all or always moor at the wharves, but had to lie out in the middle of the river or not come up to the heart of the city. New docks were built farther and farther down the river, but their value was in inverse ratio to their distance from the " Pool "; and the alternative of working the traffic by barges higher up the river was not only the more suitable, but also already established in practice. London, then, is a barge port, with a fleet of fully 12,000 barges; and the strength of the tide practically dispenses with any other source of motive-power.

There is nothing in all this in itself adverse to shipbuilding on *Thames* the river; and the disadvantages urged against the river, *e.g.* distance *Ship-* from coal and iron, are becoming continuously less important. For *building.* the materials now used are made of mild steel, not iron, and are largely worked "cold"; and this minimises the need for coal— especially as the machine tools are mainly actuated by electricity— while the steel-plates, etc., are delivered by the great producers in North-East England at the same price everywhere in the country, whether Poplar, Barrow, or Belfast. The removal of yards, then, from the Thames to the Clyde was due mainly to the better and cheaper labour, involving a saving of 12-15 p.c. at Scotstoun over Poplar, and partly to such subordinate considerations as access to a good "measured mile" for speed trials.

In some small points, *e.g.* healthiness and scenery, Southampton *South-* has natural advantages over London; and it had obvious historical *hampton* advantages so long as Winchester was the "English" capital, or *v. London.* England was governed by Norman dukes, or civilisation was west of the Rhine, or the export of "South-Down" wool was still legal. With the loss of these advantages, and after the political isolation of the country from the continent had led to great internal development, Southampton had no chance against London; but the very advantages by which London won her monopoly, eventually reacted in favour of Southampton.   Once cargoes from the Atlantic for London had to be transhipped on to rail, it was a matter of little importance whether that was done far down the Thames or far up the Itchen; and the latter saves the long détour by the foggy and crowded Dover Strait—no small advantage in the saving of insurance and in the quick transport of meat and vegetables, fruit and dairy produce.   These conditions, with the possession of very good docks, have more than doubled the traffic in twenty years.

Double Tide.   The essential advantages of the harbour, however, are its double front and its double tide.   It has a double front because it stands on the peninsula between the Itchen and the Test; its tide is double, not because two tides come in at the same time, but because the same tide comes in twice.   The obtuse-angled basin has naturally a very broad base, 23 miles of which (east and west) is

Structural map of the Hampshire basin.

occupied by the Isle of Wight; and this gives the port a double tide, the first by way of the Solent and the second—two hours later —by way of Spithead.   While this régime never involves a violent current, such as troubles the Thames, it effectually prevents there being a normal low-water minimum; and the strategic and climatic shelter afforded by the Isle of Wight are reflected in the old saying that " The Solent might make a Queen's chamber."   The shelter and safe anchorage, the easy entrance by day or night, and the four tides a day combine, therefore, to give the port exceptional advantages on the great route to the New World and the Suez Canal from London and all its rival harbours.   Cf. p. 257.

"Agricultural" Ports.   On the inner margin of the great agricultural belt, commanding the outlets of its two chief river-basins, and with easy access on or along Avon and Stour to what were—before the reclaiming of the Fens—the richest corn and cattle lands of the country, Bristol and (Kingston-on-) Hull have been our two great agricultural ports. Even the slave trade, which was so profitable to Bristol, was looked upon in those days as a trade in "agricultural implements"; and

the oldest streets in the city still bear such names as " Wine Street "
and " Corn Street."   Indeed, the strategic importance of both
places was largely as outposts of the civilised agricultural area,
though it was based fundamentally on their " peninsular " isolation—
between Avon and Frome, between Humber and Hull—and on the
protection of the Avon Gorge in the one case and of the " Holder-
ness " swamps in the other case.   It was these swamps that attracted
the attention of Edward I. when he was securing his route to
Scotland ; and he gave the title of " King's-Town " to the military
station which he founded between Humber and Hull—on a site
exactly comparable, *e.g.* in its pile-foundations and protecting [1]
sluices, to that on which his grandson built Queenborough.

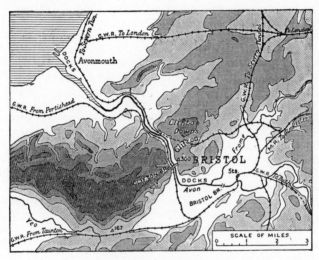

Map of Bristol and the lower Avon.
Contour-lines at intervals of 100 feet.

Historically, Bristol had the advantage—locally in nearness to **Bristol.**
the Roman station of Bath and the lead-mines which the Romans
began to work in the Mendips, and regionally, in nearness to London
landward and to Ireland (for wool) and France (for wine) seaward.
Later on, with the opening up of the Atlantic, these advantages
were increased ; and, as long as trans-oceanic shipping depended on
wind-power, no port on the north-east coast could compete with one
on the south-west coast, with its shorter and more direct, less foggy
and less crowded, access to the ocean.   Even now Bristol's main
chance of enlarging its sphere lies in the fact that it is nearer to
America than either Liverpool or Southampton, and nearer to London

[1] In the Civil War Hull was protected by deliberate flooding of the surrounding
flats.

than either Liverpool or Fishguard. And it is this that has encouraged—if it has not quite justified—the creation of very fine docks at Avonmouth and such improvement of the eight miles of river up to Bristol that vessels 325 feet long and carrying nearly 6000 tons of cargo can thread the whole gorge—under the Clifton Suspension Bridge—up to the heart of the city.

Hull. Even this, however, cannot compensate for its thinly-peopled and limited hinterland; and in this respect Hull claims an enormous advantage, with a hinterland population of perhaps 10,000,000 persons and with excellent means of transport inland by rail, river, and canal. It may lose its timber trade—a typically "Baltic" trade —to Grimsby and Immingham, as it has lost much of its old fish trade; but it must remain an exceedingly important food-depot for both man and beast,[1] and it is mainly the size of its trade that accounts for the cheapness of the port. This is its one great advantage; for instance, in sending food to Birmingham, it has had in recent years an advantage over London in cost varying from perhaps 2 p.c. for meat and 9 p.c. for butter up to 25 p.c. for apples and over 30 p.c. for eggs.

Mineral Ports. Behind the agricultural belt comes the mineral belt, and the exploitation of the latter largely depended on—or actually consisted in—the working of the coal-fields. At the two seaward extremities of the belt Newcastle and Cardiff are the most important coal-ports on the face of the earth—"Newcastle" being understood to include all the Tyne ports, as "Cardiff" includes Barry and Penarth; but some of their geographical conditions are widely different, the recent development of Cardiff being more or less based on the possession of a monopoly. As a matter of fact, both Newport and Port Talbot are in some respects better natural harbours; and Newport is likely to become a very serious rival. It taps that part of the coal-field which has been least exploited; the Usk is the deepest tidal river with floating docks in the British Isles; and it has the largest single dock in the world. These are the conditions which account for the recent removal of several very large works to Newport from the Midlands. But Port Talbot, like its neighbour, Swansea, is specifically interested in metal industries—though coal, including anthracite, is a dominating feature; and Newport was, and still is technically, "English."

Cardiff. Cardiff owes its predominance to that convergence of valleys which, ages ago, made it the capital of the British kingdom of Gwent. For the coal-deposits of Glamorgan and Monmouth lie in a series of narrow valleys, e.g. those of Taff and Rhymney, which converge on the lowland behind Cardiff and Newport, and Cardiff was the nearest outlet to the part of the coal-field first worked. A number of quite independent circumstances favoured the growth of

---

[1] It has the largest oil-seed industry in the world except that of Memphis (U.S.A.), and its river-system drains one-sixth of England.

the port—including the displacement of clippers by tramp-steamers and the opening of the Suez Canal; but the fundamental advantage was in the superiority of the coal for bunkering purposes. Fifty years ago the South Wales coal-field exported only 10,000,000 tons

a year; twenty-five years ago the export was 25,000,000 tons; and in 1913 it was *c.* 50,000,000. Our total export in 1925 was only *c.* 50,800,000 tons, *i.e.* 40 p.c. of the whole export of the country. Like all other great coal-exporting harbours, Cardiff has great facilities for importing cheaply, because steamers

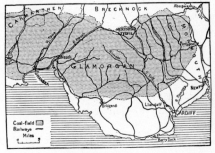

South Wales coal-field.

can always get a return cargo; and this is reflected in, *e.g.* the great flour-milling industry of the town. But its growth has been more or less of "mushroom" character, based on the "monopoly" of steam coal and anthracite, and one of its troubles now is the reduction of annual output per man from 332 tons in 1883 (275 in 1903, 260 in 1913) to 220 in 1924.

Newcastle has had a very different history. Its importance in **New-** early times was almost entirely strategic, the "new castle" of the **castle.** Normans only replacing an old one built on the same site by the Romans; and the occupational control of its strategic period seems to have favoured a political type, both of individual and of group, which has been largely responsible for its economic importance in more recent times. From the time when the Romans built their great wall, the Tynesiders, whether lead-miners in the South Tyne valley or the fishermen of Jarrow port, became typical frontiersmen, alert and independent, adaptable and not afraid of taking responsibility. Presently these frontiersmen became an important factor in the staple trade of their age and country, the wool trade, for which the relatively high winter temperature is so favourable that Northumberland[1] is still the most important sheep-rearing county in England, though Newcastle is no longer one of the chief wool-markets of Europe. The export of the wool was obviously associated with England's greatest historic industry, that of fishing; and, when the Tynesider began to handle another great staple, coal, it was one of world importance. As miner and fisherman, he had only continued the strenuous life and constant danger of the frontiersman; and, as wool-raiser, as fisherman, as coal-miner, he

[1] The neighbouring county of Durham is the home of the Shorthorn cattle, the most famous breed in the kingdom and by far the most numerous ($\frac{9}{50}$); it is the most useful "dual-purpose" (milk and meat) breed in the world.

had had for centuries his finger on the pulse of the commercial world of his age.

The Tyne. About half-way between the present head of navigation at Newburn and the probable old head of navigation at Wall's-End—an appropriate place, therefore, for the great wall to end—the low southern bank rises to the level of the high northern bank; and where the twin heights close in on the river, there the Great North Road dropped to the river at Gateshead ("Road-Head"), and the opposite end of the ford was guarded by a castle. Both above and below this point—now marked by the High and Low Level Bridges—the bed of the river was deep clay; and the constriction of the banks at the "Bridges" increased the natural scour until Newcastle became the normal head of navigation, while similar constriction at

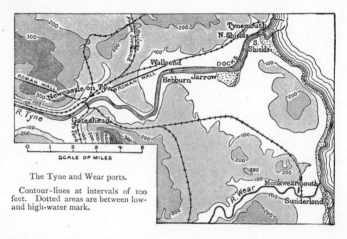

The Tyne and Wear ports.

Contour-lines at intervals of 100 feet. Dotted areas are between low- and high-water mark.

the mouth of the river made the intervening section of the river almost a natural dock. With such a population and such a river-bed (clay), it was comparatively a small thing to canalise the whole river up to Newburn, giving fully 30 feet of depth as far as the upper constriction, and to extend the lower constriction by running out great walls to the 5-fathom line, so that sand could not accumulate and vessels could enter straight from the sea.

Development of Trade. The mineral wealth justified and defrayed the expense of these great enterprises, and the distribution of it was exceedingly favourable both to export and to the development of local industries. The mines first worked were so near the river that, even with pack-horse transport, it was possible and profitable to export the coal;[1] the height of the banks makes it equally possible and

---

[1] It began to be worked in the thirteenth century, and went to London by sea—hence its old name of "sea-coal."

profitable to work the transport to-day mainly by gravitation, the loaded trucks pulling the empty ones back up the hill. The growth of the export implied more cheapness of import, *e.g.* of timber for pit-props and of ores to replace the exhausted home ores; and, as a huge export of heavy iron goods came to be added to that of coal, increase of tonnage out encouraged increase of other materials in, *e.g.* food-stuffs. Meantime, the Tyne Gap had been becoming more capable of use, *e.g.* deforested and drained; and, once it was threaded by a railway, Newcastle had obvious facilities for distribution westward. And the typical frontiersman seizes an opportunity when he sees it. It is significant that it was on the Tyne that the first steam collier was built, and that a Tyne tug was the first steam "trawler."

The modern development of textile industries depended **South** absolutely on the coal—the value of which was greatly increased **Lanca-** by its proximity to salt, as a basis of chemical industries, in both **shire.** Yorkshire and Lancashire—and the two great textile ports are to windward of the coal-belt, *i.e.* in what was in earlier times the most backward part of the country, isolated by marsh and mountain, by forest and glacial clay. At one point in the forested marsh at the foot of the mountains, "a hard rock of stone" cropped out; the whole formation, of which it was the most conspicuous point, caused four streams to converge here, and the rock[1] offered a site for a fort, while the current offered a source of "power" that was presently utilised. Along these and other streams tracks converged on the rock from the watershed, *i.e.* past the sites of Bolton, Bury, Rochdale, Oldham, etc., the Irwell valley leading to both Bolton and Bury; and, once a busy industry and a correspondingly large population had sprung up on the eastern flank of the watershed, the rock was bound to become the focus for all roads westward. In this way the woollen industry was extended, mainly by Flemish weavers, into Lancashire in the thirteenth century; and it is still an important industry in the area. But when—200 years later— Levant "*cotton*-wool" was introduced into England, it soon became evident that Lancashire could handle this new material better than any other part of the country; and, though the germs of plague were introduced by the cotton, and epidemics paralysed the industry at least twice, geographical conditions were so favourable that it was bound to recover.

Eventually Manchester became the natural focus of fully **Man-** 8,000,000 people—with obvious results. The greatly increased **chester.** value of land, capable of being covered very cheaply with houses of brick made of the local clay, drove many mills and works across the Irwell into Salford and farther afield; and Manchester became more important commercially than industrially, thus attracting

---

[1] The place still bears the significant name of " Castlefield."

(1830) the second railway in the kingdom, "The Manchester and Sheffield." The ship canal—35 miles long, with a minimum depth of 28 feet, and a minimum bottom width—for three-quarters of a

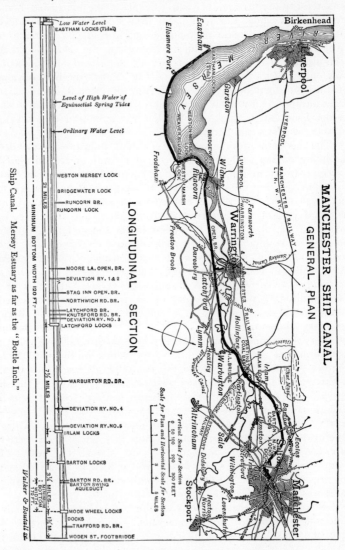

mile near Latchford—of 30 yards, was a natural sequel to the Bridge-water canal; and now, as the nearest port to 150 towns, Manchester stands fourth of all British ports in the value of her total trade, importing her staple, cotton, and such significant other products as oil, lard, fruit, timber, and grain, and exporting coal, cotton goods, and machinery, including machine tools.

As Manchester owed its start to the growth of the Yorkshire **Liverpool.** woollen industry, so Liverpool owed its start to that of the Lancashire cotton industry ; and, therefore, it started relatively late, Bristol and Plymouth, London and Southampton, having an immense advantage in this respect. But its great rival, London, was severely handi-capped—at the critical time in the development of Liverpool—by the plague and by the constant danger from Dutch fleets. And the topographical details of the Liverpool site saved it from the fate of Chester, which originally monopolised the sea-trade of the " Cheshire Gap," but which dare not—for fear of Welsh raids—move its port farther down the river, *i.e.* away from the Castle rock, as the river silted up. For Liverpool stands at the sea end of a bottle-necked estuary which runs at right angles to the prevailing wind, and there-fore could be entered or left by sailing vessels with equal ease ; and the windy exposure, added to the dry subsoil and the good " drainage " slope [1] of the red-sandstone block, made the site exceptionally healthy. This narrow neck has other advantages, two of which decided the fate of Liverpool. The one is that the concentration of the broad " Sloyne lake " on the narrows gives the current exceptional scouring force, which maintained a good depth in spite of the great volume of sand ; the other is that the facilities for coming alongside the natural bank, even before it was lined with more than 10 miles of docks and *c.* 40 miles of level quays, were greatest at the very place most suitable for the rise of a city. Incidentally, too, these conditions have greatly facilitated dredging, for they have focused the main trouble on a definite and quite limited bar, and so have not caused difficulties such as exist on the Thames, *e.g.* the " slipping " of banks. On the other hand, they have evolved the famous landing-stage. Owing to the great difference of tidal level, the docks can be open only for a short time (at high water) ; but the landing-stage (over 800 yards long) is built on floating pontoons which rise and fall with the tide.

As the " Home of Ship Owners," Liverpool's interests are world- **Man-** wide ; but the special commodities handled are raw cotton, food- **chester v.** stuffs, and tobacco inwards, and cotton goods and iron and steel **Liverpool.** goods outwards. Typical industries, therefore, are flour-milling and the making of marine engines, while the typical attitude is a broad outlook. This will probably always put the port beyond the fear of serious competition from Manchester. For the dense population of the natural hinterland of Manchester has one absolutely dominant economic interest, and that in a product which can, under no circumstances, be grown in this country ; nor are its best customers

---

[1] The name almost certainly means " The Pool of the Slopes."

for cotton goods found in this country.   Its outlook is, therefore, at once narrow and not typically British; and yet its economic interests can be pushed by sheer tyranny of numbers.

Glasgow.   Glasgow and Belfast were still later in developing, and both were made by strenuous effort.   Isolated on the ocean margin, both were secure from privateers and nearer to the sugar, tobacco, and cotton of the New World than any of their rivals; and both had chances of monopolising the foreign trade of their respective countries.   Glasgow, however—once the Act of Union was passed—was in much the stronger position, *e.g.* having both a much larger hinterland without " break of bulk " and the essential bases of industry in rich fields of coal and iron; and, until Glasgow had perfected the steam-dredger, Belfast could not be reached through the "sloblands" of the sluggish Lagan.   Within a century and a half from the time when Smeaton reported (1740) that the depth of water just east of the Kelvin-Clyde confluence was *15 inches*, there was a high-water depth of over 33 feet at the same place. Under the guidance of Telford and Watt and Galthorne—whose experience of the sands of Dee was invaluable—the Clyde was first narrowed to produce a scour which would remove loosened silt and prevent new silt from accumulating very quickly; then it was systematically dredged to a minimum of 22 feet; and so "the river made the city when the citizens had once made the river."   This has been true in a remarkable sense; for the deepening of the river has had a profoundly beneficial effect on the tidal wave, which reaches Glasgow now in 2 hours less than it did a century ago, while the flow of spring tides has been lengthened from $4\frac{1}{4}$ to 6 hours and their ebb shortened from 8 to $6\frac{1}{4}$ hours.

Woollen Industry.   The commerce of these great ports reflects especially two supremely important industries—textiles and hardware, the one almost as clearly connected with the climate now as the other was originally connected with the structure of the country.   The development of the wool trade with Flanders, in the days when Norwich was really " Norwich by the Sea "—and she is still no farther than Glasgow from the sea—made the city the natural home of the woollen industry, as also the natural asylum for refugees from the continent.   But, even before the use of coal—with the silting up of the Norwich bay and the need for removing a staple industry to a safer site farther inland—Norfolk began to give place to Yorkshire; and the latter still has special advantages, *e.g.* in water-supply, climate, and access to fuel and machinery, to markets and raw materials.   Hand-work survives in the islands only in remote places where neither fuel nor machinery is accessible, *e.g.* the Hebrides and Connaught; and these two essentials affect machine work even in places that are not remote.   Thus, climate, hill-pastures, and soft water are favourable along the Cotswolds and the Cheviots, *e.g.* at

Frome and Bradford, at Hawick and Galashiels, the Cotswold water
—like that of the Leven at Alexandria—being very suitable for dyeing "grain" colours ; but the distance from fuel and machinery is a
drawback.   On the contrary, the Leicester coal is coupled with a
more continental climate, which is more suited to hosiery than to

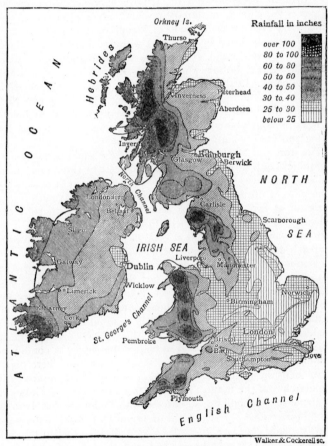

Annual rainfall of the British Isles.
Based upon a map by Dr. H. R. Mill.

general woollens.   Yorkshire, then, has the most advantages.   It
has easy access to home and foreign supplies of wool, and to
countries with winters cold enough to cause a demand for woollen
clothing ; water of the right quality is abundant ; up under the water-
parting, the "muggy" air that lodges in the valleys, e.g. in those
of Aire and Calder, is almost ideal for the various manufacturing

processes ; and the presence of the necessary coal has also involved multiplication of means of transport.

Cotton Industry. The localisation of the cotton industry round the ring of torrent-scarred hills on the windward side of the Pennines is purely climatic. Access to fuel and machinery or to markets and raw materials is no easier than in Yorkshire, but the relative humidity is higher ; and this makes the climate much more favourable to a vegetable product, as illustrated even by the division of labour on the spot. For the spinning is monopolised by the towns with the most humid climate and the best water ; and, even so, the finest spinning goes to the seaward towns, *e.g.* Bolton, while the coarse spinning goes landward, *e.g.* to Oldham. In the areas of still lower humidity, *e.g.* the Ribble basin, weaving is more typical than spinning (cf. Preston and Blackburn) ; and in still drier areas, *e.g.* in the lee of the Welsh mountains, the work is largely confined to secondary processes such as lace-making and hosiery-knitting, as at Nottingham.

Hardware : Birmingham. The iron and steel industries illustrate the same permanence of geographic control with the same progressive variations in the manifestation of the control. The permanence is most conspicuous in the case of Birmingham and Sheffield. Both have historic industries of at least 1000 years' standing ; both had, to start with, local supplies of ore and of fuel—from the Forests of Arden and Sherwood ; and both had "local" supplies of coal, and were within easy reach of imported ore, whether of home or foreign origin. But their non-local relations were different, for Birmingham is in the very heart of England. No doubt, the fact that it stands at about equal distances from navigable water on Trent and Severn and Avon encouraged the construction of canals ; but it was essentially on a site the full value of which could only be realised by railways. Both climate and relief are responsible for this. For obviously the size of a canal lock must bear some relation to water-supply as conditioned by rainfall, and the demand on this supply is greatest where population is densest, as round Birmingham and Wolverhampton ; and long stretches of the natural routes in this district are at least 400 feet above the sea, and are so covered with buildings that land has a prohibitive value. Even if the deficiency of local water-supply could be made good, *e.g.* from the Elan Valley, so that in the driest season large locks could be assured uniform and sufficient depth, the cost of improvement—at such an elevation and in such a densely populated and deeply undermined area—would be so great that an improved Grand Junction Canal *could not afford* to go through the Black Country.

Railway Transport. Obviously, under such conditions, development depends on railway transport, and this controls local industries in two directions. In the first place, such districts must specialise in goods which demand much labour for little raw material, *e.g.* pins, pens, needles,

screws, watch-springs, etc. ; and in the second place, amongst such
there must be specifically transport media—from bicycles to railway
stock.   Apart from such neighbouring centres as Coventry and
Wolverhampton, at least three suburbs of Birmingham—Handsworth,
Oldbury, and Saltley—have a world-wide reputation for the production of railway rolling-stock.   Firms wishing to do typically
" heavy " work for other purposes than transport have recently been
migrating, *e.g.* to Newport and Pontypool.   Of course, early canals
and railways made Birmingham their objective, because its essentially central position had already raised it into a very important
transport centre—associated with horse transport ; and it was this
question of the transport medium that—coupled with the presence
of fine casting-sand — gave the district its original industry in
iron-castings for harness (cf. the important harness industry of
Walsall).

In the case of Sheffield the local advantages included crucible- **Sheffield.**
clay and water-power, but the determining factor was the presence
of fine grinding-stone, which directed the local energies into cutlery
and so predestined them to import of fine iron and specialisation in
steel.   " Birmingham " ore [1] yields only 35-36 p.c. of metal, with
1·07 p.c. of phosphorus, and ·04 p.c. of sulphur ; the Furness
hematite, though yielding 66-67 p.c. of metal, practically free from
sulphur and phosphorus, was less accessible than Scandinavia from
Sheffield even in Plantagenet times ; even now quantities of pig-iron
are produced in the " Sheffield " area, *e.g.* at Rotherham and
Chesterfield, to which the blast-furnaces were removed 150 years
ago, and fully 95 p.c. is used at home—but not by Sheffield.

On the Sheaf and the Don only steel is used, made of Swedish **Sheaf v.**
or Spanish and Cumbrian iron.   Along the Sheaf there are many **Don.**
crucible steel makers, the " descendants " of the old cutlers, still
engaged in light products and still using Scandinavian metal ; and
along the navigable Don there are many makers of heavy products
(*e.g.* armour plates), but using for their new work the newer sources
of supply from Furness and Spain.   As everything except the fuel
has to bear transport, mainly by rail, the determining factor here is
the human one.   Not only is the weight of material used trivial
compared with the labour spent on it, as at Birmingham, but
centuries of experience have bred in both masters and men an
instinct which no theoretical knowledge can hope to rival.   For the
men can " divine " by the eye the quality of a piece of metal—
which metallurgical analysis can only confirm—or the amount of
smoke necessary [2] in a flame for reheating steel—which no
mechanical process yet invented can decide ; and the masters seem
to have a similar genius for seizing on new ideas or new methods,

---

[1] The corresponding percentages for Cleveland are 33-34, 1·24, and ·03.
[2] The amount, unfortunately, is not favourable to amenities of climate.

e.g. the Bessemer and Siemens patents or the driving of machinery by electricity.

Eastern Counties.

To the south-east and north-east of the great steel centre are two areas which again present interesting contrasts. The agricultural belt was bound to develop industries in agricultural machinery at such places as Lincoln and Grantham, Ipswich and Colchester ; and the cheapness and abundance of labour—and that, too, unorganised —were favourable to the extension of such industries where special facilities existed for access to fuel and metal, as the tin-plate

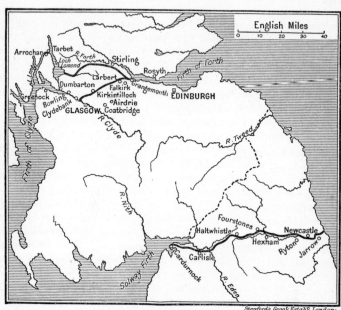

Isthmian canal routes.

industry of South Wales has been supplemented by industries in galvanised and corrugated iron. And, no doubt, the opening of the Doncaster coal-field and the local supplies of iron-ore, *e.g.* at Frodingham, will develop the industry in Lincolnshire.

Cleveland *v.* Durham.

In the north-east the industry has been based largely on the Cleveland ore, which in 1913 yielded 40 p.c. (6,000,000 tons) of the total output of the country, but mainly on the Durham coke. The Cleveland ore, however, has been getting poorer in percentage of metal, and more costly to work in other ways too ; and the output is now behind that of Lincolnshire (*c.* 2,270,000 *v. c.* 3,220,000), and still more behind the "Notts-Lincoln belt" (7,270,000), reaching a percentage of only 11 out of a total of 11,250,000 tons. But the

Durham coke, which possesses precisely those mechanical qualities [1] required in fuel for modern blast-furnaces, being large enough not to choke the furnaces and strong enough to bear great weight of ore. This, of course, is another asset for Newcastle; and it is the sum of advantages concentrated there that favours the construction of a great ship-canal from the Tyne to the Solway.

Such a canal would not only shorten the distance between our great west-coast ports and the Baltic by 300 miles or so, but would enable a fleet to be concentrated with maximum ease and safety at the very centre of our North-Sea coast, and that, too, where there are exceptional facilities for repairs, etc. An alternative route would join the Forth and Clyde, possibly *via* Loch Lomond; it would have the same commercial advantages, *e.g.* the avoidance of the stormy and crowded Pentland Firth or the foggy and still more crowded Dover Strait, and its only inferiority strategically would be that the repairing base would be on the west coast. In neither case is the difficulty or the expense prohibitive, and short ship-canals are the one form of inland water-transport that seems to be justified in these days under our conditions of relief and climate. The northern route has the more privacy and the better accommodation, and has the great advantage of its technical base (Glasgow) being at its inner end.

Note on Southampton Tides.

The double tides referred to on p. 244—the practical effect of which is really a prolonged high water of about 3 hours' duration—is certainly associated (? mainly) with the Isle of Wight; but, as there are rather similar phenomena elsewhere in the English Channel, *e.g.* at Weymouth and Havre, there is probably also at work the double influence of (1) the Cotentin peninsula in checking the tide suddenly in its access to mid-channel, and (2) a similar and more complete constriction at its exit near Dover.

---

[1] The "splint" coal of Lanarkshire has somewhat the same value to Coatbridge and Motherwell.

CHAPTER XVII

BELGIUM

THE geographical interest of Belgium is mainly historical and economic, but its geographical importance is mainly political; for it was as a Buffer State that it won its national existence at all, and it illustrates nearly all the characteristic phenomena of a Buffer State, especially the difficulties. Even such a trivial detail as the printing of a railway ticket becomes significant, when it is printed in two languages; and one of the two is always "foreign," French in the west and German in the east.[1] That is to say, it does not represent the Belgians as a nation, nor the commercial part of the population, which is made Flemish by Antwerp, nor yet the industrial part, which is made Walloon by the Mons-Liége coal-field; it does represent one of the two great political antagonists between whom Belgium is a Buffer State.

It has been pointed out, too, that Belgium is an area of geographic, as well as of political, transition, *e.g.* its great rivers both rising and emptying beyond the Belgian frontier. Its frontiers are, except on the sea-coast, far from being well-marked physical features; its surface features and even its mineral beds are largely extensions from other countries; its peoples and languages are equally transitional, for the "Latin" Walloon stands between the Romance tongue of western Switzerland and the Romance tongue of northern France, while Flemish bears a similar relationship to Dutch and Deutsch; and its political history[2] has been largely the history of other countries, France and Holland, Spain and Austria.

The frontier features are very varied, and some of their details are peculiarly significant. For instance, the Franco-Belgian frontier is a lasting memento of the many wars between France and Spain, when peace was often purchased at the cost of some choice bit of Spanish Belgium, *e.g.* the "bay" of Lille, with its river-frontier on the Lys, or the somewhat similar "bay" of Valenciennes. So, the extension of the French frontier down the Meuse valley as far as

---

[1] The internal racial division is latitudinal, not longitudinal, the north (of Waterloo) being Flemish and the south being Walloon.

[2] Cf. the battlefields of Fontenoy and Jemappes, Oudenarde and Ramillies, Ligny and Quatre Bras, etc.

the natural fortress of Givet has an obvious strategic value ; but, as a matter of fact, except in crossing the deep narrow valley of the river itself and of its Semois tributary, the course of the actual frontier eastward of the Sambre adheres fairly well to a line of maximum elevation and minimum population.

The same is true of the frontier towards Luxemburg and **Eastern** Germany, which is roughly marked by the water-parting between **Frontier.** the Semois and the Sauer in the south and that between the Ourthe and the Roer in the north, though the difficulty of drawing a line through the densely populated mining (lead and zinc) area in the Moresnet commune led to the defining of a neutral—now wholly Belgian—zone held in common by Belgium and Prussia ; but directly the Ardennes plateau is left for the Meuse lowland minimum population has no obvious relation to "maximum" elevation. Here three things are significant—the Meuse, the mesopotamian, and the marine lines respectively. On the "primitive" river-frontier the significant feature is the détour to disconnect Maastricht, as it were, from the left bank of the river—on which it actually stands—and to perpetuate its historic connection with the right bank. This is the point at which the river Geer joins the Meuse, and on which, therefore, in very early times it directed the "Rhine" overland traffic (for London *via* Ghent and Bruges) ; the confluence is just below the great sandstone block of Pietersberg, which was worked by the Romans, and which provided material for castle and bridge at this "Maas-traject" ("crossing-place," first by ford and then by bridge) ; and the only guarantee of a safe crossing was to hold the farther, *i.e.* the western, bank. Incidentally, this was associated in sentiment with the "Dutch" refugees from the political and religious tyranny of Spain, because the subterranean labyrinths in the quarries became a recognised refuge for both man and beast.

The Mesopotamian line is a meandering compromise between **Northern** two similar considerations : it was necessary to avoid the great **Frontier.** arteries of movement, whether by river or road ; and the overland route led by the Demer-Dyle-Senne valley, while the dreariest and most desolate areas, *e.g.* central Limburg, were almost bound to have the least population, even if they had not also been— previous to the cutting of the S. William's and Campine canals— devoid of natural highways.

The marine line represents a determined effort to exclude the **Western** weaker partner from the polders and tidal water, and it is profoundly **Frontier.** significant of the fundamental causes which separated Holland from Belgium in 1830. For, though the Belgian population (*c.* 3,500,000) was almost double that of Holland, and French in sympathy and Roman in creed, the King was a Dutch Calvinist, the capital was in Holland, representation was so unequal that the Dutch minority had a permanent majority for all important legislation, and official posts were monopolised by Dutchmen, only one minister out of seven being Belgian in 1830.

Coast.   The one stretch of sea-coast left to Belgium had a minimum value, except as an obstacle to invasion, for its shore-waters are shallow and the coast-line consists of typical sand-dunes. Indeed, the sands slope so gradually that the regular winds have thrown up a natural barrier of dunes, but for which—supplemented now by artificial "dykes"—the land would be submerged at every tide; and it is to this that the coast owes its popularity as a bathing-resort. Of course, gaps have been left for drainage—one at each end and one in the centre. The estuary of the Yser offers a site for a fishing-port at Nieuport,—the "Old Port" of Ypres being now 20 miles inland; the central gap obviously commands mail and passenger traffic for Brussels and the busiest fish trade, and the packet-station of Ost-end was naturally placed as far as possible inland, *i.e.* on the "East End" of the gap, thus increasing the facilities offered by the good railway service for the distribution of fish; the northern gap, at the fishing-port of Heyst, has been made the terminus of a ship-canal from Bruges, and its new harbour is the "Harwich" train-ferry port of Zee-Brugge, also a busy fishing port.

Zee-Brugge.   Much care and money have been expended on this new port and many advantages have been claimed for it, *e.g.* that it is entirely Belgian,—that the port itself, the canal, and the Bruges basin, all have a minimum depth of fully 26 feet,—that it is on or very near the greatest steamer-routes of Northern Europe,—that three great express railway routes converge on Bruges (from Berlin, Vienna, and Basel),—that the canal is only one-fifth of the length of the Scheldt below Antwerp; and great efforts are being made to develop it as a fine "free" port. But its natural hinterland is small in both population and area. In the immediate hinterland is Ghent, accessible *via* the Terneuzen canal by ships drawing 26 ft., and behind Ghent again is Brussels, now recognised as a port, with direct services—by vessels drawing 21 ft.—*via* the Rupel canal, to London and other North Sea ports; and the fundamental difficulty which even in the palmiest days of Bruges necessitated an out-port at Damme, and which by 1488 had caused all foreign merchants to move their headquarters to Antwerp, is still operative.

Silt.   That difficulty was the superiority of the mighty Scheldt over the little Zwin, not only in such obvious commercial advantages as length and volume, but also in its consequent power of pouring out silt. The success of efforts to reclaim land in the "West" Scheldt estuary, *i.e.* the rapidity of the historic narrowing of the waterway, is the best proof of the difficulties which faced ports on the old margin of the waterway. Bruges is "La Morte"; the battlefield of Sluis is a meadow; and a couple of dredgers will probably always have to be kept at work in the port.

The historical development of Antwerp has been rather **Antwerp.**
chequered, mainly because its economic importance, as based on
the river, was kept subordinate to its political importance, as based
on the strategic value of the marshes which for centuries surrounded

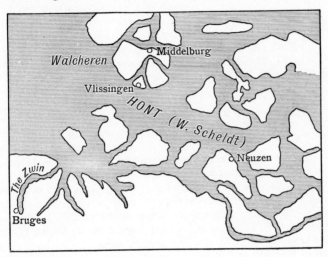

Land area before 12th century.

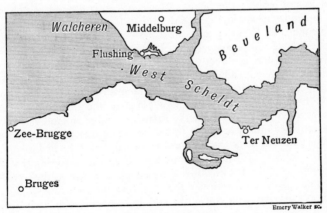

Emery Walker sc.

Land area at present day.

it ; but its indisputable popularity with "skippers" is based on its
essential commercial advantages, and several of these are obvious.
Fully 50 miles from Flushing, it is absolutely safe from storms—
though it was the work of storms in opening the estuary in the
fifteenth century that gave it its first chance—and yet has tides that

bring up the largest vessels ; it is as near as London to the centre of the world's ocean highways, and nearer than London to the great network of railways and canals that converge on the Atlantic from central and northern Europe ; and it is exceedingly cheap.   The

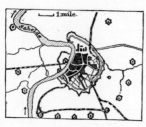

Antwerp and its historic forts.

result is a popularity which has actually outpaced accommodation, so that there is now some risk of delay or confusion, especially during fogs—the one real drawback to the harbour ; but extra accommodation can be secured, and is already projected, by a scheme which will not only get rid of the angle at Austenweel (*i.e.* just opposite the north end of the city), with its capacity for accumulating silt, but also give a continuous concave quay on a wide-radius curve such as makes an ideal frontage for a tidal river.

Surface.   The surface is partly plateau and partly plain, with a general slope from the south-east (over 2000 feet) to north-west, the two areas corresponding strikingly with the basins of the Scheldt and the Meuse.   In Flanders there is a large area of polder, at little above sea-level, which is valuable pasture, famous for its horses ; the south of Hainault and most of Brabant, at a height of 300-500 feet, is fine agricultural land, with a chalk ridge separating the Scheldt and Meuse basins ; the Sambre-Meuse valley is flanked southwards by uplands averaging perhaps 800-900 feet, the picturesque Famenne and Fagnes ; and the forested plateau of the Ardennes varies from 1200 to 2000 feet.   It is peculiarly interesting that the physical division is directly paralleled by, and associated with, the "racial" division.   Where the primitive rock of the Ardennes plateau gives place to the young strata of the Flemish plain, there the short, dark, round-headed Walloon gives place to the taller, fairer, long-headed Fleming ; there, too, the French-speaking and individualistic peasant-proprietor gives place to the tenant-farmer who tolerates no tongue akin to that of the accursed Spaniards, once the tyrants of the plain.   In view of historic events, therefore, it is surprising that the one bond of unity for this dual little people is found in their creed.

Plain.   The plain is practically the basin of the Scheldt, so that it naturally gravitates on Antwerp ; and it is ribbed with undulations which collect the abundant water in tributaries that flow more or less parallel with one another before converging on the Scheldt, thus creating a waterway out of all proportion to the length of the river (270 miles).   Except for the marshy north and a somewhat sandy centre, most of the basin is distinctly fertile, especially towards the south-east, and grows a great variety of crops, about a quarter of it giving two crops a year—with very high yield.

The real dividing line between Upper and Lower Belgium is the **Meuse Valley** Sambre-Meuse valley, equally important by relief and by structure. Fertilised from the limestone and other young rock that flanks the old hard rock of the Ardennes, rich in coal and iron, and giving a line of least resistance in peace or war, it divides the nearly un‑ disturbed Tertiary and cretaceous beds which cover the plain, from the worn-down stumps of the ancient mountains to the south, the coal being found where the younger strata are involved in the relics of the ancient folds. This is obviously along the northern foot of the Ardennes, where the Sambre-Meuse has worn a trough along the geological fault; and the scarp of the old rock was characteristically rich in metals, especially zinc, between Huy and Verviers. Cf. p. 266.

The coal occurs in three basins,—the "Meuse" field which **Coal-** stretches from Namur to Liège, — the "Sambre" field, which **Fields.** contains the chief coal‑mining centre, Charleroi, — and the "Hainault" field with its centre in Mons (cf. p. 267). The new Campine field will be still more important, because it is rich in really good *coking* coal, which is lacking in most Belgian coal-fields. In 1918 it produced less than 75,000 tons; in 1927 it produced more than 850,000. It is so near to Antwerp (another asset for the port) that it is becoming the objective of the Congo mineral wealth (cf. the Oolen radium factory); and it is also rich in fine glass-sand, of great value in the plate-glass industry.

The climate approximates to that of East Anglia, but has **Climate.** slightly greater extremes, the winter in the Ardennes being distinctly severe. The rainfall, too, is heaviest on the Ardennes; but there are two clearly marked and parallel belts of heavy rainfall, separated by a wide belt of much lighter fall. The one is an area of mainly cyclonic rains in Flanders, eastwards of—and due to—the dunes; and the other is where the cyclonic fall is more obviously accentuated by relief, *i.e.* south-east of the Sambre-Mass trough.

The river-system is exceedingly useful, providing valuable **River-** waterways and water of first-rate quality for retting, bleaching, **System** dyeing, etc.; and it is scarcely an exaggeration to say that the dense population of the country (680 per square mile) is based essentially on the development of the inland waterways. The fundamental advantage is that a small area (*c.* 11,750 square miles), forming practically the basin of a single river, is flanked by two concave curves of waterway, a sea flank from Nieuport to Antwerp and the river flank of the Sambre-Meuse between Mons and Maastricht. This was made the basis of a network of additional waterway— canalised rivers and canals—which is worked at a considerable annual loss, but which has enabled Belgium to meet the fierce competition of Holland, Germany, and France.

Canals : Western. The whole system has its morphological, if not its geometrical, centre in Antwerp ; and it may be divided into two areas by the great route from Antwerp to Charleroi *via* the canalised Rupel and Brussels, which is reached by small ocean steamers (*e.g.* from London). The western area, besides having direct communication with the sea, *e.g.* at Heyst, Ostend, Nieuport, and with Holland, *e.g.* at Terneuzen and *via* the Lower Scheldt, has at least seven good routes into France, the best being by Termonde and the canalised Dender, by Charleroi and the canalised Sambre, and by the Mons-Condé canal. The last is the most useful for the export of coal, because at certain seasons of the year all the Sambre, like the Upper Meuse, is difficult to navigate ; and the least useful in some ways is the canalised Lys, because during the retting season (whole summer) no steam traffic is allowed on it.

Canals : Eastern. The east has a much smaller proportion of waterway (though being greatly extended in the Campine), but the main line forms a continuous ring—Antwerp, Brussels, Charleroi, Namur, Liége (Maastricht), Turnhout, Antwerp—serving both the old Brabant and the new Campine coal-fields, and enclosing the most fertile area in Belgium, *i.e.* the Hesbage plain round Waremme. This communicates with Holland towards the north (for Bois-le-Duc) as well as at Maastricht, and has the same sort of competition from the Rhine as the Flemish canals have from the sea. For large barges (carrying fully 1500 tons) ply regularly from Antwerp, *via* Dordrecht and the Waal, to Cologne and Mannheim, reaching the latter within a week ; and in summer they ply even to Strasbourg, which needs another week.

Transit Trade. The total length of inland waterway in the whole area (not = twice Yorkshire) is well over 1000 miles, which gives an average of 1 mile of waterway to under 12 square miles of surface ; and this is supplemented so well by railways (*c.* 3000 miles) for quick transport and by light railways (*c.* 3000 miles) for agricultural development, that several million tons of goods converge on Antwerp every year by inland waterways, and there is a very large transit trade through the country—valued in 1913 at about £100,000,000!

Two Areas. The waterway between the heart of the coal-field at Charleroi and the great port of Antwerp roughly divides the country into two industrial areas, the western one being prominently concerned with textiles and the eastern with hardware, thus complicating the friction of racial and linguistic differences ; and while the Flemish plain is much less picturesque than the forested Ardennes, it has much more historic interest.

Flanders. The alluvial soil and the damp climate of West Flanders are very favourable to the growing of flax, and the price of labour is not prohibitive, while the absence of "salts" from the river-water is invaluable in the "cleansing" of the fibre. The Lys above

Courtrai is the special scene of the flax retting; and Courtrai itself and its neighbours, especially Oudenarde [1] and Tournai, are engaged in the linen industry. But the great spinning centre—for hemp and cotton as well as flax—is in the higher humidity of the Lys-Scheldt confluence; and this site, at about equal distances from the three great lace-making centres of Bruges, Brussels, and Mechlin, and at the limit of tide on the Scheldt, has made Ghent the textile metropolis of Belgium.

The decay of the old historic cities, Bruges and Ypres, was **"Dead"** mainly due to the silting up of their waterways, accelerated by **Towns.** neglect of them during times of constant war—civil and otherwise; but there were other causes at work. For instance, the Orient trade had been diverted from the Rhine valley to the Atlantic; this gave special advantages to the better harbours of Rotterdam and Amsterdam; and, in any case, the Flemish trade had been carried by Hanseatic rather than by Flemish vessels. It was the inheritance of Roman civilisation that gave Flanders its first start; it was the revolt against the Roman Church that gave the Flemish ports their most formidable rivals; and the most prosperous of all the old Flemish centres, Lille, is now outside the frontier of Flanders.

Once access to the sea had to be sought northward, not west- **Brabant.** ward, Brabant was bound to flourish at the expense of Flanders; Antwerp became the obvious sea-gate of the country; and sites commanding the approach on Antwerp from landward at once became important. The natural approaches were by the Dyle valley or the Senne valley. The Romans seem to have built the first castle on the hill beside the Dyle that made Louvain a good site for the capital of the Brabant dukes; but the island in the Senne at the foot of the "hill" country (cf. p. 262) gave a better relation to the great War-and-Trade route of the Sambre-Meuse valley, besides holding the balance between Bruges and Liège, the Rhine and the Ardennes, and so Brussels displaced Louvain as the ultimate site for a capital. Both cities, like Mechlin, were interested in the early import of English [2] wool *via* Antwerp; but Mechlin, still the ecclesiastical capital of Belgium, was not only nearer the port, but also commanded the approaches both of the Dyle and of the Senne.

Eventually, the balance of power was not a question between **Liège.** east and west, but between north and south, the great port and the coal-field, with the language-line marked by Waterloo except for the French "island" of Brussels; and the coal-field had the advantage of imposing an economic importance on a previous

---

[1] The first workmen for the Gobelin tapestries came from Oudenarde.
[2] Tournai is one of the few old towns, originally dependent on local wool, that still maintains an important woollen industry (carpets).

strategic importance.   Long before the mineral wealth was of any importance, the convergence of the Vesdre and the Ourthe valleys on the narrow Meuse valley—at the precise point where the Meuse works suddenly away from, *i.e.* north-west of, the historic line of movement between Arras and Aix-la-Chapelle,—had made the site of Liège of very great political and strategic importance ; and other influences were focused there as the eastern outpost of French civilisation.   With the development of the mineral wealth, it had also exceptional advantages.   Iron and lime-stone were found almost throughout the whole lie of the coal (*c.* 100 miles) ; and to the east, where the coal was nearest to the surface, there were lead and copper as well as one of the richest zinc areas on the face of the earth.   And before the local supplies were exhausted, as the purely Belgian supplies practically are now—though Luxemburg produces *c.* 4.500,000 tons a year—the Seraing surburb of Liége had come to rank with Essen and Creuzot as a metallurgical centre, and had access to a system of inland waterways second only to, and copied from, that of their Dutch neighbours.

Verviers.   The zinc deposits were also near old historic towns, Huy and Verviers—the former where the valleys of tributaries to opposite banks of the Meuse have carried a great north-and-south road for over a thousand years, and the latter on the flank of the direct road from Aix to Liège.   South of the Huy-Verviers line the Ardennes highland makes the best sheep-rearing area in Belgium ; and all these towns began their career when wool was much the most important textile in use in Europe, and when the only other of any practical importance was flax.   Verviers still has a large woollen industry, especially in washed wool and yarn ; and the special advantage of the site is that the Gileppe tributary of the Vesdre flows over only slate and sandstone, and so its water is peculiarly free from lime and other impurities.   To guarantee a constant supply a huge dam was built across the valley, which is kept heavily timbered to economise the rainfall.

Belgian *v.* British Hard-ware.   As the progress of the hardware industry in Belgium has been partly at the expense of that in England (*e.g.* Liège guns *v.* Birmingham guns)—quite apart from any question of the colourable, if not fraudu-lent, imitation of trade-marks, etc.—and as the Belgian conditions in themselves are by no means wholly favourable, it is worth while examining the question a little further.   For instance, there are obvious reasons for traffic by rail or river or canal following what is at once a direct east-and-west route and a natural depression along the northern foot of the Ardennes highland, and the only one wide enough to carry road and rail, river and canal ; but there is no obvious geographical reason for westward traffic going to Antwerp instead of Rotterdam, unless the former is the cheaper.

Now the Belgian coal has been worked for a long time, it is

quite limited in area, it is only found now at great depths—except in the new Campine field, *i.e.* along 51° N.—it lies in very narrow seams and in distorted strata, necessitating much unproductive work, and it is liable to violent discharges of firedamp, which hampers the use of explosives, etc.; and the development of it has, therefore, involved incessant care and skill,—qualities which have become quite characteristic of the Belgian miners—and has been "expensive." Till lately, however, no fiscal or other barrier has been raised to the import of coal because of the recognised necessity of keeping a cheap basis of industry. The position could only be met by very low wages and long hours of work—a possible solution where the standard of comfort has been measured by "black bread"; and it was almost entirely this that gave Belgian goods advantage over British. For instance, just before the war about £500 more was paid *as wages* in the construction of a British locomotive than in the construction of a Belgian one of exactly similar type; turners in Belgium were content with 5½d. an hour, and fitters with 5d.; and in most other industries common to the two countries, 4½d. an hour in Belgium corresponded to 9½d. an hour in Britain. Only the superior workmanship of the British mechanic and the entire absence of slackness on the part of British manufacturers saved the situation then.

Cheap labour—with a depreciated franc!—is still a vital feature in the typical industries of Belgium, *e.g.* the glass of Mons and Liège; and perhaps the next most important feature is the variety of the home products, especially those dependent on agriculture. Two-thirds of the area is cultivated, mostly in tiny holdings and by the spade; and nearly a quarter of the population (*c.* 8,000,000) is occupied in agriculture. Oats are grown on the rainy highland, rye in the sandy centre, and wheat on the Hesbage limestone; Flanders is famous for its horses and cattle, and grows the finest flax in the world, as well as tobacco and chicory, potatoes and flowers (especially azaleas and orchids, near Ghent). So, the clay of the northern plain makes as good bricks, *e.g.* at Turnhout, as its peat makes good fuel for the Campine dairies; and, besides the minerals already referred to, the Ardennes highland is rich in good stone, *e.g.* the "Dinant" marble.[1]

The dense population can, therefore, draw much food and raw materials from the highly-cultivated small holdings of their own country, from fenny plain or forested highland; but they are largely dependent on imports for both food and raw materials, partly because it is profitable to export, *e.g.* their very fine flax, and to import Russian flax for the Courtrai mills. And it is typical that the most important imports should be akin to those products

---

[1] The Lesse valley is famous for all kinds of limestone products and phenomena, *e.g.* the Grotto of Hans.

which are, or have been, the main domestic sources of the country's wealth. Much the largest imports in quantity have been normally coal and iron, while the most valuable import, except wheat, has been wool. At the same time the largest export has also been coal, and much the most valuable has been wool, "Transit" wheat coming second.

Customers.   As wheat is such an important import, in both quantity and value, Belgium has naturally a busy trade with such a large exporter of wheat and wool as Argentina; the rest of her wheat comes now from U.S.A. and Canada, not from Eastern Europe, but most of her wool still comes from France. The closeness of her links with her immediate neighbours in 1913 is seen in the fact that about 70 p.c. of her exports went to four countries—Germany (26 p.c.), France (21 p.c.), Britain (13 p.c.), Holland (10 p.c.); but the U.S.A. demand for plate-glass (for automobiles) has greatly increased the Belgian export to U.S.A., and in 1924 the figures were Britain (*c.* 30), France (*c.* 23), Holland (*c.* 18), Germany (*c.* 14), U.S.A. (*c.* 9).

LUXEMBURG

The Town.   The sovereign Grand-Duchy of Luxemburg grew up round the river-girt crag and town of Lützel-burg ("Little Castle"), which became an important fortress as early as the days of Otto the Great, and came to be considered not only very like Gibraltar, *e.g.* in its rock galleries, but also as the next strongest fortress in Europe.

The Land.   The hilly surface of Ardennes spurs and Lorraine plateau drains by the fertile valleys of Sauer and Moselle into Germany, while the barren and sparsely-peopled north makes a natural frontier towards Belgium; and so after Waterloo the area became part of the German Confederation, thus entering the Zollverein. It is mainly pastoral, and has busy tanneries and glove factories in the Alzette valley; but the great wealth of the land is in the extreme south, where the "Gut-land" of the Moselle valley grows excellent wine, with special cellars at Remich and a central market at Grevenmacher, and where the Lorraine plateau is extremely rich in iron-ore, especially round Esch. Though the mass of the people speak a Low-German patois mixed with Walloon, the business community speaks mainly the French tongue of Lorraine; and now, under the same ruling House, it may become virtually a dependency of France, but it is definitely in economic union with Belgium.

CHAPTER XVIII

HOLLAND

HOLLAND, like Switzerland, is one of those political units the **Essential** position of which can scarcely be considered apart from the **Character.** physique. For, if Holland is compared with other areas which are low and level, or which have very good or very bad access to the sea, or which have serious problems of irrigation or of drainage, everything else sinks into insignificance beside the two considerations —(1) that, in physique and climate, it is a temperate delta, and (2) that, politically, it is a Buffer State. And these two are fundamentally related, because the delta is that of the greatest German river—the Germans are the more numerous, the stronger, and the more aggressive, of the two nations between which the Belgo-Dutch "Buffer" is thought necessary—and it is precisely Holland that blocks the expansion of Germany seaward.

The very existence of the delta depends on the position of the **The Delta** area at a corner of an ocean "pocket" where tidal crest and trough so far neutralise each other as to allow the deposit of deltaic silt; but only where the coast-line lies roughly due north and south, *i.e.* in Holland proper, is it continuous. Where it lies roughly east and west, *i.e.* parallel with the prevailing winds, as in Friesland and Zeeland, it is discontinuous. The Frisian and Zeeland islands, therefore, helped to isolate the central nucleus; and this was greatly emphasised by the marshy character both of the coast-line itself and of the Ems basin which forms its natural limit eastwards.

The dominant influence seaward has been that of wind, and it **Sand-** is shown in the characteristic sand-dunes. These do not usually **dunes.** reach a height of more than 30 feet, but in the centre of the continuous coast-line, *e.g.* near Haarlem, they reach 200 feet; and they tend to widen northwards, *i.e.* with increase of width in the sea over which the S.W. winds blow, especially in summer (cf. p. 56), though the maximum (well over three miles) is actually near Haarlem. Their extension now is controlled by the planting of bent-grass, etc., the long roots of which so bind the sand that it can no longer drift landward; but some of the most famous Dutch bathing-centres, *e.g.* Scheveningen, owe their importance to the flats left by migration of the dunes landward within historic times.

Dune and Beach.   The whole coast, then, alike on the islands and on the mainland,[1] consists of a "double" line of beach and dune, the broad and sandy beach sloping very gently under the sea, while the dunes have a very steep seaward face, due to the erosion of tide or wind or both. The dunes themselves are obviously porous and dry, but drain into marshy depressions; and they thus offered sites for early settlement, with conditions to leeward favourable to the growth of timber or to reclamation for agricultural or pastoral purposes. It was under such circumstances that the Hague—still famous for its park—and Leiden sprang into early importance; ports such as Amsterdam and Flushing still procure drinking water from the dunes; and the same control makes Haarlem equally famous for bleaching and dyeing, for brewing and bulb-raising.

Arms of Sea.   Where the coast has been deeply breached, as by the Zuider Zee and the Lauwers Zee, the inland seaboard is generally formed of marine clay at or below sea-level; and here great need for dykes arises, there being *c.* 200 miles of dykes—badly broken in 1916—round the Zuider Zee alone. These arms of the sea were actually made[2] or greatly enlarged by storms in the thirteenth century; and it seems to have been the very unfavourable weather at the same time that led to the sudden and final decay of the old Roman roads, *e.g.* in the Rhine valley. That is to say, the same cause which forced traffic on to waterways inland, provided sites such as those of Amsterdam and Zwolle with exceptional facilities for traffic on the larger waterway from retired and easily defended positions. In those days, too, Zwolle or Kampen was as safe as Amsterdam, because the Bourtanger morass had not been drained; and the early influence of the ports landward may be gauged by the subsequent projection seaward of international frontier-lines in the valleys of the Vechte and the Rhine. Amsterdam was "built on herrings," and possibly old marsh-land between the Zuider Zee and the Dollart may have preserved the human type and the peculiar tongue of the "Free Frisians" in marked purity.

Deltaic Control.   In the nature of things the delta of a large river is a thoroughfare, giving access up the river and out to sea; and in early times its importance varied with the smallness of the sea in front and the length of navigation on the river behind. It is also naturally an area of marsh, all the typical deposits of Rhine and Scheldt and Maas being below normal sea-level; and the very existence of the delta implies a deposit of silt which must be constantly raising the beds of the rivers. The choking up of any one distributary, however, only led to the opening of others, until there was a perfect

---

[1] The dunes are absent on the mainland where it is fringed with islands.
[2] Ramaer's study (1928) of the Zuider Zee in Roman times is unconvincing.

network of channels ; and the natural foci must always have tended
to be the corners of the Δ, *i.e.* the extreme seaward point of the north
bank of the north branch at the Hook,—the similar site on the south
shore of the most southerly island at Flushing,—and the landward
apex of Dordrecht.   Obviously, with the development of civilisation,
the safer position on the shallower waters up the river would tend
to decrease in importance ; and, in this case, Dordrecht had—
before the year 1421—the additional advantage of being actually
on the mainland.   It was, therefore, the natural site for the capital
of the Counts of Holland ; and it was from Dordrecht that the States
practically declared their independence in 1572.   But the economic
position was impaired by the disturbance which left it an island,
and so involved transhipment for the mainland.

Obviously, too, canals make the only "cheap" and practicable **Canals.**
roads through natural marsh-land ; and many of the most important
canals in Holland were originally natural waterways of some kind
or other, *e.g.* a small stream or the distributary of a large river.
They are also the safest kind of road in a Buffer State.   Roads
on piles would only have opened the door to invasion, whereas
the opening of "doors" on canals had a precisely opposite result,
as the French discovered in 1672 ; and the one danger—from
frost—offered little help to invaders such as the Spaniards, who
were certainly not expert skaters.   It is peculiarly significant,
therefore, that the senior branch of the Dutch Army should be the
Engineers, and that they should have their headquarters at Utrecht,
i.e. the farthest point eastward from which, at equal distances from
Amsterdam and Dordrecht, the whole lowland can be flooded.

The essential problems of the water-control are to arrest, to **Drainage**
imprison, to lead off, especially in the islands of Zeeland ("Sea **Problems.**
Land") and the "hollow land" of Holland proper.   The existence
of the country depends on sea-dykes, and its prosperity depends
on river-dykes.   One-quarter of the land—practically all west of
a line through Dordrecht and Utrecht—is actually below sea-level,
and a considerable additional area is not one yard above sea-level,
and would be submerged by any high tide if the dykes and dunes
were removed ; and, therefore, not only are large sums spent on
strengthening and extending the barriers, but stringent laws are
passed against the destruction of birds (such as storks) which prey
on burrowing animals.   The dykes are placed specially where erosion
has broken the continuous barrier of dunes, as in Walcheren, and
they are reinforced by banks of boulders and moles.   The ravages
of the pile-worm can be partially kept in check by electricity ; and
experience has greatly improved the methods of reclamation.

The first step in reclamation is to "impolder," *i.e.* dyke in and **Impolder-**
then drain ; and the drainage is effected by natural or artificial **ing.**
means according to the position and character of the land.   For

the western part of the country is distinctly lower than the eastern ; the former is low fen or sea clay, while the latter is sand and gravel with stretches of heath ; and the whole slopes down gently from the south-east—where the chalk hills of Limburg reach 1000 feet —to several feet below sea toward the north-west. As the surface of the clay in the north-west is usually several feet below Amsterdam " zero," the water has to be raised before it can be discharged ; and this has been greatly facilitated by the substitution of steam-power for wind-power—greatly to the disfigurement of the landscape,— and the greater regularity of the pumping engines has increased the

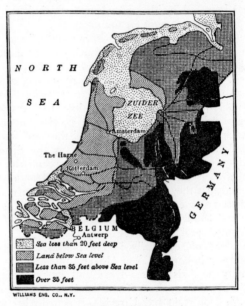

Relief of Holland.

value of the drainage canals for navigation. At the same time, the temporary storage of the drained water in basins, even in Friesland, guarantees the polders from drought even in the driest parts of the country ; and it helped the great development of butter-making in Friesland, the province producing about one-third of all the " factory " butter made in the country, *i.e.* one-fifth of the total output.

Distribution of People.   The distribution of people is intimately associated with these schemes. Marsh-land must be drained before it can be lived on ; and, as such drainage is difficult and expensive, alternatives and compromises are sought. In Holland the alternatives were to live on the water in a barge, or to drain the minimum area, and simply cover that with houses of local brick or imported wood and stone. These ran naturally in thin lines along the narrow drained streets; and when the houses stop, their places are taken by long lines of tall trees, whose roots help to bind together the friable edges of the raised causeway. For ages, therefore, the presence of Barge-life and the absence of what we mean by Village-life have been typical of the area; while the historic pre-eminence of Flanders over Zeeland and Holland was based precisely on its greater suitability for settlement because of its higher level and drier soil.

About one per cent of the population live on barges; and one reason for the cheapness of barge-transport in Holland is because the barge is a house as well as a conveyance; but such life is purely nomad, and interferes so much with the proper care and education of children, that till recently thousands grew up as little better than beasts of burden on the tow-path. For the salvation of the children, they must have a fixed home on shore, which means that barge-life is doomed; but barge-transport is an inevitable sequel to the site of Holland, as a great ocean-gate for the water-borne traffic of Central Europe. And, under such circumstances, the tendency in modern times is for all the traffic to concentrate on one or two great ports. *Barge Transport.*

The influence of this tendency is important. On the one hand, it has led to the extension of all the typical centres, *e.g.* Rotterdam, *over* the river-dyke on to the actual bank of the river; on the other hand, it has decided the relation of the various waterways to their districts and to one another. Thus, amongst the sea-isles of Zeeland the canals connect inland towns with ports, *e.g.* Middelburg with Flushing; in Holland proper they connect river-ports with the sea, as Rotterdam is connected with the North Sea by the New Waterway and Amsterdam by the North Sea Ship Canal; away from the sea and the great rivers, they are themselves the main arteries of traffic; in the drier parts of the country they are even used for irrigation, *e.g.* in Drente and Overysel. As the competition of Belgium and Germany came to be felt, rivers and canals in Holland became practically "free"; and this again increased the tendency for traffic to move in the line of least resistance on a single great port. This line of least resistance is dictated by the Rhine itself, for the Rhine coast is coherent, while the Scheldt coast is incoherent; and, while the Maas threads the South Holland archipelago, it also sends a branch to the Waal—at Gorkum—on its way to the Lek *via* the so-called Nieuwe *Maas*. The great focus, therefore, must be on the common mouth of Maas and Waal and Lek, where Rotterdam is the landward terminus of the great New Waterway. *Uses of Canals.*

The obvious rivals are Antwerp and Rotterdam. The former, as we have seen, has access with the Rhine by semi-artificial waterways, as Rotterdam has by the Nieuwe Waterweg; and Antwerp not only got the start of the Dutch ports, but also commands the *Antwerp v. Rotterdam.*

T

Scheldt as well as the Rhine, and has the additional advantage of a large "heavy" traffic of its own from the Belgium coal-field. But as ocean rates for long distances are exactly the same to all these ports and their neighbours, imports in bulk take the most direct route, *i.e. via* Rotterdam; and it is very significant that two-thirds of the imports at Rotterdam[1] consist of ore, coal, and grain. Outward goods are much more general in character, and do not travel in ship-loads, so that they may prefer Antwerp.

Amsterdam v. Rotterdam. Amsterdam, too, has historic links, *e.g.* with Dutch colonies; but till recently its two ship-canals (the Merwede and the North Sea Canals) were scarcely equal to the newer vessels, and the pace over the Merwede Canal was so slow that the extra 15 miles of distance (over Rotterdam) to the upper Rhine really counted as 50. The city has long enjoyed the partial monopoly of, *e.g.* tobacco and coffee in bulk by the North Sea Canal (now $34\frac{1}{2}$ feet), but it has even less chance than Antwerp in the competition with Rotterdam for the real Rhine trade. Incidentally, even 40 years ago the two canals made the Zuider Zee really useless as a waterway, and therefore removed objections to its being drained and reclaimed. At the same time, the city is a world-market of first rank—for colonial products; and 40 p.c. of the tonnage imported into Holland by sea for home use enters the country by the North Sea Canal. Indeed, so great is the national importance of the canal that it has now been provided at Ijmuiden with the finest locks in the world.

Relief and Climate. There is so little variety of relief that, in an area only twice the size of Yorkshire, there are 5000 miles of navigable river and canal; and the small size and the uniformly low level minimise climatic variations. But marked differences of physical structure and distinct seasonal changes of climate give rise to some variety of landscape and considerable localisation of natural and cultivated vegetation. For instance, the most effective medium of precipitation is the line of sand hills, while we find the lowest levels of the whole country to leeward of them in the polders; on the other hand, conditions tend less towards heavy rainfall, which scarcely exceeds 28 inches, than to high humidity, which is usually over 80 p.c., and which is associated with constant mist in the more dusty parts of the country. Again, wide exposure gives greater extremes of temperature than, *e.g.* in East Anglia,—canal traffic being largely ice-borne in winter—and heavier rainfall than in, *e.g.* any other part of the Great European plain; but the average temperature (50° F.) is essentially temperate, S.W. winds raising the temperature for nine months and N.W. winds lowering it for the three months of summer.

[1] Large vessels *cannot* go farther up the Rhine, and the cargoes of smaller vessels also have come to be transhipped here.

These conditions are reflected in the economic vegetation. The minimum of waste land is in the west, and the maximum is in the east, reclaimed lands being won mainly from the sea in the one case and mainly from the barren heaths in the other. The heavy land makes admirable meadow, and raises also pulse and wheat, while the light land raises rye and potatoes, and is being gradually planted with trees; and cattle are as typical of the heavy lands in the west as sheep are of the heath-lands of the east. Rather more than one-third of the whole area is pasture, while rather more than one-quarter is cultivated, and another quarter is water or waste.

Economic Vegetation.

The fundamental consideration is the cost of drainage. In the "Low Fens," where the foundation is clay, it is comparatively easy and cheap to drain the top 15 or 16 inches; and this is not only sufficient for cattle—though they may need to wear "blankets" —but produces a fine saltish grass which induces a large yield of milk. But for tillage it is necessary to drain at least twice, generally three times, as deep; and the cost in many places is quite prohibitive. Agriculture, therefore, is relatively often more important in Gelderland and Brabant than in Holland and Zeeland; and the slightly more continental climate eastward is an additional advantage, especially for the raising of cereals. Where the balance is held most evenly, as in Friesland and Groningen, there most progress is being made, especially in market-gardening; but the export goes rather to Germany *via* Delfzyl than westward *via* Harlingen.

Pasture v. Tillage.

The horticulture of the west stands by itself, but it is significant that the typical products are all of a bulbous kind and humble habit. The dunes supply the necessary sand, the pure water, and the protection from salt-bearing winds, which are the essential needs of the black peaty soil for the production of spring flowers; and Haarlem became the most famous centre because far enough north to feel the climatic benefit of the Zuider Zee, and because it possesses an ideal site in other respects in the 70 square miles of the drained floor of its old lake.

Horticulture.

Civilisation comes from the sea, and therefore the standard of comfort falls inland. The poorest and most backward elements in the population are in Drente and Overysel, in Brabant and Limburg. The cleanest and most independent are in the Frisian Islands, the sea-base of Tromp and De Ruyter. The grimmest and harshest have been the real Hollanders—the raisers of grass and hay, butter and cheese, under the leaden skies of the dyked polders, the heroes of centuries of war against the grey North Sea. There is the clearest possible distinction between the "Free Frisians," the heroes of a hundred historic fights *on* the sea, and the dour Hollanders, who have fought an equally heroic and still unended war *with* the sea. There is a similarly clear distinction between the taller western people, with their red-tiled or rye-thatched houses of

Standard of Comfort.

brick or wood, and the smaller eastern people, with—sometimes—
peat-roofed huts of clay.   It was only near the sea that—in the
earlier ages—the clay became the basis of industries, some of which,
e.g. the clay pipes of Gouda and the earthenware of Delft, still
survive, but import English clay.

Colonial Empire.   The outward trend of the delta always promised colonial
empire, still illustrated by the Dutch control of the coffee and
cocoa, the sugar and tobacco trades ; and this was emphasised and
accelerated by the need for maintaining a large fleet and the
voluntary destruction of home supplies by the flooding of the
country in the struggle for national independence.   The precise
direction of the colonial development was also wrapped up in the
same problem, for it depended on the subjection of Portugal—after
200 years of pre-eminence in geographical discovery—to the great
enemy of Holland, Spain.   It is still maintained because the
Rhine, Maas, and Scheldt form the busiest network of waterways
in Europe.   Holland still has 50,000,000 colonial subjects, and
perhaps only the Dutch could have coped successfully in early days
with the river-floods and the shoaly seas of Java ; and Holland still
collects colonial produce, and distributes it inwards.   But the East
Indian demand, though growing, is small, and the local freedom of
trade allows it to be met by direct imports from the cheapest
sources, while political pressure practically compels, *e.g.*, German
exports to go by "national" routes, so that Dutch ports and
steamers lack return cargoes.

Political Sequel.   To this economic problem there is a very important political
sequel.   In the days of wooden navies, when easy access to the
sea and to Rhine-borne timber gave the Dutch their chance of
Colonial empire, they were brought into special conflict with
Imperial Spain ; and, when Continental empires rose in rivalry of
the oceanic empires, access to the Rhine valley made these Delta
people also a Buffer State.   Still, where the land is most deltaic, *i.e.*
Zeeland, there are two racial types, Dutch and "Spanish" ; and, where
it is most continental, *i.e.* Limburg, there are two more, Flemish and
German.   But the vast improvement of land traffic in modern
times, and the size and cost of modern navies, exclude from
Naval Power a small State, especially if it is hampered by "deltaic"
deficiency of coal and iron.   And so there are difficult political
problems associated with this Buffer State delta.   For the "habit
of the sea" still counts for much, and the Dutch are the best
sailors along the whole European coast between Brittany and
Norway ; and these fine estuaries are safe for shipping, secure
from naval attack, and easily linked to Europe.   This seaboard,
therefore, became of enormous political importance as soon as
the centre of naval strategy moved from Cape St. Vincent to
the Dogger, *i.e.* from a point commanding the relations of the

Atlantic and the Mediterranean to one commanding the relations
of the North Sea and the Baltic.

Under such circumstances it was not surprising that Western **Dutch**
Europe was somewhat disturbed by the " Heemskerk " Dutch Defence **Defence**
Bill, providing for a remarkable strengthening of the seaward de- **Bill.**
fences and ignoring the gross and admitted deficiencies of the landward defences.   The difficulty in the latter case was the systematic
assertion in recent years by German strategists that " Germany
may find herself compelled, for military reasons, to disregard the
neutrality of Belgium."   The difficulty in the former case was the
extraordinary natural strength of Holland seaward.   Holland lies
on the flank of any naval movement between the Elbe and the
Thames or the Seine and on the flank of any military movement
across Belgium.   Naval attack on Holland itself is inconceivable.
Across the Zuider Zee it could only be conducted by boats drawing
less than 10 feet of water, which no doubt justifies replacing the
Helder, as a naval port, by Ijmuiden or the Hook; the coast from
the Texel to the Hook has a shelving foreshore, which would greatly
hamper disembarkation; the Hollandsch Diep and Volkerak, like
the West Scheldt,—quite apart from the forts of Helvoetsluys and
Willemstad—are only suitable for vessels of the coast-defence type
found in the Dutch Navy, and could not even be used as a naval
base by vessels of the type normal in the British and French navies.

[*These two paragraphs are retained from the 1913 edition.*]

On the contrary, invasion of Holland from the land side would **Landward**
seem to be perfectly simple.   Only Holland proper and small **Defence.**
portions of the adjacent provinces are protected at all; and even
this " Holland Fortress," as it is called, depends mainly on three
lines of defences or prepared positions—those of the Ysel, the
Grebbe Line from the Rhine to the Zuider Zee at Spankenburg,
and a line joining Amsterdam to Gertruidenburg *via* Naarden
and Muiden, Utrecht and Gorkum.   The great weapon relied on
is inundation; and, even if an enemy were to divert all river
water from the Grebbe Line, it could be flooded by salt water from
the Zuider Zee *via* Muiden.   (Cf. Marga, *Geographie Militaire*, Part
ii. vol. i. pp. 95, etc.)

Smallness is typical of Buffer States, and is eminently **Small**
characteristic of Holland.   The land itself is very small, and its **Size.**
features are all more or less in miniature.   " It is a chessboard
land, in which the average school-class numbers seven children ! "
As its international position is also delicate, some of its political
and economic phenomena are peculiarly interesting.   For instance,
the importance of the transit trade in foreign goods has involved a
need for—which has developed into a gift for—learning foreign
tongues and practising economic cosmopolitanism; and these
two considerations make Holland a most appropriate area

for International Conferences of all kinds, political, religious, etc. On the other hand, politics are merely academic, much discussion about patriotism being as typical as the difficulty in recruiting soldiers; the small physical horizon seems to be reflected in a small political horizon, and the most important political questions are of a parochial character. Again, the small size[1] and the rich soil encourage spade labour; but the high rent of reclaimed lands and severe agricultural competition depressed wages, which meant poor housing and under-feeding. Under such circumstances, the poorest agricultural workers have been attracted to the industries of Belgium and Germany, as the high pay offered to soldiers in Holland attracted adventurers from Belgium and Germany, thus causing some international friction—a typical phenomenon in a Buffer State—with two nations neither of whom relished losing good soldiers.

National Unity. The one great advantage of the geographical control is that gregarious instinct of a dense population within a closely limited area, which cannot fail to draw out national feeling; and this has been wonderfully intensified by the religious unity of the people and by their political history. Mixture of race is still reflected in differences of customs and costumes, of diet and dialect, but unity of control has ruled out all vital differences. Unfortunately this control has been associated so largely with barge-life and constant fog that it has over-emphasised every tendency to caution and deliberation—in word and deed—already emphasised by a delicate international position; and the greatest political failing of the people is the habit of thinking too slowly and acting too late. It is, no doubt, the same influence that makes them still live mentally in the days of Rembrandt and Erasmus, De Ruyter and Tromp— all natives of the misty islands and the hollow lands for which they fought Spaniard and Pope and grey North Sea.

Industries. The distribution of towns and industries, and the character of both, largely reflect these geographical conditions. For instance, though the polders raise a good type of horse in Friesland, their value is specially for cattle; and dairy industries are specially suited to a country like Holland, with important colonies to attract its male population into commerce. The success of the dairy products in Holland is largely due to the care with which quality is guaranteed by "Control Stations" in all parts—Leiden and Goes, Eindhoven and Maastricht, Deventer and Assen, Groningen and Leeuwarden. Slightly easier access to salt and slightly slower changes of temperature make cheese rather more important than butter west of the Zuider Zee, *e.g.* at Edam and Gouda, so that Alkmaar is the great cheese market, while Groningen is the great butter market.

---

[1] Of the total holdings, nearly 90 p.c. are less than 50 acres, and over 50 p.c. are less than 12 acres.

Quantities of margarine are also made, *e.g.* at Oss.   Again, rye
is the typical grain, being most important in the more continental
climate of, *e.g.* Drente ; and it is the base of the typical food and
drink of the people, the bread being made mainly of rye—mixed
with wheat—and both the " Hollands " gin of Schiedam and the
curaçao liqueur of Rotterdam having a rye base.   A large amount
of alcohol has been made from potatoes and sugar-beet, and the
country is one of the chief refiners of beet-sugar, Rotterdam and
Amsterdam being the two great centres.   The associated vinegar
industry is supplied with onions, gherkins, and cauliflowers—for
pickling—from the market-gardens of Holland proper, *e.g.* between
Alkmaar and Hoorn.

The deltaic formation being naturally devoid of minerals except
such as peat and clay, and the only coal in the non-deltaic part
of the land being in Limburg (*e.g.* Heerlen) and limited in
quantity, manufactures depend largely on imported coal ; and this
tended to localise them on the seaboard or where there was easy
access to German or Belgian coal.   A low standard of comfort,
implying a low wage, *e.g.* in Overysel and Limburg, was another
factor ; and the more modern manufactures sprang up, therefore,
along the Westphalian frontier, especially in the Twente and the
Peel districts.   The former specialises in cotton, *e.g.* at Enschede
and Almelo, and the latter in mixed cotton and wool, *e.g.* at
Roermond and Helmond.   The older industries were in flax and
wool, *e.g.* the " brown Holland " of Tilburg and Eindhoven, in the
great flax-growing area, and the carpets of Deventer, on the seaward
edge of the great sheep-raising area.   The typical " colonial "
industries in tobacco and chocolate, quinine and diamonds, are in
or near Amsterdam ; but till recently this old centre of activity was
only hampered by the isolation—between shoaly Zuider Zee and
natural moat of marsh which could be flooded from the dam on
the Amstel—which once baffled Spain and attracted the Hebrew
jewellers who fled from less tolerant lands.

The distribution of racial type, as discussed by Ripley, has, **Racial**
perhaps, more relation to physical conditions than he seems to **Type and**
think.   For the country may be divided into two regions by a line **Soil.**
similar to a large figure 3, the upper curve surrounding the Zuider
Zee and the lower one running from the mouth of the Gelders
via Nymegen to the south-west of Brabant.   This line marks
approximately the edge of a more or less continuous stretch of
diluvial, *i.e.* coarse and imperfectly stratified, sand and gravel, an
area of bleak moor and heath, on which the typical industries are
raising rye and buckwheat (cf. the millboard industry), rearing sheep
and bees, digging peat and—recently—the planting of woods.   Seaward on all sides of this diluvium are the fertile clay-lands, on
which the typical industries are the rearing of cattle and horses—

especially cattle except in the north—and the raising of wheat and barley, of flax and sugar-beet, the latter specially in the south-west, *e.g.* round Bergen-op-Zoom. The distinction is very well marked in Gelderland, where the diluvium is called Veluwe ("Bad Lands"), while the rich "apple" land south of the Rhine and west of the Gelders trough or the Ysel—which, but for river-dykes, would still be, at high water, a distributary of the Rhine—is called Betuwe ("Good Lands"). This was the home of the *Batavians*.

Racial Type and Speech. Practically all over the diluvium the characteristic dialect is Low German, Saxon north of the Rhine, and Frankish south of it, except for the Walloon infiltration down the Maas valley. In the Frisian Islands the native tongue is a "continental Lowland Scotch," gradually giving place southward along the seaboard until the Belgian influence brings in almost pure Flemish. The Frisians are unmixed Teutons, long-headed and oval-faced, tall and fair; and Teutonic characteristics are common over all parts of the land that are in direct communication with the North European plain. But in those parts originally most isolated, *i.e.* amongst the swamps of Holland and on the central islands of the delta, the broad-headed, dark, stocky-framed people show how Alpine refugees found safety in inaccessible "misery spots"; and their rather unexpected survival (cf. p. 80) may be related to the infusion of Teutonic blood, evidence of which is seen in the typical disharmonic face—which is of pure Teutonic oval shape.

Homogeneity. It has been noticed, too, that, while the intermixture is commoner in towns than in rural districts, there is very little difference of type between different social classes. This reflects the influence of (1) small area and uniform relief in producing political homogeneity, (2) a natural refuge in excluding a ruling class of alien type, and (3) spade-culture in keeping rural areas, both in density of population and in standard of comfort, comparable with urban areas. The only qualification is that areas with superior facilities of communication, *e.g.* those on the seaboard and along the great rivers, reflect this advantage in their human standard, especially in the two respects which are most closely associated with stature—food and housing.

Fishing Ports. Various conditions, however, have been adverse to the most typical seaboard industry, *i.e.* fishing. It is curious that the islanders, whether Frisians or Zeelanders, are more interested in the "inner" fisheries, *e.g.* the flat fish and "sardines" of the Zuider Zee and the Wadden, or the oysters and mussels of the East Scheldt, while all the deep-sea fisheries are worked from Holland proper, Ijmuiden being the great centre, and the others being clearly connected with Amsterdam and Rotterdam, *e.g.* Katwijk and Scheveningen, Vlaardingen and Maasluys. Old ports on inner waters, such as Zaandam—where Peter the Great served as a shipwright,—have quite fallen behind; and new ports on the seaboard, such as Flushing, have been converted into "mainland" ports by railway bridges. Walcheren and Beveland are no longer famous for fisheries; the one is the "garden," the other the "granary," of Zeeland.

The influence of the great rivers is also relatively less than it *Riverside* was. Towns such as Maasdyk and 's Hertogenbosch, on the *Towns.* navigable Aa, or Bergen and Breda on the sites of old Roman camps, had immense importance in early days as "Maas" fortresses—on the bank or the flank of the Maas; and scarcely less importance attached to similar sites on Waal and Lek and Ysel, *e.g.* Nymegen and Tiel, Arnhem and Zutphen. But even Maastricht (cf. p. 251), the fortifications of which are now dismantled, could not take full advantage of its position till it was supplied with railways (*c.* 1860); and in modern times such artificial control is still more prominent, especially in the backward diluvial areas. For instance, all the local streams are collected at Groningen, and then discharged by the Reitsdiep to the Lauwers Zee or by the Ems Canal[1] to Delfzyl and the Dollart. So, in Drente, which also slopes towards the Dollart, all southward streams are collected at Meppel and Koeverden, as in Overysel they are collected at Zwolle. The controlling factor here is the strip of rich low-fen which runs along the western edge of the diluvium, *i.e.* along the west of the railway from Zwolle to Leeuwarden, and which supports the busy pastoral industries that are supplied with such admirable "dairy" fuel from the Assen and other peat-bogs of the interior. The famous mat-plaiting of this dairy district is a home industry, based on the natural abundance of the sand-reed ("sand-vats") of Drente and Overysel.

---

[1] As German map-makers—following the German Staff Map of 1911 (sheet 172) —began deliberately printing the Dollart frontier seaward of the Reide promontory as a land and not a water line, thus making the whole estuary Prussian instead of International, it may be useful to emphasise the facts in International law and usage. The frontier is the centre line of the fairway,—the Dutch paying exactly half the total cost of lighting and buoying the whole waterway as far as Rottum and Borkum. The estuary is, therefore, an International "arm of the sea," open in time of peace to all nations without restriction. Of course, this minimises the value of Emden as a naval base, and the value of the Ems-Rhine Canal as a means of divert· ing Rhine trade from Holland (cf. p. 300). The German claim was officially repudiated by Holland, but there was one difficulty—that the seasonal régime of the river varies the fairway from one side of a certain sandbank to another. But surely the line might run along the sandbank; and, at all events, it is not a *land* line.

N.B.—The Ysel and the Grebbe lines of defence referred to in the paragraphs retained from the pre-war edition (p. 277) have been given up.

CHAPTER XIX

DENMARK

Strategic Position. THE Danish islands were not only stepping-stones to Scandinavia, but also a pivot from which the whole Baltic area was more or less controlled for centuries; for in earlier times they were on the margin of civilisation, while in later times they commanded all intercourse between the two "Hanseatic" seas. The safety of this refuge on the margin of civilisation might be inferred from the persistence of paganism in the central island of Fünen (*Odense*, "Odin's Island") or from the fact that the "Danes" have maintained continuous possession of this Sealand[1] ("Sea Land") for 2000 years. The strength of the strategic position may be gauged from the ease with which the Danes "inherited" the Hanseatic claim to charge a toll for entry to the Baltic—a charge abolished only in 1857, or from the fact that Copenhagen to-day exercises a direct control over several typical Baltic products, *e.g.* Swedish and Russian butter.

Hanseat Influence. There was, however, a time problem involved. Geographically, the Danish islands have somewhat the same command of relations between the North Sea and the Baltic as the British Islands have of relations between the North Sea and the Atlantic; but historically, as civilisation moved westward, the Baltic became only a "pocket" of the North Sea, and the influence of Denmark was bound to fall as that of England rose. Nor could Denmark itself become influential as a political unit until the politico-economic unit of the Hanseatic League had broken up. Then, however, her chance came; for her greatest rival, Holland, was occupied in a life-and-death struggle with Spain, which effectually crippled the commercial activities of both the belligerent powers.

The Straits. The construction of the Kiel Canal has affected both the strategic and the commercial importance of the Danish site, but the increased size of modern ships has almost compensated for this; for Denmark dare not have used her strategic position against either Germany or Russia, while larger vessels have to use the Drogden channel through the Sound, *i.e.* the one between the

---

[1] Zealand is a mis-spelling, due to confusion with the Dutch.

island of Saltholm and Copenhagen, and even then some have to lighten at Copenhagen. Further, the Sound is sometimes rendered dangerous for navigation by ice, though it has not been actually frozen up now for nearly a century (1836); and the fact remains that the Great Belt, which is only about 10 miles wide and entirely "landlocked" by Danish territory, is the only one of the

Railway and steamer routes in Denmark.

Straits deep enough for large men-of-war. Even merchant vessels are influenced by this, and the chance of fog in the Belt is far more than compensated by the dues on the Canal. In any case, however, the very large vessels for which the Great Belt and the Canal are suitable, are of relatively little use in the Baltic.

Commercially, too, the Railway competition of the Kiel Canal Ferries. and the demand for quick transport without break-of-bulk have been met by the development of steam railway-ferries, which carry the loaded trains across the various straits between Malmö and Esbjerg *via* Korsör and Nyborg, Strib and Fredericia, or between Malmö and Rostock *via* Masuedo and Orehoved, Gjedser and Warnemünde. This is one of the chief reasons for the great development of Danish commerce (100 p.c.) in the last thirty years, especially at the "free port" of Copenhagen; and it is significant that in 1929 Britain took 54 p.c. of the exports, while Germany took only 20 p.c., and that the Danish mercantile marine is largely occupied in carrying for foreigners, *e.g.* carrying Russian butter to Copenhagen for re-export.

The frontier features have had considerable political importance. Frontier. Danger in early times came only from the Baltic side, for the North Sea coast was very difficult and inhospitable, and the direction of the Sound enabled vessels to use the prevailing wind very easily for either entrance or exit. The dues collected by the Danes at Helsingör, on the narrowest (3 miles) part of the Sound, were nominally paid for protection from pirates; and Copenhagen was the first Danish capital on the Sound at all, earlier capitals being in less exposed places, *e.g.* at Roskilde. The isthmian frontier involves different considerations, for the fact that civilisation came from the south gave special importance to the Little Belt (not 1 mile wide at Fredericia), as it made Viborg the first capital of Jutland and the first Christian centre.

With the development of German nationality, it was inevitable

that Denmark should be dislodged from the right bank of the Elbe
estuary; for the Holstein area was south of the Ägyr Dör
("Neptune's Gate") line of the tidal Eider till Charlemagne's time,
when the same line became the Romani Terminus Imperii, and so
Prussia had some claim on it.   But in 1866 the Powers—forgetting
Bismarck's shameless falsehood in 1864—accepted his suggestion
that the decision should be left to "a free vote," and he at once
transported thousands of German settlers into the area, so that its
inclusion in Denmark became practically impossible.   Under the
circumstances the best compromise was to have the frontier where
the "German" influence died out because of the barren heaths
of Ribe; this happened to be almost the narrowest part (36 miles)
of the peninsula; and the seaward ends of the frontier dipped
southward far enough to include on the North Sea the old port
of Ribe, the great rival of Schleswig as a port, and on the Baltic
the approach to the narrow Fredericia Strait.   Even now this 1600-
year-old line is not the frontier; even Flensburg is not included
in Denmark, still less Schleswig and Rendsborg.

The dangerous character of the North Sea coast, though now
minimised by coastal engineering and provision of lighthouses, is
due to its structure and its climate.   For about 200 miles north-
and-south lies a belt of sand-dunes, averaging perhaps 2 or 3 miles
in total width, the most northerly of them forming the Skaw spit,
while in the extreme south they form part of the North Frisian
Islands.   Everywhere these are more or less discontinuous and
liable to be broken through by the sea, the resultant inundations
leaving permanent lagoons behind the dunes, e.g. the Ringkiobing
and Liim "fiords"; and the submerged dunes are exceedingly
dangerous, even where the channels into the lagoons do not shift.
The danger is increased by the fact that the dusty air greatly favours
the development of fog, thick sea-fogs being a constant phenomenon,
at all events in summer.

The Liim fiord, which was joined to the North Sea as lately as
1825, is of special importance in the Danish fishing industry.   It is
a network of salt lagoons, linking the North Sea to the Baltic and
making Northern Jutland an island group; these lagoons have a
total area of about 600 square miles, with very narrow entrances at
both ends, so that they form a lake-like strait with a depth seldom
more than 12 feet.   This has been converted into a "nursery" for
young plaice from the North Sea, and rivals the North Frisian
waters as a source of supply for the plaice market.   Obviously, the
best harbour between the two nurseries was likely to become a very
important fishing centre; and Esbjerg is that harbour, with huge
floating cages to keep the fish in till they are wanted.   It does a large
British trade—in other things besides fish, e.g. butter, cheese, and eggs.
There are a number of safe little harbours both elsewhere in

Jutland and on the islands, especially on the so-called "fiords"; **Difficult Navigation.** and, while these were a great incentive to movement by sea in the days of small ships, the conditions of navigation were such as to demand and evoke a fine type of seamanship. For the main current out of the Baltic is rapid and strong ; in windy weather it soon becomes rough ; in calm weather there is a good deal of fog ; there is a fringe of ice generally in mid-winter round most of the coast except on the North Sea ; and quantities of ice are carried by the current itself.

Under these circumstances special importance was bound to be **The Sound.** attached to the two ends of the straightest and easiest entrance to the Baltic, the toll-gate of Helsingör on the narrow entrance and the trading haven (Copenhagen, "Merchant's Haven") on the broad entrance. The trade was almost entirely in herrings, and the fish systematically used the deeper Drogden channel ; this was flanked by the Middle Ground shoal and the Saltholm flat—between which Nelson attacked Copenhagen in 1801—on the east and the two islands of Sealand and Amager on the west, *i.e.* the windward side. The channel between these two made a natural refuge, and here Copenhagen sprang up ; but now the Sound is too shallow for the largest ships, and the Kiel Canal gives a more direct route, so that Copenhagen—though now a free port—has increasing competition.

The surface features are almost entirely due to the glaciation **Surface.** which spread over the basal cretaceous limestone from the Scandinavian ice-centre, for the melting of the ice, and the action of water otherwise, left the rougher material to form morainic hills, while the finer material was distributed over the lower land within, *i.e.* to the north of, the terminal moraines. All the highest elevations, therefore, are of this boulder sand and gravel, and lie towards the south and east both in Jutland and in the islands ; and the whole area tends to slope very gently down towards the west, thus tending to expose the limestone base—to form the better coast—towards the east. Where the chalk or limestone lies in a favourable position with regard to the clay, an important cement industry has sprung up.

Over such a small area (*c.* half Ireland), however, there could **General Uniformity.** not be—under the circumstances—much variety of relief ; and no point in the kingdom much exceeds 500 feet. This maximum is found in the Himmel-bjerg district, near Aarhus, and gives birth to the only considerable river in the country, the Gudenaa (80 miles), which accounts for the early rise of Randers as a port. Similarly, the Odense river, draining from the Svendborg hills (about 400 feet), helps to account for the early rise of Odense as a port. In Sealand the maximum elevation is only some 350 feet ; and the lower elevation and the greater distance from the Atlantic combine with proximity to the Sound to make the "Faxo" hills more famous as a source of cement than as a watershed.

Variety of Detail.   Though the general level is uniformly low, however, its glacial history is not favourable to conspicuous uniformity; on the contrary, there is a considerable variety of detail—dead level and swamp being as rare, except in the west, as hills and lakes are common. This makes the problems of farming very different from those in e.g. Holland, as it gives a "Buckinghamshire" effect to the scenery—corn-fields, meadows, beech forests; indeed, the scenery is typically "pretty," as is implied by the name Fünen ("The Pretty Land "), and the small islands, e.g. Langeland (sixteen times as "long" as it is broad) or Möen, are as favoured in this respect as the large ones.

Jutland "Deserts."   The great exception, of course, is in the west and north of Jutland, where the morainic hills slope down to morainic lowlands, and the undulating farm-lands give place to moor and heath and then to peat-bog and sand-dune. Even here, however,—thanks largely to the organising genius of the numerous Jews, especially in Copenhagen—a great change has been coming over the landscape, so that it has been actually altering the relative proportions of urban and rural population. In olden days the oak was the typical tree in Jutland, but the supply seems to have been exhausted for shipbuilding. In the process of natural re-afforestation, soil and climate were more favourable to the beech than the oak; and probably the demand for a "domestic" wood and charcoal further favoured the beech. But in the meantime the destruction of the old forests had exposed the western parts of the country to encroachment by wind-blown sand, thus impoverishing still more a land of bog and moor. Within recent years, as on the French Landes, all these adverse conditions have been fought successfully. The sands have been planted with mountain pine and red fir, the windiest exposures have been isolated by scrub fences, the bogs have been drained, and the moors have been fertilised by top-dressings of marl. The total result may be best summed up by the statement that the old "deserts" of Viborg, Ringkiobing, and Ribe have been growing in population faster than any other part of the kingdom.

Climate.   The climate is something like that of Eastern England, but with a slightly warmer summer and slightly colder winter; and it is characteristic that extremes do not increase eastward, the purely insular environment giving the east an average temperature slightly higher than that of Jutland. There is a distinct four-months' winter (December–March) at about 32° F., in spite of the normal S.W. wind; and the three-months' summer (June–August) has an average of 59° F. The average rainfall is about the same as in Middlesex (25 inches), most falling in the west and least falling in the lee of the chief heights, e.g. only 15 inches falling in the lee of the Himmelbjerg on Anholt. The dry and keen east wind in April is exceedingly favourable to farm operations; but, as it works round by the north into the normal due-west wind of summer, it exposes the north of Jutland to a "skai" influence which is equally unfavourable to vegetation of all kinds.

The one great advantage which Denmark possesses over her typical Baltic rivals with regard to the typical industry of dairy farming is the greater length of her summer and the marine curtailing of her winter, thus minimising the need for indoor feeding of stock and giving a maximum growing-time for pasture-grasses. This advantage and the facilities for commerce gave the Danes an opportunity for developing an industry for which their economic system was admirably suited. Most of the land is freehold and farmed by the owner, about equal quantities being devoted to tillage and to pasture ; and the soil is fertile enough to foster a dense population (averaging 140 per square mile in Jutland and 250 in the islands), while the climate allows its fertility to be used for products so useful in the dairy industry as oats and barley, beet and potatoes. About 1,000,000 acres are under oats, producing about 1,000,000 tons of grain ; the area under barley is fully 100,000 acres less, but the yield is nearly 100,000 tons more. **Advantages for Dairying.**

The personal cleanliness of the people was equally favourable to success, while the smallness of the holdings compelled a wide development of co-operation, by which—especially in the matter of buying, *e.g.* fertilisers or feeding-stuffs—enormous economies have been secured. Butter is, of course, the great product, the yearly export having reached a total value now of *c.* £20,000,000 ; but the utilisation of the waste-products of butter-making obviously involved pig-rearing and poultry-farming (22,000,000 hens). **Human Note.**

The number of live-stock provides much raw material for the glove industry, *e.g.* of Randers and Copenhagen, and the woollen and leather goods, *e.g.* of Odense and Copenhagen ; but the difficulty of importing feeding-stuffs and fertilisers during the war, and the failure of unmanured crops, caused great reduction of stock—500,000 cattle (20 p.c.), 2,000,000 pigs (80 p.c.), 6,000,000 poultry (40 p.c.). **Live-Stock.**

The country is naturally deficient in mineral wealth, except for clays ; but between the chalk and the boulder clay in the south-west there are beds of lignite, and the peat makes an admirable fuel for dairy purposes. The china-clay, which forms the basis of the famous porcelain industry of Copenhagen, comes from the primitive rock of Bornholm, which is typically Scandinavian, not Danish, in structure. **Minerals.**

The economic geography of Denmark has a special interest to foreigners, owing to the particular lines on which the country has developed and to the inclusion of Iceland within its nominal frontiers ; for the one gives a profound lesson to farmers, especially in Britain, while the other has a unique interest for meteorologists, especially round the "British seas." **Icelandic Whirl.**

The excellence of the grass which feeds the famous ponies and sheep of the mountainous island of Iceland, is due mainly to the fact that the island is, like the Azores, close to a great centre of atmospheric action, and partly to the amount of underground heat, as evidenced by the ubiquity of volcanoes and geysers. The relation of the permanent Low-Pressure centre off Iceland to the permanent High-Pressure centre off the Azores seems likely to enable the weather in N.W. Europe to be forecast successfully for long periods ; for when pressure is above normal in the Azores, it seems to be below normal in Iceland. Now, when the difference of pressure is greater than usual during winter months, warm oceanic winds are stronger than usual in the north-east of the Atlantic, and the west of Central Europe is likely to have a spell of high temperature ; and, on the other hand, when the difference is less than usual, the oceanic winds are weakened, and the west of Central Europe is likely to have a spell of hard frost.

Danish v. British Farmer. The development of Danish farming has upset almost every Shibboleth of British theorists ; and, therefore, both the facts and the interpretation of them are of profound importance. As far as all the Danish exports to the United Kingdom are concerned, the British farmer, as a potential producer, is at no natural disadvantage ; his soil and climate are equally good, and he is actually nearer the market. But he has an invincible superstition that cows can be kept only on good grass-land, and that scientific dairy-farming is only possible where soil and climate are peculiarly favourable, *e.g.* in Cheshire or Devonshire. Indirectly this has led to the poor in England more or less giving up the use of milk and eggs !

Pasture v. Plough. Now the Danes have proved that more cows can be kept " on " plough-land than on pasture ; and, as the proportion of cattle to arable land in 1888 was exactly the same in Denmark and in Britain (214 head to each 1000 acres of tillage), any comparison of recent development must be significant. In 1913 the Danish proportion was 264 head, while ours was only 239; and the increase was accompanied by a similar development in secondary products of the dairy industry. For instance, in the same period, the quantity of margarine had risen from under 40,000 cwts. to over 350,000, the number of pigs from under 775,000 to nearly 1,500,000, the value of the butter exported from about £2,500,000 to about £10,000,000. To-day the Danes have 90 cattle for every 100 people, while we have 14 ; and in 1928 we paid them alone £16,600,000 for butter and nearly £25,250,000 for bacon.

Organisation. Now when the Danes first entered on this development, they had a practical monopoly of the British market ; but since then there has risen keen competition amongst producers, and consumers have been educated—by the Danish products—to be more critical. There must, therefore, be more in the problem than the mere influence of personal cleanliness and the taking of pains, scrupulous

---

[1] Our total import from Denmark reached a value of nearly £56,000,000.

maintenance of standard, and the economies of co-operation.   There
is absolutely scientific organisation.   This is shown in various ways ;
for instance, the yield of milk per cow was increased between 1900 and
1913—by keeping careful records and breeding only from the best
milkers—from 450 gallons per year to 585, so that the farmers were
able even to export annually over 15,000,000 kilos of cream without
decreasing their output of butter.   And, of course, the mechanical
"separation" of the cream immediately after milking minimises the
chance of infection [1] and saves the expense of transporting the milk.
The essential point, however, is the growing of green crops, especially
lucerne, acres of green crop surrounding each strip of the real grass-
land which is still absolutely necessary for summer use.   This means
that a well-organised dairy industry is the best possible method of
keeping people on the land—the proportion kept in Denmark being
double that, per 1000 acres of tillage, in England in 1913; it
is also the most profitable way of using land, as evidenced by the
fact that—incidentally to her production of roots for cattle-food—
Denmark has found that she can provide all her own sugar.

The only apparent limits to production are the small total area **Area v.**
of the country and the considerable proportion of it that consists of **Imports.**
moor and "landes."   And this difficulty is met, as far as possible,
by imports of grain (maize, rye, and barley) and oil-cake (cotton,
soya, and sunflower).   In the list of imports, with almost wearisome
iteration, two stand alone—"coal and feeding-stuffs" ; and this is
true of all parts—Aalborg, Esbjerg, Horsens, Kolding, Randers in
Jutland ; Nyborg, Odense, Svendborg in Fünen ; Nykobing in
Falster ; Nakskov in Laaland.   This concentration of economic
interest on a single industry is not dangerous, because that industry
is concerned with a wide number of products all of which have
become normal necessaries of life; and the neighbouring waters,
supplemented by the Iceland and Faroe fisheries, supply the only
other necessary food.

On the other hand, such concentration on a rural industry implies **Towns.**
an absence of large towns and a considerable import of manufactures
and minerals.   Copenhagen is responsible for 740,000 people out
of the total of 3,200,000 ; and Aarhus (76,000), Odense (52,000),
and Aarborg (43,000) are the other centres.   Aarhus is one of the
chief railway-junctions of the country, for the lake-studded Gudenaa
valley, which forms its hinterland, is as important as it is picturesque ;
and Odense has been rescued, by a ship-canal, from the seclusion
which gave it safety in olden days and made it a suitable site for
the shrine of St. Canute.   Aarborg is growing with the development of the Liim fiord.   Cf. p. 234.

---

[1] One of the great economies of this absolutely sanitary method is that the milk
keeps so well that it need not be delivered more than once a day.

U

CHAPTER XX

GERMANY

GERMANY is essentially a continental, *i.e.* a military, area, pivoting on a confined Alpine foreground in the south and expanding to an exposed coastal lowland in the north; and it is significant that the home of her recent rulers is the double principality of Hohenzollern, the drainage of which—like the Pan-Germanic ambition of a considerable section of their people—works its way out to sea by both Rhine and Danube.

Central Site. The essentially continental character of the area has an intimate relation of course to its essentially central site, the controlling influence of which has probably been at least as harmful politically in the past as it is helpful economically now, and has been equally evident in the racial elements of the area, in their strategical problems, and in their modern economic development. Relief control led various groups of Teutonic nomads westward up the neck of steppe which lay between the Carpathians on the one hand and the Baltic lagoons, the Lithuanian forest, and the Pripet marsh on the other hand; and they emerged, from between forested highland on the south and forested lowland on the north, on to a central treeless plain. This position proved to be exposed to various influences—Keltic and Slavic, Scandinavian and Roman, the Roman being based on the old Roman occupation of the great north-and-south waterway of the Middle Rhine, which empties towards what are now the chief industrial and commercial nations of the world.

Political Variety. This was likely to lead to great mixture of races and of political units—of which twenty-six still exist separately—and this mixture was largely responsible for the internal incoherence which delayed union inside the German area; but eventually self-preservation demanded definite union of kindred units against the various foreign influences and powers. State consciousness, as opposed to Imperialism, remained widely dominant in the area; for instance, Alsace-Lorraine was German, not Prussian; there is strong State patronage of art and drama; and there are more than a score of rival universities. But the very variety of relief and race which

impeded unity in early days, has been a main source of strength to
the nation since it was united.

The political frontiers[1] are varied and suggestive. The mere **Political**
fact that Germany touches seven foreign Powers lessens any **Frontiers.**
political danger, but the frontiers are least safe where they face
those neighbours who are at once the strongest and the least in
sympathy with the Germans, *i.e.* France and Russia. In the east
the frontier-line has some natural protection, and in the west there
are the Dutch moors and disjointed hills; but the position was
bound either to obliterate or to accentuate nationality, weakening
the weak or strengthening the strong; and while Germany might
have become—and has become commercially—a link between the
kindred peoples of Austria and Holland, she must have become a
barrier between the alien peoples of France and Russia, or have
disappeared from the political map. A military organisation was,
therefore, necessarily imposed on her, at the same time that her
great length from west to east forced her to be involved in both
Western and Eastern political problems.

But economic union was as much a matter of imperial strategy **Economic**
as the political union; and it was greatly encouraged by the central **Unity.**
site and the access to the Atlantic. The central site gives unique
facilities for trade with the whole of continental Europe without
"break of bulk"; and it is significant that, though there is a
difference of gauge between the German and the Russian railways,
the gauge does not actually change till Warsaw, thus throwing the
inconvenience of the change entirely on Russia. The access to the
Atlantic was of little value in early times, and therefore little was lost
by the fact that it was neglected—though the reason for the neglect
is an obvious comment on the character of the southern frontier.
For from the tenth to the sixteenth century Germany, as the
heir of the Roman Empire, was drawn to Italy so strongly that she
never became the heir of the Hanseatic League. And the very
lateness of her development on the Atlantic is one cause of the
rapid progress which her mercantile marine has made recently, and
which—for the same reason—can scarcely be expected to continue.

At the most liberal estimate, Germany has only about 1200 **Sea-**
miles of sea-coast, of which more than 900 are on the Baltic; but **Coast.**
the relative unimportance of the Baltic is suggested by the fact that,
while perhaps £20,000,000 have been spent on the improvement
of the Elbe estuary, and £7,000,000 on that of the Weser, only
£2,000,000 have been spent on that of the Oder, a river twice as
long as the Weser. The obvious defects of the Baltic are its
shallowness, its liability to ice in winter, and its relation to the
German rivers, which are deprived—by their curious eastward trend

---

[1] Pages 291-5, like pp. 201, 259, etc., seem to have had enough "prognostic"
value to be retained verbatim from the 1913 edition.

in their lower courses—of their natural hinterland in modern times; so that, since the Baltic ceased to be one of the great inland seas of the "world," trade has tended to concentrate westwards, where the sea is never frozen, and where there is easiest access to the greatest markets. The relation of this sea frontier to the land frontier, and the relation of both to the central position, are made more obvious by a more detailed analysis of the precise frontier features.

Land Frontier. The land frontier (cf. pp. 194, 251) has the great advantage of including no less than four areas that are occupied by Buffer States whose neutrality is beyond suspicion, for their future existence depends on it; and, though the Swiss frontier is partly marked by a river, the particular conditions neutralise the typical defects of a river frontier—the riverine lands being marshy eastward and including the Schaffhausen gorge westward. It is true that the Alpine valleys lie rather north-and-south, as evidenced by the

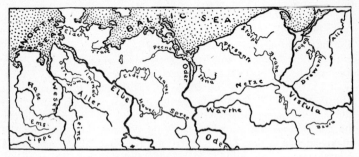

The rivers of the North German Plain.

different political units northwards; but in front of the wild wooded limestone of the Alps proper there is an expanse of peat-bogs and morainic lakes, such as made the site of Munich one of great strategic importance in early days. The frontier towards Austria is equally safe—river gorge and mountain crest; and, again, any balance of power is in favour of Germany, the slope on the Austrian side being much the steeper, especially in the Erz Gebirge, while the Riesen Gebirge have an extreme height (in Schneekoppe) of well over 5000 feet. The admirable Silesian railways, too, threaten Vienna *via* the Moravian Gate (1000 ft.) in a way in which no Austrian railway—still less several—can threaten Berlin. Only in Lorraine, where the old Roman dominion was so firmly established that the native speech has been Romance ever since, and on the Slav frontier in the east, is there any real difficulty; and in both cases the trouble is due to extension of frontier from within.

French Frontier. With regard to Lorraine, it has been urged by German authorities that the distance to Paris from Metz (200 miles) is more than 60 miles less than that from Aix-la-Chapelle, and that the route *via*

Verdun is as easy as that *via* the Sambre-Meuse valley; and this is true of the physical character[1] of the route, however false the suggestion as to its strategic character. Further, behind the wide wooded Vosges a dozen railway bridges and a score of pontoon bridges cross the Rhine, all linked to the twin objectives of Metz and Diedenhofen. Similar considerations are urged about the "Swiss" route into France *via* Porrentruy and the Upper Doubs compared with the legitimate route *via* the Burgundy Gate (1350 feet) and the Middle Doubs; and, again, as far as the physical character is concerned, the legitimate route is the easier. So, in the north, there is ample justification for the extension of *ordinary* railways to the frontier; for, since the peat was stripped off large areas of the Aremberg and Boutanger moors, and the subsoil began to be cultivated, there has been a large increase of population. And, though the drainage canals provide quite good transport, the growth of the Dutch textile industry has raised a growing market for agricultural produce across the frontier. Still the whole argument and the insistence on it, like the character of the railways, are significant; for, logically, it has only one meaning—that the possession of Lorraine obviates to some extent the "moral necessity" for violating the neutrality of the Buffer States in order to lengthen the front available for the concentration of a huge force.

Any charitable doubts must be dispelled by the character of the **Belgian** railways. South of Malmedy,[2] though the normal traffic does not **Frontier.** average half-a-dozen small trains in the twenty four hours, there is a heavily metalled and double track running parallel to, and within a mile of, the Belgian frontier. Along this track there is a station every three miles; and at these stations there is sufficient "loop" accommodation to allow from half-a-dozen to a dozen long troop trains to be side-tracked, and—without blocking the through-traffic on the main line—from 5000 to 10,000 men to be detrained, with all their immediate impedimenta. In each case, too, the sidings are provided with high platforms and all other necessary apparatus for detraining horses, guns, and wagons. These stations are close to the admirable roads which the Belgians have run through the Ardennes to encourage tourist traffic.

The eastern frontier winds through a low plain which once made **Russian** a reasonable unit for Poland, but which offered no marked relief **Frontier.** features to justify its partition; and all the sharers of the spoil suffer in consequence, if not comparably with their guilt. The eastward extension of Prussia over the Baltic lowland, though it exposes to special danger, is a legitimate inheritance from the Duchy of Prussia; and the movement of the frontier since Napoleon's time so as to

---

[1] The parallel route from Strasbourg *via* Toul is *c.* 80 miles longer than the Verdun route from Metz.
[2] Quite recently linked up to the Belgian line at Stavelot.

include Thorn southward and Posen eastward has made it fairly easy to secure connection between East Prussia and Silesia. Still East Prussia is undeniably "hugged by the Russian bear" economically, if not politically; for it is cut off from its natural hinterland by hostile tariffs, and its economic progress has been hampered by its strategic dangers. These are obvious, but over-rated. The total length of frontier from north of Memel to east of Königshutte is about 750 miles, the width of the Prussian tongue from east of Thorn to the Baltic is about 75 miles, and the distance from the Russian frontier in the Warthe valley to Berlin is little more than 175 miles. But the fact that the frontier was deliberately run directly across all the chief rivers and through all the areas of scantiest population is based on geographical conditions which minimise the dangers. For the narrow trans-continental route between Odessa and Pillau (800 miles) approaches the "Haff" coast only through an intricate maze of woods and waters, *e.g.* in Masuria, the most critical points in which are fortified, *e.g.* at Lötzen; and this forested lakeland, with its poor soil and a climate which kills out the beech, has reared a most sturdy population. The same is more or less true of Posen, though the soil is more fertile, this being compensated by the fact that the lakes run systematically north-and-south, and thus offer maximum obstacle to invasion from the east, while the roads on the Russian side are appallingly bad.

Danger-Zones. These physical conditions limit the lines of approach more or less to the main river-valleys, and even here the danger-zone is minimised. For instance, the "narrows" at Tilsit are almost the only point where the broad, marshy, often-flooded valley of the Memel can be crossed with any ease; and, on the other hand, longitudinal reaches of the great river are systematically fortified, as that of the Lower Vistula at Thorn and Graudenz and Elbing. So the Pregel is defended by the fortresses of Pillau and Königsberg, the latter being one of the famous Quadrilateral (the others being Danzig, Posen, and Thorn) which control the whole of and the approaches to the Lower Vistula, with its floodable delta. Over and above all this, two—in some places three—separate, but parallel, lines of railway, capable of carrying the heaviest trains at a high speed, run all along the frontier; and this is justified by the assertion that in times of danger offensive measures may be the best form of defence. Logically, however, this assumes that Russia is more or less equally well equipped for delivering troops in large masses on the German frontier—an assumption which cannot be justified in face of her notorious lack of proper railway facilities even for ordinary purposes. It certainly adds a piquancy to the position to note that the political pressure which caused the change of railway gauge, which theoretically takes place on the frontier, to be moved *eastward* as far as Warsaw, gives Germany the strategic and

economic advantage of being able to run right across the frontier [1]
from all her internal bases without "break of bulk" or detraining;
and, on the contrary, Russia, besides having to cover very great
distances which would greatly delay mobilisation, would have to
detrain and "break bulk."

The northern frontier involves other considerations, for—though **Baltic**
Germany now stands second in the world with her mercantile marine **Frontier**
—her maritime position is naturally worse than that of any other
Power in Western Europe, for her Baltic coast is of quite secondary
importance, while her North Sea coast is very small.   The Baltic
coast may be divided into two parts, roughly described as " Lagoon " coast in the east and " Bay " coast in the west; and in the
former direction German ports are less favoured climatically than
even Russian ports, *e.g.* Libau and Windau.   For while these are
faced to windward by so many miles of sea that they often remain
practically ice-free the whole winter, the German ports are so much
landlocked that they are always—naturally—blocked by ice for some
weeks.   Even on an open gulf like that of Danzig, too, the ports
—unlike the Russian—suffer from excess of river-water, the harbour-
water at Danzig being fully 50 p.c. below normal saltness, and consequently frozen for nearly three months every year; and, of course,
inside the Haffs, or lagoons, matters are still worse, the approach to
Memel from the Baltic being blocked for less than 14 days in
the year, while the approach from the Haff is blocked for more than
140.   On the " Bay " coast conditions are much more favourable,
Lübeck being closed for only one month; and still farther west
they are still better.   For here morainic deposits cut off the natural
outlet of the older and larger rivers, *e.g.* the Eider, leaving the old
river-valleys without rivers of any size in them; and as the submerged parts of these old valleys are—climatically—very near the
Atlantic, and have no rivers depositing silt in them, they make the
best harbours along the whole coast, except for the purely fishing
operations which flourish on the more intricate coast farther eastward.   The most southerly of them, Kiel, happens also to have a very
narrow entrance at Friedrichsort; and the strategic value of this
caused it to be chosen as the terminus of the isthmian canal

These western ports have a further advantage of being **in Haffs.**
the lee of the land as far as wind-action is concerned, and this
is the determining influence in the formation of the Haffs.   For the
surface movements of the Baltic along this coast are either a westward overflow into the North Sea (cf. p. 15) or an eastward drift
before the Anti-Trade winds; and as the latter is usually the stronger,
débris of various kinds gets drifted eastward along the coast.   Thus
Nehrungs, or sand-bars, are built up along the general line of the

---

[1] The German rolling-stock is provided with adjustable wheels capable of actually
working on the Russian 5-feet gauge.

coast, cutting off particular articulations and converting them into Haffs, or lagoons; and a large river soon converts one of these into what is practically a fresh-water lake. The river silt speedily reduces the size of this lake; and, though the reclaimed land may be exceedingly fertile, as on the deltaic dam with which the Vistula has filled the western end of the Frische Haff ("Fresh-Water Lagoon"), the value of the site as a port is ruined.

Where there is no important stream emptying through the coast, the effect is much less marked, but identically the same in character; for instance, the 200 miles of the Pomeranian coast have been converted into a monotonous series of bars backed by tiny lagoons. But the presence of an important river, especially where the coast bends northward and so is more exposed to the west wind, at once makes the feature pronounced (cf. p. 261), the Frische and the Kurische being the most pronounced. In neither case is the bar less than 60 miles long; in neither is the lagoon practically open except at its extreme north-east, *i.e.* leeward, corner—where the drainage of the Pregel [and the Niemen] maintains a channel at Pillau [and Memel]; in neither case has the natural harbour survived—*e.g.* Elbing having had to be connected with Königsberg by a canal, and Königsberg itself having been provided with a ship-canal to Pillau.

Königsberg v. Danzig. The commercial importance of Königsberg, once based on the amber trade, has recently been connected with the strategic value of its position between the two Haffs; but that of Danzig, even when German, was almost entirely commercial, based on the Vistula. The loss of Danzig will naturally affect Königsberg as a port in itself as well as in its relations with the rest of Prussia; and these will be specially affected by any new orientation of Germany *eastward*, based on the large numbers and great influence of Germans in the Baltic States and Russia. East Prussia is markedly feudal and military in spirit, and any such orientation may make use of the fact; but Königsberg is now the only sea-outlet of the province, and must be organised more on the lines of an ordinary commercial harbour. The Polish corridor is too narrow to be regarded as a possible base for military operations; and the presence (in Danzig) of the League of Nations' High Commissioners should guarantee the strictest observance of the regulations by which the Vistula has been organised as an international waterway, and freedom of transit by rail is guaranteed across the corridor between East Prussia and the rest of Prussia.

Stettin. Stettin is in a still better position for trade, because its position farther inland is at once safer strategically and nearer to the great inland centres, especially Berlin. It is, indeed, the most southerly of all the Baltic ports; and, as it is also at the mouth of the greatest Prussian river, it has become the chief Prussian port, specially interested in shipbuilding (cf. the Vulcan yards) and agricultural products (sugar and grain). The net tonnage of vessels using the port is about 2,300,000, and there is a fairway of fully 23 feet to Swinemünde, which is kept open by ice-breakers even in the severest winter. In a very mild winter the breakers may only be needed for perhaps a fortnight (in February).

The relation of these three important towns to the river-basins, **Bays.** from which they have more or less drained population, suggests another contrast between the eastern and western parts of this coast ; for in the west there has been no similar concentration except at a very few points. On the contrary, between the Lower Oder and the Schleswig peninsula no river of any size enters the Baltic—one

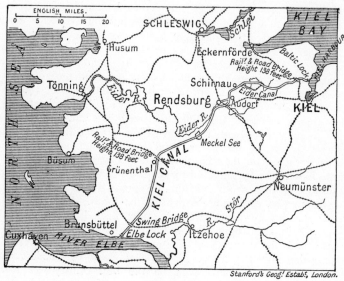

Kiel Canal.

reason perhaps for the fish having deserted this part of the sea—so that no particular point had any special control over a large special hinterland. A number of towns, however, sprang up here, some on the "dead valleys" referred to above and others on the "Boddens" or intricate bays formed farther eastward, i.e. less under the lee of the peninsula, by the débris caught between the westward overflow and the eastward drift and deposited round the outlines of existing land, as in Rügen. The numerous towns were originally all more or less rivals and yet joint-members of the Hanseatic League ; and Stralsund and Rostock were as much favoured in early times by their nearness to Falster (for Copenhagen) and the Baltic proper, as Kiel and Lübeck are now by their nearness to the North Sea and the Lower Elbe.

Lübeck.   It was the little river Trave (70 miles) that made Lübeck the head of the League, largely by encouraging the cutting of the Stecknitz Canal—the oldest in Germany (*c.* A.D. 1400)—to the Elbe and by giving it a definite hinterland ; but even the deepening of the Trave, the modern Elbe-and-Trave Canal, and the excellent railway facilities, have all failed to compensate for the advantage given to Kiel by the Trans-Isthmian Ship-canal. Lübeck does retain, however, so much of its old influence in the Baltic that it carries on a larger Baltic trade than any other German port.

North Sea Frontier.   The North Sea coast is much more important, the Elbe and Weser ports alone owning about 85 p.c. of all German shipping ; and the interaction of strategic and economic considerations makes a virtue even of its shortness, which offers minimum exposure along with maximum facility—since the construction of the Kiel Canal— for concentration on interior lines that are quite out of reach from the sea. For the approach to the coast is so shallow that navigation is far from safe even for moderate-sized vessels in time of peace, and the prodigious fortifications of Borkum, Heligoland, and Sylt (before 1914 connected with the mainland by a railway embankment) very greatly increased the difficulty during the war. Apart, too, from recent developments in air-navigation, it would be exceedingly difficult to cut the canal by a raid from Büsum or any similar railway terminus on the "North Frisian" coast or from the mouth of the Eider. For the shore-waters and the coastal-plain are two parts of a single homogeneous unit, the ubiquitous shoals seaward being the counterpart of ubiquitous marshes landward. The latter, like the moors behind them, have no doubt been largely reclaimed, especially in Oldenburg and in the Ditmarsh and East Frisian areas ; and the estuaries of the great rivers have been greatly improved. But the dyked polders can easily be flooded, and dangerous shoals extend—even on the best estuary—20 miles seaward of Cuxhaven. During the war we had no real chance of reaching the coast in force, even when it was free from the fog under which it is normally hidden.

Hamburg.   The relative advantages of the chief centres illustrate the relation of strategic to commercial considerations. Hamburg owes its importance to the fact that 60 miles up the Elbe the dyked marshes come up against a strip of relatively high "geest"; and in crossing this the river not only concentrates its power on a narrow front which makes it at this point narrower than for many miles farther up-stream, but also cuts characteristically into its right bank, thus deepening its bed on the "Baltic" bank. Here, too, it is joined by the Alster, amid a group of islands, which thus became the natural objective of a land route from Lübeck (cf. the Elbe-and-Trave Canal) and of a river route which taps, *via* the Imperial capital of Berlin, the farthest frontier towns on the Oder and the

Vistula. The damming back of the Alster to form a moat, and the development of the British Isles and of Atlantic commerce, converted this junction into an industrial and commercial centre; and its strategic importance only waited on the acquisition of Heligoland by Germany.

Bremen was an older port, nearer the Atlantic and farther from **Bremen.** the competition of Lübeck, but on a much smaller river; and the position 50 miles up the smaller river could not compete with that only 10 miles farther up the larger river. Even the development of an outport at Bremerhaven, 5 miles nearer than Cuxhaven to the sea, and the deepening of the river up to Bremen itself, have failed to enable the city to keep pace with Hamburg. Its one advantage— reaped specially in the early days of emigration—is that it is nearer to the Atlantic, and so it has come to control the trade in such typical Trans-Atlantic products as cotton and tobacco. The cotton trade is of special interest, because the hinterland of the port in this connection stretches from Scandinavia to Italy and from France to Russia—in spite of the fact that Hamburg and the Elbe intervene eastwards.

The explanation lies in what are apparently the very dis- **Its** advantages of the port. With a depth of 50 feet seaward on the **Hinter-** "improved" river, its immediate hinterland is curiously poor and **land.** useless, and its landward navigation is not half that of the Elbe. But the imports of cotton are crowded into less than six months, thousands of bales being sometimes discharged within a few days; and this means a demand for very large wharfage and store-rooms for sorting. Bremen can provide these just because of the poorness of its immediate hinterland and of its river navigation; and, there- fore, it has come to rival even Hamburg as a *sea*-port, though as a river-port it is insignificant, falling far behind such ports as Duisburg and Mannheim. Indeed, Hamburg's river trade alone exceeds the total outward trade of Bremen by sea, river, and rail. It is equally significant that, while the North Sea coast generally is superior in its wharfage, the Baltic coast—with its deeper shore waters—is superior in shipbuilding, no North Sea port except Hamburg rivalling in this respect Kiel, "Stettin," [Danzig], or even Elbing (cf. the Schielau "yard").

If the Weser, in cutting to the right, had not deserted the Jade **Wilhelms-** Bay, the great Weser port would have been at Wilhelmshaven; but **haven v.** the bay is now a sort of backwater into which the Weser current, **Emden.** and the fierce tides that are typical of the coast, drift so much silt that approach by sea is exceedingly difficult, even on the rare occasions when there is neither fog nor rough water. However useful as a naval station, therefore—and it is one of the three finest naval bases in the world—the place is useless for commerce; and, as the commercial development of Westphalia has been commensurate with the growth of the national resolve to handle their own commerce, and has far outstripped the Dutch willingness to deepen the Rhine in Holland, there has been a strong demand for a seaport in German territory at a minimum distance from the Ruhr valley. The obvious solution of the difficulty was suggested by the fact that the Ems, after flowing within 50 miles of Dortmund, empties into the Dollart at the extreme west of the German coastal plain ; and, as nearness to the Dutch frontier is no longer really a political or strategic obstacle, the Dortmund-Ems canal [1] has found an admirable sea-terminus at Emden [see p. 273].

It may be doubted whether, in spite of its commercial success, this route is the best possible between the Rhine and the Dollart, for the relief just along the Dutch frontier is exceedingly favourable to a deep canal without locks from Wesel to the Lower Ems ; but there is a strategic problem involved, which also has a bearing on the development of Emden. For the reasonable intention to guarantee co-operation between army and navy involved the conversion of Emden—in lee of the great naval base of Borkum— into a great naval station *with large military barracks*, in direct rail and canal communication with the Krupp works at Essen, and with enormous wharfage for the accommodation of transports.

Natural Divisions. The 180,000 odd square miles of Germany include two very distinct areas, a northern lowland and a southern highland, the real

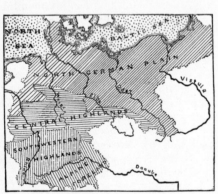

Natural divisions of Central Europe.

dividing line being the mineral-bearing scarp of the old "Variscan fragments" between the Ardennes and the Moravian Gate. The northern lowland has a uniformity of relief and structure which involved a vast expanse of forested marsh in early days, but which — once the forest was cleared and the marsh drained — gave Prussia every chance of establishing a single political unit. The southern highland, which is slightly the smaller of the two (3 : 4), is also so varied in relief and structure that its political destiny was to be partitioned amongst several political units, as its economic destiny was a minute subdivision of labour dependent on water-power ; and there is as much difference between the vivacious

---

[1] The traffic at first (coal = 75 p.c. down, and ores = 50 p.c. up) increased very quickly, then rather fell off ; but the ore traffic is very important.

vine-dresser of the Rhineland and the heavy practical Bavarian shepherd or the untidy independent Saxon miner, as between any one of these and the bumptious orderly Prussian official.

Politically, there is further complication, because these highland **National** units include three "Napoleonic" monarchies, which in origin and **Unity.** development were essentially anti-Prussian; and the lowland plain is somewhat Dutch in its political character towards the west and markedly Slav towards the east, the age-long "Polish Question" being an obvious sign of the inherent antagonism between Slavish Teutons and Teutonised Slavs. This anti-Slav attitude is by no means confined to the Prussians, but is equally strong amongst the Saxons. Economically, there is also some complication, not only in the somewhat antagonistic interests of the agriculturists of the plain and the industrialists of the mineral-bearing scarp, but also because of the variety of structure and physique in the highland. The linking rift valley of the Rhine (200 miles × 20) is a bit dropped out of the once continuous Vosges-Black Forest uplift, and so the outer slopes of the two ranges, like the opposite sides of the rift itself, are identical in structure and physique; but, as the sides of the rift obviously face steeply towards the river, and as its structural floor—once the crest of the whole uplift—is now covered with a deep alluvial carpet, its climate and vegetation mark it off distinctly from the rest of the highland, whether Variscan fragments or Jurassic scarp-lands or Alpine foreland.

Both lowland and highland in early times felt the pressure of **Frontier** Slavs from the east, the one *via* the steppe, and the other *via* the **Marks.** Danube valley; and in both directions Frontier Marks arose to meet the danger. The Eastern Mark, or Austria, arose with its back against forested Alp, while the Northern Mark of Brandenburg arose in forested marsh, boldly pivoting on the Brenni-bor ("Wooded Hill") which was the sacred capital of the Wends. Austria, being the better placed both strategically and economically, grew the faster; and, as the danger from Hungary increased, a strong Duke was always sent to Vienna, and the need for being always ready to meet sudden danger enforced a military tyranny and so only increased his strength. Brandenburg by itself, as an "Arch-Grand-Sand-Box," had no wealth or other attractions; but it got its chance when Frederick of Hohenzollern used the wealth accumulated as Bar-Graf of the Rhine-Danube link-town of Nürnberg, to purchase the Elbe-Oder link-lands along the Spree. This was a commanding position for tapping the two relatively fertile belts which edge the steppe on the north and the south, and which converge where the steppe narrows westward because of nearness to the Atlantic. And, as a military unit, its very sterility was in its favour.

The fertile northern belt runs through Prussia, Pomerania, and

Fertility of Plain. Mecklenburg, up to Lübeck and Schleswig, and is formed by the sunny southward slopes of the Baltic ridge; but, except along the great rivers, the soil is not fertile enough to discourage constant care and toil. The fertile southern belt runs through Galicia, Silesia, and Saxony, up to Hamburg and Holstein; and the great rivers join the two fertile belts across the unfertile one, and are themselves practically linked by the Havel-Spree. Obviously, as pasture gave place to tillage on the narrowing steppe, patriarchal control was bound to weaken, and individualism was bound to be encouraged; but the nomads would settle in very small units, and it is significant that still nearly 60 p.c. of the total holdings are less than 5 acres, while nearly 90 p.c. are less than 50 acres. It is mainly owing to this that fully 90 p.c. of the area has been rendered productive by the spade.

Gravitation northwards. While movement inside each belt, therefore, was naturally from east to west, all the belts had a common gravitation northwards to the coast; and so it was easy for little sea-fishing centres at the mouths of the great waterways to drain potential artisans from their agricultural hinterland, and by their help build up little local industries. With the wealth thus gained, it was again easy to buy royal protection and other liberties; and, though at first no single centre was equal to undertaking a large contract by itself, the whole Trade Area of the Baltic had even in those days common interests. From occasional and informal co-operation with immediate neighbours for a special purpose, to a formal league for all purposes between all the coastal foci and their bases inland, was a short and natural step. The only marked exception was in the maze of moor and marsh between Elbe and Ems. There an isolated and self-contained people perpetuated their fiord instincts as typical fishermen: the rivers teemed with fish; the facilities for water-traffic were so excellent in the milder " Atlantic " climate that they long retarded the building of roads and other " urban " developments; and these fishermen even avoided one another except when they brought their accumulated goods to some shrine which they were bound to attend at the great religious festivals—thus " catching two fish on one hook." Cf. p. 320.

Glaciation and Relief (1). The detailed topography of the lowland plain is intimately related to the action of ice in the Great Ice Age. Not only are very large areas, especially in the north-east, covered with morainic lakes, but the successive frontages of the ice, in advance or retreat, left a series of concentric arcs of morainic hills more or less parallel with the Baltic coast. The most northerly of these, which reaches a height of nearly 1100 feet in the Turmberg above Danzig, is known as the Baltic Ridge, and shut in the first natural hinterland of the Hanseatic League. It runs from Flensburg to Lötzen, with deep détours landward round the Lower Oder and the Lower Vistula, the détour in the latter case providing a background of morainic heights

for the Prussian frontier east of Thorn in 1914, with a subordinate
ridge along the Pomeranian coast. Landward of this Baltic Ridge
is the valley of an old " glacial " river—represented now, *e.g.* by the
Netze-Warthe and by Lake Schwerin—which offers an admirable
line of least resistance for artificial waterways, *e.g.* the Bromberg
and Eberswalde or Finow canals, and which was so swampy that
for ages it made a natural boundary, *e.g.* between the original political
units of Pomerania and Posen or Mecklenburg and Brandenburg.
The reclaiming of the swamp, which has yielded at least 500 square
miles of good land along the Oder alone, and regulation of the
waterways, removed most of the old obstacles to communication
and political union.

The second ridge forms the northern boundary of another old Glaciation
" glacial " river—represented by the Upper Warthe and the Spree— and
Relief (2).
which has played a similar part ; but its political importance, *e.g.* as
a Brandenburg frontier, was infinitely less than its commercial importance, as linking Lübeck *via* Berlin and Frankfurt to Posen—the
political importance of this in the war being equal to its commercial
importance. A third ridge forms the northern boundary of a similar
" glacial " river, represented now, *e.g.* by the Bartsch and the Lower
Elbe, and connecting Glogau *via* Potsdam with Hamburg ; and this,
like the Baltic Ridge, has a short " parallel " complement—overlooking the " Black Elster " trough between Breslau and Magdeburg.
This southern valley was the least favourable to movement east-and-
west, because it was the most marshy ; but its ridge—which ends
up against the Lüneburg Heath—is relatively low and discontinuous,
so that it favoured movement north-and-south. And the most
important centres were bound to be those commanding routes round
or through the swamps, *e.g.* Glogau and Brandenburg, especially
when these stood where the present northward waterways cross the
old westward waterways, *e.g.* Frankfurt and Posen. Both these are
in the central valley, but their importance has been dwarfed by the
overwhelming importance of Berlin as occupying the centre of the
whole plain both latitudinally and longitudinally. So, westward all
the ridges and valleys merge in the dune-girt expanse of moor and
marsh beyond the Lüneburg Heath, where Hamburg monopolises
attention.

The distribution of fertility over the triple formation of coast- Glaciation
land, ridge, and valley, is itself also related to the action of ice, as and
Fertility.
seen in the fertile stretches of boulder clay or the infertile stretches
of lake or sand, the rich sugar-beet lands and the poor potato lands ;
but the preponderance of the infertile—heath and marsh in the
west, and sand and forest in the east—over the fertile caused the
political and economic unity of the plain to be retarded, waiting
for the rise of agricultural and engineering science. So we have
now in Prussia, as over the whole German Empire, a more or less

voluntary association of units whose internal rivalry is no bar to unity against external powers. And it is significant that the predominance of Prussia should be associated with the stimulus of a sterile land which *could* be made fruitful by toil and care and science.

Southern Highland. The uniformity of the northern plain under the action of ice finds a strong contrast in the varied relief of the southern highland, which lies as persistently S.W.–N.E. up to the Harz as the plain lies S.E.–N.W. down to the North Sea. This variety of relief, like the economic value of the various areas, is due mainly to structure: the Variscan "fragments" from the Eifel to the Ore Mountains are rich in mineral wealth, the rift valley of the Rhine is equally rich in agricultural wealth, and both are cut off by the real obstacle of the Jurassic ridges from the Alpine foreground, where alone the relief of Germany approaches a height of 10,000 feet (in the Zugspitze). South Germany, therefore, is not physically, and was not politically, a natural unit; but the natural pivot of Hohenzollern did something to unify the Alpine foreland and the Jura terraces with the Rhine valley, while the large proportion of the South German frontier which faces a Neutral State has favoured commercial union by the peaceful development of industries.

Political Distributions. The great Lake of Constance, too, which ought to have been a natural focus for commerce (cf. p. 85), has an obvious relation to present political distributions, for Bavaria, Würtemberg, and Baden, all front on its navigable waters. But Bavaria is naturally a Danube area, cut off westward by the Swabian Jura near the head of navigation at Ulm, and penetrating across the Franconian Jura only in virtue of the historic continuation by land, *via* Nürnberg to the Main, of the essential *north*-westward trend of the Danube from below Ratisbon. Expansion was easier to than from the north-west; for, though the Danube runs along the south face of the Jura limestone, as along the south face of the crystalline Bohemian Forest, the gradient on the south side is much the gentler, the altitude 20 miles from the water-parting between Ulm and Stuttgart being 800 feet lower on the northern than on the southern side. Further, where the cave-pitted Jura were bent northwards by the resistance of the older rock, the special strain caused such weakness at the curve that volcanic action and rapid weathering developed the pass (1300 feet) which divides the Swabian from the Franconian Jura, and by which the Ludwig Canal follows the Regnitz and Altmühl rivers between Bamberg and Kelheim, dropping nearly 400 feet below the Danube level before it reaches the Main.

Alpine Foreland. The Alpine foreground is a high plain of largely morainic character, its southern belt being an area of morainic hills and lakes, which merges northward in a belt of gravel so porous that it can support only deep-rooted plants (*e.g.* trees); and, where the gravel gets thin, *i.e.* northwards again, the underground water comes so near to the surface as to cause real swamp, as along the Amper and the Isar north of München. A safe and healthy site was thus found for München between the forested background of the Alps and the swampy foreground of the lakes (*e.g.* Ammer and Würm), commanding east-and-west routes both over its own gravel belt and on the rich alluvial lands along the Danube, and north-and-south routes converging on the Seefeld Pass and the Brenner. Political distributions, however, were decided more by the old north-and-south valleys than by the east-and-west ridges or rivers; and, as the Alpine rivers are mainly unnavigable torrents,—though useful for floating timber,—they made convenient political frontiers in early days, as the Lech did between Swabia and Bavaria. The fortunes of Bavaria, too, were associated with the sequence of land-forms in the Upper Danube valley, which—like the Alpine Foreland —slopes from forested hills, past the marshy gravel flats of, *e.g.* Ingolstadt, to the alluvial plain of Ratisbon. And the natural continuation of the general trend from the south-west on this reach had access through the Bohemian Forest at the Pass of Fürth (c. 1500 feet) to Pilsen and Prague.

The water-parting of the oolitic ridges would in any case "throw **Oolitic** off" human activities, like river-water, in opposite directions—to **Ridges.** Rhine and Danube; but their influence as an obstacle is increased by the somewhat incoherent character of the limestone rims and ridges that shut in isolated clay plains, and by a harsh climate which has given the name of Rauhe Alb to the central part of the Swabian Jura. This was specially effective in isolating the basin of the Neckar, so that Würtemberg forms naturally a separate political unit on the east of the Black Forest, as Baden does on the west. Originally, too, the Franconian Jura formed the natural frontier of the Franks, the heart of Francia being the fertile lowlands that focus from east and south on Mainz; and, though the Rhine valley led Baden south-eastward through the gap between the Swiss and the Swabian Jura, the essential continuity of physique made the Swabian Jura the natural northward boundary of the Suevi, as the thinly-peopled highland of the Odenwald is the natural northward boundary of Baden to-day.

The northern end of the Franconian Jura abuts, like the Erz **Fichtel** Mountains and the Bohemian and Thuringian Forests, on the **Focus.** Fichtel ("Fir Tree") pivot, which forms an ethnic and hydrographic, as well as an orographic, focus; and the basins of its radiating rivers—Saale and Naab, Eger and Main—have had intimate relation to the formation of political units, *e.g.* Bohemia and Thuringia. The whole region between the Thuringian Forest and the Harz is a succession of trough and ridge, through which the Saale-Weser valley gives easy communication more or less east-and-west, and from which there is easy communication northward round the

Harz, *e.g.* by the Leine or the Saale valley; but southward the Thuringian Forest stretches a barrier much longer than the Harz (*c.* 50 miles, E.–W.) and rising to a height of over 3000 feet. Here, too, obviously the easiest gradient was found round the ends of the range, *via* Eisenach and Coburg,[1] and this increased the importance of the great east-and-west road *via* Eisenach, Gotha, Erfurt, and Weimar (cf. Jena). But various tributaries of the Saale, *e.g.* the Gera and the Ilm, give direct approach to the range from Halle and Leipzig *via* Naumberg; and their valleys encouraged the multiplication of routes and so of petty States.

Thuringian Routes. The most important of these valleys, at all events in early days, was that of the Gera, the "Garden of Erfurt," because it has the advantage of a mild climate, with Föhn winds (cf. Quedlinburg, N.E. of the Harz) and a very fertile red-marl soil. Eisenach, with the harsher climate and the infertile soil of the Werra plateau, still commanded the north-and-south route of the Werra valley, as well as the east-and-west route round the north end of the range. Better known than either are Weimar and Gotha, with their famous literary and geographical associations. There was a somewhat similar result on the northern side of this belt. Here, in the southern lee of the Harz, another tributary of the Saale, the Helme, not only gives an easy route along the foot of the Harz between Halle and Göttingen, but also enjoys a peculiarly mild climate, so that its valley is known as the Goldene Aue ("Golden Meadow"). And the importance of this fertile area was greatly increased by the mineral wealth of the wooded Harz, especially the silver of the Upper Harz—now of no importance compared with the iron of the Lower Harz. The political importance of the towns here, however, is much less than on the Thuringian slopes, because there are no cross-routes, and the Helme valley itself is only one small piece of the great Unstrat-Leine route that deploys in front of Hanover.

German Race Home. Between the Thuringian Forest and the Rothaar Mountains, the Harz and the Vogelsberg, the Teutoburger Forest and the Rhön, lies the core of Germany and the racial home of the Germans. For these wooded Hessian highlands were never held by Roman or Frenchman or Slav, and have always held the balance, and controlled the natural routes, between North and South Germany, between the Thuringian States and the Rhenish Palatinate. For the volcanic mass of the Vogels separates the Fulda from the Wetter and the Lahn, as the volcanic ridge of the Rhön separates it from the Werra; and the seclusion and safety provided in olden days by the mountain-girt and forested valleys of the Fulda and the Werra, were compatible with facilities for movement between the Vogels and the Westerwald or the Spessart which only needed railways to be of maximum utility. Thus Frankfurt sends main

---

[1] Now less important, in this respect, than Lichtenfels.

lines of rail round the Vogels by both the Wetter and the North
Kinzig valleys, and the great strategic route *via* the Lahn and
Moselle between Marburg and Metz is very nearly a straight line.
Northward, again, Eder and Fulda and Werra converge on Kassel;
and Kassel in turn has wonderful facilities for movement eastward
and northward, by the Unstrut, the Leine, and the Weser.   The
final exit from the highland is *via* the Westphalian Gate and
Minden or along the Teutoburger to Osnabrück.   Both Osnabrück
and Hanover, therefore, have become great railway junctions where
longitudinal and latitudinal lines cross; and, as Hanover has the
advantage of a local coal-field and less distance from the North Sea,
it has now far outstripped its old rival Brunswick, which is practically
the same distance as Hanover from the Baltic.   So, Osnabrück
occupies somewhat the same relation to movement westward from
the Leine valley, as Goslar used to occupy to movement eastward.

The Rhineland consists essentially of two oblong blocks of old **Rhine-**
rock, both lying generally S.W.–N.E.—both graved deeply by the **land.**
Rhine, the northern block across the "grain" and the southern
one along it—and both giving a natural route S.W.–N.E., by
the Moselle-Lahn and the Rhine-Kinzig valleys.   The Rhine
and the Lahn-Moselle gully divide the northern block into four
sections, of which the north-eastern is much the most important.
Along the whole of the northern scarp of the block the old rock,
as in the Ardennes—of which the Eifel is actually a continuation,
—is rich in metal, and it overlooks a "bay" of fertile lowland
underlaid and flanked by coal.   The southern scarp, though
characteristically rich in slate in the Hunsrück, where it overlooks
the Saarbrücken coal-field, is generally much less rich than the
northern both in metal and in fuel; but it has some compensation
in the greater area of volcanic formation, the bleak Eifel being
much less important than the fertile Taunus, as the hot-springs of
the latter, *e.g.* at Wiesbaden, Ems, and Homburg, are more
numerous than those in the north, *e.g.* at Aix.

North of the Lahn-Moselle gully conditions are exceedingly **The Ruhr**
favourable to human activity, for the land slopes down—from the **District.**
breezy, healthy highlands of Eifel and Westerwald—both to the great
waterway and to the North Sea through an ore-bearing scarp and
a fertile lowland flanked by coal, and for ores and fuel and crops
alike there is easy movement to all points of the compass.   As the
highland rises eastward, the rainfall is as heavy there as in the
west; and the great cities that have risen along the lines of
movement draw excellent stone and timber from the wooded
heights that also give them health.   The basins of the Ruhr and the
Sieg are specially important, not only because they are exceedingly
rich in minerals, but also because they are fed from the highest
and most northerly, *i.e.* most exposed, part of the highland, and

yet give very easy access round it, *e.g.* by the Sieg to the Lahn and the Eder, and by the Ruhr to the Eder and the Diemel. In the 1000 square miles that form the immediate hinterland of the " 50 " miles during which the Ruhr is cutting through coal, there is a population of over 3,000,000, including a dozen cities that reached at least 100,000 in 1920, though some have *decreased* since then.

Düsseldorf, 435,000.	Essen, 470,000.
Duisburg-Ruhrort, 275,000.	Dortmund, 455,000.
Barmen, 190,000.	Gelsenkirchen, 330,000.
Elberfeld, 170,000.	Bochum, 210,000.
Crefeld, 130,000.	Mulheim, 125,000.
Oberhausen, 105,000.	Hagen, 100,000.

And just outside this ring are Cologne (634,000) and Aix (150,000).

Rift Valley Section. The southern block of the whole area dropped a central strip to form a rift valley parallel to its axis, but was not broken across transversely, so that the outer edges of the block present a different appearance, and have had a different history,—sinking, not in an abrupt scarp as in Westphalia, but in more or less gentle terraces somewhat similar to those in which the Swabian Jura sink to the Danube. But, while the old hard rock extends much farther in the Black Forest than in the Vosges, and falls—in the lee of the range—to the relative poverty of the Upper Neckar valley, the windward western terraces fall to the fertile flats of the Moselle and the rich iron-fields of Lorraine. Here was the irresistible attraction in 1871—of a warm, sunny wineland, with rich deposits of iron along the west bank of the river and of salt along the east bank (Château Salins), and even with the Saarbrücken coal crossing the political frontier to Forbach. But the Romance tongue of Lorraine, like its political inheritance, was firmly based in the Roman occupation of the land behind Trèves (Augusta Trevirorum), and could not be displaced in a generation.

Its Exits. The general direction of this southern block, as shown by the rift valley which ends northward at Frankfurt, is from south-west to north-east, *i.e.* as distinctly towards the Baltic as the direction of the Bingen Gorge through the northern block is towards the North Sea ; and this gave additional importance to the Burgundy Gate (1150 feet) below the frowning heights of the Jura (*c.* 5000 feet), as the direction of the Lower Rhine gave additional importance to the Main connection with Ratisbon. The dip between the Vosges and the Hardt is not much higher (1325 feet) than the Burgundy Gate—though the Rhine and Marne Canal goes through a tunnel—and so the valley of the Zabern gives an easy route between Strasbourg and Lorraine, while movement eastward finds a fairly easy route up the valley of the South Kinzig to Ulm, and a still easier one round the north end of the Black Forest at Karlsruhe.

The climate is more or less continental everywhere, but reflects

accidentally the fundamental S.W.–N.E. trend of the old rock of **Tempera-**
the country, extremes increasing towards the north-east. Thus, **ture.**
the average annual temperature is 53° F. in the south-west, 49° F.
in the centre, and 43° F. in the north-east; and the range of
temperature shows the same general tendency, increasing more with
distance from the sea than with distance from the equator. The
actual range is due to excess of cold rather than of heat, for the
warmer latitude is counteracted by the higher altitude except in
the Rhine valley; and uncongenial springs—due to the amount
of snow and ice that have to be melted—greatly shorten the
summers in the Baltic provinces. The average range is 42° F. in
the north-east, and 30° F. in the north-west; in the centre of the
north it is 35° F., and in the centre of the south 38° F.—distance
from the sea being in the latter case the predominant influence
in winter, while latitude is predominant in summer. The mean
January temperature varies from 22° F. near Insterburg up to 34° F.
near Cologne; and Cologne has also the highest mean temperature
in July (68° F.), while the lowest is on the Schleswig peninsula.
The lowest January temperature is in the extreme north-east,
e.g. Königsberg (at sea level) having 7° F., while the highest
July temperature is on the Rhine lowland at the end of the Black
Forest, *e.g.* Heidelberg having 93° F. There are, therefore, two
exceptional areas—the north-west and
the rift valley. West of the Elbe the
mean summer temperature is not much
above 60° F., while the mean winter
temperature is above 30° F.—west of
the Weser even above 32° F.; and in
the rift valley shelter and latitude and
altitude combine [1] to give the highest
average temperature for the year, including both the highest summer
temperature and the highest winter
temperature. It was these conditions,

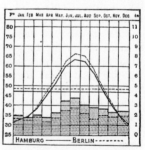

Mean monthly temperature and rainfall curves for Hamburg and Berlin.

coupled with the unfailing water-
supply and the fertile soil, that made it the Palatinate ("Land of
Palaces"). Roughly, then, we may note four climatic areas—(1) of
warm summers and cold winters in the north-west, (2) of very warm
summers and very cold winters in the north-east, (3) of very warm
summers and cold winters in the south, and (4) of hot summers
and cool winters in the rift valley. Areas (2) and (4) are most
favourable to agriculture; but it is in them that Germany has
suffered most of her total loss of 15 p.c. of her arable land and 24
p.c. of her vineyards.

[1] This is also true of the lowlands of Main, Moselle, and Neckar, with an average summer temperature above 66° F. and an average winter temperature above 32° F.

Rainfall.   The range of rainfall, as of temperature, is modified by the fact that the lower latitudes have the higher altitudes; it is also modified by the fact that no uplift in the west is sufficiently high or continuous to cut off the wet west winds entirely from the eastern part of the plain. The rain is not limited to any season, but most falls in summer (cf. p. 56), only the extreme west having any appreciable winter rains, and only the coast-lands having any considerable rains in autumn—when the sea is still warm, but the land has been chilled. The fall generally may be compared with that in the south-eastern quadrant of England. On the higher parts of the west, from the Harz southward and including the Alpine foreland, it averages 34 inches; on the intermediate levels in the west and the higher parts of the east (Erz and Sudetes), as on the lower levels in the extreme north-west, it averages 31 inches; on the exposed lower levels of the north-east it averages 24 inches, decreasing southward even on the slightly higher levels, *e.g.* in Brandenburg and Lusatia, Saxony and Silesia; and it reaches both a minimum and a maximum in the Rhine valley— below 20 inches on the sheltered fruit-lands of the Palatinate and Baden, and above 80 on the Black Forest. Here, too, the fact that vintage-time is remarkable for the absence of rain and the presence of warmth is of prime importance to the vine-growers, as the high percentage of bright sunshine is to the beet-growers between the Oder and the Elbe.

River v. Canal.   The relation of these climatic conditions to the general relief is more favourable to communication by canal than by river; for while the relief is very favourable to the construction of canals linking the great rivers together (cf. p. 303), the climate is scarcely favourable either to continuous navigation or to uniform volume. Rhine, Elbe, and Oder, all have a course of nearly 500 miles in Germany; but only the Rhine is free from serious interruption by ice or by low water, and the régime of even the Rhine has been affected adversely by the clearing of the old forest.

The Oder.   The Oder is relatively the least useful of the large rivers, mainly because of its exposure to frost and because of the nearness of its channel to the "Giant" Mountains in its upper course. It rises only some 2000 feet above the sea, and has a total length of 560 miles; but it has a rapid fall in its upper course, and receives a number of mountain torrents, *e.g.* the Neisse, through its left bank in Silesia, so that there are frequent floods. Its right bank tributaries, on the other hand, *e.g.* the Warthe-Netze, have relief conditions which would be very favourable to transport, if they were not unfavourable to precipitation, so that the main stream suffers normally from lack of depth in summer. The floods carry with them quantities of silt, which have contributed to the fertility of the riverine lowlands, *e.g.* the Oderbrüch below

the confluence of the Warthe, but which are constantly obstructing the waterway.[1] Important works have been undertaken to
improve the conditions, *e.g.* (1) canalisation to enable barges
"always" to reach Ratibor and larger vessels to reach Breslau; (2)
link-canals, such as the Oder-Spree canal from Fürstenberg
to Fürstenwalde (cf. the Finow Canal to the Havel, and the
Bromberg Canal to the Vistula); and (3) regulation of the mouth
in order to concentrate the whole force of the current on the
Swine channel, so as to make it available for large ocean vessels
to Swinemünde. In its picturesque upper course the river runs
through what has been a disturbed frontier area; and its chief
"flood-foci," *e.g.* Glogau and Küstrin, in early days became
important strategic centres, and are now heavily fortified. Frankfurt is the natural pivot of the basin.

The Elbe has obvious advantages over the Oder in length and **The Elbe.**
climate, and over the Rhine in having its lower as well as its

Site of Hamburg.

middle course in Germany. Indeed, its historical associations are
as Teutonic as its name. Its upper course is dotted with strategic
crags such as those of Lilienstein and Königstein, and with battlefields, such as those of Magdeburg and Dessau, Dresden and Pirna;
its middle course has acted as an important frontier to various
political units past and present, *e.g.* Hanover and Prussia, Mecklenburg and Brandenburg; and its lower course has had profound
political and commercial importance since the days when it was
a bulwark against Slav and Viking. The strategic importance of
the gorge through the Mittelgebirge basalt and the Saxon sandstone
is focused at Pirna, and the commercial importance of its middle
course begins where it drops on to the lowland north of Meissen,
Dresden holding the balance; and from Dresden, where the river
is nearly 1000 feet wide, it has a total fall of only 280 feet in the
whole 430 miles of its course to the sea. One adverse result
of this is that in the last 100 miles, during which it has to struggle

---

[1] The spring and summer floods on the Vistula cause similar trouble in Poland.

with the tide, its bed is much troubled by sand; and its meandering course over the plain leads to the dissipation of strength in
numerous branches, especially in the Hamburg reach.   But the
fact that these reunite at Blankensee, and careful artificial regulation
of the river, minimise the difficulty; and the construction of link-
canals, *e.g.* between Elbe and Havel, between Elbe and Trave, the
canalisation of tributaries such as the Saale, and the laying of a
towing-cable from Hamburg to Aussig, have helped to give the
river the largest fleet of river craft in Germany, in spite of its lack
of depth and its liability to periodic floods.

The Weser.   Historically the Weser has been even more interesting than the
Elbe (cf. p. 291), but its conditions were adverse to its progress, for—
before 1866—the joint stream (Weser-Werra-Fulda) passed through
no less than thirty-five separate political stages, representing the rival
claims and rights of a number of separate States.   Its course as far as
Minden is picturesque, but has a rapid fall, while in its lower reaches
it is sluggish and shallow, uninteresting and subject to drought.   But
here again Prussian organisation has made vast improvements,—by
canals, *e.g.* to Elbe and Ems, by canalisation, *e.g.* near Cassel, and
by very extensive works on the estuary, where—before 1894—the
depth at low water did not reach 2 feet.

The Rhine : Historic.   The Rhine was for centuries, and still is, the chief natural
waterway of Europe; and the causes which made it predominant
in early days, have more or less justified the improvements which
account for its predominance to-day.   Besides its natural advantages, it inherited a Roman organisation, and eventually took the
place of the Roman roads as the great Mid-European link
(cf. p. 262); and even the discovery of the New World, which
affected so greatly most transport routes and foci, scarcely affected
the Rhine at all except that supreme control of the through
route passed from its southern termini in Venice and Genoa
to northern termini in Antwerp and Amsterdam.   That is to say,
traffic began to go up-stream rather than down-stream; and to-day
it is predominantly "up-stream," four-fifths of the traffic down-
stream from Mannheim going empty!   Again, its traffic in early
days was essentially a "road" traffic, and so it suffered in the same
way as the Roman roads from bad weather.   Now boats are towed
both up and down, because drifting down-stream is both too slow
and too dangerous; but then, in the less crowded state of the river,
they drifted down-stream, and were only towed up-stream—with or
without the help of sails in each case.   But, while towing is now
done usually by a tug, it was done in those days from the tow-
path; and, as only small boats were used, lowness of water was a
trifle, and the one trouble was from flood.   Here, again, all *is*
changed.   And it was profoundly fortunate that, at the critical
time in the history of the river, it was so specifically French that it

received uniform attention throughout both in improvement of waterway and in simplification of tolls, etc. At the same time, in the transition, towns which owed their importance to staple or transfer rights sank into relative insignificance; Mainz became less important than Frankfurt northwards and than Mannheim southwards.

The river is now under a really International Commission, on **The** which France, Belgium, and Switzerland—with *no* representative **Rhine:** in 1913!—as well as Britain and Italy, are represented, France **Economic.** to excess, for she owns only *c.* 110 miles of one bank, while Germany owns *c.* 150 miles of one bank and *c.* 300 miles of both banks; enormous improvements were made in the waterway itself, especially by Prussia. From the very position and the direction, the river deals specifically with foreign trade, which great exception in the list of important articles being the coal that is carried up-stream from the Ruhr basin. Another feature is that the trade is largely in bulk, especially towards the north, *e.g.* grain and ore, building material and coal; and this has an important relation to the size of boat and the method of transport. Boats carrying less than *c.* 600 tons do not pay on the main stream, and yet they can seldom be used on the tributaries. Indeed, the latter seldom can take boats of more than 400 tons, and this limit is not nearly reached on the normally navigable portions of the Lahn or the Lippe, the Ruhr or the Moselle. Traffic, therefore, tends to come to the main stream by rail, and this involves at once other considerations, *e.g.* of transfer and of limit of draught. Barges of as much as 4000 tons burden are actually used, but the standard is *c.* 1500; and the reason lies in the character of the river-bed. For 80 miles of gorge separate 220 miles of rift valley from ·230 miles of lowland plain; and, while a width of 200-300 feet is easily provided in the valley or on the plain, scarcely 80 can be obtained in the gorge. This means that real safety forbids the regular use of boats more than 40 feet wide; and this practically implies a length of not much more than 300 feet, a draught (loaded) of 9 feet, and a capacity of 2000 tons. Of course big boats pay best even at low water, because the variation in draught is relatively less than that in capacity, and rates are then highest; and the rough loading of coal from "tips" soon proved so destructive to the old wooden barges that they have been replaced by steel ones, which of course are lighter and draw less water.

But it is stated that transfer from rail to river pays only when **River and** the goods are in bulk and going a long way (at least 50 miles), **Rail.** unless the relations between rail and river media are very close and

---

[1] "Staple" right prevented goods being carried past the town without being exposed for sale, and "transfer" right prevented them from being carried past in a boat not owned by the town, the only and occasional exception being at fair-time. Cf. Clapp's *Navigable Rhine.*

very friendly.   This is the case in South Germany, where goods for or from Rhine-transport receive the minimum rate on the railway before or after transfer ; but on the Prussian railways the case is different, for the interests of rail and river here are often antagonistic, as those of Hamburg and Bremen are to those of Rotterdam and Antwerp.   The only obvious exception is in the case of Rhine *sea*-traffic ; but that is only open permanently to steamers drawing not more than about $7\frac{1}{2}$ feet when loaded, and they can only reach Cologne, *e.g.* from London.   Even if the depth were permanently increased and curves were widened, these small steamers are relatively costly to work (cf. p. 66).

Conditions of Navigation.
The traffic is, therefore, predominantly river-traffic and done by barge ; and the typical barge-trains (4 or 5 barges, aggregating *c.* 6000 tons) are a response to the conditions of navigation.   The Rhine being an ice-fed river, low-water is not a trouble except in autumn, when, unfortunately, there is most traffic ; but ice, fogs, and floods do cause trouble.   The low-water and the flood troubles may be removed by the canalisation of the river from Basel to Lake Constance, for the lake can easily be made into a reservoir which will regulate the flow ; but any attempt to regulate the pace of the river, which is the great drawback above Mannheim, will only increase the ice-trouble.   A tug which has brought four or five barges from Rotterdam to Mannheim (350 miles) in four or five days, and can take them back in three or four days, can only take two of them on to Strasbourg (80 miles), and requires two days for the journey ; and the journey is only possible at all for five or six months in each year, while the total load must not exceed *c.* 2000 tons.   From Strasbourg to Basel (80 miles) the difficulty is still greater, the load limit being *c.* 1000 tons, and the time limit six or seven months.   North from Mannheim, however, conditions are very different, and the river is a scene of very busy traffic. Indeed, the largest port, Duisburg-Ruhrort (including the railway harbour of Hochfeld), which does specially a "bulk" trade,[1] has a water traffic greater than the whole ocean traffic of Hamburg ; and Mannheim (including Ludwigshafen and the railway harbour of Rheinau), which does specially a "piece" trade, has a water traffic twice that of the whole ocean traffic of Bremen.   Of course, Duisburg, which is only 130 miles from Rotterdam, is the port of the "Black Country" ; and Mannheim, though 350 miles from Rotterdam, has, as natural head of navigation, an enormous hinterland stretching from France into Austria and as far south as Italy (cf. p. 334).   But obviously the natural resources and needs of the area must be such as are well served by river traffic.

Two points deserve special attention.   One is that four-fifths

---

[1] Duisburg lists only a dozen special articles, while Mannheim lists four or five dozen.   Between them they do *c.* 75 p.c. of all the Rhine trade.   See Clapp.

of the up-stream traffic is in iron ore (*c.* 60 p.c. of Germany's total **Political**
import), grain, coal, and timber, and that about half of the down- **Rivalry.**
stream traffic is coal, and nearly one-sixth is building materials, *e.g.*
bricks from between Mannheim and Speyer, or stone from
Badenheim. The other is the influence of political rivalry. This
is seen both in the inter-relations of the various river ports and in
the relation of all of them to outside seaports. Thus political
rivalry on the river itself has led to the development of rival ports
on opposite banks and on every natural reach of the river ; and
the rivalry has led to continuous progress. Even inside the
Zollverein this has not been confined to purely political rivalry, *e.g.*
between Strasbourg (Alsace) and Kehl (Baden), or Ludwigshafen
(Bavarian Palatinate) and Mannheim (Baden), or Frankfurt and Kastel
(Wiesbaden ports) and Offenbach and Mainz (Hessian), but has
been found also inside the Rhine Province, *e.g.* between Cologne and
Mülheim or Neuss and Düsseldorf. Cf. the "Company" rivalry of
Rheinhausen (Krupp), Homberg, Walsum, Alsum, and Schwelgern.

The outside rivalry works by rail and canal, and is focused **Northern**
on the North Sea coast, where the great shipping companies of **Relations.**
Antwerp and Bremen and Hamburg have a great lever in their
large fleets and their old-established trade relations, and are all as
jealous of the Dutch ports as the Prussian State Railway is of the
river. Thus, the Rhine-and-Marne canal gives Antwerp more
hold on the upper part of the Middle Rhine than the Dortmund-
Ems canal gives to Emden on the lower part ; and the Midland
Canal from Ruhrort to Hanover can serve Bremen as well, *via*
Minden, as the Dortmund-Ems canal serves Emden. Under these
circumstances, Emden seems to have little chance against Antwerp
or Bremen ; but the Rhine traffic has an obvious advantage.
With the railways the case is rather different. Rhine barges
usually travel from Rotterdam to Mannheim as fast as any
ordinary goods trains ; but, when all transfer charges and deterioration risks (*e.g.* of coal in "tipping") are taken into account, it
seems that railway transport is always normally cheaper than
transport by inland waterway. The two together have enabled full
advantage to be taken of the central site, and have greatly helped
to unify an area where complex highlands and radiating rivers in
olden days were the main causes of political division.

The different attitudes to the transport problem in North and **Southern**
South Germany are based on a geographical foundation. In the **Relations.**
north the rivers flow uniformly, and more or less parallel to one
another, northwards ; and some of the chief towns are specifically between two great rivers, *e.g.* Berlin. Economic needs and
physical features, therefore, alike encourage the construction of
link canals,—though the "Agrarian" party are hostile to any
development which in their opinion would be adverse to the

interests of local agriculture, and prefer congested railways to the cheap import of grain by canal. In the south, on the other hand, rivers flow in various and opposite directions; and the torrential character of many of them is more favourable to the development of "power" than of navigation, while the relief is less favourable to the construction of canals. Political influences also are at work. For instance, the Neckar, though essentially a Würtemberg river, empties through Baden, and the Bavarian Main empties through Prussian territory; on the contrary, Augsburg and Nürnberg,

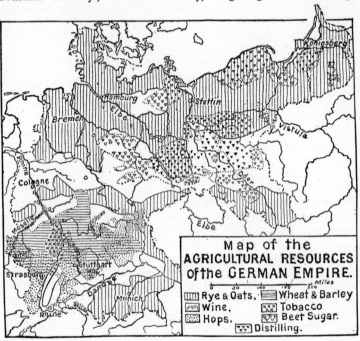

Agricultural map of Germany.

Mulhausen and Esslingen, are noted for their electrical machinery and apparatus.

Farming.   About half the total area of the country is under cultivation, while fully a quarter is under forest; and there is a natural antagonism of interest between the purely agricultural and purely industrial areas, based largely on the demand for labour and on the fact that Germany cannot provide herself with all the food she needs. Indirectly, the lack of labour for farm-work has led to a wide use of machinery; but it has also often led to a large import of foreign labour. There is also a natural antagonism between the less fertile lands of the north and the more fertile lands of the south, distinguished generally as grain lands and wine lands; and it is in the Elbe valley that the potash deposits exist which are "the sheet-anchor of German agriculture." The most important crops of the northern plain are wheat and rye, sugar-beet and potatoes; and it is mainly the root crops that have been responsible for the wide manufacture of alcohol and starch and for the decrease of sheep compared with cattle, fed on the "refuse." The number of sheep dropped between 1871 and 1913 from 25,000,000 to 5,500,000; and, on the other hand, there are 300 potato-starch factories in Silesia, Brandenburg, and Mecklenburg. To the north-east, too, flax becomes a typical product—wherever the Scotch fir is abundant, as sugar-beet is associated with the beech. The Palatinate (cf. p. 309) is by far the most important wine-grower, while Bavaria is the great wood-grower, being the only part of the empire which—with 95 acres for every 100 persons—can supply all its own needs.[1] Obviously, areas with abundance of soft-wood and water-power, e.g. the Harz and Thuringian forests, have special advantages for the manu-facture of paper in all its forms, including pasteboard toys, etc.; and Bavaria still has the largest "paper" centre in Germany, Aschaffenburg.

Again, the northern part of the country is specially associated **Mining.** with mineral wealth, e.g. the coal and iron of Westphalia and Rhenish Prussia, and the metals of the Harz and Silesia. But the most typical product is the potash. A large area, including the plains on every side of the Harz, contains enormous beds of rock-salt above or amongst deposits of potassium minerals, held in place and so preserved by an extensive sheet of impervious clay. To the east of the Harz is the famous Anhalt district with its centre at Stassfurt, where the "Rubbish-salts"—as they were called fifty years ago—were first found; to the north are the Brunswick and Hanover districts, the latter a scene of great activity; to the south is the Nordhausen district; and less important deposits exist in the west of the Thuringian Forest. These give Germany easily accessible supplies of what has been a world-monopoly; and they are the definite link between agriculture and industries, especially the manufacture of ammunition. For they consist mainly of carnallite and kainite—the former easily soluble and therefore naturally suited for industrial purposes, the latter ready for use as a fertiliser.

The northern plain has a unity of relief even on a rainfall map, **Unity of** the slight elevations, e.g. of the Lüneburg Heath, the Fläming or **Prussian** the Baltic Heights, being faithfully reflected in a slight increase of **Plain.** rainfall; but it contains a considerable variety of political units with considerable variety of geographical conditions. For instance,

---

[1] The limit for this is said to be eighty-five acres for 100 persons; in the British Isles the proportion is not eight acres to the 100 persons.

while East Prussia is a typical morainic lake-land, West Prussia is a fertile carse; while Pomerania includes the less fertile lower "basin" of the Oder, Silesia occupies its more fertile upper "basin." So, Brandenburg pivots on the flood-lands of Spree and Havel, while the Province of Saxony includes the Golden Mead and other fertile valleys. The unity of relief and climate has, however, outweighed all other influences,—religious, linguistic, and even racial, so that to-day there is marked unity of national type and even some approximation to a German physique.

"German" Physical Type.
No doubt the type on the ocean border is distinctly different from that on the densely forested heights of (cf. p. 79) the Black Forest, the tall Longheads of the north-west being of very pure Teutonic type, while the stocky Roundheads of the south-west are purely Alpine; but these extreme types are exceptional, the normal type being an intermediate one—seen at its best in that most typically German area, the Weser highlands. This intermediate type is intermediate specially in height and head-form, the mixture of race in it being betrayed by the disharmony between the round Alpine head and the long Nordic face; and the fact that the one influence came in from the north while the other came in from the east, is still reflected in the regional variations. The natural route for the Teutons to move south by was the Weser basin, which brought them into the "basin" of the Middle Rhine; and the relative tallness and fairness of the people in the rift valley and the Main and Neckar basins must be attributed to this influence. Naturally, too, the older inhabitants — real Alpines, of round head and stocky frame—were pressed up into the less accessible and less fertile heights, especially in the Black Forest and the Jura, where pure Alpine types are still normal. The natural route for the Slav (Alpine) people to move west by was the unfertile plain; but the infertility was always favourable to speedy, if not premature, "saturation"—as well as to limited rights of inheritance, *e.g.* to primogeniture—and the overflow had easiest access to the fertile south by the Saale basin. In this case, however, it was the Slav people who were pressing; and here, therefore, it was the older Teutonic people that were pressed up into the highlands, *e.g.* in Thuringia, leaving permanent traces of themselves in the relative tallness of the modern Thuringians. In both cases the influence spread along lines of least resistance, Slav influence spreading *via* the Oder through Brandenburg and Mecklenburg, while Teutonic influence spread *via* the Rhine to the Burgundy Gate. The darker colour of the real Alpine grass-lander is reflected in the more Slavic areas even of the north, *e.g.* Brandenburg, as the lighter colour of the forester-fisherman is reflected in the more Teutonic areas even in the typically Alpine climate, *e.g.* in Hohenzollern; but colour is relatively transient, and

so we find blonde colouring everywhere within reach of the sea, even to the north-east frontier, and wherever else humidity—with or without much shade—is high. Thus, even amongst the short, stocky "grass-land" Roundheads of the Black Forest—with the maximum rainfall in the empire (a mean of 80-83 inches)—in the most secluded part of the forested heights one person in three is distinctly fair.

PRUSSIA

Fully three-fifths of Prussia belongs to the Great European Plain, forming a wedge of lowland that narrows westward until at the Westphalian Gate it is only 100 miles wide. The total population is about the same as that of England, the non-German-speaking element not being more than 10 p.c. of the whole; the local density is greatest in the mining and manufacturing part of the Rhine area, closely followed by the similar areas in Saxony (where the density is less "local") and Silesia.

The railway mileage, though very high (5 miles per 10,000 Strategic persons), has little relation to this dense population, as its funda- "Control." mental principle has been strategic; that is to say, an enormous proportion of the total mileage represents trunk lines radiating from Berlin impartially in all directions or running along the political frontiers. Indirectly, however, this has a valuable economic influence. For the surface qualities of the area are very diverse, rather less than one-third being good, rather more than one-third being fair, and just one-third being simply sand; and, apart from strategic considerations, there was little in the barren sands of the north-east or in the barren heaths of the north-west to attract railways. But the spread of railways through these districts has been of real service, e.g. to the great rye and oat lands of the north-east. Agriculture generally has also profited by the—more or less consequent—spread of beet-growing for sugar, for the deep cultivation necessary leaves the soil in a magnificent condition for succeeding crops, e.g. barley and chicory. At least equally valuable has been the influence of compulsory military training, e.g. on habits of obedience, punctuality, attention to detail; and both in agriculture and in manufacturing industries the Prussians came into the field so late that they were able to make a fair start on lines dictated by the previous experience of other nations, who have been handicapped in their subsequent competition by the difficulty of getting rid of established procedure which that experience has proved to be inferior.

Physical history, climate, and position have all been somewhat East adverse to the progress of East Prussia. Though one of the Prussia. largest provinces, and sharing in the general character of the great plain, it has only one important town, Königsberg (cf. p. 296). It is a morainic lake-land, sloping down to a dune-fringed and

Haff-fronted coastal plain from the lake-strewn plateau of the Seen-platte, which rises in the south-west to 1000 feet. About one-fifth is covered with coniferous forests, which support wood industries, *e.g.* at Allenstein, and in which wolves are still found; there is a large area of barren sand or bog; and the climate is the coldest in Germany, the mean January temperature of Tilsit being only 25° F. At the same time, thanks to the alluvial lands along the Niemen, Pregel, and Passarge, about half the area is under cultivation, mainly with rye, potatoes, and flax—the last specially in the Passarge basin, which is specifically Roman Catholic in creed. But the two characteristic products of the province are the amber of Samland and horses, the chief Government stud-farm of all Germany being near Gumbinnen. Cf. Trakehnen and Marienwerder.

Pomerania. The long straggling province of Pomerania ("On the Sea") well deserves its name, and in the early days of its history it stretched even farther along the coast, including Pomerellen or West Prussia eastward and Slavinia or Mecklenburg westward. But its position between Sweden and Brandenburg and its old division into Vorpommern (or Nearer Pomerania) and Hinterpommern (or Farther Pomerania) involved it in such constant hostilities with the Brandenburg Electors, such devastation in the Thirty Years' War, and such endless redistribution of territory between its two native dukes, that its progress was terribly hindered. Nor did its physical conditions help. Though it includes a typical belt of the Baltic Lake Plateau, it is one of the flattest areas in all Germany and correspondingly marshy; and even where there is neither lake nor marsh, the soil is thin and sandy. Its typical activities are, therefore, in four directions. The enormous original expanse of "bog" is now represented by very extensive peat-bogs; the great portion of "lagoon" coast-line and of lake ($\frac{1}{20}$ of the area) is very favourable to fishing—the lampreys being famous—and to the rearing of aquatic fowl, especially geese; and a busy commerce centres on the Oder. **Cf.** the junction of Stargard.

The latter was the centre of early civilisation, Christianity reaching the area — characteristically — *via* the island of Wollin (Jolin), as the commercial centre is now divided between the island of Usedom (Swinemünde) and the head of the estuary (Stettin). The "Bodden" coast farther west was equally favourable to civilising influences from the sea. Both Stralsund, which is still a flourishing harbour, and Greifswald, with its famous old Church-reared university, were important Hanseatic centres; they are both typically on the mainland side of the Strela Sund; and the island of Rügen, the capital of which is at a little railway junction called *Bergen*, was even in heathen times a Holy Island. But Stettin is, of course, much the most important centre (cf. p. 296), being the most central town on the whole westland of Germany.

Silesia was not only the largest province of Prussia in 1914, with **Silesia :** an area half the size of Ireland, but also one of the lowest and most **Mineral.** level. Even at the head of navigation the Oder at Ratibor is only *c.* 500 feet above the sea, and so it was easy to canalise the river for large barges up to Kosel, the terminus of the Klodnitz canal from the coal-field at Gleiwitz ; and, as the part of the field nearest to Berlin was naturally the first to be developed, Beuthen, Zabrze, and Gleiwitz became re-spectively great mining, smelting, and glass-working centres. But they are only on the north-western edge of the coal-field, while the new frontier runs in an almost straight line E.N.E. from Ratibor to Beuthen, and then roughly N.N.W. ; and, as the metalliferous rock is, typically, "behind" the coal, Germany has lost practically all the iron, zinc, lead, and silver of the area as well as 77 p.c. of the coal. The German mines (*c.* 7,000,000 tons a year) do, how-ever, include a large percentage (50 p.c. of the whole region) of the good *coking* coal, though it was heavily drawn upon during the War. The frontier site, with its strategic problems and its foreign tariff, has been naturally adverse to pros-perity ; but the mineral wealth is great and so easily won that the plain has become the "Black Country" of Eastern Germany.

Silesian Frontier.

In the valleys of the Sudetic system there has been almost equally great development on the textile **Silesia :** side; for not only is there a rich coal-field in the Weistritz basin, but the **Textile.** wooded heights are almost everywhere supplied with abundant water-power. The confined coal-basin of Waldenburg has very important mining, smelting, and chemical industries (cf. the Bunzlau glass), which account for a population of nearly 40,000 per square mile ; and local pro-duction of flax and wool helps to supply raw material for textiles on both sides of the basin, though wool is the more important in the Lausitzer Neisse and Katybach valleys, *e.g.* at Görlitz and Liegnitz, and linen in the Glatzen Neisse, *e.g.* at Neisse. The need for access to "power" causes this industrial part of the province to show very high density of population even at very considerable altitudes ; and this, of course, affects the average temperature, some villages in the Riesengebirge having the lowest mean (below 40° F.) of any in Prussia. A typical "mountain" home industry of lace-making centres round Hirschberg; but the great historic industry is the weaving of linen (cf. the splendid damasks of Neustadt and Glatz).

Silesia : Agricultural. The foreground of this industrial "mountain" zone happens also to be very fertile, especially between Ratibor and Liegnitz; and, as the rainfall is also heavy (cf. p. 57)—heavy enough, indeed, to account for forest [1] covering nearly 30 p.c. of the area—agriculture is greatly favoured, the crops of wheat and rye sometimes giving a surplus for export after feeding a very large local population, while hops and tobacco, and even wine and silk, are typical products. To the north and north-west, especially along the Brandenburg frontier, the soil is much less fertile, and the density of population decreases from 300-500 per square mile to scarcely 100.

Brandenburg. Brandenburg is now the largest province, but thinly populated; for, though its infertility is exaggerated in its old nickname of "Sand-Box," it does consist essentially of a sandy plain, interspersed with large areas of coniferous forest and small areas of fertile soil. Timber and sheep are its two typical products, the wool being the finest in Prussia (cf. the excellent woollen mills of Rummelsberg and Nieder Schonweide). Barley and rye, hemp and flax, and even tobacco and hops, are widely cultivated, and the large production of honey and wax may be associated with the wealth of aromatic vegetation ; but the excessive number of swamps, lakes (700), and rivers—supporting quite a busy fishery, especially for carp, and making the punt a common transport medium—causes the climate to be unusually raw in winter, while the absence of shelter and the loose, easily-heated surface expose it to violent winds both in winter and in summer. Commercially, however, the abundance of navigable water and the central site have made it the pivot of inland navigation in Prussia, as the low level and central site have made it the pivot of the Prussian railways. And where the chief waterways converge, by a chain of lakes, on the "mathematical" centre of the Prussian railway-system, the Berlin-Spandau-Potsdam area has an aggregate population of 4,000,000.

Berlin. Berlin itself, with over 1,900,000, is historically a typical island-bridge centre, half-way between Elbe and Oder, half-way between Hamburg and Breslau ; and it is significant that some of the largest "new" cities in Germany, e.g. Charlottenburg, Rixdorf, and Schöneberg, are simply decentralised suburbs of Berlin. The metropolitan area, in which special districts, e.g. that of Teltow or of Nieder Barnim, have populations of 500,000, is now the chief manufacturing centre in Central Europe, its great industries—as in

---

[1] It is significant that the densest forests are in the lee of the "Giant" Mountains, e.g. south of Liegnitz, or of the Sudetes, e.g. south-west of Oppeln.

so many foci of dense population, *e.g.* New York—being in clothing and machinery, including scientific instruments. Its two outposts on the west of the Havel represent "war and the chase." The unhealthy, marsh-girt fortress at the confluence of the Havel and the Spree became the chief military arsenal of Germany, while some relatively healthy lake-girt hills to the south offered beautiful sites for the palaces of royal fishermen, *e.g.* the Sans Souci. Potsdam now has busy industries, but only in such products as silk, chocolate, and furniture. Spandau is an older centre than Potsdam, but was hampered by its unhealthy marshes.

Outside the metropolitan area the towns have been characteristically dwarfed by nearness to the metropolis (cf. p. 222), even Frankfurt having only 70,000, and Brandenburg only 60,000. As the Mark

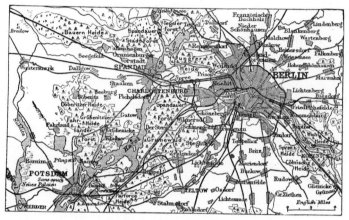

The surroundings of Berlin.

developed eastward, the " wooded hill " (Brenni-Bor), in its girdle of forested marsh, that had been the old sacred capital of the Wends, was bound to give way to some place farther east ; and the Oder-Spree Canal similarly deprived Frankfurt of its old commercial importance as the natural head of " sea " navigation on the Oder, while its strategic importance passed to the marsh-girt fortress of Küstrin. The other centres are still less important, most being engaged in the typical wool industry, *e.g.* Kottbus and Forst ("shoddy ").

Eastern Prussia is separated from western Prussia by the double Duchy of Mecklenburg, which is a typical Baltic plateau area between the Oder and the Elbe ; but the plateau is unusually low, not reaching 600 feet even in the Helpter or the Ruhner hills, and its seaward drainage is less important than its southward drainage, *i.e.* to the Elbe. Indeed, its only important Baltic river is the little Warnow (80 miles), which is navigable from Butzow for small

Mecklenburg.

vessels, and which made Rostock an important Hanseatic port, with a University that dates back to Hansa days. On the other hand, there are at least 400 lakes scattered over the plateau; and the rivers which are connected with them, are navigable for long distances, *e.g.* the Elbe and the Havel, the two being connected by a canal *via* the Müritz See. These lakes are very rich in fish, and the Müritz—like the Baltic coast of the State—even produces amber.

The history of the area—under Vandal, Slav, and German rulers—has also been adverse to its progress; and its industries are still backward. It is one of the typical instances of a population in which the nobles are mainly of Teutonic, and the peasants of Slav origin, the Slav element being still prominent even in speech. The two capitals of Schwerin and Neu-Strelitz occupy very beautiful sites in wooded lake-land; but they have very different histories. For while Neu-Strelitz is quite a modern town, built in the form of an 8-pointed star, Schwerin is one of the oldest towns in the whole area. Its modern appearance is due to the destructive fires which utterly wiped out the old wooden houses of the forest-settlement (*Schwerin*, "Game-Preserve"). Commercially, it is overwhelmed by the old Hansa ports of Rostock and Wismar, both admirable harbours from the Hanseatic point of view, and both still doing a busy commerce, though some of the "Rostock" commerce is now done through its outport of Warnemünde.

Bruns-wick and Anhalt.   Western Prussia includes the large and fairly coherent areas of Schleswig-Holstein, Hanover, Westphalia, Rhenish Prussia, and Hessen-Nassau; but these are grouped round a confused nucleus of small States, whose territory is generally dotted about in a number of incoherent fragments. For instance, Brunswick consists of 3 large and 6 small areas, scattered along the banks of Aller and Ocker, Leine and Weser, including such diverse units as the Lüneburg plain, the Drömlin marsh, the Harz Mountains. The city of Brunswick, on the fertile Ocker plain, with rich surrounding forests, was very important as a Hanseatic inland centre; but, now that traffic does not move normally between the Middle Rhine and Lübeck, it has only local importance, *e.g.* as a manufacturer of sugar and sausages. In the northern part of the duchy, where the climate is most favourable, scientific agriculture is very productive, especially of sugar-beet; the Harz is, of course, a very busy mining area; and in the intermediate area timber-cutting is a typical industry. The Duchy of Anhalt, with its Harz foothills, the reclaimed pastures of its Elbe marshes, and its fertile Saale plain, is in a very similar position; its agriculture is excellent, sugar is a typical product, and mining is a typical industry (cf. the famous salt-works of Leopoldshall, on the left bank of the Bode, opposite Stassfurt).

Thu-ringia.   The Thuringian States form a more coherent unit in spite of their subdivisions, for these correspond more or less to the opposite slopes of the Thuringian Forest. Generally speaking, Saxe-Weimar-Eisenach lies across the north of the area, and Saxe-Meiningen across the south, while Saxe-Altenburg is to the east, and Saxe-Coburg-Gotha runs from north to south towards the west; and the Thuringian Road—*via* Eisenach, Gotha, Weimar, and Jena—bridges the base of the angle which is formed by the Upper Werra and the Middle Saale, and which has its natural apex at Coburg. To the forest and mineral wealth the mountain environment has given a special direction, the subdivision of territory being reflected in a subdivision of labour—occupied in making articles which demand a vast amount of work on a tiny quantity of raw material. Glass-making is the typical industry along the crest of the range, including such products as thermometer tubes and glass eyes; on the eastern slope the special product is various kinds of porcelain, terra-cotta, and earthenware; on the western slope it is toys—of glass, wood, paper, china, metal; and the metal industry is also prominent in the north, where, too, Ruhla has an unique industry in pipe-making —using wood, amber, and meerschaum.

The toy industry is associated at Gotha with the making of all kinds of instruments—mechanical and mathematical, surgical and musical; in the extreme south Coburg shows "Bavarian" influence in its typical brewing industry, as in the extreme east Neustadt shows Saxon influence in its population. Saxe-Meiningen, with a less fertile soil and mainly to the south, has long specialised in wooden toys, *e.g.* at Sonneberg, and papier-maché, *e.g.* at Hildburg-hausen; but the industry has now reached such proportions that it is "international."

Saxe-Weimar-Eisenach is much the largest state (*c.* 1400 square miles), and has the most varied physique and resources. The Eisenach area is renowned for its natural beauty—of forest and mountains, the former specially "Thuringian" and the latter specially "Rhön"; the Neustadt area is specially "Saxe," being physically a slice of the Vogtland and racially Slav; the Weimar area, though not rich in minerals, has important industries in such typically "Saxe" products as woollen hosiery, *e.g.* at Apolda,—porcelain, *e.g.* at Ilmenau,—scientific instruments, *e.g.* at Jena (optical). Jena is also in a very fertile district, famous for its fruits; and, as the eastern road round the Thuringian Forest was originally more important than the western, Jena was always the most important of the towns at the angles of the great triangle—Eisenach, Coburg, and Jena. More important than either of the north-and-south roads was the great "Thuringian Road" from east to west, linking Dresden to Cologne *via* Gera, Jena, Weimar, Erfurt (not politically Thuringian), Gotha, and Eisenach. Weimar and Gotha, "the Holders of the Gates" where the road crossed the Ilm or branched north-westward to the Lower Werra, were intimately interested in Itineraries and

Thuringian Road.

Road-plans centuries before they won their most honourable place in the modern world of Geographical publishing.[1]

Province of Saxony. The province of Saxony is divided by Anhalt into two main areas, pivoting respectively on Magdeburg and Halle, and the southern area is flanked by a chaotic intrusion of scraps of territory belonging to Anhalt, Brunswick, and the Thuringian States. The determining influence on this side was the Harz, diverting all roads along their north flank to Magdeburg or along their south flank to Halle. The northern roads diverged over an area that was largely moorland, while the southern ones threaded fertile mountain-girt valleys, *e.g.* that of the Helme ("The Golden Mead"). At the same time a certain unity is given to the province by the fact that $\frac{9}{10}$ths of it belongs to the "basin" of the Middle Elbe, the flood sediments of which have for centuries manured it so richly that it is now the most fertile province in Prussia, with a very large output of wheat and sugar-beet.

The special wealth of the province is essentially underground— in brown coal and salt, to the west and south-west of Magdeburg. Though the oldest salt-workings were along the Saale ("Salt"), *e.g.* at Halle (cf. the Merseburg chemicals), the richest are now found along the Bode, *e.g.* at Stassfurt, and along the Elbe itself, *e.g.* at Schönebeck; and a ring of brown coal—almost continuous along the west—surrounds the salt, *e.g.* at Oschersleben, Aschersleben, Weissenfels (where the Saale is canalised), Bitterfeld and Wittenberg. Below the old Salziger See near Eisleben there are the richest copper mines in Europe — at Mansfeld; and both this district and the similar copper area in the Harz are rich in silver.

Magdeburg. Magdeburg, which is the smallest (300,000) of the great cities of Germany, might have been the largest. The site is certainly the natural centre of Prussia,—a central position on the central river of the plain, where the great westward bend comes so near to the Harz that the hilly foreground of the mountains enabled a German population to hold its ground and divert the Slav flood north-westward over Hanover, and where the Elbe is put into close relations with the Aller and even with the Westphalian Gate as well as with the tributary Saale. Here the presence of islands, in a stretch of the river otherwise devoid of islands for many miles, offered facilities for a defensive position and for building a bridge. On the western, *i.e.* the non-Slav, bank the city was a valuable outpost of German strength, and then a base for German expansion, while its importance as a market made it an inland member of the Hanseatic League. But its old salt industry, like that of Halle—which was worked in the sixth century—was its political ruin, for it gave it such a value (*e.g.* for preserving fish) that Otho gave it to his wife,

---

[1] Road maps of Central Europe were quite common by A.D. 1500, and the present house of Justus Perthes was founded in 1785.

Edith, and she gave it to the Church. From that time its industries began to be stifled; and, when eventually reaction came at the Reformation, the city suffered terribly under Tilly. By the time that it recovered, the old Thuringian Road was becoming less and less important, while Berlin had the advantage of being nearer to the Baltic, which was becoming more important. Now the north-eastern bend of the Elbe to the Havel confluence has not only no importance as far as Baltic trade is concerned, but has even lost a considerable portion of trade gravitating north-westward, the latter now often leaving the river at Magdeburg and proceeding direct, *e.g., via* Hanover for Bevergern on the Dortmund-Ems Canal.

Practically the whole of the rest of the Prussian plain south and **Hanover.** west of the Lower Elbe and north of a line joining Osnabrück to Hildesheim is included in the province of Hanover, which stands now next in size to Brandenburg, with an area roughly half the size of Scotland; for the total area of the Grand-Duchy of Oldenburg and the Free Territory of Bremen is not much larger than Norfolk, and the most important strip of the old Duchy — the "Jade territory" round Wilhelmshaven—was purchased by Prussia in 1873. The province slopes gently down from the Harz to the North Sea, but may be divided into two areas. The greater portion is a sandy plain crossed from north to south by the moor and fen of the Lüneburg Heath, through which shallow valleys join the city of Hanover to the port of Harburg, now joined to Hamburg by a tunnel under the Elbe. The most fertile parts of this are the water-meadows along the Elbe frontier and the dyked lands along the North Sea. In the south a generally hilly area—broken by Lippe and Brunswick territory—slopes up to the Harz, and—like the eastern part of the plain—is densely forested, mainly with fir and larch, though there are also fine oak and beech woods. The chief artery of the whole province is the Leine-Aller-Weser, *i.e.* a river line wholly isolated eastward by the Heath; and this fact, coupled with the rich river fisheries and with the poor soil, resulted in the area, which was originally peopled from the Norwegian fiords, being always somewhat backward in agriculture. The same conditions were more or less responsible for the rural type of civilisation, *e.g.* the making of roads being discouraged by the excellence of the waterways, and so the rise of real towns being delayed by the practice of accumulating goods at home until successive Christian Fasts or Festivals necessitated attendance at some shrine which became for the time a fair-ground. They are also reflected in the fact that in Hanover alone of all the German provinces there is a typically "Viking" preponderance of male over female births, and that 85 p.c. of the population are Protestants, the Roman Catholics being practically confined to the neighbourhood of the old episcopal cities of Hildesheim and Osnabrück.

Pastoral and Mineral Wealth.

The Heath—famous also for honey and wax—has a fine breed of native sheep; the "polders" of Aurich and Stade, like the water-meadows of Celle, are renowned for their horses; and before the War the number of cattle and pigs was exceedingly high per head of population. The marsh-lands are also the home of enormous flocks of geese, while the chief fishing-port of Germany is still appropriately in the "Viking" province — at Geestemünde. The chief mineral centre is, of course, the Harz, and there is a well-known Mining Institute at Clausthal; but fuel is widely spread in different forms, *e.g.* coal, lignite, and petroleum— mainly between Osnabrück and Celle—and enormous beds of peat —mainly in the north and the south-east. Salt was partly responsible for the early rise of Hanover and Lüneburg; and the province is now a main centre of the potash trade of Germany, exporting very large quantities of chemicals, dyes, medicines, etc.

Towns.

More or less robbed, by Free Town and other "foreign" territory, from her proper development on the coast, or induced to sell points of vantage, *e.g.* Bremerhaven, Hanover has her most important centres in the south; and here they have special opportunities of controlling movement north-and-south, *e.g.* by the Leine and the Weser valleys. Even Osnabrück, like Bielefeld, owes much of its importance to the command of a pass across the Teutoburger; but the older lines of communication led by the two great valleys, *via* Münden (and the *Westphalian* Gate at Minden), and *via* Göttingen and Hanover. As more or less local movement round the Harz was in olden days more important than trans-continental movement along the southern edge of the plain, Hildesheim and Göttingen were more important than Hanover. Even Göttingen, however, is a modern creation; for its old woollen industry is quite forgotten, and the University was only founded by King George II. (of England). So, Emden only sprang into importance as a cable terminus; and the great opportunity before Harburg has had to wait for modern congestion of traffic, especially coal, at Hamburg. Even the old towns, including such important Hansa markets as Celle, Hildesheim, and Lüneburg, were remote from the sea, most of them being at the natural head of river navigation. For instance, Celle is at the natural head of navigation on the Aller, and so became an old seat of water traffic with Bremen and the site of the Ducal residence; and it still possesses, as a legacy of this, the supreme Court of Appeal for the whole province, while its relations with its episcopal neighbour survive in its wax (and honey) market. Hildesheim itself, as a great cattle and linen market, was an original member of the Hansa League; and Lüneburg still exports its lime and gypsum (or cement) and salt by the Ilmenau,—faithful to its old motto of *Mons, Fons, Pons, i.e.* the quarries of the "Kalkberg," the salt "springs," and the conditions which made it a suitable place for a "bridge."

Schleswig-Holstein gives an interesting epitome of the Prussian plain and a significant illustration of Prussian domination. Its eastern coast is skirted by the Baltic Ridge, which reaches 500 feet on the mainland behind Fehmarn; the centre is practically a continuation of the Lüneburg Heath; and the west coast is fringed by dune-ribbed islands, such as Sylt, and by dyked polders landwards. The centre is, therefore, of little value except, *e.g.* for bee-keeping; but the glacial soil of the plateau raises good flax, while the polders raise rape, and give excellent pasture. For these products the marine climate is very favourable, for the width of isthmus even in Holstein —*i.e.* south of the Eider—does not reach 100 miles, while in the narrower parts of Schleswig it is under 40; and in the small area there is naturally very little variation of temperature or rainfall. Exposure to wind is reflected in the tiny percentage of forest (6 p.c.), and yet fogs are very common (cf. p. 284). The obvious advantages of the area are for rearing cattle—large numbers of which are exported [1]—and for sea-fishing or sea-trading; but provincial interests are of slight importance. Kiel is wholly an Imperial interest, and Altona is practically part of Hamburg. Only in Schleswig, *e.g.* in the old Danish capital of Flensburg and the great fishing-port of Eckernförde, is there any real provincial strength. Even the original German element suffered so much from the Prussian "mailed fist" that the sympathies of many were with the Danish element—in whom the official persecution, as in Posen, so far from Prussianising the area, only embittered a racial antagonism which was in existence before the Angles had left Angeln. But for the shameless equivocation by Bismarck in 1864,—which encouraged Denmark to hold out against Prussia and Austria— it is practically certain that a European Congress would have confirmed Denmark in her historic possession of Schleswig, while giving to Prussia the Holstein fief of the old Germano-Roman Empire. Cf. p. 284.

Westphalia is a rough oblong, which lies N.W.–S.E., and its south-western frontier runs generally parallel to the Teutoburger at an average distance of about 20 miles from the Rhine, while its south-eastern frontier runs along the Rothaar mountains generally parallel to the Dutch frontier. Political influences, mainly Napoleonic, took its natural limits north of the Teutoburger to include the Westphalian Gate and east of the Egge mountains to tap the Weser waterway between the territories of Cassel and Hildesheim. Within the natural limits the province is divided into two contrasting areas. The north, *i.e.* essentially the Ems-Lippe drainage, is really Westphalia ("Western Plain"), while the Sauerland ("South Land") is a roughly slaty plateau drained by the Ruhr; and there is a corresponding difference of climate, the Munster

---

[1] The proportion per head of population is the largest in Prussia.

lowland having an average annual temperature of about 49° F. with a rainfall of only 25 inches, while the average annual temperature of Sauerland is only 41° F., but the rainfall approaches 40 inches. The northern area is, therefore, predominantly agricultural; and, though the constant outcropping of rocky beds, the wide area of fen in the Vechte basin along the Dutch frontier, and the dry sand of the Senne below the Lippe frontier, minimise the available land, this is to some extent compensated by the great number of peasant proprietors and by the fertility of the heart of the province, *i.e.* a belt running along the south of the Lippe (the "Hellweg") and continued beyond the Egge mountains to the Weser, where Beverungen is an important grain market. Hardy cereals and roots are the typical products except in the north-east, where flax is very largely grown, and where there has been a flourishing linen industry for at least 500 years, *e.g.* at Bielefeld, the old "hill" capital of the Countship of Ravensberg. As at Dundee, the old linen industry has attracted a modern jute industry; but this is mainly confined to Bielefeld, the other towns, *e.g.* Herford and Warendorf, being specifically engaged in linen. Below the Egge heights Paderborn is a busy wool market; but away from the hills the typical live-stock are pigs (cf. the famous Westphalian hams).

"Sauer-land." The southern area of Sauerland, in the widest sense of the word, presents a very great contrast, being monopolised by mining and manufacturing interests (hardware), the rougher work mainly between the Ruhr and the Emscher and the finer in the Ruhr-Lenne valley. The production of coal is much the largest in Prussia, and that of iron[1] is second only to the production in the Rhine-land. The chief mining and smelting centres are on the north bank of the Ruhr, *e.g.* at Dortmund and Gelsenkirchen, at Bochum and Recklinghausen, with some specialisation in the manufacture of tools, armour, and ammunition, and a very large output of coke; but the more distinctly manufacturing industries are to the south of the river, *e.g.* Hagen and Iserlohn, interested respectively in

Ruhr coal-field.

"Birmingham" goods and "Redditch" goods ("cutlery," including needles and fish-hooks). The use of surface gases for "power"

---

[1] Of the total 10,000,000 tons of raw iron produced in Prussia, the "Dortmund district" was credited in 1913 with about 5,400,000 and the "Bonn district" with about 3,300,000. The 1928 report gave 6,300,000 tons for all Germany.

and of slag for cement have become so important, *e.g.* at Gelsenkirchen, that it is said—not altogether in jest—that "iron is the great by-product of the industry."

Hesse-Nassau is a small and hilly, but densely-peopled province **Hesse-** which lies between the Rhön and the Rothaar heights, and between **Nassau.** the Bingen-Coblenz reach of the Rhine and a rather longer reach of the Weser - Werra beyond Cassel, entirely surrounding the Oberhessen province of the Grand Duchy of Hesse and roughly divided by it into two main areas, the basin of the Lahn and the basin of the Fulda. The northern, or Hessian hills, are more or less isolated, while the southern, or Taunus, and western, or Westerwald, form a continuous block. The most characteristic features of the province are the very large proportion of forest (40 p.c.), the volcanic sheet that clothes the slopes of the old Taunus core, and the mineral wealth (iron, manganese, and lead) of the Lahn valley. The ore goes—*via* Oberlahnstein—almost entirely to the Krupp furnaces opposite Duisburg-Ruhrort ; and the influence of the forest (largely oak and beech) is reflected in the important tanning industry, *e.g.* at Hamburg and Fulda, Marburg and Hersfeld—in the history of the old educational centres of Cassel, Fulda, and Marburg—in the fairy tales of the Grimms, whose home was at Hanau, now famous for diamond-cutting. But the volcanic area is much the most important, with its characteristic springs, *e.g.* at Ems, Homburg, and Wiesbaden, and its magnificent vineyards—in the shelter of the Taunus, on rich volcanic soil, and facing full on to the Rheingau "lake," off which sunshine is reflected or mist is sent up to the slopes of Hockheim, Johannisberg, Geisenheim, Rudesheim, Rauenthal, etc.

The province is administered from Cassel and Wiesbaden—the **Frank-** transport centre typically associated with locomotive and rolling **furt.** stock works, and the fashionable centre with the manufacture of furniture ; but much the largest centre is Frankfurt (540,000), famous alike in industry and finance, historically and commercially. As the natural head of the rift valley, and the natural junction of great routes from all points of the compass, it became an enormously important political, financial, and commercial centre ; and, though its political importance was rather bound up with the Holy Roman Empire, and its financial importance has passed to the new political capital of Berlin, its commercial importance remains, based on the conditions of relief and climate which originally enabled the Franks of the Ford on the Main to dominate the Saxons of the Weser plain, the Swabians of the Neckar valley, and the Bavarians of the Danube plateau.

The Rhineland is in several ways the most important province **Rhine-** in Prussia—politically important because of its great length from **land.** north to south along the French, Belgian, and Dutch frontiers,

commercially important as containing 200 miles of the navigable
Rhine and exceptional railway facilities, and industrially important
as containing great mineral wealth both of coal and of metals, and
as having the most favourable climate in Germany for textile work
and the best access to foreign markets.   The province contains a
typical North German lowland, and a typical South German highland, and has a great variety of rock and soil, while the average
temperature is about 50° F., and the rainfall varies from 24 inches
in the Rhine valley to 37 inches on the Eifel, and 36 across the
Moselle on the Hunsrück.   The division between northern plain and
southern highland is roughly marked by a line from Aix to Bonn,
which is almost the direction of the isotherm of 68° F. in summer.
To the north the land is very flat, and so low that towards the Dutch
frontier it is largely marshy ; the highland exceeds 2200 feet in the
Eifel, with its cones [1] and crater-lakes (maare), and 2500 in the
Hunsrück ("Dog's Back"), with its busy slate quarries.   But, in
spite of marsh and mountain, there is a large proportion (*c.* 70 p.c.)
of really fertile land in the province, and about 50 p.c. of the
whole is under tillage.   On the higher land, which is heavily wooded,
little but rye, oats, and potatoes can be grown : but the various
river valleys are not only, like the northern lowland, exceedingly
fertile, but also, unlike that, blessed with a climate which favours all
kinds of valuable crops, *e.g.* hops and tobacco, fruit and wine, the
last specially in the valley of the Moselle (at Berncastle, Zeltingen,
etc.).   The northern lowland makes rich cattle pasture, but the
draining of rivers to make canals, *e.g.* the Lippe for the Dortmund-
Ems Canal, has done damage to the water-meadows.

**Mineral
Wealth.**
　　The great value of the province, however, is in its mineral
wealth, which lies all round the old rock, especially the coal in
the Ruhr basin ; the Moselle valley, even after it leaves Lorraine
and Luxemburg, is fairly rich in iron-ore ; the "Meuse" scarp above
Aix is rich in zinc, and overlooks a valuable coal-field ; and the
name Bleiberg ("Lead-Hill") speaks for itself.   The coal is so much
the most important, because—with the favourable climate and the
facilities for transport—it has made the province the most important manufacturing district in Germany.   Indeed, the Ruhr basin
contains the most productive coal-field in Germany ; and, owing to
its fine coking qualities, the eastern, or "Düsseldorf," field is more
important than the western, or "Aix," field.   The great iron and steel
works are at points where transport and access to the coal are best,
e.g. Essen and Oberhausen, Duisburg-Ruhrort ("Ruhr Mouth") and
Mülheim-on-Ruhr.   Farther afield there is more attention to smaller
ware, *e.g.* the cutlery of Solingen and the tools of Remscheid ; and
glass is a special product on the Saar, though iron is also very

---

[1] The trachytic cones are repeated in the Siebengebirge ("Seven Hills") across
the Rhine.

important at Saarbrücken and Neunkirchen. The great hardware centre is Düsseldorf, the seat of the Steel Syndicate and other similar bodies, and the site of hardware works of all kinds—from blast-furnaces to bridge-building, and with the largest glass-bottle factory in the world; the great transport centre of the hardware district is Duisburg-Ruhrort, the largest river harbour in Europe, with nearly 500 acres of water, nearly 600 acres of wharfage, and fully 160 miles of railway.

The textile industry is more scattered. The cotton centres on the **Textiles.** Wupper valley, where the climate encourages weaving and "open-work" rather than spinning Both Barmen and Elberfeld specialise in laces, ribbons, braids, etc.; and there is a great deal of calico-printing, Elberfeld having the largest chemical works in Germany, where over 200 chemists are employed on dyes, especially Turkey-red. The woollen industry centres on the Belgian border, at Aix; the linen is on the old flax-lands farther north, at Gladbach; Crefeld spins cotton, but specialises in silk. These west-bank industries are all largely worked by Roman Catholics, while on the east bank the population is mainly Protestant. Cf. p. 335.

The great centre of the whole province is Cologne ("The **Cologne** Colony"), with a population of 700,000, engaged in all the typical **and** industries of the area—textile, chemical, glass, etc., with special **Coblenz.**

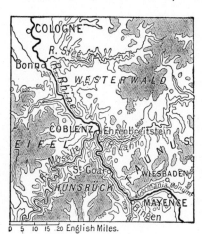

D 5 10 15 20 English Miles.

The Bonn-Bingen gorge.

interest in scent and chocolate. As an old Roman "Colony," it is naturally on the "Roman" bank of the river—at the normal head of "ocean" navi-gation (180 miles from the sea), between plateau and plain, where—below the scarp of the old metal-bearing rock—high-land and lowland routes cross between Paris and Berlin, Strasbourg and Rotterdam. It has also, with Deutz, become an important fortress; and a number of industrial[1] "suburbs" have sprung up across the river, e.g. Mülheim. Coblenz ("the Confluence"), however, is the political capital —itself on the "Roman" bank, but with the Ehrenbreitstein fortress on the opposite bank. The Romans attached great importance to this "confluence," where the narrow and tortuous Moselle route

---

[1] The lignite field round Cologne (cf. Aix) is some 45 square miles in area, and has some very thick seams (an extreme of 300 feet !).

round the Eifel from Metz and Trèves, and the narrow and tortuous Lahn route round the Taunus from Thuringia converge on a fertile basin in the very centre of the easily defended Bonn-Bingen gorge.

Chemical Monopoly. This is the area on which Germany depended during the War, for her economic strength had been built up essentially on a world-monopoly, engineered and subsidised by the Government for the Interessen Gemeinschaft; and the "I.G." organic chemical factories were simply a chemical arsenal. Before the French seized the Ludwigshafen aniline works, the "I.G." could make the whole stock of shells allowed to Germany by the Versailles Treaty *in less than two days.*

Baden. The Grand Duchy of Baden is essentially a Rhine-bank State, though it stretches round the Odenwald to the southern bend of the Lower Main, and round the Swabian Jura to the north of the Upper Danube. A very large proportion of the area is mountainous (nearly 80 p.c.); but the average height of the Black Forest does not much exceed 3000 feet except south of the South Kinzig valley, and the lowland is exceedingly fertile, growing quantities of fruit (almonds and walnuts) and wine, hops and tobacco. The large proportion of highland and of forest (nearly 40 p.c.) have forced the people into industrial lines, and there are now very important industries in typical articles, *e.g.* light machinery, china and glass, clocks and jewellery, toys and small articles especially made for sale to the numerous visitors who patronise the medicinal springs to which the State owes its name, and of which the best known is that at Baden town. Naturally, the physical character of the area has greatly influenced communications, and most of the chief centres of population now are river-side railway junctions; but fully 50 p.c. of the population is purely "rural," though engaged in industries. These centre on little towns in the neighbourhood, *e.g.* textiles round Constance, where water-power is near to a main line of rail,—making of clocks and toys round Furtwangen, in the heart of the Black Forest, and round Villingen on the Kinzig-Brigach line,—manufacture of tobacco and chicory along the Rhine-valley railway, *e.g.* at Rastatt and Freiburg. At each end of the country there is a famous University, *i.e.* at Heidelberg and Freiburg; the capital, Karlsruhe, is on the line of least resistance round the north end of the range between the Rhine and Neckar valleys; and on the same line French refugees started, at Pforzheim, an industry in cheap jewellery, now the largest in the world.

Mann-heim. But the one supremely important centre in the Duchy is Mannheim. It is the confluence of the Neckar that decides the normal head of navigation on the Rhine; and, therefore,—though in years of exceptionally high water, *e.g.* 1910, Kehl and Strasbourg and even Basel may profit at the expense of Mannheim—the latter must, in the long run, have a great advantage. As the northern terminus of the Baden railways, as well as the southern terminus of normal navigation, it has a literally enormous hinterland; and as four-fifths of the traffic down-stream goes empty, rates for export are exceedingly low, while those for import are not high, and there are no dues. Besides this direct aid, the State has been most careful to maintain absolute harmony and co-operation between river and rail; it has provided a special coal-port at Rheinau, where land is cheap, although it lies just along the main lines of rail to the south *via* Schwetzing and to the east *via* Heidelberg; and it has thus made the city the great wholesale depot of South Germany, especially in grain, coal, and petroleum. No ordinary regulation of the river higher up in the future can do Mannheim much harm —for two reasons. During the natural low-water stage no place farther south dare take much advantage of an accidental and temporary rise of level, *e.g.* a few days' flood, to send barges up the river; and no normal regulation can affect the pace of the river on the steeper gradient to the south, even though it made it always navigable. Like Pforzheim, the city owed its rise to French refugees, who found safety in the marshy peninsula between the Rhine and the Neckar, *i.e.* on the non-French side of the river, after the massacre of St. Bartholomew. Over 20 p.c. of the total artisan population of Baden is centred in Mannheim. [1]

The Grand Duchy of Hessen is divided into two approximately **Hessen.** equal parts by the Prussian territory round Frankfurt. The eastern area, both north and south of the river, is mountainous (Vogelsberg and Odenwald); but the western is part of the Rhine plain. The soil is very productive, excellent wine being produced in the west, *e.g.* round Bingen and Openheim; and the large proportion of oak-forest and the valuable cattle-pasture account for the importance of the old leather industry. Darmstadt, the political capital, is a route-centre at the north-west corner of the Odenwald, the steep western scarp of which (the Bergstrasse) is famous for its wine; Giessen ("By the Rivers"), at the Lahn-Wieseck confluence, is the educational capital, but its School of Organic Chemistry—in spite of Baron Liebig—is far behind Höchst in the manufacture of war chemicals; and Mainz is the commercial capital. Like Worms, also an old Roman centre, it stands on the "Roman" bank of the river, where the inflow of the Main tends to keep that bank free from sediment. Under purely natural conditions this was a position of very great importance, and it was long maintained by exercise of "transfer right" (cf. p. 313); but the loss of transfer right (in 1831) began what artificial regulation of the river has completed, *i.e.* the displacing of Mainz by Frankfurt for eastern traffic and by Mannheim for northern traffic.

---

[1] Some of its prosperity is due to the huge chemical industry of Ludwigshafen.

Würtemberg

Würtemberg is a little kingdom the size of Wales, shut in by Bavaria on the north and east and by Baden on the south and west in such a way that it has only inferior connection with the great east-and-west or north-and-south highways of South Germany except at one point.   But for the same reason it is fairly compact, and the fact that it still contains many miles of Roman roads suggests an early civilisation.   A further advantage is in the relief, which is hilly rather than mountainous, and has the Rauhe Alb (Swabian Jura) as its natural centre.   On both sides of the S.W.– N.E. backbone the land falls in fertile terraces, the northern (Lower Swabia) having a more genial climate than the southern (Upper Swabia).   The latter still has a typical Swabian (Suevi) population, while west of the Neckar the population is Alemanni, and east of the Neckar it is Franconian.   The natural centre of the country is at Stuttgart, where the Neckar is navigable[1] after its great northward bend; and the neighbouring town of Esslingen is a great transport centre.   The country is specifically agricultural, with rich corn-fields, vineyards, and orchards (apple and pear), and lush meadows which were so famous for their horses that they gave its name to Stuttgart (" Stud-garden "); and over 30 p.c. of the area is forested, paper-making being a typical industry, e.g. at Ravensburg and Heilbronn.   The mineral wealth is small, being mainly confined to iron; but the industry in this is probably as old as the Romans, and the people have a traditional skill in metal-working (cf. the pianos of Stuttgart, the engines of Esslingen, mathematical instruments, etc.); and, as the abundant water-power compensates largely for the absence of coal, old textile industries (woollens and linens) still flourish, e.g. at Esslingen and Göppingen.

The most important centre politically is Stuttgart, with an industrial bulwark at Esslingen and the State University at Tübingen.   Though it is rather isolated from the outside world, the compactness of the kingdom and the energy of the people have combined to attract to it all the typical activities of the country, including the clock-making of the Black Forest; but it is relatively modern—the old capital having been Cannstatt—and owes its architectural beauty and artistic treasures to royal patrons attracted to the place by its fine climate and beautiful surroundings. The most important centre strategically is the old city of Ulm. It stands where the confluence of the Iller makes the Danube navigable, and marks the terminus of the long Alpine valley by which the Suevi originally moved northwards.   It thus guards the approach from the east to the Burgundy Gate, and is still a fortress

---

[1] The actual port is at Cannstatt, c. 900 feet above sea-level.

of first rank, the base of operations for the German army behind
the Black Forest, and capable of accommodating a force of fully
100,000 men. Its grand old cathedral, which is said to be able to
hold 30,000 persons, suggests its importance in the Middle Ages; and
the city still retains its old leather and cloth trades. The most
important centre commercially is Heilbronn, on the site of a
Roman settlement. It is a very old town; and much of it—like
Ulm, but unlike Stuttgart—looks old, with its turreted walls and
gabled roofs. Old industries, too, in delicate metal-work (gold and
silver) still flourish. But it is so far north that it has become a
great rail and river junction, the natural head of steam navigation
on the Neckar and commanding railway traffic round the end of
the Black Forest.

BAVARIA

In Bavaria, except for a fringe of Longheads dotted about Its Charthe main lines of movement, *e.g.* along the Danube or on the acter.
approaches to the great Alpine passes, we are in a land of Roundheads. No doubt, there is a considerable mixture of influences,
e.g. Germanised Slav in the north-east, Swabian in the centre, Frank
in the north-west; but the dominating strain can probably be
traced back to times before Odoacer's troops swept the country,
and its physical qualities and mental activities are very significant.
Indeed, it seems to represent an approximation to that original
stock which found its highest expression in the ancient Greeks,
and from which the Slavs have degenerated. The geographical
conditions were favourable to the survival of such a stock—at
least, off the line of the main routes; for the core of the area is an
old "Variscan fragment" with a Steppe climate. It may be
divided into five natural regions—(1) the high plateau between the
frontier streams of Iller and Salzach and south of a line joining
Ulm and Augsburg to Mühldorf, (2) the riverine lands north of
that up to the Danube, (3) the constricted valleys of the Naab and
the Regen between the Bohemian Forest on the one hand, and the
Franconian Jura and Bavarian Forest on the other, (4) the basin
of the winding Main from the Fichtelgebirge, and (5) the alien
Palatinate. It is, therefore essentially a highland area walled in by
mountains, for the Bohemian Forest (4800 feet) falls abruptly on
the Bavarian side, and the Noric Alps have, in Zugspitze (9700
feet), the highest peak in the German Empire. The most
characteristic feature of the high plateau, which is simply a
continuation of the Swiss plateau, is the number of important
streams which cross it at short and regular intervals, and which flow
more or less parallel with one another in deep gullies that form
natural barriers to movement east-and-west. The section of the

Jura that faces the riverine lands has been so much denuded that there are relatively easy valleys across it, *e.g.* those of the Wörnitz and the Altmühl, while to the north the uplift becomes an expanse of hilly land rather than a consecutive scarp—thus facilitating the construction of the Ludwig Canal.

Economic Geography. Agriculture and forestry are the natural occupations of the area, and the importance of the forestry is intimately related to the relief and to the lack of mineral wealth, for much of the hilly country is not favourable to agriculture, and there is an almost total absence of coal. These conditions have re-acted on a poor population of pronounced artistic leaning in such a way as to account for some of the typical modern industries. For instance, the very important glass industry, although now centred at Fürth, flourished at least 500 years ago on the forested sandstone of the Spessart; and to-day the great paper industry of Aschaffenburg gets, not only much of its raw material, but also the whole of its workmen from the same poverty-stricken highland. Cheap labour, again, accounts for the huge ready-made clothes industry of the town. The crochet and glass-bead embroidery, the basket-work, the polishing of cedar-wood for pencils, were all at first home industries undertaken by the women to eke out the earnings of the men in the quarries and as navvies or foresters. The largest forests are in the south, but the best timber comes from the north, *e.g.* the Spessart oak. About half the area is cultivated, and a sixth is pasture. The latter is most important in the extreme south, where the alp pasture is very favourable to cattle, especially in the Algau. The riverine lands produce barley, rye, oats, and wheat in large quantities, the first two sometimes to a weight of 7,000,000 tons apiece! Hops are widely grown, especially in the Regnitz basin, the finest coming from the Halledau and Spalt districts; and the same area grows the best tobacco in Germany. Wine is a special product in the Lower Main valley, *e.g.* round Würzburg, and in the Palatinate; and the sandstone of the same two areas grows famous potatoes.

Industrial Divisions. The position of the three Universities of Munich, Würzburg, and Erlangen, almost suggests a three-fold industrial division of the kingdom. The Erlangen, Fürth, and Nürnberg area is the centre of the hop and tobacco trades and of the glass and toy industries— Nürnberg being the "capital of toy-world" in all materials except felt (normally cheaper in England), and having local supplies of wood, paper, and celluloid. The Munich centre is specially concerned with chemical and electrical work, having abundance of salt in the Inn and the Salzach valleys, *e.g.* at Rosenheim and Traunstein— abundance of water-power, used near Traunstein for nitrogen works —and some coal or lignite both south-west and south-east of the city, providing both Munich itself and Augsburg with perhaps one-third of their supply. The Würzburg centre is more interested in wine and "wood" products. The genius of the people seems specially developed in the working of metal, from gold-leaf and spun silver (for trimmings) to various transport media, both Munich and Nürnberg having important locomotive and motor works, and both Munich and Würzburg having important industries in surgical and mathematical instruments. Water-power is largely used in textile as well as in mechanical works, especially on the Lech, *e.g.* at Augsburg, and on the Upper Main valley, where Hof and Beyreuth, Bamberg and Lichtenfels, are important centres, the "textile" industry of Bamberg and Lichtenfels including basket-weaving. The most widely-distributed industry is the brewing; and the best known breweries, *e.g.* those at Munich and Kulmbach, Erlangen and Nürnberg, have special advantages of nearness to the best barley or the best water or the best hops. The best known product is probably the pencils of Nürnberg,—the lead of which comes mainly from the graphite mines near Passau—or the lithographic stone of Solnhofen. The great lack of coal is largely compensated by the abundance of water-power and the facilities for importing fuel by water, *e.g.* Rumanian petroleum to Ratisbon.

In many ways the Palatinate is more favoured than Bavaria **The Pala-** proper, but it produces much the same products, *e.g.* tobacco and **tinate.** wine, wood and grain. Its special products are the chemicals of Ludwigshafen and the boots and shoes of Pirmasens; and the military routes westward from Ludwigshafen and Spires (the capital) have given facilities for transport which have encouraged a great development of textiles in the humid forested valleys on the windward face of the Haardt, *e.g.* at Kaiserslautern.

Four towns are of special interest. Munich—on the central **Munich** river of Southern Bavaria, on the north edge of the Alpine foreland, **and Augs-** between moor and forest, in the rear of the Danube, controlling the **burg.** junction of the Brenner route with the great "Piedmont" road from Vienna to Basel (cf. Hohenlinden, Blenheim, Mühldorf, etc.)— was the natural south-eastern outlet of Southern Germany, and so the natural political centre of old Bavaria, as it is the natural economic centre of modern Bavaria, and the largest city in Southern Germany. It "inherits" the old university first founded in the fortress-town of Ingoldstadt, and then moved to the industrial centre of Landshut, where textiles and scientific instruments are as typical products as in Munich itself. Augsburg, on the western river of Southern Bavaria, had a somewhat similar position; but the Lech does not lead so directly to the Brenner as the Isar does, and the importance of the place was specifically local, as a fortress between the Lech and the Wertach. Indeed, the fact that the Lech still divides Swabia from Bavaria and Alemannian from Bavarian types is sufficient comment on its torrential character—shown in its endless arms, its rush-grown islands, its terrific floods, or the recent progress in textile industries with power from the curbed torrent. Cf. the Walchensee, the Mittlere Isar, and the Jettenbach-Toeging power-stations.

Ratisbon and Nürnberg. Ratisbon and Nürnberg represent the lowland rather than the highland control. Both are on the line of least resistance between the Middle Danube and the Middle Main, *i.e.* a more important route in olden days than the direct north-and-south route *via* the Wörnitz or Altmühl valley ; and the change in the relative value of these routes has been compensated, as far as Ratisbon and Nürnberg are concerned, by the increased importance of the routes by the Naab valley into the Eger valley, and by the Regen valley into the Beraun. Ratisbon (Regensburg) had, and still has, easy access *via* Landshut to the Brenner, and the advantage of being on the northerly bend of the Danube, at the limit of " deep " navigation ; but, though once the meeting-place of the Imperial Diet, it is too near the frontier to have permanent political importance other than in war. Nürnberg, though more important even politically and owing its rise to the command given by its castled rock over the sandy plain, was essentially a commercial centre in the Pegnitz gap ; and it still is one of the most important junctions (rail, river, road, and canal) in Germany.

SAXONY

Its Character. The triangular kingdom of Saxony, from its base on the Erzgebirge (" Ore Mountains "), intrudes so far into the great European plain that its apex, at Leipzig, has had for ages special facilities for tapping trans-continental trade, while the abundant water-power and the mineral wealth of the Ore Mountains made it an industrial as well as a commercial area. The actual amount of lowland is not great, but the soil is exceedingly fertile ; and, on the other hand, the Erzgebirge nowhere reach 4000 feet, while the Lusatian heights do not reach even 3000. The mountain base, however, lies S.W.–N.E., throwing off its water-supply naturally towards the north-west, *i.e.* parallel to the course of the Elbe ; and one important result of this is that very few of its numerous rivers flow directly to the Elbe, thus providing the area with a succession of separate arteries more or less parallel with one another. The sub-tributaries converge, however, on the tributaries, *e.g.* the Mulde, the Pleisse, and the Elster, within the frontiers of the kingdom, thus making the " apex " site of Leipzig almost deltaic. Saxony, therefore—since it got rid of the futile Slav subdivision of its land into microscopic fragments—has become one of the most advanced agricultural States in the world, the richest grain-lands (rye and oats) being just where these rivers drop on to the lowland, *e.g.* at Bautzen, Meissen, and Grimma ; and, though its climate is somewhat severe, it grows enormous quantities of hardy fruit,

especially cherries, plums, and apples, *e.g.* round Grimma, while
the Vogtland grows equally large crops of potatoes.

The prosperity of the kingdom, however, is based essentially on **Mineral**
the mineral wealth and water-power of the mountains, thanks to **Wealth.**
which the population is the densest in Europe, the total of over
4,800,000 for an area of under 6000 square miles giving an average
of just about 860 per square mile.   The Erz have a steep southward
fall to the valleys of the Eger and the Biela, but a gentler slope
northward, *i.e.* on the windward side ; and the varied course of the
rivers, through open " bay " or narrow gorge, betrays the alternation
of hard old rock with soft sedimentary rock.   The hard old rock is,
or was, characteristically rich in metal, *e.g.* silver and tin ; and the
neighbouring sedimentary rock (cf. p. 49) is rich in coal.   There
are still nominally four ore-mining districts—round Frieberg, where

The industrial areas, Saxony and Silesia.

silver has been worked for 800 years, round Scheeberg (cobalt and
nickel), round Johann-Georgenstadt (silver and iron), and the
Müglitz valley round Altenberg (tin) ; but the metallic wealth
is largely exhausted, and the economic life of the area has
gravitated to, or been entirely remodelled by, the coal-fields of
Zwickau, Oelsnitz, and Chemnitz.   There is also a small field
between Dresden and Freiberg, and both Dresden and Leipzig
have fields of brown coal.   With this wealth of coal, and enough
water-power elsewhere to run almost as many factories as are
worked by coal, Saxony has come to monopolise more than one-
fourth of all the textile industries of Germany.

There was, however, a third influence at work—in the "after- **Industries.**
results " of the old tin and silver mining.   This had attracted
population almost to the very crest of the Erz, *e.g.* at Annaberg and
Altenberg ; and, when the mining began to fail, the inhabitants did
not desert their mountain homes, but sought employment in other

directions.   As agriculture was out of the question at such altitudes, and as forest industries were limited, home industries sprang up in "textiles," *e.g.* lace and straw-plaiting, or toys (Vogtland) and fine metal work, *e.g.* the gold lace of Freiburg and the watches of the Altenberg-Glashütte district.   Climatic conditions are more favourable to secondary than to primary processes, and cotton is naturally more suited to the windward than to the leeward range of mountains. The great cotton district is in and round Zwickau and Chemnitz, *e.g.* at Meerane and Glauchau, Werdau and Krimitschau—Chemnitz being the metropolis, and the special product being hosiery.   Nearer the mountains, *e.g.* from Reichenbach to Plauen, lace is more typical, Plauen being specially known for its white embroidery and muslin (cf. Falkenstein and Auerbach), as Annaberg is for passementeries.   In the drier east, wool takes the place of cotton. The other chief industries of the kingdom are in hardware and stoneware, *e.g.* all kinds of "machinery" (mining, textile, printing, locomotive), especially at Chemnitz and Dresden, and of "china," especially at Meissen (porcelain) and Pirna (earthenware).

Towns.   Pirna, with its famous sandstone quarries, stands at the exit of the Elbe from the Saxon "Switzerland."   Though very far from being typically *Swiss*, the district is exceedingly picturesque, owing its beauty to the deep gorges and quaint isolated peaks easily worn by water and ice in the soft sandstone ; and it was this gorge that gave such political importance to a site within easy access of the fine building-stone and the beautiful scenery that the capital was moved to Dresden ("The Forest") from Meissen ("The Frontier,")—the latter placed, typically for a frontier fort, on the west bank of the Elbe.   Dresden still has a strategic value, and its industrial importance has grown with the development of the coal-field to the west ; but, except for Dresden itself, the whole balance of power has moved to the west of the kingdom, and Dresden (like Halle) never had a tithe of the non-local importance possessed by Leipzig.   For Dresden was too far south, as Halle was too far north, to be the natural meeting-place of the Thuringian Road from the west with the road that skirts the Lusatian plateau from the east, and crosses the Elbe at Riesa—still a busy river-port, on the "German" bank of the river.

Leipzig.   Leipzig, too, had the commercial advantage of being at the great bend on the Elster and the strategic advantage of the Elster-Pleisse marshes within the bend.   As far as internal commerce is concerned, it has the most central site in the Empire, and has thus come to be the seat of the Supreme Law Courts of the Empire ; it has also the most central site strategically in what is called the "cockpit of Germany"; it has one of the oldest Universities in Germany and one of the most important printing and publishing[1] trades in the

---

[1] As a bookselling centre, it has been more important than either Paris or London.

world. A fishing village, between forest and pasture and marsh, it had natural facilities for local collection of skins and furs ; and it is now one of the most important fur and leather markets in the world, with a very large book-binding industry. The substitution of metallic for wooden type did it no harm, for it had easy access to practically all the necessaries for modern type-founding (copper, tin, lead, bismuth, antimony, etc.) ; and the substitution of " wood " for textile materials in paper-making only gave it a new use for its forests. Its two greatest fairs are held at Easter and Michaelmas, and the chief articles sold (to the value of perhaps £10,000,000), are still furs, skins, leather, wool, hair, and bristles. But the city has very important industries of its own, including scientific and musical instruments (cf. Dresden), artificial flowers (cf. Dresden), and chemicals— the last founded on the salt of its old rival, Halle, which provided its earliest cargoes.

The city illustrates specifically the process referred to above (p. 291), by which the central position of Germany enables her more or less to monopolise many of the markets that she can reach without " break-of-bulk."

Output of Coal and Lignite

The following table gives the output of coal and lignite for (a) all Germany and (b) the chief fields separately for 1922 and 1923, with similar figures for such parts of Germany in 1913 as are still within the republic.

Coal (in Millions of Metric Tons)

	Germany.	Ruhr.	Silesia.
1913	$140\frac{3}{4}$	114	11
1922	119	$96\frac{1}{2}$	$8\frac{3}{4}$
1923	$62\frac{1}{4}$	$42\frac{1}{4}$	$8\frac{1}{3}$

Lignite (in Millions of Metric Tons)

	Lower Rhine.	Central Germany.	East Elbe.
1913	$20\frac{1}{4}$	$38\frac{2}{3}$	26
1922	$37\frac{1}{2}$	$59\frac{1}{4}$	$36\frac{1}{2}$
1923	24	$55\frac{1}{2}$	$34\frac{3}{4}$

If the lignite is converted into its equivalent coal, the aggre-gate of 1923 was fully 61,000,000 tons below that of 1922, and 59,000,000 below that of 1913 (excluding the Saar and "Polish" Silesia); and at that time the figures were thought to suggest that Germany could not make good, by increased output elsewhere, any marked decreased output in the Ruhr district. The figures for 1929, however, show a very remarkable recovery and development both in coal and in lignite production. The coal out-put for the Ruhr district had risen to 110,000,000 tons (*i.e.* almost the 1913 level), that for Upper Silesia to 19,700,000, that for the Aachen field to 10,700,000, that for Lower Silesia to 5,700,000, while the Saxon was just over 4,000,000. The lignite[1] output varied from nearly 11,000,000 tons for Lower Silesia and 12,000,000 for the Saxon field, to 48,000,000 for the Bonn field and nearly 79,000,000 for the Halle. There is also potential water-power estimated at 7,500,000 h.p., nearly 3,000,000 being in Bavaria and 1,000,000 in Baden; and of this already nearly 1,500,000 is being exploited.

The loss of Alsace-Lorraine has deprived Germany of fully 73 p.c. of her home supplies of iron-ore, and has reduced her iron resources from *c.* 25 p.c. of the European total to rather less than $7\frac{1}{2}$ p.c. The Sieg basin is now the chief source of home ore, and the import from Sweden has increased by nearly 40 p.c., while that from "France" has fallen by more than that.

[1] The lignite can be converted into coal value at 3 for 1.

CHAPTER XXI

SWITZERLAND

THE Alps spread through five different countries, and fully two-thirds of their area, including the two highest peaks, is outside the Swiss frontier; but Switzerland does contain the heart of the system, with all that is most typical in feature and phenomenon. To Europe as a whole the system gives a beautiful playground, a useful barrier between conflicting racial elements, and a magnificent hydrographic focus; to the Swiss it has meant survival, character, prosperity. Even the name has been applied for centuries by the natives not to the snowy peaks, but to the grass-land which spreads in a broad belt almost everywhere between the snow-line and the forest, and which in summer dominates both the whole colour-scheme of Alpine scenery and the characteristic occupation of the people. *Alp v. alp.*

Between Lake Geneva and Lake Constance, between the Jura and the seaward wall of the Engadine, between a northward expansion beyond the Rhine in Schaffhausen and a southward expansion to the latitude of Como in Ticino, the country lies in a fairly compact oval across the whole plan of the Alps (cf. Ch. IV.). It has, therefore, no real physical unity, nor are its political frontiers consistently related to natural features. Thus, the whole canton of Ticino, the Poschiavo basin and several other tongues of the Grisons, and a fraction of Valais, overlap the southern water-parting; the whole of Schaffhausen and part of Basel overlap the line of the Rhine in the north; and all the land beyond Mont Terrible—some even east of it—is as naturally French as the Engadine is naturally Austrian. The thirteen cantons which formed the Swiss Confederation down to 1798, were *inside* the natural boundaries, so that modern Switzerland has encroached on all her great neighbours, France and Germany, Austria and Italy. *Lack of Unity.*

These natural boundaries are of a kind which greatly favoured the political independence of the small area within them, but cut it off from access to the outer world except by the courtesy of its neighbours. For it is too small ($= \frac{1}{2}$ Ireland) to be dangerous to any of them; it is too strongly defended for any of them to be really *Foreign Relations.*

345

dangerous to it ; and its dependence on all of them alike for access
to the outside world guaranteed perfect neutrality in all directions.
It made, therefore, an admirable Buffer State ; and the cutting of
Alpine tunnels, while enormously increasing the commercial possibilities, has in no way affected its political or strategic independence.

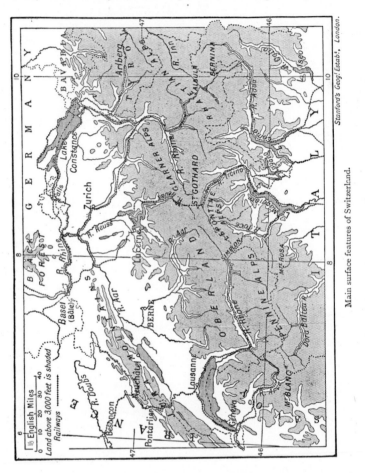

Surface. The surface is divided into four natural belts, running generally
S.W. to N.E., with a tendency to expand in the latter direction ;
for the sandstone plateau of the Aar basin is flanked by the
limestone of the Jura on the one side and the limestone of the
northern Alps on the other, while the whole is buttressed seaward
by the crystalline wall of the southern Alps. The tendency to
expand towards the N.E., *i.e.* towards Germany rather than France,

has been emphasised by the position of the country between Genoa and Frankfurt, and by the encouragement of tunnelling, owing to the thinness of the ends of the crystalline range, especially near the St. Gothard and the Simplon passes. The northern outlier of the Alps, however, in the Bernese Oberland and the Tödi, is really the key to the whole position, separating the two wide and undulating valleys of the Aar and the Thur from the two deep and narrow gorges of the Rhine and the Rhone ; and, as the highest ranges and almost all the great glaciers of the system are inside the Swiss frontier, the rivers have had maximum power. On the one hand, they have cut back their valleys to a common source in the area of maximum precipitation round the St. Gothard ; on the other, though radiating in all directions, they consistently cut transverse valleys, *e.g.* between Chur and Lake Constance, or Martigny and Lake Geneva, thus greatly facilitating access north and south across the whole system.

If we compare a political map of the cantons with a physical **River** map of the whole country, it at once becomes obvious that the **System.** four large cantons of Valais, Grisons, Bern, and Ticino, correspond roughly with the valleys of the four great rivers that radiate from the St. Gothard—Rhone, Rhine, Aar, and Ticino. It is obvious, too, that where the country is narrowest from north to south, it is divided equally into a western and an eastern area by the one river which consistently cuts a transverse valley throughout its whole course. This is the Reuss—on its way from the common source of the other four rivers, near the fortress of Andermatt, to what is practically the confluence of the Rhine and the Aar at the historic site of Habsburg. The basin of the Upper Reuss is the precise area in which the Föhn wind is most favourable to the northern slope of the Alps—though its extreme heat and dryness are relatively unfavourable to trees in the canton into which it swoops first, Uri ; and the basin of the Lower Reuss was originally part of the old Duchy of Swabia, the natural limit of which northward was the Swabian Jura.

These circumstances throw considerable light on the early **Forest** importance of Uri and its two neighbours in the Reuss basin, **Cantons.** Schwyz and Unterwalden. Three results were specially significant. The most important was their success in pushing the native Hapsburgs northward into the Danube valley—thus "anticipating" the Schaffhausen expansion of frontier beyond the Rhine, and in pushing the Savoy intruders southward into the Po valley—thus "anticipating" the Ticino expansion beyond the crystalline crest. Less important was the subsequent connection, through the Swabian part of the Danube basin, with the Hapsburgs in Austria. Locally, it was entirely appropriate that the three great "battles of deliverance" should have been fought round the most northerly, *i.e.* the most exposed, of the three cantons—at Sempach, Morgarten, and Näfels. Lucerne was, therefore, so much involved that the natural sequel was a unit of the "*Four* Forest Cantons" round the Vierwaldstättersee; and the natural expansion of this unit into the eight ancient cantons was controlled by the plateau of the Aar.

Climate.   The great average height of the area (= summit of Snowdon) and the northward exposure make the climate generally one of considerable extremes, especially to leeward, *e.g.* in the Engadine; but there is great variety of level and of exposure. With a southern exposure and an altitude of only 900 feet, Lugano has an average annual temperature of 53° F., a range of from 36° F. to 72° F., a winter of only three months, and a rainfall of 64 inches. In the Upper Engadine (6000 feet) there is a range of over 90° F., the summer highest mean reaching 77° F., though snow may fall in August, and the winter lasts for six months. There is also, of course, immense variety of local conditions, *e.g.* slope and shelter, which makes generalisation almost impossible; but, quite generally, the annual mean varies little, being, *e.g.*, about 49° F. at Sion or Geneva (50° F. at Montreux), 48° F. at Bern and Zurich, and 49° F. at Basel, while the extremes over the plateau (*c.* 1600 feet) range roughly from a winter mean of 30° F. to a summer mean of 60° F. The same is true generally of the rainfall. There are a few glaring extremes, as between a maximum of *c.* 90 inches on or round the Adula Alps, and a minimum of *c.* 22 inches in the Rhone valley to leeward of Mont Blanc; but generally the variation is not great, *e.g.* from 33 inches at Geneva and 43 at Montreux to 36 at Bern and 46 at Lucerne. Davos has a mean annual temperature of *c.* 37° F., and a mean annual rainfall of about 37 inches. Two features of the rainfall are important. The average fall is greatest and most even, not on the higher elevations, but where winds blowing over a wide space are suddenly "contracted" into a narrowing valley; and greater exposure to rain and sun make the Aar and the Ticino valleys more fertile than the gorges of the Rhine and the Rhone. The average rainfall is about half the extreme, *i.e.* fully 40 inches; and the snow-line varies, mainly with the precipitation, from 8000 to 9000 feet.

Lakes and Glaciers.   Under these conditions, the rivers have great pace and great volume, which makes them as useful for "power" as they are useless for navigation—except, to a certain extent, the Aar; and the one danger from such a régime, from flood, is obviated by the number of lake-reservoirs. As these lakes, too, are generally of the typical "ribbon" type which is left in a deep U-shaped valley that has been glaciated, they are very long for their width, *e.g.* Lake Zurich being 10 times as long as it is wide; and, therefore, they are very useful for transport. They are placed characteristically along the edge of the plateau, *i.e.* where the morainic dams would naturally accumulate; and, therefore, their value for filtering silt and for checking flood is increased. It is significant that the three cantons which *still* have by far the greatest area [1] of glaciers, Valais (375 square miles), Grisons (139), and Bern (111), have the least proportion of lake. In spite of the lakes, however, the larger rivers, *e.g.* the Rhine below Ragatz, require careful embanking (cf. the Rhone); and the whole plain of the Aar is widely covered with alluvial accumulations.

As some 25 p.c. of the area is unproductive, and there are no **Natural** important minerals except asphalt (Neuchâtel), salt (Bex and Basel), **Resources.** and iron and manganese (St. Gall), the country is far from being naturally rich; but care and diligence have made it rich. Of the 77 p.c. that is productive, fully 29 p.c. is forest, nearly 20 p.c. is arable, and the rest is pasture; and the last is of predominant importance. It is essentially Alpine and concerned with cattle. The heights give the summer pasture on the real alp, and the valleys supply the hay for winter food and accessible centres for dairy industries, *e.g.* condensing milk and manufacturing cheese; and, in spite of the small area, the number of cattle exceeds 1,600,000. The explanation lies in the peculiar richness of the alp pasture.

The Alps are so young that they are still weathering very **Real Alp.** quickly, especially under the influence of the glaciers; and the finer rock-waste from the glaciers is distributed over broad shelves of rock below the snow-line. These elevated shelves are normally above the clouds in winter, but below them in summer, so that they are fully exposed to the action of frost in winter and drenched with moisture in summer. The fine soil and abundant moisture produce a very quick growth of such plants as can exist at this high elevation; and the quick growth, aided by the rare atmosphere and the bright light, produces a most nutritious and wholesome type of vegetation. It may be knee-deep in flowers, but all is of unique value as fodder for cows; and it is far too valuable to be wasted on sheep. A few large flocks of sheep are to be found—*e.g.* in the Muttenalp part of the Tödi—and goats [2] are numerous in very rocky places and actually amongst the ice; but wherever the underlying rock-form is covered with sufficient vegetation to conceal its precise character, there the cow monopolises all attention. Climate and facilities for transport are naturally more favourable on the northern slopes of the mountains—the highest proportion of land used as pasture being towards the north-east, *e.g.* in St. Gall and Appenzell, but the best returns being towards the south-west, *e.g.* in the valleys of the Great Emmen and the Saane. Cheese—made up on the alp—is the great product, especially Gruyère and Emmenthaler (both full of holes and with hard rind); but condensed milk is

---

[1] This is actual area, not relative proportion; for these three cantons comprise nearly half Switzerland.

[2] The goats do not number more than *c.* 300,000, while the sheep are only *c.* 170,000.

more important, especially on the lake-lowlands, *e.g.* at Vevey and Cham, Bern and Lucerne.

Agriculture.   Agriculture is relatively unimportant, local supplies of food being insufficient even for the local population, and the additional demands of visitors raise the import of cereals to 100,000 tons, *i.e.* 50 p.c. of total imports. Only 14 or 15 p.c. of the total productive area is under grain, mainly in the south-west, especially in Vaud ; and Vaud also is most advanced otherwise, growing—like Ticino—good wine, *e.g.* round Montreux, and good tobacco, *e.g.* in the Broye valley. Good wine is also grown in Valais, and to some extent in Neuchâtel and Basel ; but in the more northern latitudes the vine is replaced by hardier fruit (cf. the jam and cherry-brandy trades of the Lower Reuss basin), and the increasing demand for sugar is encouraging wide cultivation of beet.

Other Industries.   The wealth of the country, therefore, obviously depends on its other industries ; and there are already nearly as many persons occupied in these,—*i.e.* practically in textiles, watch-making, mining and machinery—as in agricultural and pastoral work in its widest sense — *i.e.* including horticulture, forestry, and some fishing Even so, but for the visitors, there would still be a balance against the Swiss ; and the problem is not becoming less acute. Dependence on foreigners for raw materials—as well as for access to the outside world—is complicated by the growth of foreign industrial competition and of prohibitive tariffs, especially in countries where the home demand is much larger than in Switzerland ; and the (qualified) prosperity of the Swiss industries is due only to the character of the people and the abundance of water-power on the one hand, and to the type of product and the attention compulsorily paid to foreign taste, etc., on the other hand. Activity is, therefore, concentrated on fine work, in which relatively high value is coupled with relatively small bulk ; in other words, a vast amount of labour is spent on a small amount of raw material. This applies more strictly to such products as lace and silk, watches and chocolate ; but it is also more or less true even of the ordinary cotton and woollen textiles (cf. the great decrease in the number of spindles during the last thirty years—amounting to at least 500,000 !). The two most prosperous industries are those in chocolate (helped by the increased local output of sugar) and watches ; and about 95 p.c. of all centres, *i.e.* 90 p.c. of the entire population, have access to electric power.

Textiles and Metal Work.   The textile industry is the most important, attention being largely monopolised by silk[1] and cotton (4 : 3) ; and Zürich, which is the largest town in the country (*c.* 223,000), is interested in both. The other silk centres, of which Basel (*c.* 145,000) is much the most important, are to the west of Zürich, on the route of the

---

[1] Artificial silk is becoming as important as floss silk, especially in St. Gall.

St. Gothard railway—by which the raw silk is imported from Italy—
and the other cotton centres are to the east, where St. Gall and
Appenzell use their abundant water-power specially in embroidery
and similar products, *e.g.* net.   Machinery, both for the textiles and
for transport, is made in the chief textile centres, specially at Zürich
and Basel, at Bern and Winterthur.   The fine metal work is,
however, as distinctly "French" as the textile work is "German";
and it has spread from its old home in Geneva to the Neuchâtel
portion of the Jura.   Geneva, though still famous for watches, is
also noted for its jewellery and scientific instruments; Neuchâtel is
more specially a watch-making centre, though also interested in
electrical apparatus, while La Chaux-de-Fonds and Le Locle are
specifically devoted to watches, and Ste. Croix makes musical boxes.
Aluminium is manufactured in Schaffhausen, and aniline dyes are a
special product at Basel.

The small area, the very definite routes by which it can be **Political**
approached, and its intricate relief, have combined to dominate the **Character.**
economic distribution of population.   No equal area elsewhere has
so many "confluence" and "lake-end" towns—*e.g.* Solothurn and
Aarau, Martigny and Sion, Bellinzona and Samaden, Geneva and
Zürich, Lucerne and Zug, Thun and Brienz.   As the lines of least
resistance run along the edges of the plateau and up the great
valleys, Geneva ("The Mouth") ought to be the most important
centre; but the character of the relief, like the Federal constitution,
is adverse to the marked supremacy of any one town, least of all
a town in a corner of the country.   Historically, too, conditions
were adverse to Geneva.   For Swiss history is said to begin with
the gravitation of bits of Burgundy and Bavaria to a focus from
which they could defend themselves against the common enemy,
the Hapsburgs.   The Confederation was, therefore, German in
origin and in character; and 16 out of the 22 cantons to-day are
predominantly German, French only prevailing in Fribourg, Vaud,
Neuchâtel, Geneva, and the Valais.   Historically, however, Geneva
—even apart from Calvin—has exercised more influence in Europe
than any other Swiss town; and, industrially, it has a magnificent
asset in the Rhone.

The widening of the plateau northwards, while accounting for **Constance**
the predominantly German origin and character of the Confedera- **and**
tion, does not give any similar monopoly of routes to any northern **Schaff-**
centre.   For instance, Constance, even if it had stood at the end of **hausen.**
the lake, could never have monopolised the Lower Rhine trade as
Geneva has monopolised the Lower Rhone trade since the days of
Julius Cæsar; and, of course, once Switzerland had separated from
the Empire, any distinctively German town was more or less in
hostility to the distinctively Swiss interests.   Schaffhausen, almost
as favoured with water-power as Geneva, is off the natural gravitation

by the Thur valley to the Rhine *below* the falls ; and it had an unfortunate connection with Constance, being the " Skiff-town " where
goods from Constance were transferred to land routes because of
the falls.   The great bend on the river and the castle-crowned hill
of Unott gave it both commercial and strategic importance, and its
wealth enabled it to acquire—especially at the time of the Reformation—the various estates which now make up the canton ; but it
suffered so much in the Thirty Years' War that it remained of
little or no importance till its revival as an industrial centre in the
latter part of the nineteenth century.

Basel.   Basel, commanding the relations of the Upper Rhine with both
the Middle Rhine and the Burgundy Gate, was still more important
—first as an imperial and then as an episcopal centre, and then as
the chief city of Helvetia and as the site of the oldest Swiss University
(A.D. 1460) ; but internal rivalries, *e.g.* between bishops and burghers,
and destruction by earthquake—a penalty of commanding a great
fracture-gap—minimised its progress, while the attempt to hold—
to its own financial advantage—the balance between the Rhine
cities and the Swiss Confederation destroyed its influence with both.
The same grasping attitude alienated its own territory, so that to-day
Basel-Land is independent of Basel-Town.   Since the opening of
the St. Gothard tunnel, however, the town has prospered wonderfully ; and it is now one of the chief centres of the silk-ribbon
industry in Europe, and is said to be the richest town in Switzerland.
The port handles 350,000 tons of shipping (barges) a year. Cf. p. 365.

Zürich.   At the same time the Rhine in its longitudinal reach is
essentially not a Swiss river, and the essentially Swiss basin of the
Aar-Reuss is well within the strategic bulwark of the Jura.   Here,
therefore, was the natural site for the chief political centre, even if
it could not rival Geneva as a route-centre ; but even here an
advanced point, such as Habsburg or Baden, was too dangerous
to be able to make full use of the commercial possibilities where
Aar and Reuss and Limmat converge to enter the Rhine at
Coblenz.   The two obvious sites that fulfil all needs are at the
great bend on the Aar, and where the Limmat leaves the long lake of
Zürich ; and the latter is undoubtedly much the more important now.
For the Lake of Lucerne diverted the St. Gothard route eastward
of the Reuss valley, so that Zürich became its natural objective ; all
north-eastward traffic from Geneva must work round the west end
of the lake, while south-eastward traffic from Basel follows the
Limmat-Linth valley to the Prättigau.   Before the days of railways,
however, it had much less commercial importance ; and, largely
owing to many favours received from the Frankish emperors, it
inherited an attitude so hostile to the Confederation that it only
entered it under the compulsion of a war in which it was beaten.
It is now the most important town in the country, even politically,

while in commercial, industrial, and educational [1] importance it is far ahead of all the other towns except Basel.

But by the time that a single capital was chosen for the Con- **Bern.** federation (1848), Bern—on the great bend of the navigable Aar— was the most central place of any importance; and, thanks to the vigour of its people, it had extended its canton until it was the most representative area in Switzerland—divided into Oberland, with its magnificent alps, especially in the Simmen valley, the agricultural plain of the Mittelland, and the Jura Seeland ("Lakeland"). Perched, too, on a river-girt bluff guarded by the castle of Nydeck, it had long held the balance as a frontier town between the French-speaking Burgundians and the German-speaking Alemanni. Though its population is only 110,000, it is an exceedingly convenient centre for such resorts as Thun and Interlaken, Mürren and Grindelwald.

But the Geographic Control exercised by the critical, central **Racial** position and by the varied, intricate relief was not confined to the **Distribu-** economic distribution of population. As a focus which was also a **tion.** thoroughfare, especially between Lake Constance and Lake Geneva, the country should show a profoundly heterogeneous population; and, according to Canon Taylor, there are, or have been till quite recently, 35 different dialects of German, 16 of French, 8 of Italian, and 5 of Romonsch. The small proportion speaking the last two languages (7 p.c. and 1 p.c. respectively) is due only to the greater obstacle presented to intrusion from south and east by the lofty crystalline zone of the Alps; and similar reasons account for the relatively small proportion speaking French (20 p.c.). But there are no internal antagonisms based on difference of speech, nor is there any disqualification or inequality; for the political urgency of internal unity against external danger is supreme, and Switzerland is an inviolable Confederation.

But this political and commercial focus of Europe is also its **Internal &** orographical centre, with extremes of elevation and isolation,[2] a **External** forested refuge to "the sweepings of the plains" (p. 209) and **Relations** uninviting to the sweepers. Here all the tendencies of highland life and of geographical isolation make for individualism—in a people whose ethnic base is the individualistic Alpine Roundhead (cf. p. 80), and almost every important natural unit of river-valley becomes a canton, so that the Confederation is ruled absolutely by independent cantons, a minimum of common action "internally" being found with a maximum of common action "externally." And where extremes of ruggedness give a maximum of isolation and safety, there Alpine type and individualism are most marked.

---

[1] It was the home of Pestalozzi and Lavater.
[2] Illustrated by the mere existence of Latin (Ladin), even in a debased form, in the Romonsch dialects of the Rhætian Alps.

**Racial
Elements.**
For the original population of Roundhead Lake-Dwellers—whose settlements were actually in the lakes, especially in Lake Neuchâtel (50 villages) and Lake Biel (20), Lake Constance (32) and Lake Geneva (24)—were ousted from the fertile lake-side lands by Helvetians and Burgundians and other Teutons; and the intruders have left a zone of relatively fair Longheads all over the great thoroughfare of the Aar plain, especially at the two entrances, *i.e.* at Geneva and from Basel to Constance. As the intruders came from the north and the west, the natives retreated to the south and the east, surviving in wonderful purity in the south-east, *e.g.* Disentis, till modern times; and this meant higher elevation, poorer soil, more forest, thinner air, longer winters, especially on the northern slopes. These conditions are all reflected in the physical types to-day. The tall Burgundians in the fertile "Jura" lands have kept their stature, as their French speech, and to some extent their French brunetness; the shorter Alpines have been bleached and dwarfed in the forested glens of the Oberland and the Pennines; the Rhætians in the Romonsch area retain Roman stature and speech on the broader, sunnier, and more fertile valleys of the Grisons; and on the Aar plateau there is the modern "disharmonic" Swiss, with round head and moderate stature, but with long face and grey eyes.

**Forest
Nucleus.**
The nucleus of the country is the heart-shaped "basin" of the Four Forest Cantons and Zug, of which the essential and typical focus was the "Helvetian Cross" of the Lake of Lucerne, or Vierwaldstättersee, the "Lake of the Four *Valleys*." This lake gives an admirable instance of the profound political [1] and economic importance of a long navigable unit in the heart of a land where natural lines of communication are few and difficult. Its German name actually refers to the *valleys* of the four chief rivers which feed it—those of the Reuss, the Emmen, the Aa, and the Muota; but it is geologically most appropriate to a lake which is formed of four main basins, representing four distinct valleys. This is the secret of its beauty—of great promontories, deep bays, and steep mountain walls. Its political and economic importance is bound up with its great length,—of 24 miles, with a maximum width of 2 miles—which puts one-third into the canton of Lucerne, nearly one-third into Unterwalden, one-sixth into Schwyz, and one-sixth into Uri.

**Scenic
Attrac-
tions.**
The last three, the original "Three Cantons" of the Ever-lasting League (A.D. 1398), are typical river-valley sections, the natural approaches to which round the Rigi are commanded by Lucerne and Zug, with their larger proportion of arable lowland; and the latter, if no longer more exposed to danger, are still the richer, the more inviting, and the more accessible. Lucerne had the advantage of Zug in its larger area and its easier access—by its

---

[1] It is worth noting that Brunnen was the *port* of Schwyz.

long lake—to the foot of the St. Gothard route, while its central position in the Roman Catholic area of the country made its town of Lucerne for ages the headquarters of the Roman Church in Switzerland.   In modern times Zug has the advantage of nearness to the textile district of the north-east, in the industries of which the town of Zug has some share.   The whole group now, however, owes its prosperity to its scenery.   This is locally pretty and picturesque rather than grand or sublime, for its peaks do not "challenge," like those of the Oberland, nor do its passes link different climatic worlds, like those of the Pennines; but the eternal snows are always in the background, and access to them is only too easy.   Even the Jungfrau is now desecrated by one of those ingenious railways that are the culminating product of an engineering skill appropriate to, and engendered by, centuries of adaptation to a land of difficult and dangerous communications; and nearly half a million persons "climb" the Rigi and Pilatus every year by train !

The canton of Lucerne (= Herts), so far from containing glaciers, **Lucerne** does not rise to the snow-line even in the Rothhorn (*c.* 7700 feet) and Pilatus (*c.* 7000), and nine-tenths of it is "productive," the Emmen valley being famous for its pastures, especially round Entlebuch, and having some mineral wealth.   Its people are still noted for their devotion to old customs and costumes, to the Roman Church, and to wrestling; but the canton is merely an appendage to the town.   Even historically this is true, for it grew out of various districts acquired from time to time by the town ; and the Confederation itself was the direct result of the purchase of Lucerne by the Hapsburgs from the Abbots of Murbach (in Alsace).

Though the old canton of Schwyz gave its name to the whole **Schwyz.** country of Switzerland, its strength must not be judged from the fine strategic position occupied by the modern canton, wedged in between the lakes of Zürich and Lucerne, and with the Rigi and the Lake of Zug in the foreground.   The old canton was confined to the Muota valley, *i.e.* the Lucerne drainage, while the Sihl valley of the Zürich drainage was under the ecclesiastical rulers of Einsiedeln, who were definitely hostile.   Indeed, the Austrian campaign which ended at Morgarten, was provoked by a Schwyz attack on Einsiedeln.   The influence of Schwyz, both in the naming of the country and in its political existence, was, however, largely based on its geographical conditions.   As the most northerly of the three cantons, it stood—to the Hapsburgs—for the whole group, and bore the brunt of the danger ; and for this both the canton and its capital were well equipped by highland physique and a typical Highland population.   The relief of the canton rises to above the snow-line (Boser Faulen = 9200 feet), and is even slightly glaciated, while the town stands on a rocky terrace—with a magnificent view

—below the peak of Gross Mythen (6240 feet), and with a port at Brunnen, where the Everlasting League was renewed in A.D. 1315. Here again the canton grew piecemeal from the town centre, especially after the victory of Sempach; but expansion into the Zürich basin threw the balance of power from Schwyz, though still the capital, to Einsiedeln, still the site of the famous Benedictine monastery. For relative inferiority of scenic attractions in the south is coupled with marked superiority of industrial possibilities in the north; cf. the silk-weaving along the Lake of Zürich, *e.g.* at Lachen and Pfäffikon (*Pfaffe*, "Monk").

Unter-walden. Behind Pilatus and the Lake of Lucerne, the canton of Unterwalden (= Middlesex) had little chance for expansion; and its rugged relief, rising to over 10,600 feet in the Titlis and with nearly 2 p.c. of the area glaciated, was not favourable to dense population.[1] A considerable portion, too, especially between Stans and Kems, was densely forested; and the forested ridge divided the valleys of the two Aa's so completely that Obwalden and Nidwalden, as representing the "Upper" and "Lower" sections of the canton, had somewhat diverse interests, for Obwalden had relatively easy access by the Brünig Pass (3400 feet) to the Brienz valley of Bern. At the same time, it is, of course, much the more mountainous. The most important place in olden days was Engelberg, with its famous Benedictine House; but now the only places of any size are the junction of Stans, the Lower capital, and the Upper capital of Sarnen, which is 4 or 5 miles from the lake that bears its name.

Uri. Considerably more than half Uri is barren, no less than 11 p.c. being glaciated, and the relief reaches very nearly 12,000 feet (in the Dammastock); but it has special importance as being essentially the upper valley of the Reuss, *i.e.* the line of approach by rail to the St. Gothard. The torrent has cut a very deep bed except round Ursern and Altdorf; and the valley is very picturesque, and contains some wonderful engineering work, *e.g.* near Wassen and Göschenen, the northern entrance to the great tunnel (9¼ miles). Like Unterwalden, the canton had little chance of expansion; but it used such chance as it had, and it still holds the Urnerboden Alps on the outer slope of the Klausen Pass (*c.* 6400 feet). As the St. Gothard "Roman road" rose to importance again, after the 13th century, the valley began to prosper; and by the 15th century the canton was able to encroach on the Italian slope of the Alps, winning or buying—with the help of one or more of the other cantons—*e.g.* the Val Leventina and Bellinzona. Altdorf, the capital, is indissolubly connected with William Tell, and—like so many of the other capitals—*not*[2] actually on the lake; and Erstfeld is a great

---

[1] Even now the population does not reach 33,000 persons.
[2] Thus, the port of Stans is at Stanstad, that of Sarnen (on L. Lucerne) at Alpnachstad, that of Altdorf at Fluelen.

railway depot, where the "Bank" engines used to be attached to the trains—now worked by electricity.

The best justification for the annexation of Ticino by the Swiss **Ticino.** lies in the fact that the watersheds of the Reuss and the Ticino make a single land-form, the St. Gothard "Bridge," with its termini on the long waters of Lake Maggiore and the Lake of Lucerne. The whole valley of the Ticino from Airolo to the lake is the Val Leventina, and its acquisition by Uri was facilitated by the easy support of the main route by the side route from the Lukmanier Pass to Biasca ; but the Maggia basin is quite separate and essentially Italian, while the extension of the Swiss frontier across Lake Lugano so as to command the route along Lake Como was just a foolish piece of bravado to irritate the Duke of Milan. Till recently the capital was alternately—for six-year periods —at the chief town of each natural division, Bellinzona, Locarno, and Lugano ; but now it is permanently at Bellinzona, the most appropriate, if not the largest, centre — owing its historic importance to its command of the defile on the so-called Riviera (Val Blenio) at the junction of the St. Gothard and San Bernardino routes.

The St. Gothard tunnel.

Locarno has an im- **Locarno** portant historic connection **and** **Lugano.** with Switzerland, for it was a body of Protestants expelled from the town in the middle of the sixteenth century that re-introduced the silk industry into Zürich. Lugano, as both an industrial (silk and leather) and a tourist centre, is the largest town ; but the St. Gothard railway, the main line of which goes through Lugano and not along Lake Maggiore, has so much encouraged emigration of men (mainly as waiters) that the canton has no industrial importance. In population, as in climate and products (chestnuts and wine), it is purely Italian, over 135,000 out of a total of under 140,000 being Italians.

Grisons.
The canton of Grisons, or Graubünden, does not take its name —as the story goes—from the "grey" cloaks of the Leaguers in the fourteenth century, but from the *Graven* or Counts of the Vorder Rhine highlands who led the Oberbünd; and the real basis of the canton in its present, somewhat incoherent, form was the alliance of the Upper Rhine and Upper Inn peoples against the bishops of Chur, *i.e.* the "Lower" Rhine, after their alliance with the Hapsburgs of the Lower Inn. The canton is, therefore, at once the largest, the most easterly, and the most sparsely peopled in Switzerland, being entirely mountainous and largely glaciated (*c.* 140 square miles). Indeed, its glaciers are a very valuable source of power, even Zürich—at a distance of 120 miles—drawing supplies from them. Its essential parts are the "Trinity of Rhine Valleys and the Unity of the Inn Valley"; and the two basins are closely linked—betwcen the "Ragatz" frontier and Süs by the fertile Prättigau or Landquart valley, and between Thusis and St. Moritz by the Albula valley, itself linked to the Prättigau by the Davos or Landwasser valley. In spite of this apparent skeleton of routes, communications are very difficult, many of the valleys being in places only gorges, *e.g.* the well-named *Via Mala* ("Evil Way") between the Domleschg and the Rhinewald parts of the Hinter Rhine; and the little centres of population are at a great height, St. Moritz being over 6000 feet above the sea, and Davos well over 5000 feet. Of course, it is precisely to this and to their position to leeward of the prevailing wind that they owe the pure dry air which makes them so valuable as health resorts.

Its Population.
The natural distribution of the population has an economic as well as a historic base. In the relatively fertile valleys of the "Lower" Rhine, *e.g.* the Prättigau and the Schanfigg (Plessur), where antagonism to the Bishop of Chur was originally fiercest, the relatively dense population is German and Protestant; in the poor valleys of Vorder and Hinter Rhine, *i.e.* in and west of the Julier valley, a very sparse population adheres to the Roman Church, and speaks the Romonsch dialect of the old *lingua rustica* of their Romanised Rhætian ancestors; in the Inn valley a sparse population is again German and Protestant, but speaks the Ladin dialect of the same Romance tongue; in the various protrusions of frontier which attempt to tap the fertile Valtellina—by the Moesa, Maira, and Poschiavo tributaries of the Adda—a relatively dense population is purely Italian in race and speech and creed. Typical centres are in

the Rhine basin,—Disentis [1] ("The Desert"), at a height of nearly 4000 feet, now with a narrow-gauge railway from Ilanz,—Thusis, where the Albula (with its tributary, the Julia) joins the Hinter Rhine at the exit of the Via Mala,—and Chur (*Curia Rhaetorum*, "the Court of the Rhætians"), the capital. The latter is less than 2000 feet above the sea; it taps more important passes than any other place in the Rhine valley, *e.g.* the Lukmanier, the Bernardino and the Splügen, the Septimer and the Maloja, the Julier and the Albula; it commands the flank of the main Rhine valley from the entrance of the fertile Schanfigg valley; and its bishopric, which seems to date from the fourth century, still exercises jurisdiction over the Three Forest Cantons of the League and over the "Austrian" principality of Liechtenstein.

The Engadine (*eng*, "narrow") strictly begins at Sils, for the **Engadine.** Maloja plateau is slightly *lower* than the beginning of the Inn valley, and it ends in the wide gorge of Finstermünz below Martinsbruck; and roughly half-way between the two, *i.e.* near Brail, is the formal frontier between the Upper and the Lower divisions. The Upper Engadine is a straight and nearly level trough averaging fully a mile in width between the glaciated Bernina (13,300 feet) and the Albula, with its political capital at the objective of the Bernina and the Albula passes in the middle of the trough at Samaden. It is a much-frequented tourist centre,[2]—for various reasons; but its open floor, dotted with villages and lakes, is *not* particularly picturesque. The mineral springs of St. Moritz have been famous for centuries—since they were recommended by Paracelsus; the "fresh-air cure" has immensely added to their importance recently; and the expansion of the Inn which makes the St. Moritz "lake," is so shallow that— like those of Sils and Silvaplana—it remains frozen for six months (November to May). But the Lower Engadine is much the more picturesque, for the valley is so "narrow" that the villages are perched up on rocky terraces, and the fall of the river is much greater. Its political capital is the central village of Schuls, famous —like its neighbour, Tarasp—for mineral springs; but its most important points are where the Flüela and Ofen passes converge, *i.e.* Süs and Zernetz. The climate is, of course, more favourable to vegetation in the Lower division, but in both there is great exposure to wind; and this, in the dry climate, led to such destructive fires that for generations now all the villages have been built of stone. The Bernina glaciers attract climbers to Pontresina, and the whole valley is a paradise for botanists; but the natives

---

[1] Called in Romonsch *Munster* ("Monastery").
[2] Twice as many persons still speak Ladin as speak German, but—owing to the tourists—the latter is relatively much more common than in the Lower valley, where Ladin is to German as 5 : 1.

have no natural resources beyond the alp pastures and the conifer forests. In these wild life is still abundant, and even the bears kept in the famous bear-pit at Bern come from the Spöl forests near Zernetz.

Glarus.   Behind the natural frontier of the Walen See, with its Linth Canal connection with the Lake of Zürich, the canton of Glarus is formed of the upper basin of the Linth, so much hemmed in by the Tödi and other lofty mountains that it is a real *cul-de-sac*. The Linth in its rapid descent from the Tödi glaciers,—besides throwing some magnificent waterfalls, *e.g.* Pantenbrüche,—has carved a very deep gorge, so that a number of villages have sprung up on the narrow strip of lowland along the river; but the Grossthal, or main valley, is cut off from its two side valleys, the Klönthal and the Kleinthal, by heights of *c.* 10,000 feet (Glärnisch = *c.* 9600, Hausstock = 10,300). Its German and Protestant people have developed all its possibilities, especially the slate quarries of the Kleinthal (Seruf); but, in spite of the abundant water-power, outside competition from areas with easier access to markets has so affected the old textile industry that for some time the population has been slowly decreasing. There are some mineral springs, *e.g.* at Elm and near Linthal, which attract tourists; but again difficulty of access is a great drawback. The characteristic industry of the canton is cheese-making, especially the production of the Schabzieger, or Sapsago, cheese, made of a mixture of skim-milk and butter-milk (from cows or goats), and coloured and flavoured with the local blue melilot.[1] The little capital of Glarus is the natural focus of the basin; and, as such, it is full in the path of the Föhn[2] as it rushes down the Linth gorge between the Vorder Glärnisch (7600 feet) and the Schild (6400 feet). In consequence, it was burnt to the ground during a Föhn storm in May 1861. The approach on the town round the west end of the lake makes Näfels a strategic centre. Here the men of Glarus defeated the Hapsburgs in A.D. 1388, and the French turned the Russians in 1799.

Appen-zell.   Appenzell (*Abbatis cella*) was the summer retreat of the Prince Abbots of St. Gall, and the town still has a very ancient Chapel of St. Gall; and its forested domain was carved out of the larger domain of St. Gall, an arrangement which accounts for the modern canton being entirely surrounded by that of St. Gall. Its value as a summer retreat depended on its Alpine and forested character; it reaches a height of over 8200 feet in the Säntis, and a large proportion is still forested. The forest "clearings" were originally known as *Rhoden*, and the canton is still divided into Ausser Rhoden and Inner Rhoden. The division is partly physical and

---

[1] The Gruyère type of cheese is coloured and flavoured with yellow melilot.
[2] The lake of Walenstadt (or Walen See) has never been known to be frozen!

partly based on religious differences. For the people of the mountainous south, though all Germans in race and speech, belong to the Roman Church; they are exceedingly backward and conservative, even the herdsmen still adhering to the historic red waistcoats and yellow breeches for festival attire. The Outer Rhodes have a much more favourable relief, nearly one-fourth of which is still forested, and easier access to the outside world, both by ordinary railways and by light railway to the St. Gall port of Rorschach; and the Protestant population is distinctively industrial, muslins and embroidery being typical products, *e.g.* at Herisau, Teufen, and the political capital of Trogen. The industry is also carried on at Appenzell, the political capital of the Inner Rhodes, where—though the Sitter provides abundant power—much work is still done by hand as a typical home industry of pastoral mountaineers. The most characteristic industry of both areas, however, is really in goat's whey—some of the "cure resorts" being quite large villages, *e.g.* Heiden (*c.* 4000); and these resorts are scattered all over the canton, *e.g.* at Urnäsch and Gais, at Weissbad and Gonten. Herisau is the largest town in the canton; and in alternate years the interesting Landsgemeinde (or primitive democratic assembly of all adult males) is held in the neighbourhood, at Hundwil, instead of at the other end of the area at Trogen.

St. Gall, like its enclosure, was, and one-fifth of the area still is, St. Gall. well-forested; but it has also considerable areas of alluvial plain and a relatively large proportion of lake frontier—on Lake Constance, the Walen See, and the Lake of Zürich. On each lake it has at least one very useful little port, *e.g.* Rorschach, Rapperswil, and Weesen; and its relations to the Rhine and Lower Linth valleys give it exceptional frontier railway facilities (cf. the frontier junctions of Sargans and Weesen, Rapperswil and Wil), while the mass of the canton has such a relation to the basin of the Upper Thur (the Toggenburg) that internal communications are equally good. In the mountainous south, where the Ringelspitz reaches nearly 10,700 feet, dairy work is the typical industry; elsewhere there is a considerable amount of agriculture, including fruit-growing, but it is generally combined with manufactures. For the canton is the centre of the Swiss cotton industry,—almost all branches of the work being followed,[1] though the special development is in machine-made embroidery. The output for export is about one-sixth of the Swiss total, the value of the embroideries exported in a good year having approached £10,000,000 and practically dominating the world-market, though the total population is only *c.* 300,000, and the factory hands number only *c.* 55,000. Much the largest place is the capital, St. Gall (*c.* 65,000), with its two large suburbs of Tablet

---

[1] Though between 1885 and 1915 the number of spindles in Switzerland declined by 500,000 (cf. p. 350), the number for the whole world doubled.

and Stranbenzell ; and its lake-port of Rorschach (scarcely 1200),
only 9 miles away, comes next. A few places are specially
important as rail or road junctions, *e.g.* Gossau and Richenbad,
Altstatten and Flawil, and Uznach is proud of its patch of lignite as
Gonzen of its iron and manganese; but nearly all are interested in
cotton, *e.g.* Rapperswil spinning, Walenstadt and Wattwil weaving,
Wil embroidery. Cf. Rorschach artificial silk.

Thurgau.　　The Thur-Gau originally included not only the whole basin of
the Thur, but also the basins of the Limmat and the Lower Reuss ;
and it still includes the richest land of the Thur basin, with a " lake-
side " climate very favourable to agriculture. As the highest
elevation of the canton is at its southern extremity, and does not
much exceed 3000 feet, while the physical landmarks between the
lake-basin and the Murg valley, and between the latter and the
Thur valley, are only low lines of wooded hills, the climate is uniformly continental over the whole area, and there are great facilities
for agricultural operations and for transport. The main industry is
agriculture, special attention being paid to fruit, including the vine,
from which quite good wine (red) is made, *e.g.* at Weinfelden
("Wine-Field ") ; but, as in St. Gall, the agriculture is almost everywhere combined with some textile work, especially cotton-spinning
and artificial silk. The chief centre, handling silk, cotton, and
wool, and making textile machinery, is the capital, Frauenfeld ;
its position gave it such political and strategic importance that for a
considerable time it was the capital of the whole Confederation ;
and it is now a busy railway junction. A large proportion of the
trade of the canton still goes through the lake-port of Romanshorn,
which has taken the old place of Steckborn or Arbon ; and the fate
of the latter, like the vagaries of the northern frontier (*e.g.* the
"foreign " Horn, the intrusion of the German frontier to include
Constance, the Diesenhofen lake, etc.), is largely bound up with
the ecclesiastical history, especially with that of Constance.

Schaff-　　The vagaries of the Schaffhausen frontier are still more curious,
hausen.　but in this case they are mainly due to the deliberate policy of the
town itself, for the canton is merely an annex of the town. Thus,
the Rudlingen and Buchberg "island," commanding the great
swerve on the Rhine below the Inchelberg, was purchased (A.D.
1520) ; and the lake approach was secured by the acquisition of the
district round Stein, one of the oldest and most frequented of the
crossing-places on the Rhine. The northern edge of the main
portion of the canton is, however, the highest part (*c.* 3000 feet),
and so makes an appropriate frontier, while the general south-
eastward slope (cf. p. 217) of the land is very favourable to the
vine, *e.g.* at Hallau. As a great transport centre,[1] the capital is
still interested in fodder-stuffs, which are a typical product of the

---

[1] The old Roman road to Ratisbon passed through the fertile Klettau district.

canton, *e.g.* round Schleitheim and Thayingen; and it has a busy modern industry in the manufacture of railway rolling-stock. The famous " Falls," which are rather rapids than falls, have supplied power for the last fifty years; and the cheap power has encouraged all sorts of industries, *e.g.* aluminium works in the Neuhausen suburb.

Like Schaffhausen, Zürich slopes gently down to the Rhine— **Zürich.** through a series of four fertile valleys, which give natural routes N.W.–S.E., and which are separated by such low hills that they present no obstacles to communication N.E.–S.W. The nodal point was at the west end of the lake, and the canton is merely an annex of the town, the most important purchase having been that of the Winterthur district from the Hapsburgs. The fact that each of the chief rivers, Linth-Limmat, Glatt and Töss, expands into a lake and sends its waters direct to the Rhine, has had great effect in the checking of floods, and accounts for the wide extent of fertile alluvium and the considerable subdivision of the land, while the old commercial relations of the town with Italy and its political relations with the Hapsburgs have had a very marked influence on its economic development. Thus, its great silk-weaving industry was revived, if not actually started, by Protestant refugees from Italy and immensely improved by Huguenot refugees from France; and it now " conditions " more silk than any other centres in Europe except Milan and Lyons. Under the same influence it became the intellectual capital of the German cantons, and this fact reacted most favourably on its industries, especially the silk-weaving, the cotton-spinning, and the manufacture of machinery and rolling-stock. In the last fifty years its population has increased 400 p.c., and its international character is marked by the presence of thousands of foreigners, anxious to avoid active military service and asking very low wages; it is now very much the largest town in Switzerland (cf. p. 350). The busy little junction of Winterthur (*c.* 55,000), the Roman *Vitudurum* (" The Vineyard beside the Water "), is still famous for wine and has important cambric and calico-printing industries. But there are numerous large villages busily occupied with both silk and cotton industries, especially beside the lake. Indeed, so many are engaged in the silk industry round the Pfäffikon Lake that the chief source of power there, the Aa, is known locally as the " Millionaire's Stream."

Though the geographic control may not be obvious, it can **Aargau.** scarcely be a mere accident that in Aargau, or within an easy day's ride of its frontiers, are the race-homes of three Royal Houses— Guelph, Hapsburg, and Hohenzollern, while within a long day's ride is the race-home of a fourth House—Savoy, always dominating the southern horizon. Within the little triangle where the waters meet, stand, or stood, the old Roman station of Vindonissa, the sulphur springs of Schinznach—recommended by Tacitus—and of Baden (the old *Aquae Helveticae*) the castles of Habsburg, Lenzburg, and Wildegg, the monastery of Weltingen, the free bailiwick of Mellingen ; and close at hand is Aarau, the present capital of the canton and once the capital of the Helvetian Republic. The fundamental control in all this is position, greatly accentuated by relief and structure, with their obvious effects on communications and fertility. Four things are of special importance—the multitudinous folds of the Jura, the relation of the Aar valley to the Reuss valley, the régime of the Aar, and the fertility of its "fans." As we have seen (p. 34), the multitudinous parallel folds of the porous limestone are such an obstacle that normal traffic has always been forced to go round them rather than across them ; and this tendency has been encouraged by the great facilities offered by the low Burgundy Gate and the navigable Rhine. The valleys of the two rivers which give the best routes across the Alps, the Aar and the Reuss, converge where the extreme north-eastern corner of the Jura approaches the head of navigation on the Rhine, and where the relief falls suddenly from the 3000-foot to the 1200-foot contour immediately below the Habsburg heights ; and the Aar valley is the more important of the two because by the tributary valleys of Thièle (Orbe) and Broye—and even Saane—it taps both ends of Lake Geneva, *i.e.* both France and Italy.

The Aar.   The Aar, too, is a real river, not a mere torrent. It is fed through every important lake that is wholly inside the Swiss frontier —from Walen to Neuchâtel, and from Zürich to Thun. Its main stream is actually navigable up to Brienz, and at its confluence with the Rhine—after a course of over 180 miles—it has the greater volume. The breadth of level plateau which encourages navigation, has discouraged quick "run-off" of glacial and fluvial silt ; and, as its largest tributaries enter by the right bank, while the Aar itself hugs the Jura, a series of fertile fans has been distributed between the lines of morainic hills. These hills are now well-wooded, they aid good drainage, and they add variety to the landscape, while the fertile valleys between them are very productive. Grain, wine, and tobacco are typical products, and amongst the typical industries are straw-plaiting and cigar-making. Most of the important old centres are now busy railway junctions, *e.g.* Coblenz, Brugg, and Lenzburg, and the old mineral springs are still important, *e.g.* the sulphur of Baden and Schinznach, and the saline springs of Rheinfelden and Rybourg ; but the one industrial centre is Aarau, specialising in silk-ribbons and cutlery.

Basel.   The canton of Basel is overwhelmed by the importance of the town of Basel. Its two "Jura" valleys, those of the Birs and the Erzolz, have rich pastures, and produce quantities of fruit, including grapes ; indeed, the famous "Swiss Blood" vintage comes from the old battlefield in the Birs valley, watered by the blood of 1500 Swiss in A.D. 1444. The internal quarrels (cf. p. 352) which led to the division of the canton into two half-cantons, have been adverse to the prosperity of the rural part. This, with an area of 165 square miles out of the total area of 177, has a population only half that of the town of Basel alone (*c.* 140,000); and even Liestal, the capital, though rather an important railway junction, has only a few thousand inhabitants. The special industries of the town of Basel (*Basilea*, "The Royal City") are the weaving of silk ribbons, the spinning of silk, and the making of chemical dyes, the Schweizerhalle mines being one of the four great sources of salt in the country. The town has now a Free Customs Zone, and the Basel Stock Exchange has some International importance. Cf. p. 352.

The irregular shape of Solothurn and the name of its capital **Solothurn.** suggest that it is a typical mountain section of the Jura, and that it grew gradually from the town-centre. Amongst the isolated districts, that of Hofstetten seems to have been acquired mainly in order to control the pilgrim routes to the famous shrine at Mariastein; but the access into Burgundy round the Weissenstein ridge was also a matter of importance. The Roman camp of Salodurum—of which remains still exist—was up against the scarp of the Weissenstein (*c.* 4750 feet); and the place, though now dismantled as a fortress, has ever since been of great strategic importance, especially when it was on the borders of the Alemanni and the Burgundians and in the latter half of the seventeenth century. Its sympathies were rather with Burgundy, and its industries to this day are more French than German, watch-making and shoe-making being typical; but, as 98 p.c. of its population speak German, it is better called Solothurn than Soleure. Its commercial importance has been greatly increased by the Weissenstein tunnel—which is adversely affecting Olten, hitherto much the more important junction—and the number of visitors to the place is also increasing, attracted by the "air-and-whey cure" on the Weissenstein ridge and by the Passion-play of Selzach.

Though Zürich is really the senior canton, Bern may fairly **Bern:** claim the sovereign position; it is the largest canton except the **Jura and** Grisons, and it includes the three typical belts of the country— **Plateau.** Jura, plateau, and Alps, unified by their respective relations to the Aar. It is therefore divided naturally into three areas—Seeland, Mittelland, and Oberland, all of which were acquired gradually by the town of Bern. The Seeland ("Lakeland"), which was only acquired after the Battle of Waterloo, and which is still French in speech and Roman in creed, extends right across the Jura from Lake Biel to west of Porrentruy, and its typical industry is watch-making, especially at Biel and St. Imier, Porrentruy and Delémont, the last also with an iron industry (mining and working). The Mittelland, or Aar plateau, is the agricultural part of the canton, and its northern and southern limits have largely historic interest.

For instance, Laupen, at the confluence of the Sense and the Saane, was the site of the great battle in A.D. 1339; the indentation of Solothurn behind Wangen, where the railway now crosses the Aar, commands the approaches to the Dünnern Pass. Much the most important place is the Federal capital, though its importance is now only political; but there are a number of small places interested in the silk and ribbon industries, *e.g.* the cheese-depot of Burgdorf at the mouth of the Emmenthal.

Bern: Oberland. The Oberland, in the wider sense, includes all the canton east or south of Thun and the neighbouring parts of Valais, etc.; but in the stricter sense, it is restricted to the valleys of Hasli, Grindelwald, and Lauterbrunnen. The culminating peaks of Finsteraarhorn (*c.* 14,000 feet) and the Jungfrau (*c.* 13,670) are not within the frontier of Bern, but the natural focus for them is Interlaken, and the natural approaches are by the Grindelwald and the Lauterbrunnen valleys. In the easterly valleys, *e.g.* at Brienz and Meiringen, where tourists are very numerous, there is a great deal of wood-carving and mosaic work; in the west, *e.g.* in the fine pastoral Simmenthal, the relative lowness of the peaks and the absence of glaciers make the dairy industry more important, and catering for tourists less important. As the old commercial importance of the Grimsel Pass has been annihilated by the St. Gothard tunnel, so that of the Gemmi Pass has been by the Lötschberg tunnel; and the latter is greatly increasing the military and industrial importance of Thun, with its famous Military School and "Heimberg" potteries. Interlaken gives an admirable illustration of the normal destiny of such a youthful feature as a lake; for it stands on a fan of rock-waste brought down by the Lütschine in such quantities as to completely cut off the Brienz part from the Thun part of an originally united and single lake. It is therefore "Between the lakes," even structurally (cf. p. 32).

Valais. In the fullest and most literal sense Valais is "*the* Valley," though the historic struggle between the French and the German elements in it gave rise to the attempt to explain its name as the *Wälsch, i.e.* non-German land. It illustrates almost perfectly some of the most interesting features and processes of river development, and its chief political phenomena have obvious relation to those features. Although it has been deepened and widened by ice until it is characteristically steep-sided and flat-floored, *i.e.* U-shaped, it is a valley by origin and structure as well as in form and function; for it is simply the single downfold between the two upfolds of the Oberland and the Pennines. It lies, therefore, parallel to the axes of both and more or less level, an excellent instance of a synclinal longitudinal valley. Obviously any tributaries of the main stream are not likely to be long or to enter it at accordant grade, *i.e.* from about the same level as the banks of the main stream. On the contrary, they plunge down the steep sides of the mountains in a series of cataracts, and deposit fans of rough débris when and where their current is checked by the confluence. In the case of the larger or stronger tributaries, these fans are gradually pushed out into the Rhone until they force it to encroach on its opposite bank; and, as the fans themselves are sufficiently porous and elevated to have been—before the days of dykes and drainage—free from the swamp and safe from the floods of the main valley, they were of great value as sites for villages and gardens. At Martigny the Rhone leaves its young longitudinal valley for the old transverse gorge maintained by the Drance through the rising folds; and the original canton, therefore, stopped at Martigny. When it did expand (A.D. 1536), it made no attempt to hold both sides of the St. Maurice gorge.

As the canton includes, in an area no larger than Northumber- **Linguistic** land (2000 square miles), heights of 15,000 feet, over 40 square **Frontier.** miles of lake, and nearly 400 square miles of glacier, the proportion that is "productive" is very small (*c.* half); and it is, therefore, one of the poorest cantons in Switzerland, redeemed only by its scenic attractions and by the excellent wine made on its 10 or 11 square miles of vineyards. Its commercial importance was, however, greatly increased by the Simplon tunnel, and is being still further increased by the Lötschberg tunnel. The former, which deploys characteristic- ally on the Brieg gorge, has considerably strengthened French influence and extended the use of the French language. The old linguistic frontier was the Morge valley west of Sion, up to which Savoy was so dominant that the valley was divided into Savoyard or Lower and Episcopal or Upper Valais; but now German dialects are only normal east of Sierre, while to the west the normal speech is a Savoyard patois of French. One advantage gained by the warring elements was the construction of really good roads over the passes, the Simplon (*c.* 6600 feet), the Grimsel (*c.* 7100 feet), the Furka (*c.* 8000 feet), and the Great St. Bernard (*c.* 8100 feet); and Valais was able to encroach on alp pastures—still within its frontier—south of the Simplon and north of the Gemmi.

There is a nominal working of various minerals, and there are mineral springs at Leuk and Saxa; the dairy industry is important, especially in Lower Valais, the canton having over 500 separate alps—capable of supporting 50,000 cows; the lateral valleys, *e.g.* that of the Visp, are wonderfully well cultivated; and their torrents, *e.g.* in the Anniviers valley, drive important aluminium and other works—Martigny being now an important "power" centre. The chief villages, *e.g.* Sion and St. Maurice, are on Roman sites, for the valley was completely Romanised after the battle of Octodurus (Martigny); and the most flourishing are at the foot of historic passes, *e.g.* Brieg at the foot of the Simplon and Leuk at that of the

Gemmi, while Visp commands the railway to Zermatt (*c.* 5300 feet) for the Matterhorn. Sion, the capital, stands on the sunny northern bank of the river in the broadest part of the valley floor, opposite the mouth of the Borgne, just above the point at which the Rhone drops below the 500-foot contour, *i.e.* half-way between the route northward to the Gemmi pass from Leuk and the route southward to the Great St. Bernard from Martigny.   Here differential crosion left isolated elevations, suitable for and crowned by Roman fort and medieval castle.

Vaud.   Vaud presents a great contrast to Valais, having fully five-sixths of its area productive, being largely in the basin of the Rhine, and consisting (except in the south-east) of more or less level plateau, though—like Bern—it actually includes specimens of all the typical Swiss belts, the Alpine belt reaching 10,650 feet in the Diablerets.

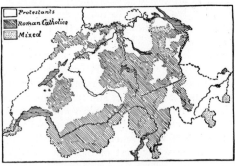

The religions of Switzerland.

The main occupation is agriculture, 16,000 acres being under the vine ; and the land is very highly cultivated. The best wine is grown under the lee of the Alpine heights in the south-east, Vevey and Cully being important centres, though good wine is grown all the way from Lausanne to Aigle.   Tobacco is also grown, especially in the Neuchâtel basin, *e.g.* near Payerne and Grandson.   Other industries are few ; but clocks and watches are made in the Jura villages, *e.g.* St. Croix, and the hills [1] supply the condensed milk factories of Vevey (Nestlé) and Lausanne.   Like its neighbour, Geneva, the canton attracts many foreigners, especially to its educational centres, *e.g.* Lausanne and Vevey, Morges and Yverdun ; but, of course, there are other attractions—scenic, climatic, and historical, *e.g.* at Montreux, Château d'Oex, and Chillon.   Much the largest town is, however, the capital, Lausanne, which combines a central position landward with a port at Ouchy.   The area was thoroughly conquered and settled by the Romans (cf. the Roman remains at, *e.g.* Avenches and Nyon), and has been distinctly Romance in character ever since ; but at the

---

[1] It should be noted that the condensed milk and other *factories* (of Nestlé, Peter, Cailler, Kohler, etc.) are very dependent on easy communications, and, therefore, find more suitable sites on the undulating hill-country of the plateau—where, too, the streams are less torrential in pace and constancy of volume, and the supply of hay for the winter is ample—than in the more difficult mountain-country of the real alp pastures.   Bex supplies Vaud with local salt.

Reformation it became, and—unlike Geneva, and in spite of its considerable foreign element—it still is, overwhelmingly Protestant.

In this respect Fribourg presents a great contrast. For, though **Fribourg**
the linguistic frontier runs due north-and-south through the very
heart of the canton, *c.* 120,000 out of its *c.* 150,000 people are
staunch adherents of
the Roman Church.
This unity of creed
and political develop-
ment is based on a
physical unity, the
canton being practic-
ally the basin of the
Saane and having
grown from what is
at once the most im-
portant détour on the
river itself, and the
chief hydrographic
centre of the basin, at
the town of Fribourg.

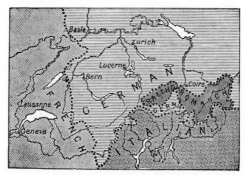

The languages of Switzerland.

Indeed, Duke Berchthold of Zäringen chose
the site for a fortress on the Alemannian - Burgundian frontier;
and the town is still on the left bank of the Saane, and protected
by the river on all sides except the west, *i.e.* towards Burgundy. As
the canton grew, it became noted for its cloth and leather, typical
"pasture" products represented now by Gruyère cheese. For,
though no part of the canton approaches the snow-line, the upper
part of the Saane basin is the most famous pastoral area in Switzerland, the home of the "Ranz des Vaches" cattle-call. There is
some agriculture, *e.g.* grain in the north and tobacco in the south;
and there are industries in straw-plait and paper. But the great
interest of the canton is pastoral, the cheese-making being of
predominant importance, especially between Bulle and Gruyère;
and the great chocolate factories (Cailler's) in the same district are
essentially a bye-product of the dairy trade. Cheese, chocolate, and
straw hats are the typical exports. As the canton spans the plateau,
it gets the advantage of the through-lines of rail, and it has access
to Lake Neuchâtel both directly, *e.g.* at Estavayer (with its most
interesting relics of lake-dwellings) and indirectly *via* Lake Morat,
which is joined to its larger neighbour by the canalised Broye.

Neuchâtel is the only canton that is simply a section of the **Neuchâtel**
Jura, and it is essentially Jurassic, consisting of parallel ridges
and river valleys more or less linked transversely by *cluses, i.e.*
depressed saddles (in the ridges) that have been cut back by streams
until they have been definitely eaten through. The canton may,
therefore, be divided into natural zones from east to west. The

narrow strip along the lake and the foot-hills up to 2000 feet are known, from their vineyards, as Le Vignoble; and good wines, both sparkling and still, are exported from Boudri, Cortaillod, and Neuchâtel town. Westward of this zone is that known as Vallées, *i.e.* the two chief valleys in the canton, the Val de Ruz or Seyon valley and the Val de Travers or Reuse valley, which converge on the lake-side junction of Serrière, the site of more chocolate factories (Suchard's). Here, too, vineyards are still common, and absinthe is a typical product in the Val de Travers; but the special products are fine metal-work and asphalt, Travers itself being noted for its "cement." The metal-work is mainly in connection with the watch-making industry, *e.g.* the actual watches at Fleurier and fine screws, etc., at Couvet. This industry has "percolated" through the *cluse* which makes Fleurier an important road and rail junction, from Les Montagnes, the long valley between La Chaux de Fonds and Le Locle, both typical *cluse* junctions. Here watch-making is the one great industry, and has been for 250 years. Le Locle was the original home of the industry, but La Chaux de Fonds is now the largest centre, boasting itself "the largest village in Europe" and exporting watches and watch-cases to a value of fully one-fourth of the total Swiss export. The population is naturally very French—though Protestant—all through the canton; and the capital owes its importance, as an educational centre for foreign students, to the good French which is spoken.

Geneva.　　Like the canton of Basel, that of Geneva has no importance compared with the town from which it takes its name; but the southern canton (= ⅔ Rutlandshire) is too small to have had any interests separate from, still less alien to, those of the town, and it is quite modern, dating only from Waterloo. The town had previously acquired the land immediately round it, but the Romanist majority of the Swiss cantons had steadily refused for 200 years to admit the "Protestant Rome" to membership of the Confederation; and when it was eventually admitted, it was allowed only sufficient (French and Savoyard) territory to give it some protection, as an outpost of the Confederation, against foreign interference. The town itself is one of those which, like many old Cathedral cities in England, are living on their past. For the conditions which gave it importance in early times are now relatively unfavourable, if not positively adverse; but it inherits from those old days traditions of educational standard and industrial efficiency which enable it to compete more or less successfully with more favoured modern rivals. Perched up 1300 feet above the sea, in the narrow line of least resistance between Jura and Alps, it commanded a gate of immense importance in peace or war; and this position was at once favourable to its commercial prosperity and unfavourable to its political progress. For the difficult nature of its

westward "hinterland," and the domination of Savoy from its
position of vantage astride the Alps, made political expansion
westward practically impossible, while expansion over the fertile
plateau was blocked by towns earlier in the field, *e.g.* Fribourg.
What delayed the start of Geneva was largely its frontier position.
Even in the times of Julius Cæsar it was an important frontier post
between the Allobroges and the Helvetii ; and, though it was the
capital of the Second Kingdom of Burgundy, it never had any
real political importance of its own except as a frontier post.   On
the other hand, its International utility, commercial and political,
was obvious.   For instance, it was a suitable site for Charlemagne's
great council in A.D. 773, as for the Convention of A.D. 1864 ; and
its four annual fairs were of such importance that (to secure freedom
for their export of cloth) the burghers of Fribourg maintained the
freedom of the town from the attacks of Savoy, while Louis XI. not
only forbad French merchants to attend them, but also established
fairs at Lyons *on the same days.*

Indeed, the whole history of the town—and largely that of **The Rhone**
Central Europe—was intimately bound up with its International **Gate.**
relations.   For, though its regional position as a frontier town was
adverse to its independent political prosperity, its local position was
one of great strength on the flank of the Rhone Gate.   The lake
which brought it so much trade was also a great protection on the
one side, while the turbid Arve was a still better bulwark on the
other.   Between the two, on island and hill washed by the Rhone
and backed by the Salève wall of the Mont Blanc group, the town
offered at once a safe refuge and a bridge to tap the trade-route
along the northern bank of the river ; and refugees, who were also
traders, flocked to it.   So Steinschaber of Schweinfurt introduced
the printing trade ; Cusin of Autun brought to it the watch-making
industry; the revocation of the Edict of Nantes gave it an immense
impulse, Calvin himself being a Huguenot refugee.   Latterly, of the
University students *75 p.c.* have been foreigners, including many
Russians ; and its environment on almost every side is one of "free
zone," in which no customs duties are levied by Swiss or French.
Indeed, the influx of South Europeans has been so great that in the
city of Calvin now the majority of the population belong to the Roman
Church, so that some day it may add to the somewhat limited attractions of its extraordinary list of great men in almost every branch of
learning, some of the more popular attractions of architectural adorn-
ment which were denied to it by Calvinistic ideas of art.   Its
economic importance has been increased by the Franco- Swiss Free
Customs Zone (cf. Basel), and its political importance by its being
made the headquarters of the League of Nations.

CHAPTER XXII

MIDDLE DANUBE STATES

15° E.
45° N.
THE Austro-Hungarian empire occupied a very significant position, indicated by longitude 15° E. and latitude 45° N., the one linking the Adriatic to the Baltic, and the other linking the Adriatic to the Black Sea. All the important political relations of the empire were implied in this. Many of its most important historical relations were also suggested by it. For north and west of 15° E. and 45° N. was the "Land of the Cross," while south and east of it was the "Land of the Crescent," so that it afforded routes alike for Crusaders moving towards Asia and for Asiatic hordes and Ottoman armies moving into Central Europe. West of 15° E. is still typically European, in its manufacturing industries, its "Western" civilisation, its adhesion to the Roman Church, while east of 15° E. is still somewhat Asiatic, a land of raw materials, of predominantly Slav interests, and of adhesion to the Greek Church.

Peoples.
The constant warfare to which the area was condemned in early times, was adverse to agriculture or any other fixed occupation and to the accumulation of wealth ; but highlanders, foresters, and nomads, while not naturally accumulating wealth, are all naturally devoted to personal liberty But in this case personal liberty and national existence were alike involved in successful resistance to the swarms of Asia in their expansion up the broad Danube and over the vast plains of its middle "basin." In later times, too, the varied interests—often emphasised by variety of creed—have encouraged healthy racial rivalry as some compensation for the political incoherence ; at all events, they have helped to perpetuate old customs and costumes, old languages and literatures, in the attempt to "express racial patriotism in racial emblems."

Racial
Divisions.
The great difficulty was that no one race was sufficiently strong or numerous to attract or dominate all the others, though the finest type—the Magyar—had much the most influential position. There was, therefore, no common language or literature, just as there was no common creed, and little unity of political aims. Most of the people were neither Austrians and Roman Catholics, nor Hungarians

whether Roman or Protestant, but Slavs who were devoted to the
Greek Church, and whose name was ignored in the title of the
empire.   The natural bond here might reasonably have been
between White race and White against Yellow, *i.e.* between Roman
Church and Greek Church, Teutons and Slavs, Germans and
Russians, against the "Asiatic" Magyars.   But the political tendencies were rather in favour of linking the Greek Church Slavs
with the Magyars ; for there was no outside Magyar Power which
either threatened or attracted, while common jealousy of the outside
German Power was a very real bond, and the typical Austrian was
peculiarly exclusive.

The purely Alpine area, *i.e.* Austria to-day, presents normal **Austrian**
Alpine features in the most favourable form—lower crest, easier **Con-**
passes, wider valleys, so that the percentage of absolutely barren **ditions.**
land is small (10 to 20 p.c.), and the means of communication are
good.   Of special importance are the great longitudinal valleys by
which the central crystalline zone is cut off from the limestone
zones, and lines of movement radiate eastward from the Brenner—
by Salzach and Enns, by Drave and Mur.

AUSTRIA

The problems and the future of Austria may be viewed, perhaps **A**
most hopefully, by reference to the experience and the prosperity **"Swiss"**
of Switzerland.   The Austrian Alps are, of course, wider and lower; **Area.**
and the extension of frontier to include the old Hungarian, but
German-speaking, Bergland has added some good, low, agricultural
land to that along the Danube.   The area (= Ireland) is just twice
that of Switzerland, and the proportion of waste land, even in Tyrol
and Salzburg (20 p.c.), is rather less than that in Switzerland (23 p.c.),
while in Styria and Upper Austria it is not even 10 p.c.   But just
because the Alps are lower, the scenery is less fine ; and they are
less easy of access to the chief " Tourist " peoples.   The Austrian
population is not much more than half as large again as the Swiss
(6·5 : 4), and the density per square mile is actually less (*c.* 190 :
c. 250), mainly because of the large proportion of forest (40 p.c., *i.e.*
very nearly double the Swiss) ; indeed, except in the very "Swiss"
Vorarlberg, forest has been encouraged rather at the expense of
pasture.   Austria, again, has a fair amount of mineral wealth (coal,
lignite, iron, etc.) ; and, though only 10 p.c. of her potential water-
power has been developed (22 p.c. in Switzerland), her total amount
is as great as that of Switzerland.   And, if the latter has exceptional
facilities for international railway traffic, she is not much more central
than Austria, and has no cross-road centre really comparable with
Vienna ; nor is she as near to the great agricultural lands of Eastern
Europe, with their surplus of food and their need of manufactures.

Problems involved. The two most important problems to be faced are (1) Vienna and (2) raw materials. The country is a dwarf with a large head. Even now, with its population reduced below 1,850,000, Vienna is far too large, and is in many ways a great burden and embarrassment to the country; its typical population consists of the officials needed by a vast empire, and still one-seventh of the whole population of Austria seems to be formed by officials and their families. At the same time, the city is the country's greatest potential asset—the most important financial and commercial centre in south-eastern Europe as well as the chief centre of culture and civilisation; and it already has a busy international trade, especially with the Balkan and the "Succession" States. As to food and other raw materials, the position is only fairly hopeful. The vital agriculture has not done well, even since the Bergenland was acquired, partly because of bad grain-seasons, e.g. in 1922; and so in 1929 c. 21 p.c. of import values represented foodstuffs. With her wealth of forest, however, Austria has a large surplus of forest products—supplying nearly one-third of her total annual exports, paper being the largest item, followed by wooden goods and sawn wood. Even in mineral output the position is fairly good. Before the war these Alpine iron-fields supplied 45 p.c. of the whole Imperial demand; the Erzberg ore is of fine quality, very useful for steel, and there is a normal output of nearly 2,000,000 tons a year—apart from the other sources of ore, e.g. the Styrian pyrites. Of course, the country possesses no coking coal; but the total output of coal suffices for c. 40 p.c. of the consumption, though as much as 98 p.c. is brown coal of poor heating value, e.g. from the Burgland. There is some oil-shale in Tyrol; and, in any case, the use of water-power, especially in the electrification of the railways, is markedly decreasing the demands on the available supplies of fuel. Still less has the Austrian salt industry been completely ruined by the loss of Galicia; besides the deposits in Tyrol, Salzburg, and Salzkammergut there are useful beds south of Wels and near Krems. Of course, the country feels the loss of the large protected market of Empire days; but she has 30 p.c. of the old industrial population out of only 22 p.c. of the total population, and economic considerations will no longer be subordinate to political in Vienna.

Austria Proper. Austria proper is the immediate valley of the Danube between the lower Inn and the lower March, i.e. the most important east-and-west route in Central Europe and one of the oldest, as illustrated by the discoveries at Krems (cf. p. 44). Upper Austria, i.e. the land above the Enns, is entirely hilly and mountainous, rising in its most southerly point of the Salzkammergut—where Austria, Salzburg, and Styria meet—to a height of nearly 10,000 feet; but Lower Austria has a considerable strip of lowland along the north of the Danube, while the plain of Vienna stretches from the Thaya to

the Leitha.   Lower Austria has, too, the easiest means of exit from
the Danube valley, *e.g.* by the March to the Moravian Gate and by
the Leitha to the Semmering Pass.   This greatly encouraged
expansion into Bohemia and Moravia.

Upper Austria is divided by the Danube into a typically **Upper**
Bohemian and a typically Alpine area, the latter largely composed **Austria.**
of terraces of wooded hills, *e.g.* the Hausruck, rising to the beautiful
lake-land of the Salzkammergut.   This area is rich in brown coal,
iron ores, salt, and mineral springs ; and its beauty attracts many
visitors, *e.g.* to Ischl and Gmunden.   The salt-mines at Hallstatt
(famous for its lake-fishing) have been worked for 2000 years ; but
Ischl is now the chief centre, and the district provides nearly half
of the total output of salt in the kingdom.   The natural gravitation
of traffic is down the Traun valley, which opens on the reach of the
Danube where for the first time the river leaves its gorge, at Linz,
the natural capital of the Duchy.   The brown coal lies along the
Alpine foreland parallel with the Danube, and is tapped by the
railway from the frontier junction of Braunau *via* Ried and Wels to
Steyr, the great commercial and industrial (paper and hardware)
centre being where the two routes cross at Wels.   Steyr, however,
with easy access *via* the Enns valley to the Styrian iron-fields, is
much the most important hardware centre.   The relatively dense
population (175 per square mile) is also partly due to the fertility
of the soil, one-third of the area being cultivated and one-fifth
providing excellent cattle-pasture ; and the large proportion of
forest (one-third of the whole) supplies raw material for the paper
industry.   The Bohemian scarp, now crossed by canal and rail,
provided the wool which gave rise to the old textile industries of
Linz ; and wool (raw, yarn, etc.) is still an important export.

Lower Austria in relief corresponds closely with Upper Austria. **Lower**
It is divided by the Danube into an Alpine and a Bohemian area, **Austria.**
the former much the more hilly and very much the more important ;
but the importance is almost entirely commercial and industrial.
The proportion of forest is the same as in Upper Austria, while the
proportion of arable land is greater, though its average fertility is
less ; but excellent wine is produced on the sunny slopes of the
Wiener Wald, and the Marchfeld—an expanse of natural pussta,
and for long made an artificial desert by war (cf. the battles of
Aspern and Wagram)—has been brought under cultivation.   But
the high density of population (400) is essentially due to the
encouragement of industries by the exceedingly important political
and commercial position.   There is a hardware industry at
Waidhofen (almost a suburb of Steyr), and the important junction
of St. Polten has some coal-mines ; but the foundation of the main
industries is the water-power of the Wiener Wald (cf. the cottons of
Neustadt and Klosterneuburg—another important export).

Vienna. As its name implies, this beautiful forested range, which reaches a height of nearly 7000 feet in the adjacent Schneeberg, makes Vienna its objective, the great longitudinal valleys of the Eastern Alps having access along its eastern flank *via* the transverse ridge of the Semmering. The hot springs, *e.g.* at Baden, suggest the line of fracture which makes this the eastern terminus of the Alps; and, although rivers such as the Inn and the Enns have transverse reaches which carry them across the northern belt of limestone, this is the natural route round all the belts. On this point, too, converge the routes of the Austrian Gate (the Upper Danube), the Moravian Gate (the March), and the Hungarian Gate (the Lower Danube); and here,—with the Alpine bulwark behind and the Marchfeld plain in front,—Vienna became first an outpost of the "Eastern Mark," then the capital of the Eastern Alps, and eventually the focus of the Alpine highland, the Bohemian plateau, the Moravian Gate, the Hungarian plain, the East European railway system. It stands where the Danube leaves its Austrian gorge for the Hungarian lowland, is joined by the Wien, and swings nearest to the Adriatic. With its germ in the Roman camp at Carnuntum, the city sprang up naturally on the Roman bank of the river; and, as only recent engineering has made the left bank sufficiently safe from floods to be really habitable (cf. the industrial suburb of Floridsdorf), the city originally spread up the western hills. It is the great industrial centre of Austria, specially interested in all kinds of metal work, furniture, and leather goods, and rivals Paris in the production of *objets de luxe*, especially textile and metallic.

Alpine Provinces. Although the Alpine provinces stretch strictly from Vienna up the Inn valley and on to Lake Constance, those which are connected closely with the two great longitudinal valleys of the Eastern Alps are so specifically "Swiss" in character that they may be treated separately. The two valleys have an average height of fully 2000 feet, and their relations to the three lines of uplift are important. The central crystalline belt is broken in the west into groups which allow the whole saddle to be easily crossed by the Brenner at a height of only 4470 feet; but east of the Brenner it forms a very distinct wall, especially in the Gross Glockner, reaching nearly 12,500 feet and with no pass under 7500 feet for a distance of 100 miles. Farther east again it sinks to half that height, with low passes and wide valley-basins. The two limestone belts are lower than the central belt in the west, which helps to account for the importance of the Brenner, but higher in the east, which accounts for the relatively heavy rainfall.

Vorarlberg. The Vorarlberg, like the neighbouring independent principality of Liechtenstein,[1] is peculiarly "Swiss"; and, since the construction of the Arlberg tunnel, it has become a serious competitor with

---

[1] Now inside the Swiss Customs Union.

Switzerland, *e.g.* in dairy produce and embroideries. The name means the "land beyond the Arlberg Pass" (5900 feet), *i.e.* north-west of Tyrol; but access to Tyrol was comparatively easy, *via* Bludenz, while the lake-port of Bregenz faced a political frontier. The latter, though the political capital, is even now not nearly so large as Dornbirn.

Historic Tyrol is divided by the Alpine water-parting into a **Tyrol.** "Swiss" and an "Italian" area, joined by the Brenner; and sitting, like Savoy (cf. p. 84), astride of the Alps, it has had great political and commercial importance, and has been the scene of much conflict. Under the old régime, for instance, political causes added part of the Lech basin to the Inn watershed, and part of the Drave basin to the Adige watershed; and though the population had always adhered almost entirely to the Roman Church, more than half of it was German. The purely German Innsbruck became the proper capital, however, only because no place in the Adige basin com-bined such advantages for east-and-west, as well as north-and-south, traffic. But the oldest capital was in the Adige basin at Meran, the terminus of the medieval "Brenner Road," while Innsbruck was for centuries—from Roman times—simply a strategic post (cf. Kufstein) to hold the great "Inn-Bridge" which carried the old road across the Sill-Inn confluence to the Brenner; and modern railway develop-ment is now tending to decrease its commercial and increase its strategic importance. The people are typical highlanders, famous for marksmanship and for music—including the training of singing-birds, especially canaries—and their strong devotion to the House of Austria makes them valuable frontiersmen. But the crowds of visitors have done much to spoil their simplicity and other highland virtues, and the picturesque native costumes have died out almost everywhere except in the Passeierthal, the old home of Andreas Hofer—now no longer Austrian! There is some mining, *e.g.* for lead near Landeck, at the entrance to the Engadine, and for iron and salt in the extreme north-east, where Hallein is one of the most important salt-working centres in Austria. But the main occupations are pastoral, with a typical Alpine dairy industry.

The doorway to Tyrol is Salzburg, with an importance out of all **Salzburg.** proportion to its tiny size (*c.* = Devonshire). For, though locally *Tauern* is the name given to the passes, the Hohe Tauern is far from easy to cross, the chief pass (the old bridle-path from the Gastein valley into Carinthia) being at a height of over 7900 feet; and the natural route between Vienna and Tyrol follows the Upper Salzach, while the Lower Salzach commands the north-and-south approach to and from the International frontier. Most of the area is occupied by the Limestone Alps, noted for their *Klammen* or narrow gorges; and access to the main valley is commanded by such a gorge, at the Lueg Pass, the scene of tremendous fighting, especially between 1800 and 1809. Though the climate is very changeable, with extremes of temperature and very heavy rain, it is quite healthy; and the people are, therefore, of a peculiarly strong and healthy type, invaluable on the political frontier at a strategic point. The large proportion of summer rain accounts for the large proportion of forest ($\frac{1}{3}$) and pasture ($\frac{2}{5}$), dairy-farming and forestry being the two great industries; and it is quite typical that, under these circumstances, the population should be sparse (not 70 per square mile), but education relatively advanced. There is a certain amount of mineral wealth, including salt, *e.g.* at Hallein, copper, *e.g.* at Mitterberg, and marble, *e.g.* at Adnet; but the old gold-mines of the Tauern, like the old silver-mines of Schwaz, are exhausted, and the duchy is noted only for its mineral springs, *e.g.* at Gastein, St. Wolfgang, and Hallein. The area has had a very definite ecclesiastical development, associated—by cause—with the old salt deposits (cf. p. 326), and—by result—with Church music,[1] and the city of Salzburg, besides occupying a site of great beauty, and with its architecture characterised by lavish use of the local marble, has a very strong strategic site between two isolated hills, one crowned with a citadel (now barracks) and communicating by a tunnel with the river plain.

Carinthia.   Though twice the size of Salzburg, and much richer in mineral wealth, Carinthia has essentially similar character, conditions, and importance. It is a mountainous basin, rising to nearly 12,500 feet in the Gross Glockner, and divided by its main river, the Drave, into a crystalline and a limestone belt, with easier access east and west, *e.g.* into Tyrol, than across the crystalline belt into Salzburg. In the west the limestone belt is a military and political frontier, and its passes have been the scene of heavy fighting, especially the Pontebba (Pontafel) and the Predil (cf. the famous battle-place of Malborgeth). Indeed, it was for this strategical reason that Italy laid a strong claim to the little junction of Tarvis, though in Carniola, and obtained it—and, of course, the Predil Pass to the south of it—by the Rapallo Treaty. Practically the whole drainage centres on the Drave, which is made navigable for rafts and punts at Villach by the confluence of the Gail. Parallel with the river, too, *i.e.* lying longitudinally, are a number of Alpine lakes, *e.g.* Millstadt and Worth, Ossiach and Weissen. The Hohe Tauern makes the climate rather severe, especially in the Moll valley; but easier access to the Adriatic makes it much milder in the south and east, especially in the long meridional valley of the Lavant. This valley, too, like the parallel neighbouring Gurk valley, is rich in iron-ore, *e.g.* round Wolfsberg, and its value for north-and-south traffic has encouraged railway development—to the great advantage of the mining industry, etc. (cf. the foundries of St. Leonhard and Pravali).

---

[1] The capital was the birthplace of Mozart.

Still more important is the lead-mining of the Gail valley, *e.g.* at Bleiberg.

The focus of the area has always been near the eastern end of Lake Wörth. It was here that the Romans had their great camp of *Virunum*; Ferbach has a busy industry in small-arms; and for centuries the political capital has been in the Glan valley, first at St. Veit and then at Klagenfurt ("Glan-ford"). The latter, though connected with the lake by a canal, is not on it nor on the Drave-bank route. But the lake basin was the line of least resistance, and so the town is not only on the main ("Interlaken") line of rail, but also the junction for the line into Styria *via* the Glan-Gurk valley and the Friesach iron-field. Villach, however, has had more commercial importance, mainly as being on the great route from Ratisbon to Venice. Indeed, for 700 years it was under the rule of the bishops of Bamberg. Recently, with the decrease of importance as a strategic outpost, which made it an unsuitable site for a political capital, it has become a busy industrial and railway centre, interested in all the typical industries of the duchy, *e.g.* lead articles, steel wire, wood, and paper. The proportion of pasture ($\frac{1}{7}$) is much less than in Salzburg, but *c.* 45 p.c. is forested.

Under the Romans Styria was divided between Noricum and Pannonia, and the old division is more or less perpetuated in the modern division into Upper and Lower provinces, the one really mountainous and the other only hilly, with a difference of fully 9° F. in their average annual temperature—the annual mean at the famous mineral springs of Aussee not reaching 43° F. Stretching from the Salzkammergut to the Karawanken, it embraces all three zones of the Eastern Alps, and so monopolises most of the chief entrances to the system (cf. the Roman road across the Pyhrn Pass).

North of the Enns one limestone zone rises to over 9800 feet in the Dachstein, and south of the Drave the other rises to over 8400 feet in the Grintouz, where Carniola, Carinthia, and Styria meet. Between the Enns and the Drave the crystalline zone rises to 9400 feet in the Radstädten Tauern, and ends eastward in the Semmering group—famous not only for beauty, but also as the scene of the first continental mountain railway, a 35-mile experiment in tunnels, viaducts, and galleries. The political and commercial importance of this command of east-and-west traffic along the longitudinal valleys has been immensely increased by the great southward bend on the Mur, which gives a natural north-and-south link between the longitudinal routes ; and the natural site for the capital of the area was obviously in the centre of this link—at Graz. Here the Romans found, and fortified, a lonely cone-hill (the Schlossberg), rising 400 feet above the river-plain in the first important expansion of the Mur valley ; and in modern times the place has been able, by means of railways, to make better use of its natural connection eastwards with the Raab valley, and has had the additional advantage of easy access to the excellent lignite of the Kainach valley, *e.g.* at Vortsberg and Köflach.

Its Products. Though the area is far from being infertile—nearly 50 p.c. being well forested, over 20 p.c. being under tillage, and nearly 20 p.c. providing good meadow or alp pasture—the great wealth is in the minerals. There are thick deposits of "Miocene" lignite also near Leoben, where the Enz valley gives as easy access northwards to the "elbow" of the Enns at Hieflau, as the Mürz valley gives eastward at Bruck from the "elbow" of the Mur; the Sulm valley gives Leibnitz easy access to similar fields at Wies and Eibiswald; and in the extreme south the important junction of

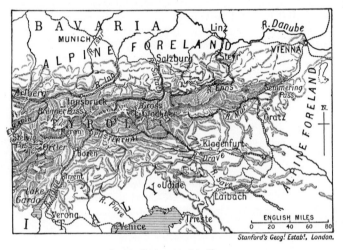

Longitudinal routes of the Tauern.

Cilli is equally well supplied, *e.g.* from Trifail, Tüffer, and Hrastnig. Iron ore is, however, the special product. The Erzberg above Eisenerz ("Iron-ore") has been worked by open-air quarries for 2000 years, and still supplies nearly 50 p.c. of the total Austrian output. The Enz valley has thus become a succession of foundry towns, *e.g.* Eisenerz and Hieflau, Vordernberg and Trofaiach. Several other minerals are worked, especially magnesite, graphite and zinc, alum and salt. Except for the engine-shops of Marburg, the chief ironworks are in and round Leoben, *e.g.* at Donawitz and Maria Zell, where there is a famous Shrine of the Virgin; and they have always been worked by a German population. The zinc industry has been more dependent on the Slavs of the south, *e.g.* at Cilli; and alum is a special product round Judenburg ("Jews' Castle"), where there was a horrible massacre of Jews in 1496.

HUNGARY

The great Alföld is the nucleus of Hungary to-day even more truly **A Steppe** than it was before the war. In origin, partly an old sea-floor, it came **Area.** at once under the influence of the relative desiccation that followed the disappearance of the sea ; and its eastward position and the encircling rim of mountains accentuated the tendency to drought, with consequent extremes of temperature—whirlwinds of snow in winter and of sand in summer. It developed, therefore, into a piece of typical " prairie " or rich steppe, with an almost typical steppe climate ; but it is near enough to the Atlantic, and the highland rim is not too high, for the strictly seasonal rainfall to be enough for successful agriculture (20-24 inches). At the same time the mountainous watershed is high enough to involve regular floods of great extent along both the great rivers, especially the Theiss (Tisza) ; and this natural " irrigation " also renews annually the fertility of the soil by a rich top-dressing of mud.

Hungary has suffered more than any other of the Central Powers. **The** Like Austria, she was not fought over during the war ; but after the **Trianon** Armistice she went through a terrific Bolshevist upheaval, and was **Treaty.** then invaded by the Rumanians, who swept her as bare as the Germans swept France, and did so with as much inhuman ingenuity and brutality. The Magyars are a proud and ancient nation, and have shown the greatest courage and tenacity in maintaining their independence and institutions ; and for centuries they were the real bulwark of Europe against the Turk. But they have been treated with great injustice, based on political spite and such ignorance of geography as allowed a great British official to speak of the town of Kharkof as a general ! The new frontiers were drawn with a reckless disregard alike for geographical features and human distributions, and violate almost every sound principle of self-determination. Thus along the whole of the north there is a solid belt of Magyar popula-tion beyond the frontier, especially in the north-west, where the Grosse Schütt district is entirely Magyar ; and here over 1,000,000 Magyars have been transferred to Czecho-Slovakia—on the flimsy excuse that the Slovaks on the southern face of the Carpathians must have access to an at present non-existing railway ! Along the east there is a similar belt, not quite so wide or quite so continuous, but overwhelmingly Magyar ; and the frontier is drawn so as to give all these Magyars—as well as the 600,000 Szeklers in the south-east of Transylvania—to Rumania and to deprive Hungary (by a few miles in each case) of such important centres as Szatmar Németi, Nagy Várad, and Arad. In a word, 20 p.c. of the total Magyar population in the world, all of which is concentrated in this middle Danube basin, is put outside the frontiers of Hungary.

This is said to be just punishment for past crimes, for which **Whose** the Magyar nobility is held guilty ; but the excuse only reveals gross **Tyranny ?**

ignorance of historic facts.   To the Magyar, whether peer or peasant, there are only two honourable forms of occupation—farming and serving the State; trade and industry have been left to foreigners, specifically Germans and Jews, and especially the latter.   The Magyar nobles were seldom tyrants, always loyal, and often unselfish; the so-called "gentry" were certainly very exclusive and domineering, but they were too few and too unintellectual to be of much importance. And the Magyar peasant—the great "aristocrat" of the area—is one of the finest types in Europe, the pride and mainstay of the country. There is no room for doubt that it was more than time to rescue several subject nationalities from tyranny in Hungary; but the method of doing that should not have ignored both the source and the distribution of the tyranny.   If it had been solely or even mainly oppression of non-Magyars by Magyars, it is most improbable that 28 p.c. of the emigrants in the decade before the war would have been Magyars.   The cause at work in that was not political but economic —the rapid exhaustion of some of the mineral wealth, the development of Austrian industries under Pan-German encouragement, and the rise of food prices, due mainly to the operations of the Jews.

The Jews.   Even in 1910 the Jews in Hungary were approaching 1,000,000 in number.   Perhaps a third of them were very useful and thoroughly Magyarised citizens; but the rest were either typical Ghetto-dwellers or frankly revolutionary, and they have been a great curse to the country, strangling the peasantry by their financial control and poisoning urban life.   It is this debased internationalism, not militant nationalism, that has been mainly to blame for the evil reputation that the "Magyars" have gained in the last generation.

Indeed, this is the great internal problem of Hungary—as its great external problem is how long 2,000,000 of the finest peasantry in Europe will be content to remain cut off from neighbours with whom alone in the whole world they have ties of blood and speech. And the new distribution of territory has raised the number of Jews in Hungary by 2 p.c.

The Alföld.   Reduced from the size of the British Isles to that of Ireland, and with its population reduced from 21,000,000 to 8,600,000, and deprived of practically all its metal-bearing highlands, its access to the sea, and a third—the best (in the Banat)—of its Alföld, Hungary has little prospect except in its rich soil and its fine human type.   The Great Alföld extends across the Danube right up to the line of the Bakony Forest; but west of the line of weakness, where the margin of the old sea-floor was abruptly fractured and detached from its rim, both structure and relief change, the dead level being replaced by an undulating lowland, in one of the shallow downfolds of which lies the brackish Lake Balaton (50 miles by 10), while the highest of the upfolds rises into the Bakony.   As this range—continuing the feature-lines of the Noric Alps, but structurally

Carpathian—reaches 2000 to 2300 feet, and lies parallel with the prevailing wet wind, it is thickly forested, mainly with oak and beech, and provides such a magnificent feeding-ground for pigs that it raises the distribution to 70 per square mile (compared with 50 cattle, 42 sheep, and 25 horses). Its marble quarries are one of the few sources of mineral wealth left to Hungary. Beyond it, Alföld begins again, the Little Alföld, nearly as rich as the Great Alföld, but so much isolated by the Bakony, that German and other than Magyar settlement was favoured ; and thus Hungary has lost the Bergland to Austria as well as half the lowland to Czecho-Slovakia.

The hopes of Hungary, then, depend on her magnificent peasantry **Actual** and her rich soil; and she is bound to become even more agri- **Losses.** cultural than she used to be, and to try to develop a much smaller area by still more intensive cultivation. For she lost about 32 p.c. of her old area, including 43 p.c. of arable land, 31 p.c. of natural pasture, 25 p.c. of meadow, and 14 p.c. of forest; incidentally to this, too,—and to the Rumanian invasion—she lost 33 p.c. (2,000,000) of her old stock of cattle, 50 p.c. of both her pigs (3,500,000) and her horses (750,000), and 25 p.c. (1,750,000) of her sheep. The greater part of the arid sands of the old kingdom are also within the new frontiers, especially between the Danube and the Theiss and south of the Theiss, where waterlogged and reed-covered hollows are divided by long lines of sand-dunes ; and the same is true of the lands most liable to bad flooding, *e.g.* between the Theiss and the Maros and south of the latter.

With a range of temperature from about 25° F. to 71° F., and a **The** rainfall which, though seldom reaching 25 inches, is essentially a **Crops.** summer fall, the land is well suited to both wheat and maize; and they are grown in roughly equal quantities, but the distribution is different. For maize, as a local food for man and beast, is grown practically in all parts of the area ; but wheat is concentrated in the " peninsula " between the Theiss and Maros. The Theiss, indeed, marks the main line of fertility in the country, all the best tobacco being grown east or west of it, while the same is true of sugar-beet, except that a good deal is grown in the south of the Little Alföld. A large sugar-beet area might also be reclaimed by draining the shallow Lake Balaton, for the relative saltness of the water, in spite of the (Sio) outlet to the Danube, is due less to the excessive evaporation than to the presence of numerous salt springs ; and the saline soil would be admirably suited to sugar-beet. Of course, the draining of the lake would increase the risk of sudden and severe frost in autumn (when now latent heat is freed in the freezing), but accelerate spring (when heat is now absorbed in melting the ice). The vine is associated with the volcanic banks, *e.g.* at Tokay and round Buda(-Pest), where the light drift-sand that covers the volcanic subsoil has been found curiously unfavourable to the phylloxera.

Minerals. Even before the war the mineral wealth was not fully exploited, and Hungary used to import one-third of the coal that she used. Now she produces about 7,300,000 tons a year, scarcely 10 p.c. being bituminous—from Pécs (Funfkirchen) and Ajk; but the lignite is good (with 60 p.c. of coal value), produced mainly in the Bakony district, *e.g.* at Totis, and along the Slovak border, *e.g.* at Gran. Here, too, at Rudobanya is the only iron-mine left to Hungary— north of Miskolcz. The natural gas, like the salt, has become Rumanian; and the loss of the salt means the partial ruin of the Hungarian chemical industry, though the bauxite industry is flourishing. All the iron-work and $\frac{7}{8}$ of the coal used now are home products.

Agriculture. Even in pre-war Hungary nearly 70 p.c. of the population found occupation on the land, and extraordinary progress had been made in scientific farming, arable and pastoral. The wide stretches of pussta offer special facilities for rearing cattle and horses, while the huge production of maize is very favourable to the rearing of pigs and poultry. With the spread of intensive agriculture, sheep-farming has become less and less important, though wool is still exported; for there is full appreciation of the need for tillage to supply stock-food (maize, beet, lucerne), to counteract drought, and to expose the deep rich loam to the beneficial action of frost. Nor is cultivation in any way restricted to grain.

Industries and Towns. Even more than ever, then, all the chief industries are bound to be "agricultural," *e.g.* flour-milling, brewing and distilling, tobacco-curing, sugar-making, while the most typical iron products are agricultural implements and machinery. And, under the circumstances, urban centres are few and far between. The real "towns" were mostly of German origin, for "the Magyars founded the State, but the Germans built the towns"; and this accounts for the large proportion of towns with the affix Nemet ("German") or Szasz ("Saxon"). The largest centres are, however, Hungarian, and are simply enormous villages, in which the isolated farms are dotted along a bush-road or round a Steppe fair-ground. For instance, Debreczin does not number a population of 120,000, and Szegedin only just reaches that limit; but both have an area of *c.* 350 square miles, *i.e.* the size of Huntingdonshire. The position of such towns is equally typical. The most important, Szegedin, stands at the confluence of the Theiss and its chief tributary, the Maros; and two other important places, Hód Mezö Väsärhely and Tokay are also on the Theiss, Tokay at another important confluence. All the others are at the limit of the Theiss lowland, *e.g.* Kecskemet, where naturally there are no rivers, and Békés, where rivers drop from the 350-foot level on to the lowland.

Sandstorms and Floods. Most of them are subject to either floods or sandstorms. The sand is, of course, naturally worst away from the great rivers, *e.g.* at Kecskemet and Debreczin; but persistent efforts, *e.g.* in planting

acacia, etc., have checked the movement of the sand, and enabled
agriculture to be firmly established (cf. the Debreczin vineyards).
The floods are also being mastered, but very slowly. The great
difficulty is the very small fall of the Theiss after it reaches the
lowland, *e.g.* 1 foot in 10 miles south of Szegedin. Though the
Theiss basin is fed essentially from forested sandstone, it is flooded
by melting snow, like the Danube ; and the increased pace of the
latter, due to its greater fall, is emphasised by greater volume, with
the result that heavy flood on the Danube blocks back the Theiss.
This accounts for the entire absence of important towns on the
Lower Theiss. Indeed except for Zenta, with its "accidental"
historic importance, there is no place of any importance below
Szegedin, which has been practically swept away time after time.
Since the last great catastrophe, in 1879, however, its dykes have
been materially strengthened.

To reach the Great Alföld from the west the Danube has Buda-
to cut through the linking uplift between the Bakony and the Pest,
Matra by the Waitzen gorge ; and in the days before their conversion to Christianity the Magyars found a more appropriate
and safer capital at the *eastern* end of the Little Alföld, on the
precipitous rock of Gran, commanding the Gran valley northward
and the land passage southward round the "Ofen" highland to
Buda. But the ultimate capital was bound to be on the Great
Alföld ; and undoubtedly the best place was where hard rock on
each side of the river and an island in the channel offered special
facilities for bridging the river before it deploys in its full natural
width on to the plain. This, too, was the natural objective of
traffic from the south-west along the Balaton Lake ; and it was
here that the old Roman road reached the Danube. On the
"Roman" bank there are several steep hills from which hot springs
flow—minimising ice in winter; and the Romans chose the site
for their great camp of Aquincum (? *Aquae Quinque*),[1] which
has grown into Buda ("Oven"). Here, too, was the natural
meeting-place of the agricultural and pastoral industries, the
mining and forestry, along with abundance of good stone for
building purposes. The one drawback was that the town could
only spread on the "Roman" bank by leaving the hills to which
it owed its essential character ; but on the opposite bank there
was unlimited room for expansion over the flat sandy plain and
a fine frontage on to the broad river (averaging 500 yards).

Pést ("Stove"), therefore, is essentially the commercial and
industrial centre, while the official centre is cramped amongst
the Buda hills, of which the Blocksberg (770 feet) rises 400 feet
above the river-level. Obviously, too, the population of Buda

---

[1] Celtic scholars consider it a transformation from the former Celtic name of
Ak-ink ("Rich Waters") ; but the Roman camp certainly had "five springs."

remains more or less stationary, while that of Pest has grown enormously (1000 p.c. in the nineteenth century). The population has always been absolutely permeated by Magyar influence, energy, and national ideals, and the Magyars have made the city the one great centre, intellectual and economic, of the kingdom. It is the seat of all the typical industries—milling, brewing and distilling, leather, agricultural machinery, etc., with a special export of mineral waters, *e.g.* Hunyadi-Janos and Apenta; and the zone traffic on the railways has so facilitated access from the farthest corners of the kingdom that it even attracts trade from beyond the political frontier. It possesses the one [1] great university in Hungary, and is to the kingdom what Paris used to be to France; and the fact is not forgotten that for some 400 years the old Maygar Diets were held on the Rákos camp just on the north of the city.

Trans-port. The zone traffic is not the only transport advantage of the area. The great rivers are navigable throughout the whole of their course in Hungary, and this means about 700 miles of navigation in home waters, with a fleet of about 2000 steamers (including tugs, etc.); nearly 600,000 tons of cargo (with as many passengers) worked in and out of Buda-Pest alone, and the Cszepel harbour is to be made a free port. Further, just because of the serious floods on the rivers, both roads and railways avoid the river-routes, and so means of transport are widely spread; and, though the roads—in the absence of " metal "—are very poor, the railways are good.

CZECHO-SLOVAKIA

Political Position. The State is included in the middle Danube basin, not only because of its political associations in both the near and the more distant past, but also because more than half its drainage now is definitely Danubian, though its most important unit drains to the Elbe; but, in a sense, its physiographic relationships are the less important. The vital factor is that it has been a pioneer peninsula of Slavdom in a setting of Austrian oppression and German penetration; but two of the units, the Bohemian basin and the Moravian corridor, are West European in most of their essentials, while the other two, the Slovak and Ruthenian highlands, are East European, the former agricultural and industrial,. the latter backward and largely forested. Thus there is a steady decrease in population density and in economic importance from west to east. This distinction is going to be exaggerated by the straggling incoherence of the configuration—about 600 miles long with a maximum width of 160; this makes it as difficult to govern as to defend. The difficulty is still further increased by the differences of creed.

[1] There are universities also at Szegedin, Pécs, and Debreczin.

The Slovaks are mainly descendants of refugees who refused to **Different** accept the creed or dominion of the conquerors in the Battle of **Creeds.** White Hill (A.D. 1620), and who took refuge in the mountainous recesses of Hungary under the dominion of the Protestant Magyars. Here they were safe and free ; but the conditions of safety involved bad communication and poverty, which have been reflected in the backward condition, educationally and otherwise, of the area.   The typical product is a sheeps'-milk cheese made under exactly the same conditions as the Roquefort product of the Aveyron "crater" pastures.   The Czechs became adherents of the Roman Church under the compulsion of the Thirty Years' War, and so remained on their rich plateau—rich in fertile soil and mineral wealth, where small holdings could be supported by industrial earnings.   With their natural ramparts of mountains and a small area, they developed a self-contained and very exclusive type, sufficiently united to prove a strong obstacle to German influences.   In the struggle the maintenance of the Czech language and the great efforts made to develop intellectual supremacy, in place of the political supremacy that was forbidden, were of prime importance.   The Ruthenians are practically "Cossacks"—typically brave, adherents of the Greek Church, and somewhat pro-Russian ; but constant war, Slavic subdivision of land, and Slavic subjection to Jewish middle-men have left them as poor as they are unintellectual.

At the same time the economic advantages of the area, especially **Economic** on the commercial side, are obvious.   Almost in the core of Europe, **Position.** and yet just between "East" and "West," it can draw food and other raw materials from Hungary and Rumania and supply them with textiles and hardware, while supplying West Europe with specialities such as china and glass.   With no sea-coast, it has yet three internationalised rivers giving access to the sea, and on the Elbe it has free ports at both Magdeburg and Hamburg and on the Oder a bonding warehouse at Stettin.   Of course, the upper Oder is not yet canalised ; the Elbe in Saxony cannot take the 1200-ton boats that can ply between Aussig and Prague, though traffic is increasing very rapidly, especially as regards exports ; and the section of the Danube that serves the country is one of the less easily navigated sections.   But the difficulties are purely mechanical and removable ; the rivers can easily be supplemented by canals, between Elbe and Danube, and Oder and Danube ; and the railway facilities are already admirable, including even a Czecho-Slovak Customs' House at Trieste.   The prospects of the State, with an area of 54,200 square miles and a population of over 14,500,000, may be estimated from the fact that before the war the area produced 100 p.c. of the porcelain of Austria-Hungary, 90 p.c. of its gloves, its glass, its sugar, 80 p.c. of its woollens, 75 p.c. of its cottons, its chemicals, its boots, and 60 p.c. of its paper.

Bohemia.   Bohemia, though only two-thirds the size of Scotland, is the most important province of the State ; and its importance, political and historic, or economic, is and has been by no means merely local. Much more truly than Switzerland, it is the heart of Europe, at about equal distances from all the great seas, a marked physical unit cut off by forested mountains, and yet with easy access to those seas by the Saxon and Moravian, the Austrian and Magyar Gates, holding the balance between the north-westward-flowing Elbe and the south-eastward-flowing Danube, for centuries a focus of political, intellectual, and ethnic interests, and to-day—partly owing to the racial rivalry, which led to the existence in Prague of separate universities for German and for Czech—one of the most important industrial areas in the world. The rivalry may now be rather industrial than racial, as the impossibility of divorcing the frontiers alike from natural features and from historical associations has involved the inclusion of a large German population.

External Relations.   Its historic external relations have been largely coloured by three facts. One is the easy route given by the Pass of Neumark (Neugadin) between the higher southern and lower northern sections of the beautiful Bohemian Forest ; for this area, now noted only for the little lace-making villages which converge on Klattau, has been the scene of terrific fighting, *e.g.* in 1040 and 1431. The second fact is the relative lowness of the Erzgebirge (averaging under 3000 feet), and even this is emphasised by the easy passes and by the height to which the mining villages[1] have climbed (cf. p. 343). The third is the relation of the Nollendorf Pass round the east end of the Erz to the frontier head of navigation on the Elbe at Aussig and to the exit from the Elbe defiles above Dresden. This was, *e.g.*, Napoleon's route in 1813 (cf. the battles of Kulin and Arbesan).

Internal Activities.   Its internal activities centre on the Moldau (Vltava), with a basin twice as large as that of the Upper Elbe (Labe), a course fifty miles longer, and the supreme advantage of being naturally navigable—up to Budweis. This Moldau basin falls in terraces from a plateau ridge of 2500 feet in the south to a level of 367 feet, where the Moldau-Elbe leaves Bohemia ; but south of the latitude of Prague (50° N.) it is predominantly highland, while north of that it is mainly lowland. Every part is linked to the Moldau main stream by rivers—Wottawa and Luzniza, Beraun and Sazawa, Eger and Elbe ; but as the definite lowland is north of 50° N., and as the gorge between Budweis and Prague is very deep and narrow, Prague has become the practical head of navigation, although the Upper Moldau is connected by canal with the Danube.

Climatic Control.   Except for a patch of drought between the Lower Beraun and the Lower Eger, where the rainfall is under 20 inches, the whole

---

[1] Gottesgab is at a height of *c.* 3344 feet.

"plateau" has a very even rainfall, mainly confined to the summer; but the mountain bulwarks have much heavier falls, rising to 40 inches on the Giant Mountains and even 70 inches on the Bohemian Forest, for the rain-bearing winds come from the west. Temperature varies in much the same way—Prague, with an annual mean of 48° F., having an average range of from 30° F. to 67° F. With such a climate and an industrious population (Slav [1]) on the lowlands, agriculture is greatly favoured, especially in those numerous areas where the soil is peculiarly fertile, *e.g.* the "Golden Road" (Königgrätz), "Paradise" (Teplitz), and "The Garden" (Leitmeritz). At least half the total area is under tillage, and in 1924 *c.* 4,500,000 tons of grain were raised, rye and oats one-fourth each, and barley and wheat one-fifth each; but various causes, especially the competition of Hungarian grain, have caused more attention to be given lately to potatoes (a staple food of the Slavs) and beetroot, the output of sugar recently (1,480,000 tons in 1925) having been the most important in Europe. The most typical products, however, are hops, especially round Saaz, and plums. Agriculture is largely "industrial," and the crops are "cash" crops.

The mineral wealth is, however, still more important. Almost **Minerals.** the whole length of the Beraun valley, which flows roughly between sedimentary rock (on the south) and crystalline rock, there are valuable coal-fields, and the upper Eger valley is equally rich in lignite. The largest area of coal is round Pilsen-Radnitz, and the largest area of lignite round Karlsbad; but the thickest seams of coal (20-36 feet) are in the Kladno-Rokonitz main seam, while the thickest seams of lignite (nearly 100 feet) are in the Teplitz-Brux-Dux field, the Biela basin producing 78 p.c. of the whole Bohemian output. Silver is extracted at Pribram and Joachimsthal, radium near Joachimsthal, and graphite at Budweis, etc.; and there are the clays of the crystalline and the quartz of the sandstone areas, on which the china and glass industries are based.

With this wealth of fuel, backed up by abundant water-power **Industries.** and great facilities for transport, Bohemia has become one of the chief industrial centres of Europe. The glass industry, imported originally from Venice, is most prosperous where various metals (for colouring) are found near silica and fuel. The finest work is done near Böhmisch-Leipa, but Pilsen is also famous for cut glass, and Gablanz—in the textile area—has an industry in glass beads and embroideries (associated with imitation jewellery). The porcelain industry is concentrated in the Karlsbad district, where, too, there are numerous mineral springs, especially at Karlsbad itself and Marienbad. The textile industries are along the foothills of the border ranges, especially where there is most water-power and best access to coal,

---

[1] The German population is largely confined to the higher districts and the towns; 71 p.c. of the agricultural, 56 p.c. of the industrial, population is Czech.

e.g. along the Giant Mountains; and there is considerable division of labour locally.   For instance, linens are a specialty in and round Trautenau, though made elsewhere, *e.g.* at Rumburg; Reichenberg makes cloth, and Kuttenberg makes calico (with local supplies of copper for rollers); Warnsdorf and Chrudim are specially cotton centres, while Jungbunzlau handles both cotton and wool.   Lace is a special product along the Erz, *e.g.* at Weipert, and along the Bohemian Forest, *e.g.* at Taus.   Hardware is most important near the coal, *e.g.* at Kladno and Pisek; sugar is more widely spread —though largely associated with the lignite,—*e.g.* at Dux and Pardulitz; Tabor has tobacco factories.   Amongst the most typical industries are the brewing of Pilsen, the pencils of Budweis, the musical instruments of the Karlsbad districts, notably of Graslitz (wind) and Schönbach (string), the gloves of Prague.

Prague.   Prague (Praha), with a population of over 675,000, shares largely in all the typical industries, especially machinery, textiles, and leather; it is the centre of the railway system, able to draw abundance of good coal from both Kladno and Kuttenberg, and it has even displaced Leitmeritz as a river-port.   The influence of outlying towns, such as Eger and Budweis on the outskirts of the Bohemian Forest, or the confluence-town of Pilsen (Plzen) commanding its centre, is also passing largely to the capital; and the latter even possesses, in its sheltered basin—where Melnik produces the finest wine in Bohemia—a climate comparable with that of the sheltered Eger and Biela basins.   It is a very old town with a characteristic nucleus of river-girt hill, and its modern development may be associated with the Kladno coal-field, which produces 13 p.c. of all the real coal in Czecho-Slovakia (over 14,000,000 tons, apart from over 20,000,000 tons of lignite), and with a local field producing 5 p.c.

Moravia.   Moravia is a very exact complement of Bohemia—a hilly plateau falling to a lowland basin, and girt with forested heights, but sloping southward, not northward.   Its population is specifically, though not nominally, Czech (over 70 p.c.)—with its German element on the border heights or in the towns,—advanced educationally and industrially, and in creed Roman.   The March, with its direct meridional course and its monopoly of the drainage, corresponds closely to the Moldau except in its inferior navigation. Even more than Bohemia, however, the land has been a thoroughfare, for the former has no outlet corresponding to the Oder valley in Moravia; indeed, its physique and the direction of its line of least resistance—parallel to the prevailing S.W. wind—are reflected in the rather deficient rainfall, which varies from under 20 inches on the lower levels to not much more than 30 even on the higher levels.   The easy access for bitter easterly winds is also reflected in the great difference of temperature between north and south, though, of course, the latter is also the lower.   Brünn (Brno), with a

rainfall of just under 20 inches and a temperature range of from
under 29° F. to over 68° F., is quite a typical centre.

Owing to the industry and intelligence of the people a very **Its**
large proportion of the area (fully 55 p.c.) is under tillage, mainly **Industries.**
for grain (oats and rye) and sugar-beet, while the important wood
industries reflect the high proportion of forest (33 p.c.). Ease of
transport, however, and good supplies of coal and iron have made
the area predominantly industrial; and the special development has
been in textiles. Brünn, at the foot of the hills between the Zwittawa
and the Schwarzawa valleys, and near the Rossitz coal (lignite), is
the woollen metropolis of the State; but the woollen industry was
important long before the development of the coal—first at the old
silver-mining town of Iglau and then in the Upper March valley
at Olmutz, the old political capital and still the seat of the
archbishop. The fall of Poland, the commercial importance of
the valleys converging on Brünn (cf. the site of Austerlitz), the
development of the coal-field, especially between Brünn and the
limit of navigation on the March near Göding, and nearness to the
political frontier, entirely diverted (*c.* 1640) the old balance of power
from Olmutz to Brünn; but the development of the better
Silesian coal-field is again attracting a textile population to the
north-east, *e.g.* to Schönberg (linen) and Sternberg (cotton), to
Zwittau (linen and cotton) and Russwitz (linen and woollen).
Iron ore is worked in both areas, *e.g.* round Schönberg and
Sternberg, and between Rossitz and Blansko, as well as on the
Ostrau coal-field, *e.g.* at Ostrau and Witkowitz. Both the Iglawa and
the Zwittawa rise in Bohemia, and thus Iglau and Zwittau have
commanded for centuries important routes; and Trebitsch, on
the approach to the former—still noted for its military school,—
developed a typical industry in horse-cloths (cf. p. 204). The great
transport centres now are, however, Brünn and Prerau, the latter
being the pivot for the Beczwa-March and Luha-Oder connections
via Weisskirchen, *i.e.* the real Moravian Gate. Vastly different
from this eastern area, with its commercial and industrial, political
and strategic importance, is the placid valley of the Thaya in the
west, famous only for its scenery, *e.g.* round Znaim, though in
olden days the beauty was somewhat discounted by the odour of
ubiquitous tanneries. This area, like Brünn—but unlike Prague,
—has been German in both population and sympathy; but it is
significant that even Brünn itself has only commercial disadvantages
from its military advantage of standing on the flank of the
Moravian Gate route instead of directly on it, and the same is
more or less true of Prossnitz and Kremsier.

The old crown land of Silesia (= Northumberland) was divided **Silesia.**
by the tongue of Moravia which is underlaid by the Ostrau-
Karwin coal-field, *i.e.* the lowest line of the Oder valley, so that

industrially as well as physically it centres on the Oder. The dry slopes of the Sudetes supply excellent wool; and the fibrous soil of the Oppa-Olsa lowlands, especially below the forested Jablunka Carpathians, produces abundance of flax. And, as the local wealth in coal and the facilities for transport have greatly encouraged industries, the special products are woollen and linen goods, the woollens mainly at the junctions of Jägerndorf and Kielitz—though also, up on the Sudetes, *e.g.* at Engelsberg—and the linens mainly behind the junction of Troppau, *e.g.* at Freudenthal and Bennisch. Even Troppau, however, is somewhat off the main lines of movement —by the Oder itself or the Jablunka Pass—as well as off the coal-field, to which the convergence of traffic from the Jablunka Pass, the Moravian Gate, and Galicia has given exceptional importance. Indeed, the Ostrau coal-field produces 66 p.c. of all the real coal in the State; and though the Oder is the least useful of the three great rivers, the Ostrau ironworks do import ore by it from Sweden.

Slovak-Ruthene Relief.   The nucleus of Slovakia is formed by the "Hungarian" Ore Mountains, with their foreground in the Matra, their background in the Tatra and the Beskids, and their flanks in the Neutra and Hegyallya. If this condemns the area to a large proportion of poor soil — though some of the valleys, especially that of the Hernad, are very rich—there are some compensations in the mineral wealth and the possibilities of developing water-power. For it is an important hydrographic focus, the major streams radiating from the central meridian in such a way that even the core of the region has relatively easy access, *e.g.* by the Waag and the Gran on opposite sides of the Neutra, and the Hernad and Toplya on opposite sides of the Hegyallya. There is also easy access into Poland, the Jablunka Pass being under 2000 feet, and both the "Poprad" and the Vereczke well under 3000. But the difficult and circuitous connection with the rest of Czecho-Slovakia leaves little hope of any economic development except in relation to Hungary.

Natural Resources.   The mineral wealth is less, however, than one would expect from "Ore Mountains." Under Hungary a large iron industry was built up, based mainly on the rich Gömör and Szepes deposits round the head waters of the Gran and the Hernad, *e.g.* in the Vashegz ("Iron Mountains"), and there were important works, *e.g.* at Reina and Brezno; but the industry collapsed with the change of political ownership.

The richest opal mines in Europe are near Kaschau (Kosica). Gold and silver are still mined, *e.g.* near Kremnitz and Schemnitz (Ban Bistrica), and the Handlova lignite in the Neutra provides some 300,000 tons of fuel annually. But the railways which—with the tariff—accounted for the old prosperity, ran north and south, and do not properly serve for east-and-west traffic. The result is that two-thirds of the Slovaks and four-fifths of the Ruthenes are engaged in agriculture. A great variety of grain is raised, mainly barley and wheat, but also oats, rye, and maize; sugar-beet is important, with nine or ten sugar factories in Slovakia; hardy fruit thrives, especially plums and apples [1] (cf. Jablunka, "Apple-Tree"); "Tokay" is made from the vineyards near Kaschau and Munkács (Munkacero).

There are, of course, no important centres except Bratislava (Pressburg); and the efforts that are being made to develop that as a great Danube port are not likely to be immediately successful; for at high water the bridges are too low, at low water boats run aground, and the heavy traffic is definitely up-stream. Still, presently the economic importance of the town may almost rival its historic interest. **Bratislava (Pressburg).**

The Danube, cutting into its right bank under the influence of the earth's rotation, as it leaves the Theben gorge, makes Pressburg a frontier fortress, upon a low platform (250-300 feet) to the east of the gorge and the north of the river, where it thus controlled communication into the old mining area of the Waag valley. Eastward, instead of a gorge, there is the sudden expansion of the river round the Schütt islands, which offers maximum obstacle to crossing until the main stream collects the Raab and Waag drainage at Komorn. From the time that the Magyars accepted Christianity, and became at once a "bastion of Latin Christianity against Oriental barbarism" and a wedge to split the Slavs in two, the inevitable community of interest between German and Magyar in opposition to the Slavs favoured the concentration of Magyar influence on the old Roman site of Posonium, in touch with the old civilisation and the new religious focus. The fertile Little Alföld made this also a great market for grain and wine, as now for tobacco; and it became the terminus of the first railway in Hungary (up the Waag valley).

---

[1] The apple crop in 1928 weighed nearly 181,000 tons.

CHAPTER XXIII

THE ISTHMIAN STATES

Belt of Change. THESE two States occupy the most important part of the great belt of recent political change in Europe—the belt which spans the continent from Greece to Finland, and which for hundreds of years has been a belt of continual political instability. Three thousand years ago this purely "isthmian" part of the belt—between the mouths of Danube and Vistula, between the Black Sea and the Baltic—was carrying a thoroughfare between Phœnicia and "Amberland"; but the unifying influence of the north-and-south trade was less potent than the disrupting east-and-west influence of the critical position between Asia and Europe proper. This is well illustrated by recent events. For all the new States of Europe lie within this belt; they have all been formed mainly by the break-up of three empires which grew out of the very difficulties of the position—with their old capitals still practically within the belt, at Leningrad, Vienna, and Constantinople; and their smallness is really based on the diversity of "race," speech, and creed which made them incoherent and impotent to win self-government sooner. The problem has been still further complicated by the eastward push of Prussia in the north and Italy in the south, on which the recent history of Danzig and Fiume is a significant comment.

POLAND

Historic Importance. Of the two States, Poland is in many ways the more important, though her importance was as much under-rated by the treaty-makers as that of Rumania was over-rated. Its historic importance has, of course, been overwhelmingly greater; and the fundamental reason for this has been that it has been—like the other area of very pure Slav type, Bohemia—Central Europe in the only sense in which the words can be used truly and geographically. For neither structure nor relief in any way justifies the term "Central Europe" as used by German geographers of a separate Natural Region. But Poland has occupied the critical, central position for at least

394

1600 years.   In Early-Neolithic times round-headed, wavy-haired
Alpine peoples from the western plateaus of Asia moved into
Europe over the grassland ; and one group settled round the Pripet
"sea," on the great divide between east and west, between Baltic
and Black Sea drainage.   From this area of characterisation they
spread northwards along the west bank of the Dnieper and westward along the northern foot of the Carpathians, reaching the Oder
by the fourth century (A.D.).   They were organised politically by the
seventh century, and by the ninth their six tribes were merged in a
Poland.   Their biological unity and the unity of speech and culture
were prime factors in this process ; and, unlike their relations to the
north and the east, but like the Czechs, they were organised, not by
Viking or other foreign rulers, but by representatives of their own
fine peasantry, *e.g.* the Piasts.

North of the Carpathians, Europe is not a simple plain sloping **River**
gradually down to the Baltic, but a broad longitudinal valley **Units.**
between two latitudinal uplifts, the Baltic Heights and the
Carpathians ; and this has been the dominant fact behind even the
historical geography.   For instance, in the sixteenth and seventeenth
centuries Poland consisted mainly of three belts, Great Poland
along the open valley, Little Poland on the Carpathian foreland, and
Coastal Poland on the Baltic fringe.   But these units were essentially
riverine, and so were their subdivisions : Silesia lay along the Upper
Oder ; Polonia along the Warthe—once, *via* Lake Goplo, a tributary
of the Vistula ; Mazonia along the great east-and-west tract of the
Vistula ; Sandomiria along its great north-and-south reach.   For the
broad open valley was less one valley than the convergence of
several valleys—in two main lines, that of the Narew, Vistula, and
Netze, and that of the Bug, Warthe (Warta), and Oder ; and the
basal limit eastward was the north-and-south Dnieper, *i.e.* roughly
longitude 30° E., while the western objective was Lake Goplo.
Here, between Posen and Gnesen, was the race-home of the Poles,
and to this focus running water and human activities alike gravitated
from the water-parting between the northern and the southern Bug.

This position was fundamentally transitional [1]—in features, **Transi-**
phenomena, and functions.   By structure as well as site, it was a **tion Area.**
broad passage-way, with all the accompanying advantages in peace
and disadvantages in war.   It was also the mathematical centre of
Europe, half-way between the north of Sweden and the south
of Crete, between Ushant and the nearest frontier of Asia, and
crossed by both the Amber routes—the Roman *via* the Moravian
Gate and Cracow, and the Byzantine round the Carpathians *via*
Lemberg.   Here the Poles developed as both Easterns and
Westerns, the former in origin and physical type, the latter in mind
and creed—not Teutons, though Roman in creed, and not Greek in

---

[1] Cf. Nalkowski's admirable *Poland as a Geographical Entity.*

creed, though Slavs; and to-day their great economic opportunity is as a link between the industrial peoples of the west and the eastern raisers of raw materials, as they were once a link between the civilised south and the barbarous north.

Structure and Climate. The structure and relief are quite typical of Europe as a continent (cf. p. 1). Across the whole south of the region there lies the Sudetic-Sarmatian core of old rock, which we expect to find rich in metal (pp. 37 and 49). This is buttressed southward by the young folded mountains of the Carpathian system, and merges northward in the young plain of the Vistula; and, if the passage is essentially an east-and-west route, north-and-south rivers, such as the Goryn and the Styr, the Bug and the Warthe, and even the Dniester, facilitate concentration on the main line. In flood times, indeed, at least before any of the Pripet basin was reclaimed, there must always have been 500 miles of almost continuous navigation along latitude 52° N.; and yet the general level of the waterway must have been fairly constant and moderate owing to the fact that the eastern rivers flood in spring from lowland snow, while the western flood in summer from mountain snow. This is a response only to relief control. The climate is uniformly transitional, with no strong contrasts. The mean mid-winter temperature in the extreme west (29° F.) is only 5° F. above that in the extreme east, while the corresponding mid-summer temperature (66° F.) in the west is only 1° F. below that in the east. The north is slightly more marine and so more forested than the centre, and the south is slightly more continental and so has more steppe than the centre; and the forest and the steppe gave Poland useful cultural and faunal contrasts, while the steppe carried the eastern Amber route between lands of summer rain and summer drought.

The Partition. In this Vistula basin, then, the Poles played a very important part in the progress and even the survival of Europe. It was a small matter, perhaps, that they defended Russia and Lithuania from Teutonic aggression; but it was practically the whole civilised continent that they protected from Asia, from Tatar and Turk, from Islam and barbarism. Sobieski was not an Austrian! But when these neighbouring autocracies were at their zenith, Poland was a prey to social revolution; and the consequent partition has left its mark specially in great differences of social and economic development, due mainly to the different treatment received from the different Powers. The Austrian part certainly fared best; only in the Prussian part was there brutal persecution; but the largest area and the greatest number of Poles were under the most backward Power, Russia. For that very reason Russia offered a promising sphere for exploitation, and the only obstacle to a German monopoly of Russian markets was—and is—Poland; hence the desire to crush the Poles. But in the partitioning each of the three Powers

was unwise enough to take one of the three great foci of Polish
patriotism—Posen, the cradle of their nationality—Cracow, the home
of their culture, with the tombs of their kings—and Warsaw, the
pivot of their trade, past, present, and future.

For practical purposes Posen is the "basin" of the Middle **Posnania.**
Warthe, the general low level being broken by low lines or wedges
of disconnected hills between the main stream and its Netze and
Obra tributaries ; and the natural result is a labyrinth of swamps
and bogs, *e.g.* the Obrabrüch, which is the old course and therefore
the natural link—now canalised—between the Warthe, as it leaves
Poland, and the Oder, as it enters Brandenburg.   Though much of
the soil is light and sandy, the reclaimed lands are distinctly fertile ;
and over 60 p.c. of the total area is under cultivation, even hops
and tobacco being grown, while nearly 60 p.c. of population is rural.
The majority of the people even in 1914 were Poles belonging to
the Roman Church, and their relations with their Prussian rulers
were not only a great obstacle to progress, but a notorious scandal.
Even within this twentieth century Polish parents have been im-
prisoned for withdrawing their children from religious instruction
given by Prussians (Agnostics or Protestants) in German, and the
children have been thrashed for refusing to say the Lord's Prayer
in German.   Almost the only redeeming feature in the Prussian
administration was the typical insistence on education, so that these
western Poles are now the best educated in the State.

Even Posen, an old capital of Great Poland, illustrated the
racial and political tension, for the river flows due north through
the district, and the old Polish town, like the modern Polish quarter,
was on the east bank, while the Prussian town, which arrogated the
title of Alstadt ("Old Town"), was on the west bank.   The site, in
the centre of a wide sandy plain, was quite suitable for the capital of
a kingdom which included also the upper "basin" of the Warthe ;
but both trade and industry have been cramped since it became a
first-class frontier fortress near to a great tariff barrier.   As a fortress,
on the other hand, it is strongly defended by the marshy banks of
its sluggish, navigable river.   Bromberg, the great industrial and
commercial rival of Posen, has a somewhat similar position to the
west of the Vistula ; and as the great westward elbow of the Vistula
at the confluence of the Brahe makes the town the natural terminus
of a canal to the Elbe *via* the Netze, so the southward drainage of the
Netze from the Baltic Lake Plateau gives it easy access northwards.

The eastern limit of Upper Silesia is a Jurassic escarpment, **Silesia :**
which dominates the eastern bank of the Warta, and is the western **Political.**
limit of the Sarmatian platform ; and, in contrast to the latter,
Silesia is a real foreland, only seamed with faults, which—though
concealed by thick surface deposits, alluvial and glacial—have been
of great importance in the mining industry.   North of the scarp,

i.e. of Tarnowitz, a belt of " Chelm " (limestone) is so porous that it
is unforested; but in both the north and the south less porous belts
are forested, and north and south again are unforested belts—the
northern of poor, sandy soil, but the southern enriched by loess.
Before the development of the mineral wealth this southern belt was
very important both for its fertility and for its command of the
Moravian Gate. Indeed, the meeting of great routes here has led
to "racial" and linguistic problems such as were illustrated by the
recent plebiscite. For there was no correlation between speech and
votes; even close to the Polish frontier, *e.g.* at Kreuzberg, where
Polish was spoken "as the mother tongue" by 57 p.c. of the people,
only 3 p.c. voted " Polish." This was mainly due to the fact that
the whole organisation of the area and its industries had been
German, and all the concentrations of population voted "German."
The rural districts, like the miners, voted " Polish," and so the
region nearest Poland passed to Poland, carrying with it such German
towns as Tarnowitz, Königshütte, and Kattowitz. The industrial
triangle, however, is divided fairly equally between the two States,
each getting three of the great towns, *i.e.* Beuthen, Zabrze, and
Gleiwitz remaining German; and it is so truly a single great
"conurbation" that special Customs arrangements have been made
for running both the transport and the power systems (with Chorzow
as the centre) for fifteen years as a single system, allowing perfect
freedom of movement to labour and materials, raw or partly
worked.

Silesia : Indus-trial. The present importance of Silesia is based on its mineral wealth,
and its three great industries are associated with coal, iron, and zinc;
and the recent " Partition " has given decisive control of all three
to Poland, while Germany controls only such subordinate industries
as the sugar, cement, and textiles. The coal-field, which is the
richest in Europe, seems to be warped under the central belt of
limestone; and so, while it is near the surface on its northern and
southern edges, *e.g.* at Beuthen and Tarnowitz, Rybnik and Pless,
it is very deep down (1000 feet) in the centre. Naturally, the
north-western corner, as nearest to Breslau and Berlin, was worked
first; and Germany has 20 or 25 p.c. of the present output, including 50 p.c. of the coking coal. But the concealed field, *i.e.* 90 p.c.
of the reserves, and at least 75 p.c. of the present output are Polish.
In 1913 Silesia supplied 90 p.c. of the coal used in German Poland,
50 p.c. of that used in Austria, and 18 p.c. of that used in Russia,
this 18 p.c. including 40 p.c. of that used in Russian Poland. As
the total output was 43,000,000 tons ($\frac{3}{4}$ from the area now Polish),
and Russian Poland produced 70,000,000, the Polish output
now—apart from any Teschen contribution—ought to be above
100,000,000 tons per annum; and this would make Poland the
third producer in Europe, with a big surplus for export. But in

1929 the output was not much above 46,000,000 tons, of which *c.* 14,000,000 (coal and coke) were exported; and Königshütte and Kattowitz have no *Polish* coke nearer than Rybnik. With regard to metals, Germany has fared still worse; Poland has 82 p.c. of the whole zinc-field, with an output of 162,000 tons. And there is abundance of iron—of rather low (*c.* 35 p.c.) metallic content—in the west of the old Russian Poland.

The State has to face one serious internal problem, the Jews. **The** For here, as in Hungary, only on a far larger scale, they are **Jews.** identified with both petty and great finance, and *c.* 8 p.c. of the inhabitants of Poland to-day are Jews. Their ancestors were encouraged to settle here in the thirteenth and fourteenth centuries —not from any religious tolerance, but for economic reasons. For Poland was then purely "agricultural," and the nation consisted only of (1) land-owning nobles and (2) land-tilling peasants; the nobles had ruthlessly blocked the rise of any towns or any middle class, and the Jews were invited in as traders, occupying the position of middle-men. The recent rise of a Polish middle class has roused their deepest hostility. The consequent struggle between the middle class and the Jews has been very bitter, and has been largely responsible for the campaign of calumny abroad against the Poles wherever International Finance has been strong. At the same time, the greater part of Polish industry is still financed by the Jews, who are keenly pro-German—Yiddish, of course, is only a dialect of Low German—and who supply practically all the supporters of Bolshevism, economic and political, in Poland.

Galicia has considerable variety of relief, $\frac{1}{3}$ being Carpathian high- **Galicia.** land and more than $\frac{1}{3}$ being Sarmatian plateau. It is dominated by the Carpathians, as the old kingdom of Poland was, but it is linked naturally by the plateau to Russia, and the Dniester is navigable up to the point (Sambor) where it swings nearest to the "Vistula" navigation at Przemysl. Though the East Beskids are crossed by the Vereczke and other good passes, they are a great obstacle to wet winds; but the short summers are hot enough to be very favourable to the growing of grain, potatoes, and beans, and any deficiency of precipitation is partly compensated by the large proportion that falls as snow. Fully half the area is under tillage, and over 83 p.c. of the relatively dense population (240 per square mile) are engaged in agriculture, the products including beet-sugar —especially round Stanislau—and tobacco, especially on the loess near Lemberg. The mineral wealth in salt, petroleum, and zinc is very great. The zinc, which supplied 40 p.c. of the total Austrian output, is on the Silesian frontier near Cracow. The richest salt-beds are also near, being centuries old and now carried on in a subterranean town, 2 or 3 miles long and 1000 feet below the surface. Rich salt-beds are also found in the Dniester basin, *e.g.*

at Sambor, Drohobyez, and Dolina. The Drohobyez district, too, is a very important oil centre, with a special trade in ozokerit, Boryslau being the chief town ; and oil is found parallel with the axis of the Carpathian arc almost all the way from Kolomea to Jaslo. The Boryslau-Tustanowice-Mraznica field, though producing seven-eighths of all the Galician crude oil, is producing only 35 p.c. of the 1914 output; the eastern field round Bitkow is doing very well.

Cracow.   Transport in this region has been relatively good, because Galicia, as a typical frontier area, developed its lines of movement more or less in duplicate—one inside the old frontier and the other along the mountain base, *e.g. via* Tarnow, Jaroslau, Lemberg, and Tarnopol, and *via* Sandec, Sanok, Stryi, Stanislau, and Kolomea, the natural focus of Galicia alone being on the water-parting south of the old fortress of Przemysl. This has been a thoroughfare for centuries, though neither the old capital of Cracow nor the new capital of Lemberg stands on it, for Galicia can no more be isolated from the rest of Poland than it could be from the rest of Austria. Cracow stands where the Vistula becomes navigable on leaving its narrow valley, and this is the natural objective of all traffic converging from the Mediterranean and the Black Sea on the point at which —*via* the Arva and the Poprad—the plain of Poland has easy access round the Tatra to and from the plain of Hungary. The abundance of salt gave the place extra importance commercially in early days ; and the relations of the Dniester valley to the Carpathian arc and to the forested marsh on the Russian side of the Dniester-Bug water-parting concentrated the commerce from the Black Sea as directly on Cracow as that from the Mediterranean was concentrated by the Moravian Gate. But the relative inferiority of the Vistula navigation, and the positive drawbacks of the frontier position, have been adverse to the growth of the city (182,000).

Lemberg.   Like Przemysl, Lemberg (Lwow) stands on the water-parting ; and, as the rivers—in the "Russian" climate—have cut their beds deep down into the old platform, traffic for centuries has avoided alike the river trough and the riverine marsh, *i.e.* has always worked more or less along the water-parting, *e.g.* between Cracow and Kief. The town stands, however, in the middle of a predominantly Ruthenian population, characteristically backward, while Cracow is on the edge of an area predominantly Polish and relatively advanced ; but the large Hebrew population in the town itself has made it the most important industrial and commercial centre in the province, and therefore an appropriate capital. It is also the capital of three archbishoprics—Roman, Greek, and Armenian,—while its university rivals that of Cracow ; and its rise has kept pace with the development of railways across the Beskids and with the growth of the Hebrew population, though the latter may now be a cause of trouble rather than help. The population is about 220,000.

The basin of the Middle Vistula, with its fertile soil and good **Great** communication by land and water, was the cradle of the Poles; but **Poland:** it consists of two very different parts, between which the capital of **North.** Warsaw roughly holds the balance.   The northern half is a low, undulating, wooded plain, from 300 to 400 feet above the sea, rising northwards to the lake-dotted Baltic plateau—of which the detached Wilno-Suwalki area is a typical piece,—growing almost nothing except oats and rye.   Across this plain the rivers meander, in broad shallow valleys so little below the level of the surrounding land that their basins overlap in a most intricate manner, and are subject to terrific floods—caused by ice blocking their lower courses, or by heavy rains on the Carpathians, or by both.   The whole lowland has been, in geologically recent times, a vast glacial lake or series of lakes; and it is to this that it owes both its complicated river-system and the fertility of its soil, which is largely composed of the silt deposited in the old lakes.

The southern half is an expanse of forested plateau, averaging **Great** 900 feet, and rising southward to spurs of the Carpathians, *e.g.* the **Poland:** Olkusz (*c.* 1600 feet); and down through this plateau the rivers **South.** have cut deep gorges, which make the country exceedingly rough and difficult, especially to the east.   The Vistula bisects the plateau by a relatively wide valley, which—in spite of embankments—is sometimes completely inundated, the only compensation being that the river is navigable by steamers right up to the elbow at Sandomir. This highland also has its wealth, for it is rich in minerals, especially in the Olkusz area, *e.g.* at Sosnowice; besides copper, tin, iron, and zinc, there is a large coal-field, with its chief centre at Bendzin; and, of course, the main line from Breslau to Warsaw passes through the coal-field.   With its Silesian "extension" (p. 398), this field will probably become an exceedingly important metallurgical focus.

The combination of agricultural and mineral wealth is largely **Economic** responsible for the density of the population; and though there **Geo-** are only two really large towns, Warsaw (936,000) and Lodz **graphy.** (450,000), and about a dozen with populations from 50,000 to 200,000, there are a great many small towns.   The prosperity of the area has been stimulated by the "native" Jewish population and by the large immigration of Germans a generation ago.   Of course, the country suffered terribly in the war, even from malicious barbarity.   For—as in France and, to some extent, in Belgium— immense quantities of valuable machinery were stolen or broken to pieces by the Germans, farm and factory buildings were burnt or blown up, animals maimed or massacred wholesale, and orchards cut down.   But this meant that at least some relatively old equipment was replaced by better, and Poland has a valuable legacy from the Germano-Hebrew organisers, *e.g.* in the organisation which allows her now to be exporting nearly 4500 tons of eggs and nearly

25,000 tons of sugar every month. Under these influences agriculture has become widely "industrial," beetroot being extensively grown for sugar-making and potatoes for distilling ; and the variety of crop has helped the soil to recover from the ravages of the old "Three-Field" rotation, while the root-residue has given a great impulse to the stock-breeding which was always important, and to which Poland owed the rise of its valuable leather trade (cf. the tanneries of Warsaw and Radom). The progress in other respects has been at least equally great. The textile output in the 50 years before 1914 rose from a value of £5,000,000 a year to one of over £50,000,000. Lodz, between the Silesian sheep-farms and the Polish flax-fields and importing cotton by the Vistula, is the great centre, its cotton industry being very important ; and it is surrounded by a number of small towns—especially on the standard-gauge line *via* Czenstochowa to Sosnowice, and on the broad-gauge line *via* Lodz to Kalisz—all interested in textile work, *e.g.* yarn, cloth, lace, etc.

Warsaw.   All the industries of Poland are represented at Warsaw ; and its central position in Poland and its advanced position with regard to Russia, coupled with its immense advantages for rail and river traffic, have made it not only the natural political and commercial capital of Poland, but also the chief centre for the distribution of West European goods over the whole of Russia. The special site was marked out for the rise of an important city by the presence of a steep terrace, 120 feet above the river and so safe from its floods, between its confluences with the Narew and Bug, and with the Piliza and Wieprz, *i.e.* the arteries of plain and plateau, representing respectively Lithuanian and Polish tendencies. With easy access to the minerals of Piotrkov (Petrokov) and Kielce, it has developed a very important hardware industry, especially in transport materials; but its most typical industry is in boots and shoes (almost entirely in the hands of the Jews). It controls a sugar industry which, supplemented mainly by the Lublin and Ploch districts, produced 400,000 tons of sugar in 1924 ; it shares with Kalisz an important lace and embroidery trade; and, like Radom and many other centres in the chief potato-growing areas, it has enormous distilleries and starch works.

Danzig.   Though historic circumstances have torn Poland from its natural port, the whole importance of Danzig lies in its being the great clearing-house for the traffic of the Vistula; and this has been emphasised by the fact that the railways of the whole region were built with a view definitely to military rather than commercial ends. Though a free city again, it is under the Central Customs Administration of Poland and under Polish suzerainty for foreign affairs ; but the artificial colonisation of the area by Prussia in recent years must complicate the future of the port, especially as the town did five times as much trade by rail as by river in 1914—mainly owing to the great need for proper regulation of the river.   At the same time, the navigation could be immensely improved without much difficulty or expense, and more than half of the large towns of Poland ($\frac{23}{40}$) are actually on the river.   The whole of the " corridor " is rich, and its dyked deltaic lands are exceedingly so, very fine wheat being raised north of Marienburg on the high right bank of the Nogat distributary.   Moreover, only two distributaries—and both minor ones—now enter the Frische Haff at all, the main body of water entering the sea near Danzig in the lee of the Hela peninsula.   Consequently, by means of a ship-canal to its outport of Neufahrwasser, Danzig has maintained its position not only as handling large quantities of agricultural products, but even as a shipbuilding centre.   The strategic importance of the city rests on the complete facilities for flooding the dyked lands, and it had value as a base of supplies for Germany in connection with warlike operations in the Baltic ; but it has a serious rival in the new Polish port of Gdynia, where cargo to a total of *c.* 2,500,000 tons was cleared in 1929.

The possession of Wilno (Vila), no doubt, does cut off **Wilno.** Lithuania from its natural hinterland, and so may draw some Russian trade to Poland ; but the Polish attitude has been as unwise as it has been discreditable, and Wilno will probably not have a tithe of its old importance.   It certainly will no longer be a clearing-house between Russia and West or Central Europe ; it has no local resources of any real importance ; and the shipment of its timber and flax depends on the possibility of its using the Niemen. For this the Lithuanians can scarcely be expected to give facilities, even if the river is re-established as an international waterway.

RUMANIA

The exceptional generosity that Rumania received from the **Roman** treaty-makers was due rather to her real and imagined links with **and** Imperial Rome, *i.e.* to her claims to be considered as a typical **Romance.** " Latin " or West European Power, than to her actual assistance and sufferings during the war ; and her intrusion into the Banat lowland will probably prove to have been a serious blunder, for it is the only new area in the kingdom which neither makes a fairly coherent unit nor seems to have any appropriate place in the organic whole.   At the same time, it will probably be an advantage to Europe to have this critical isthmus under the control of two states which may be fairly regarded as " Romance "—the one in creed and mentality, and the other in nominal origin and speech.

With an area of over 120,000 square miles and a population of **Mountain** 17,000,000, the country has doubled its pre-war size and man- **Axis.** power, and its natural divisions are so far complementary of one another that it makes a compact and well-balanced political unit. But it is not really so compact as it looks on a political map, for its mountain backbone is a serious obstacle—all the more serious because it so definitely divides new from old areas, and these new areas contain 1,500,000 Magyars and 400,000 Germans, a large proportion of them concentrated in the very core of the kingdom. Against this, however, must be set the fact that this highland core was really the "race-home" of the people. The Walachian and Moldavian lowlands were so much exposed to raid and invasion that they were scarcely peopled at all till about half a century ago, when they began to be peopled from the highland; and the absence of permanent snow, even on the Transylvanian Alps, and the presence of mineral wealth, especially oil and salt, have caused the highland to be widely settled, and even cultivated with orchards (damsons, etc.) and vineyards.

Commer-cial Products. The new areas are specifically rich in minerals and timber, while the old are food-producing. Indeed, Transylvania, in spite of some rich valley-floors, e.g. at Fogaras and Brasso (Kronstadt), actually lacks bread-stuffs, though fairly rich in cattle and sheep; but its copper deposits carry gold and silver; the Maros-Ujvar district is rich in salt; the lignite field of the Upper Schyl produces 2,000,000 tons a year, close to the Vajda-Hunyad ironworks, and the Banat contains abundance of good iron. Even so, 82 p.c. of the whole population is still rural, and 75 p.c. of it is engaged in agriculture; Bucharest itself has only c. 350,000 people, and no other town except Chisinau (Kishinev) has over 100,000. Cereals, of course, are of prime importance; but maize (12,000,000 acres)— grown everywhere for local food—is now much more important than wheat (under 7,000,000)—grown where convenient for export,—and barley (over 5,000,000) is also greatly increasing in importance. Indeed, with the wholesale breaking-up of the large estates, the State is very unlikely ever again to be the second in the world for the export of maize or the fifth for that of wheat. And of its two other great exports, oil and timber, there must be a much heavier local demand on the former because of the great increase in railway mileage and mining activity, but the country may continue to produce $2\frac{1}{3}$ p.c. of the world's output, though it has fallen from fourth to seventh place as a producer, with between 32,000,000 and 33,000,000 barrels. The timber is a valuable asset which has been little exploited, owing partly to purely economic causes, e.g. difficulties of transport, and partly to its historic value as increasing the defensive rôle of the mountains against the mounted hordes of Asia.

The Old Kingdom. The old kingdom, with its forested Carpathian base, inherited from the days of Trajan an infiltration of South European stock which was alien in origin and type to all the surrounding races, and the influence of which is still seen in the use of the French language in the country, and, as it was protected rearwards by the Carpathians and had the riverine swamps of the Danube in front, the position was suitable for a Buffer State. As the essential purpose of the Treaty of Paris (1856) was to curtail the Russian frontier and—above all else—to keep it away from the Danube, it was natural to add to Rumania the whole of the similar Moldavian plain, with its forested Carpathian background, up to the river Pruth; and even then to secure the Danube mouth, in days before the nominal independence of Bulgaria, Rumania must possess not only the best distributaries of the Danube, but also the hilly steppe of the Dobruja at least as far south as Trajan's Wall, *i.e.* the shortest distance between the non-deltaic part of the river and the Black Sea. As a matter of fact, the frontier has been carried on to the Bulgarian plateau.

The mouths of the Danube.

Tolerated as an independent Power therefore, only as a weak guardian of the international waterway, Rumania realised that only commercial influence would be allowed to her; and all her energies **International Influence.** have been devoted to developing the natural resources of the country and to securing the political peace necessary for such development. She has, however, considerable political influence, not only because of the great volume of her trade, but also because of her racial unity. Though some 3,000,000 refugees at various times took refuge from the Tatars *behind* the Carpathian wall (cf. p. 35), and though the great schism in the Russian Church drove a number of " dissenters " into neighbouring lands including Rumania, more than 90 p.c. of the population is essentially Rumanian and belongs to the Orthodox Greek Church.

The commercial position is exceptionally good. The sea-coast **Commercial Position.** includes all the channels of the Danube delta and the old Genoese port of Kustenje (Constanza), which is seldom ice-bound, and which, therefore, since the construction of the Chernavoda bridge across the Danube, has given constant access to open water in winter. By rail there is, of course, easy access across the Pruth, the only really navigable tributary of the lower Danube, *via* both Jassy and Galatz, while the Iron Gates of Orsova give easy access into Jugo-Slavia; and the wide belt of riverine swamp, which has such a strategic value, especially in flood-time, forced the main line of rail northward on to the edge of the loess terrace, where the fertility of the loess and the central site make it of maximum utility.

Climate.   The climate is markedly continental, with sudden and treacherous changes of temperature; it ranges from below zero to 120° F.
—though the average range is only about 50° F.—with little or no
spring and, therefore, little or no spring rainfall. This, however, is
compensated by a very heavy snowfall, which is more valuable on
the porous loess than a rainfall double the present fall (20 inches)
would be; and, as large areas of the loess are rich in humus, the
supply of moisture is economised to the utmost. The result is a
remarkable fertility, wheat and maize crops being amongst the heaviest
in Europe, and a considerable variety of products. About one-sixth
of the country is well forested; and on the outskirts of the deciduous
forests various kinds of stone-fruit, especially damsons, are very
prolific. The steppe, especially between the Sereth and the Pruth,
is excellent natural pasture; and pigs are very numerous in the
oak and beech forests.

Towns.   The distribution of towns and their railway connections reflect
strongly the Buffer State origin. In Walachia, Craiova and
Bucharest stand facing the Bulgarian fortresses at Vidin and
Ruschuk, but well back from the riverine swamps, while Jassy and
Galatz face Russia from the high firm banks of the Pruth and the
Sereth. The great grain port of Braila (with Macin) is now more
important than Craiova, though the latter is still an important
junction; and the junction of Ploesti, in the petroleum district,
has become more important than Jassy. But all the railways to
Bucharest—from Craiova, Giurgiu, Pitesti, Ploesti, Kustenje—
approach the city by a single trunk from the west, *i.e.* the "safe"
side; and all the typical river-side towns stand on the "home"
bank with regard to Bucharest, *i.e.* the eastern bank in the west of
the country and the western bank in the east (cf. Craiova and
Slatina, Jassy and Galatz). It is equally typical that, except Sulina
and Galatz, no town is at the mouth of a river, because the lowness
of the left bank of the Danube and the great volume and rapid
descent of the affluents from the Carpathian watershed make their
lower courses too swampy and too much liable to flood to be either
safe or healthy. For the same reason practically all the river-side
towns are at the few points where the loess terrace actually touches
the river. Cf. Giurgiu, with its pipe-lines from Ploesti.

**Economic
Geo-
graphy.**   In the economic geography of this "old" part of the kingdom
two points are of special importance. It is really a non-Balkan area,
with almost the financial position of an ordinary European Power; so
its stable finance has encouraged foreign capital for the development
of the area, which is about equal to England, and has a population
(8,000,000) that increased more than 40 p.c. in the 40 pre-war
years. This development runs on three special lines—agricultural,
pastoral, and mineral. About 40 p.c. of the area is under cereals,
barley and oats covering respectively half as much area as wheat and

maize, with a yield that is slowly, but steadily, improving; and the
wheat is not only peculiarly heavy to the bushel, but also peculiarly
rich in gluten (cf. p. 207). The pastoral industry has been concerned
largely with export of live stock; but the great opening is for dairying
(including the raising of bacon), for at least 3,000,000 acres of the
Danubian swamp could be converted into most valuable polders quite
free from the typical local danger of drought. The mineral industry
is concerned mainly with the petroleum and salt. The oil-zone
extends over the whole anticline of the Carpathian foothills (300
miles × 10); the wells are very easily bored, 400 yards being an
exceptional depth; and the quality of the oil is excellent, that at
Bacau coming to the surface almost pure. The value of the total
yield 25 years ago was about £100,000; 15 years ago it was
£500,000; and the average for the next 5 years was about
£2,000,000. More than two-thirds of the 32,500,000 barrels (1929)
is raised now in the Targoviste (Dambovitza) district, especially at
Moreni; but one-third of the refineries are still in Ploesti (Prahova),
and one-fifth in Bacau. The oil is largely used mixed with lignite.

The distribution of population and facilities for transport, of **Distribu-**
course, reflect these conditions, Walachia being in both respects **tion of**
much more important than Moldavia. Walachia is a typical **Popula-**
agricultural area, even its towns being really huge villages with **tion.**
typically agricultural suburbs; and the density per square mile is
only 130 with the towns included as against 102 without them!
There are two chief zones of density—the old zone along the
Carpathian foot-hills, where both the Walachian [1] oil and the
Moldavian salt are found, and the new zone along the Danube,
where commerce gives a high density (75) considering the large
area of swamp. Forestry is an important industry at the back of
the upland zone, as fishing is on the front of the riverine zone—sea
and river fisheries being focused under Government control at Tulcea.
It is partly due to the use of oil-residue for fuel that transport both
by rail and by steamer is so good in spite of the practical absence of
coal; and perhaps nothing could illustrate the important relations
of the water and rail transport better than the relative size of the
great shipping port of Sulina (7100) and the rail and river junction
of Turnu Severin (90,000). Even in the war, with great improvements of the Iron Gates channel, up-stream traffic (*e.g.* 1,500,000
tons of grain and hay in 1916) was put on to *rail* at Orsova.

There are several other largish river ports, *e.g.* Giurgiu, and **River**
Galatz and Braila have populations of about 70,000; but they are all **Ports.**
unimportant compared with swamp-girt Sulina, with its massive jetties
and artificial channel. In the last fifty years the deltaic channel has
been shortened, *i.e.* straightened, by some 25 miles, and now has its

---

[1] Salt is also found in Walachia, *e.g.* at Ploesti and Campalung, as oil in
Moldavia, *e.g.* at Bacau.

depth maintained 50 p.c. lower (22 feet). Inside the great jetties there is smooth water when the wildest storms are raging on the Black Sea; along the new channel, though 12,000,000 tons of mud were estimated to be carried through it in 1910, it was never less than 21 feet deep except for four days in August; the old risks and delays of river navigation are avoided; and, above all things, the International Authority guarantees absolute equality of treatment to all vessels, and provides thirty floating grain-elevators. In recent years, then, about half the total amount of grain shipped out by the Danube has been transhipped (from lighters) at Sulina for export, but the percentage has fallen below 20. At this swamp-girt depot, with no exports of its own, no local industries, no possible local development of agriculture, British interests have been (in normal times) paramount.

The reasons for the choice of the particular branch are very

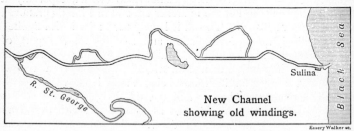

Lower Danube.

significant. Though the river falls only some 120 feet in the 600 miles between Orsova and Sulina, the régime guarantees a more or less violent current, as might be inferred from the way in which left-bank "tributaries" between Galatz and Sulina have been dammed back to form lakes. This suggests, too, that the Kilia branch, which carries two-thirds of the total volume, has also the strongest current. For that reason it was avoided, as was the main stream of the St. George branch; and the Sulina stream was chosen just because it carries only one-twelfth of the volume, with less force and less silt. The long jetties seen in the illustration, like similar ones at Newcastle (cf. p. 240), not only ensure river-silt being carried well out to sea but also prevent sea-silt from entering the river.

The New Territories. The new territories not only double the area and the population, but also the amount of arable land, of forest, and of salt; and the recent discoveries of natural gas near Kolozsvar are almost certainly associated with reservoirs of oil. Further, they supplement the mineral wealth of the old kingdom where it was most defective, in metals and coal. The latter is small in amount (c. 600,000 tons in 1922), but of good quality, and represented 40 p.c. of all the coal raised in pre-war Hungary. It is also found near both limestone and large deposits of fine iron, *e.g.* near Resicza-banya (with its output of 100,000 tons of iron a year); but any substitution of coal for charcoal will not improve the quality of the steel. Both the iron and the coal are in the highland part of the Banat, *i.e.* the part which may be reasonably linked with Transylvania; and Transylvania is said to be richer in gold than any other part of Europe outside Russia. At the same time, the new elements will not change the essential character of the kingdom; for, except in the Banat, everywhere at least 70 p.c. of the population is engaged in agriculture, even though the large proportion of forest in Bukovina and Transylvania has slightly decreased the percentage of the arable land.

Transylvania ("Beyond the Forest"), as its Latin name **Transyl-** implies, is separated from Hungary by the "Bihar" forest; but, **vania:** as its Magyar name (*Erdely*, "Forest-land") implied, it is itself **Physical.** heavily forested, nearly 40 p.c of the area being forested. It is a circular plateau basin, with relatively easy access into Hungary by the Szamos and the Maros valleys, but made into a natural fortress (*Siebenburgen*, "The Seven Strong Towns") by the lofty Carpathians and the Transylvanian Alps. In the dry climate within these mountain walls the rivers have cut wonderful ravines and cañons, the most remarkable being that by which the Aluta (Olt) works its way out in the Roteturm Pass. In each great valley there is a fertile plain; and, though the amount of arable land is small, there are magnificent pastures, on which excellent cattle and horses are reared. Flax and fruit are typical products. The main artery of the country is the valley of the Maros, which is only navigable to the 350-foot contour, near Arad; and it was a Roman thoroughfare to the salt mines of Torda (once Salinæ) *via* Gyula-Fehérvar ("White Castle of Julius"), now famous for its magnificent vineyards (Karlsburg). The connection northward *via* the Szamos valley and Satmar (Szath) is easy, and another Roman colony stood where the Szamos valley was tapped, at Cluj or Kolozsvar (Klausenburg). The connection southward into the Aluta basin was shortest and easiest *via* Nagy-Sibiu (Hermanstadt), which was said to be the capital of the Seven Strong Towns; and a legacy of its old importance, or a proof of the fertility of the Zibin valley (to the Aluta), is seen in its possession of the Transylvanian university. The natural continuation southward of the Upper Aluta valley had its objective at Brasso (Kronstadt), as the natural continuation northward of the Upper Ysil had its objective at Hatszeg; and both routes are now followed by railways. But neither pass could compete with the Aluta gorge, and east-and-west traffic went by the Maros—cf. the railway centres of Broos and Maros Vásárhely ("Maros Market")—not by the Aluta, where even Fogaras has only recently had rail connection.

**Transyl-vania :
Political.**

Transylvania, with its five nations, its five languages, its five creeds, was said to be an epitome and climax of the racial phenomena of the Dual Monarchy. The Hebrews are essentially sedentary and urban, as the Gypsies are essentially nomad and rural, though largely occupied in agriculture and gold-washing—*e.g.* in the Aranyos ("Golden") river. There are real Magyars and Magyar Szeklers, who speak almost pure Magyar. The latter claim to be descendants of Attila's Huns, but, as their name suggests (*Szekely*, "Frontier-Guard"), they are almost certainly Magyars transplanted by Ladislaus to Transylvania for strategic reasons—*i.e.* to hold the connection between Kronstadt and Maros Vásárhely *via* the Upper Aluta. They thus correspond exactly to the Saxons, who are the descendants of colonists brought from the Low Countries 800 years ago, to hold the passes and occupy the lands that had been devastated by the Turks. It was thus the land won its German title of Siebenburgen ; and their origin accounts for their being Protestants, while the Magyar population here is—generally—Roman Catholic or Unitarian. The typical Saxon centres are Kronstadt and Hermanstadt, in fertile basins on the Tömös and Roteturm routes respectively, protected by the mountains, and equipped for war—with stone houses, in wide shelterless streets, connected by underground passages, pivoting on a fortress-church, and the whole surrounded by a stockade. Much the largest element, however, is Rumanian all over the area ; and even where stone is abundant, they cling to the custom of their old home on the forest-girt loess of Walachia, and still build their houses of wood or of mud and wattle. Some of them, as shepherds, have typical transhumance habits ; but their focus is the wool-working town of Brasso (or Brasov), industrialised by the old German settlers. These "old" Transylvanian towns are in a much better position now than the "old" Alföld towns, even those on the railway skirting the plain, *e.g.* Satmur, Nagy Károly, and Nagy-Varad ("Great Fortress," *i.e.* Grosswardein), Békés and Gyula, Arad, and even Temesvar, which commands the Teregova Pass to Orsova ; for all these are now just inside the political frontier, cut off by a tariff barrier from their old economic hinterland and relationships.

Bukovina.

With nearness to the source of the summer-rains, *i.e.* the Black Sea, the area of forest spreads until it gives a name to the forested offshoot of the Carpathians that drains into the Danube, Bukovina ("Beech-Land"). The height of the range, which reaches 6100 feet, and the Danubian drainage linked the area originally to Moldavia, the old capital of which was Suczawa ; and 35 p.c. of the population is pure Rumanian. The relations with Russia and the large proportion of Ruthenians (40 p.c.) have in recent times been the controlling elements, and the province was more backward educationally than any other part of Austria except Dalmatia. With a relatively mild climate and a fertile soil the limited agriculture prospers; but nearly half the area is forested, and almost the only industries show a typical "forest" control, *e.g.* the paper of the marsh-girt capital and frontier fortress of Czernowitz (Cernauti), the glass of Radantz, the leather of Suczawa.

Bessarabia has been such a typical frontier land that it is poorly **Bessarabia.** provided with roads and railways; but it is very fertile, being mainly a typical wedge of Black Earth, similar in origin, relief, climate, soils, and products to the Russian—only rather better cultivated, jus. because it was so largely Rumanian in population. Nearly 70 p.c of it is actually under cultivation (maize and wheat, barley and tobacco); and the stock, as in the Banat and Transylvania, includes large numbers of horses and cattle, the latter especially south of a line from Bendéry to Akkerman. The standard of cultivation here will probably rise, as that of the Banat (famous under Hungary for both the yield and the quality of its wheat) may fall. Indeed, this has already happened so far as stock-raising is concerned. The number of cattle, pigs, and horses in the lands acquired from Hungary is falling, that in the lands acquired from Russia is rising. In the latter, too, an important vegetable-oil industry is developing, especially in the north, where it is based mainly on sunflower-seed, *e.g.* round Khotin, but also in the south, where it is based mainly on rape-seed, *e.g.* round Ismail.

The two great difficulties of the country are both related to the **Natural** Carpathian relief—political incoherence and difficult transport. **Incoherence.** A marked opposition seems to be growing up between the old kingdom (Regat) and the new territories; and it is in the latter that the chief transport difficulties are felt. For instance, the old Hungarian lands,—which produce all the iron, gold, and silver of the country, six-sevenths of its coal, more than half its salt, nearly half its natural gas, and more than a third of its timber,—are behind the Carpathian wall. There is nearly as much difficulty in getting Bukovina timber to Galatz, and even more in getting it to Danzig. There is, of course, abundance of oil-fuel, the total coal supply exceeds 3,000,000 tons (nearly 2,600,000, however, lignite), and the river is occasionally open the whole winter, *e.g.* in 1922–23; but the "season" does not begin till September, and the traffic is very badly balanced. Constanza is only a transit station (oil and grain), very poorly equipped, and badly linked to its political hinterland; Braila is merely an export—the chief export—centre; and nearly 40 p.c. of the vessels entering Galatz come in ballast.

CHAPTER XXIV

THE NEW BALTIC STATES

Balt States. THE three "Balt" States may be regarded as in a position rather different from that of Finland. For, owing partly to the result of historic oppression and partly to the absence of such special advantages—*e.g.* coal, harbours, scenery—as have justified the independence of Belgium, Holland, and Switzerland, not one of the three is quite capable of or fit for separate existence. As they are also closely similar in structure and relief, soil and climate, forming a single typical section of the Natural Trade Area of the Baltic, their proper destiny might seem to be in Federation; but they have no common history, or speech, or creed, or even human type. The Letts and Lithuanians are pure Europeans, speaking a very old Aryan tongue, while the Esths—like the Finns—are of Asiatic origin, and speak an Asiatic tongue; but even the two European peoples differ in creed, for the Lithuanians are Roman, while nearly 60 p.c. of the Letts are Protestant. There is really more in common between Esthonia and Finland, but their politico-economic relationships are very slight; and only between Esthonia and Latvia has there been, so far, any economic co-operation, including a permanent economic bureau at Riga, unification of harbour dues, and even a defensive alliance.

Port Rivalry. These three "Balt" States control four of the chief pre-war gateways of Russia—Reval (Tallinn), Windau (Ventspils), Libau (Liepaja), and Riga. Esthonia, the smallest state (18,350 square miles), has the longest coast; and Tallinn and its outport of Baltiski (Baltic Port) are most convenient for Petrograd (? Leningrad), and have a relatively large import trade, which will be increased by the new direct line from Tallinn to Moscow. Latvia, however, has two better ports in Ventspils and Liepaja, and a much larger commercial centre in Riga; and there is already direct rail communication from all three ports to Moscow, so that Latvia is far more important for exports than Esthonia is for imports, even though Baltiski is very seldom ice-bound, and during the past twenty-five years there have only been ten instances of vessels having to be diverted from Tallinn to Baltiski because of ice. Of course, Riga, at the landward end of a long bay, is much more troubled with ice. Lithuania, the largest state, though of disputed area, has not much more than a dozen miles of coast; and, even if she is able to dominate and greatly improve Memel, railways west of of the Dvina are not on the " Russian " gauge. Further, though she leads in population (more than half the 7,800,000 of the three states) as well as size, she is the most backward and suffered most in the war.

Structurally, the area is mainly a platform of old rock, with **Resources.** some variety of relief and soil from the "mask" of morainic deposits; and this means generally poor soil and a superabundance of peat bog, with wide stretches of coniferous forest. Indeed, timber is still a very important export, but has been exploited to such an extent that there is a good deal of " cleared " meadow and rough pasture. There is little mineral wealth except for peat; but Esthonia has beds of oil-shale and phospherite, and possesses also considerable water-power on the Narova, while Lithuania has some amber. Agriculture and forestry are, therefore, the mainstay of the people; and the breaking up of the large "Balt" estates has left the former in great confusion.

The agriculture is chiefly concerned with hardy grains (oats and **Agri-** rye), flax, and potatoes (for human consumption, alcohol, and cattle- **culture.** food); but various causes favour dairy-work, especially to the north. Flax, which was the chief crop grown for export, is losing ground, partly because of the rise in the cost of labour; the cheapness of Russian grain made grain-growing precarious; and the people have been cattle-raisers as far back as there are any records. But the spirit of oppressed nationality showed itself, at least amongst the Letts and the Esths, in a determined effort to raise the standard of civilisation, especially by education; and this and the lessons learnt from the Danes—incidentally to the transit butter trade, always dominated by Copenhagen—have led to a great development of co-operative farming, specialising in butter and eggs. For somewhat similar reasons the timber industry has been tending towards some specialisation in subordinate products, e.g. pulp, paper, and woodwork. Thus, either flax or forest products stand first on the list of exports for all the states; and, in all, industries are few and feeble, neither Riga nor Narva having their pre-war importance.

The Domberg crag at Tallinn was crowned by an Esthonian **Tallinn** fort in very early times, and the deep harbour in the shelter of the **and** castled crag attracted the Hansa merchants; and the town formerly **Narva.** profited greatly by its relative nearness to the industrial district round Petrograd, c. 62 p.c. of its total imports being cotton. It is more important than all the other Esthonian ports put together, the only others with any considerable tonnage being Pärnu and

Kuiwaste, the former mainly oceanic and the latter entirely coastal. Narva, the famous Rugodin of the Teutonic Knights, is still less flourishing. Historically, it was in turn the prey of Danes and Swedes and Russians, and in more recent times has been overwhelmed by its nearness to Petrograd. It has some importance as commanding the coast-railway in crossing the Peipus isthmus, but its only real life is associated with the textile industries that are supported by the falls on the Narova, with a potential power of 100,000 h.p.   Cf. Ugava (Mitau) on the Aa.

Riga.   Riga has always owed its importance to the (Western) Dvina. As the high granaries and huge cellars in the Old Town still suggest, it was founded as a storehouse, and became a very important member of the Hansa League, though its prosperity was somewhat hampered by its strategic importance, which involved it in the constant warfare of the Teutonic Knights, Poles, Swedes, and Russians.   Even after formal incorporation in Russia, it still suffered from the same cause, *e.g.* being burnt on the approach of the French in 1812 ; and the bar on the river and the exposure to frost and wind were for long adverse to its commercial growth.   Consequently, its population did not amount to 100,000 until within the last fifty years, when it rose to 500,000.   Its very speedy rise was due to its easy access by river and canal *via* Vitebsk to the basins of the Dnieper and the Volga.   At the same time, all the most important Russian railways had to converge on the south end of the Riga Gulf to reach " open " water, which made it supreme as an export centre, while the great development of industries in the Baltic Provinces made it also very important as an import centre, importing such significant products as coal, dye-woods, fertilisers, cotton, and rubber.   Improvements on the spot and at Ust-Dvinsk (protected by the castle of Dvinamünde) and the use of ice-breakers enabled the largest vessels to use the port at all seasons, so that its total trade was considerably more than double that of Windau, more than three times that of Libau, and nearly ten times that of Petrograd.   Under these circumstances, too, it naturally developed many local industries, *e.g.* in transport and other machinery, cotton and linen yarns, leather and oil.   Its future, however, is far from bright, and its population is now only 340,000 ; but its historic prestige—as that of Tartu (Dorpat)—or geographic inertia may enable it at least to hold its ground.

Libau and Widau.   The historic influence of Petrograd has been as adverse to the prosperity of other ports on the Gulf of Finland, *e.g.* Narva and Reval, as the modern influence of railways has been favourable to ports farther out on the Baltic itself, *e.g.* Windau and Libau.   The latter, the old Lyra Portus of the Livonian Order of the Sword, has a fine strategic site at the end of a sandy peninsula which cuts off the Libau lake or lagoon from the Baltic, and through which a canal was cut in the seventeenth century ; but it had to wait for railway connections, *e.g.* with Moscow and the Black Earth district, before it became prosperous. In the thirty years before the war its population more than trebled, and a large influx of visitors is attracted in summer by its facilities for bathing. Ventspils, which is also a large bathing centre, is surrounded by sand-dunes— evidence of the exposure to Atlantic gales to which it largely owes, like Liepaja, its freedom from ice; and what railways have done for it may be gauged from the fact that before the war its export of butter had risen to nearly 60,000 tons, valued at nearly £6,000,000.

The lands to the north of the Gulf of Finland are of the same **Finland :** essential type as those to the south of it, being low morainic lands **Isolation.** dotted with marsh and lake and covered with forest; both have felt the civilising influence of the sea; and both are essentially non-Russian in the character and influence of their people, though in both cases great efforts have been made to Russify the area. But, of course, the more northern latitude (60°-73° N.) involves a harder climate, and this fact and the secluded position of the area involve great isolation, especially in winter. The northern waters of the Gulf of Bothnia, like the eastern waters of the Gulf of Finland, begin to freeze in November; and by February the Finn coasts are often entirely blocked by accumulations of ice, which form a barrier of pack-ice right out into the Baltic. On the Bothnian coast, after the beginning of January, when Mäntyluoto and Raumo are frozen up, Åbo is the only port that can be entered; and in the Gulf of Finland Viborg is closed in November, and Helsingfors early in January, so that only Hangö remains open. Ice-breakers can be used with some advantage at Åbo and Hangö, but even there, just because of the exposure to the S.W. gales, which helps to keep them open, the ice-barrier is often exceptionally large. Though they are more favoured in climate, and have some fine harbours, the Åland Islands are of strategic rather than commercial value; and though the North Atlantic "Drift" keeps Pechenga always free from ice in spite of its latitude (*c.* 70° N.), its hinterland is so bleak and barren as to be almost unpeopled.

The Finns are even more interesting than the Letts, and their **Finland :** land has a stronger fascination than can be felt for the relatively **Relief.** young sandstones and limestones of the Baltic Provinces; for its crystalline platform is perhaps the oldest expanse of rock on the face of the earth, while its glacial mantle is, geologically, but of yesterday. After centuries of wandering—from "summer drought" over Alpine [1] crest to "summer rain," or from southern steppe over

---

[1] The evidence of, *e.g.*, their great epic (*Kalevala*) is somewhat opposed to Ripley's suggestion (cf. pp. 80, 81), and their Ural-Altaic speech remains a real difficulty, even if it is freely admitted that speech can never be pressed as a test of race; but physiologists support Ripley because they will not as yet admit the direct climatic control of somatic qualities. One thing, however, is certain : no one who is familiar with the Economic Geography of the Baltic area believes that any part of that area

gold-bearing Urals to northern lake-land—the Finns found themselves isolated on a huge slab of grey granite, destined to be a buffer between Slav and Scandinavian. This slab, like the Baltic Provinces, slopes gently gulfward and seaward; and in the Great Ice Age it was worn into shallow depressions and covered with slight upswellings. These ridges of boulder-clay are too near the source of the ice-flow to radiate much, and run almost parallel with one another from N.W. to S.E., forming the shores of innumerable lakes left by the melted ice. As the country slopes gently, but steadily, down towards the south-west, these lakes overflow by short cascades across their south-western barriers; and the richest land —partly old lake floor—lies in a belt from east to west through the heart of the lake-land, securely cut off from the Gulf shore by the rough barren obstacles of the terminal moraines. Here, in times of danger, when the people were driven back from the coast-land, there was a maze of forested marsh and lake (*Suomi*, "Fenland"), in which food and safety were assured. In times of peace, on the other hand, the relations between the relatively fertile interior and the coast led to considerable development of the barren intermediate area, although to this day the main line from Viborg to Hangö runs not *via* Helsingfors and the marshy coast, but along the top of the relatively dry moraines that form the southernmost shore of the lakes; and the water-power is as valuable—to a country that has no coal—as it is superabundant (a potential 3,000,000 h.p.).

Finland: Climate.   The slope admits the S.W. Anti-Trades to every part of the country, and the lake-land is in the regular path of the winter cyclones—a condition very favourable to the growth of hardy trees, such as Scotch pine, fir, and birch; and latitude, forest, and high humidity have combined to bleach the people into the purest blonde type—though their stature may have been rather lessened and their heads broadened by intermarriage with Lapps, *or* their stature increased and their heads lengthened by intermarriage with Teutons. The climatic influence is illustrated, too, by the fact that the mean annual temperature only varies 1° over the whole country; that it averages 37° F., *i.e.* fully 10° F. higher than the normal for that latitude; that it deviates from the normal specially in winter; and that the coldest month, at least over the area of densest population, is February. Over 70 p.c. of the land is still forested, and clearings being devoted to pasture and barley, and—in recent times—to potatoes and beetroot; and the export trade of the country is absolutely dominated by "forest" control, the chief items being timber, wood-pulp (raw and manufactured), and dairy products. Two influences are of special importance. One is that, owing to

---

was the *source* of great migrations of men in the earliest times. So *initial* movements with regard to the area are represented here, *e.g.* pp. 105 and 282, as being inward, not outward.

the relatively late winter, the maximum snowfall ($2\frac{1}{2}$ feet to 3 feet) does not accumulate until the middle of March, and a month later a short spring of rapidly increasing temperature puts the whole amount, so to speak, at the service of growing vegetation in a land where the shortness of the summer puts a premium on quick growth, and where the annual rainfall does not exceed 25 inches. The other is that the cheapest way of clearing the forest, and the way always adopted till recently, was by fire; and the top-dressing of potash thus secured was, in such a climate, exceedingly favourable to the growth of pastoral grasses and such hardy plants as barley and flax. The export of forest products—mainly as news-paper, sawn timber, and wood-pulp—has an average value four times that of all other products, Björneborg and Abo,[1] Viborg and Uleaborg, being special export centres; Hangö exports specially bobbins (of birch wood) and butter.

Industrial development is mainly in textiles, though there is **Finland:** abundance of fine iron-ore between Åbo and Helsingfors and **Industries** between Kuopio and Viborg; and the chief centre is, of course, towards the humid south-west, at Tammerfors, which is very conveniently situated for water-power and for access to a variety of ports—Helsingfors and Hangö, Åbo and Björneborg, and even Wasa. Cotton is the chief material handled; and the ports which supply Tammerfors with the raw material (and with food, especially coffee and bread-stuffs) have begun to work the cotton, e.g. Björneborg and Wasa. The old capital of Åbo, now only the ecclesiastical capital, has a fine strategic position behind the Åland archipelago, and it used to build vessels (torpedo boats) for the Russian navy; but the political capital and the national university were moved to Helsingfors, mainly because of its nearness to Russia, and because it has a fine, double, deep-water harbour well protected by the fortified island of Sveaborg. Viborg has a somewhat similar position, protected by the naval station of Björkö; and the Saima Canal gives it access to the chief lake of the country, with its 700 square miles of navigation. It is a very popular tourist centre, e.g. for the famous Imatra rapids, which fall over 100 feet in 4 miles between Lake Saima and Lake Ladoga, and from its castle Christianity spread in olden days. With its outport of Trångsund, it comes next to Helsingfors (above it in 1923) as a port, and is said to be the largest timber harbour in Europe. Cf. Koivisto (Björkö) and Kotka.

[1] The new names are Helsinki (Helsingfors), Turku (Åbo), Tempere (Tammerfors), and Viipuri (Viborg).

CHAPTER XXV

RUSSIA

Historic Expansion. THE initial idea in the expansion of Muscovy was to follow the two drainage slopes included in the original unit, the northward slope to the Arctic Ocean, and the southward slope to the Caspian Sea. Ivan III. saw the complete expansion over the former between Lapland and the Urals, and Ivan IV. saw the complete expansion over the latter between the Donetz and the Urals, so that by A.D. 1584 Russia spanned Europe from north to south. It remained for Peter the Great to add the Baltic Provinces, and for Catharine II. to link up the Baltic Sea with the Black Sea and the Sea of Azof, thus linking the Black Sea with the Caspian by A.D. 1796. Except, then, for the strip of frontier joining the Dniester and the Bug between Kovno and Lemberg, the whole of the pre-war frontier westward from the Tana to the Pruth was the creation of quite modern times.

Isolation. This implies centuries of a practical isolation from the rest of Europe, which largely accounts for some of the historic drawbacks of Russia, and which would justify its geographic exclusion from what is typically European, even if it were not non-European also in relief and climate. The worst of those drawbacks was that the land remained untouched by the intellectual stimulus of the Renaissance or by the religious stimulus of the Reformation; but scarcely less adverse were the obligation to face unaided invasion from the steppe by Tatar pagans—who presently became Muhammedans, but remained always Asiatics,—and the fact that European Christianity had been received *via* the Black Sea, *i.e.* in a debased Byzantine form.

Sea Frontier. Although a considerable part of the frontier is still sea, it is almost true to say that the sea portion is less useful, if less dangerous, than the land portion. As we have seen (pp. 14-16), the four seas in question are all typical inland seas, either absolutely landlocked or provided with ocean-links that are so narrow as to be dangerous to shipping even in time of peace, and very easily held and fortified in time of war. In any case, ice renders them practically useless for months every year except at one or two points, or with great expenditure, *e.g.* on ice-breakers, etc.

418

Strategically, the White Sea is faultless, for it has direct access **White Sea** to the Arctic Ocean, and the entrance is through the narrow Gorlo **Basin.** Strait (48 miles); but this very fact, added to its division into three landlocked bays, makes it so much exposed to continental influences that large portions of it are frozen for eight months (October-May). On the other hand, its intimate relations with the basins of the Northern Dvina, the Onega, and the Mezeñ, give it large supplies of fish-food, and it has in consequence very valuable fisheries, especially for herrings. Though the Onega is more or less navigable right up to Lake Lache—from which, and *not* from Lake Onega, it flows—it is of infinitely less importance than the Northern Dvina. For the latter is a much finer river, flowing for over 1000 miles in a wide, low, flat valley; it is formed, like so many rivers in Asiatic Russia, by two large "tributaries" from opposite directions; it is completely free of ice from their confluence at Kotlas to Archangel for nearly six months (middle of May to beginning of November) every year; the Sukhona rises as far west as the Onega, and the Vychegda as far east as the Mezeñ; and the one is joined to the Neva, and the other to the Kama, by canal. Archangel is, therefore, much the most important port; it was the first, and for a long time the only, seaport that Russia possessed; and, though its mean annual temperature is only 1° above freezing, it is still a really busy and valuable harbour both for purely Russian and for Siberian produce.

The tiny Baltic frontier, though more favoured commercially, **Baltic** is inferior strategically and not much superior climatically; and the **Coast.** best strategic positions, *e.g.* those of Kronstadt and Leningrad, suffer climatically from being at the eastern head of a long gulf. The port of Leningrad can be kept open by gigantic ice-breakers fully six weeks after the Neva itself is frozen up, and the restricted channel for foreign communication can be maintained throughout the winter, but only with great difficulty and at great cost.

Leningrad has been, however, a most important harbour, **Lenin-** even from a purely commercial point of view. For the Russian **grad:** lake-land plays, climatically and commercially, much the same part **Geo-** between the White Sea and the Gulf of Finland as the Swedish lake-**graphic.** land plays between the Kattegat and the Gulf of Bothnia, with Leningrad playing the part of Göteborg and the Neva that of the Gota. The isthmus between Lake Ladoga and the Gulf is not 30 miles wide, and the importance of the river as route or barrier across its southern end had been recognised ages before the days of Peter the Great. From very early times trade had worked northward down the Volkhof from Novgorod, and the town established fortresses on the lake end and on the sea end of the river, at Schlüsselburg and Peterhof; but a Swedish fortress at the confluence of the Ochta with the Neva, *i.e.* the apex of the delta, prevented permanent occupa-

tion even of the south bank of the river.   At last, in A.D. 1703,
Peter the Great took this fortress (of Landskrona), and proceeded
to secure both banks by building the fortress of St. Peter and St.
Paul—beside a cathedral dedicated to the same two saints—on the
large island in the mouth of the Neva 3 miles farther west.   This
island, since then known as Petersburg, and the corresponding
Basil's Island divide the Neva into three branches, thus forming a great
obstacle to flood-water ; and, as their deltaic origin puts them very
little (10 or 11 feet at the most) above the normal level of the river,
they are easily flooded when strong westerly gales "hold up" the
river, or when easterly winds in spring drive block-ice down from
Lake Ladoga.   Consequently, the main part of the city now is on
the peninsula made by the river on the south-eastern edge of the
delta, and it was here that Peter had his first shipbuilding yard
erected ; but the commercial centre remains on the landward end of
Basil's Island, which is connected by a ship-canal (c. 18 miles long
and fully 22 feet deep) with the outport of Kronstadt on the landward end of Kotlin Island.   This obviates the banks and rocks
which cumber the seaward front of the delta ; and the peninsula is
crossed by a series of roughly concentric canals, by which flood-
water can not only make its escape, but also be concentrated on
the line of the ship-canal.   As the river, of course, brings no silt out
of Lake Ladoga, and gathers little in descending the (navigable)
Ostrovki rapids, it is only the actual flood-water that causes
much trouble.

Lenin-
grad :
Political.

In spite of all the expense thus involved, the city even before
the war was not increasing in importance.   It has a detestable
climate, and its site was a pile-studded marsh—which cost the lives
of thousands of the original builders ; and since railways began to
develop the southern and western provinces of Russia by intercourse with Europe, the less favoured provinces on the Lower Volga
have relatively fallen into the background.   Thus Leningrad lost the
old advantage of being the commercial "mouth" of the Volga, and
lost it just at the time when the Baltic ports of Libau and Riga
were beginning to grow.   Cheap railway fares, great financial
encouragement of industries, and the growth of centralised administration did maintain the city in much of its old political importance,
and immensely increased its economic importance, but not as a
port.   Even politically it suffered from the rapid increase of
population in the Black Sea hinterland, though it still remained
"the interpreter to Russia of West European civilisation"—a
position won in the days when it became a profoundly cosmopolitan
centre under the influence of the innumerable foreigners who
flocked to it to supply the maritime commerce that the country
itself could not supply.   But even as the political capital of the
empire, it was always handicapped by the fact that the Baltic coast-

lands south of the Neva were specifically not Slav, but German
("Balt"), while north of the Neva they were not Slav, but Finn.

In spite of the place in history taken by the Crimean War, **Black Sea.**
the Black Sea coast of Russia is relatively unimportant except
from the purely economic point of view; and even in this respect
it must be remembered that its possession by Russia is comparatively recent, and its development correspondingly primitive.
For instance, the great port of Odessa is at present served
by only *one* line of railway, and that is practically a strategic line,
running north-westwards parallel with the frontier—just east of the
Dniester—*i.e. not* towards Russia, but towards Poland and Germany.
This is partly remedied now by the construction of a line running
north-eastwards, but it runs *via* the head of navigation on the Bug
at Voznesensk, so that it will help to feed the inferior ports of
Nikolaief and Kherson, which are already provided with rail into
the Dnieper basin. Indeed, Odessa would be in a much worse
position than it is, if it were not that it has the most favourable
site for commanding Russian sea-trade with the East, and that
it has had a large and able Jewish population. Again, the ports
at the head of the Perekop Gulf have been hitherto entirely
neglected, *e.g.* Khorli and Shadovsk, although they enjoy even more
climatic advantages than Odessa (cf. p. 15). Cf. Theodosia.

The Sea of Azof is so much shallower, fresher, more exposed, **Sea of**
and more shut in by land, than the Black Sea, that its navigation is **Azof.**
very precarious, even apart from the silt brought down by the Don.
If that river were diverted bodily *via* the Manych Depression into
the Caspian, both the sea itself and its climatic influence would be
greatly improved; and it would then be quite practicable to make
and maintain a deep channel from Taganrog and Rostof to the
Kerch Strait, and this would be almost equally useful to the coal
port of Mariopol and the grain ports of Berdiansk and Yeisk.

From these Azof ports, in normal times, 45 p.c. of the Russian ex- **Berdiansk**
port of wheat comes. Rostof, much the most important, does 17 p.c.; **and Yeisk.**
the sheltered "Riviera" port of Novorossiskaya—which, like
Theodosia, is counted an Azof port, though actually on the Black Sea
—does 9 p.c.: and, as a rule, Taganrog stands third on the list.
Nikolaief and Kherson are always among the first six ports—which is
not always the case with Odessa, but all three together are not as
important as Rostof, though navigation is possible on the Dnieper
for 250 days in the year against only 230 on the Don. And the
reason for the importance of these Azof ports is that the spring
wheat belt lies parallel with the rain-bearing S.W. winds, *i.e.* north-
eastward from the Azof, along the July isotherm of 71° F., on
both sides of the Lower Don, while the winter wheat is mainly
confined to the lowland immediate east and south-east of the Azof.

In its essential plan European Russia somewhat resembles **Area.**

France, for it consists of a central plateau surrounded by lowlands which span Europe from north to south, and which rise outwards to frontier heights—plateau or mountain, *e.g.* Finland and the Sarmatian platform, the Urals and the Caucasus. There, however, the resemblance to France largely ends; for of all the essential characteristics of the area the two most significant are enormous area and profound uniformity, each of which tends to intensify the climatic influence of the other. Even north of the Manych Depression from the Sea of Azof to the Caspian, pre-war Russia exceeded 2,000,000 square miles, including some fifty Governments. At least thirty of them contained about 20,000 square miles apiece; three of them contained 120,000, *i.e.* were as large as the United Kingdom; and one, that of Archangel, contained 320,000, *i.e.* was equal to the United Kingdom and France put together.

Population.
Although this has been reduced by over 550,000 square miles, Russia still contains a total population of probably quite 150,000,000; but, compared with the area, these millions of people are relatively insignificant. The average value of the individual is, therefore, at a minimum; even towns are normally of little or no importance outside a limited area in the west; only on the rich Black Earth is population really perceptible—one reason for, as well as one result of, population moving steadily southwards. On the steppe-lands the aver-

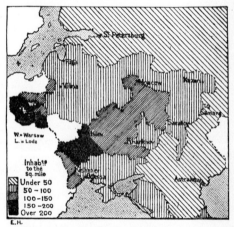

W = Warsaw
L. = Lodz

Inhab⁺⁹
to the
sq. mile
Under 50
50 – 100
100–150
150 –200
Over 200

European Russia. Density of population—pre-war.

age per square mile is 3 persons; in the forest it is 15; on the Black Earth it is 75. The total urban population is only 12 p.c. of the whole—apart from a temporary inflow into the towns; and the significance of it is even less if only real Russians are included. For one-third, and the most vigorous third, of the urban population is foreign—alien alike in blood, in creed, in speech, and to some extent in political and economic interests. One result of this is that urban influence, so far from civilising the rural areas, only complicates their economic and political problems, especially in parts where the mass of the land belongs to the peasants; and, as a matter of fact, there are nearly 100,000,000 peasants holding land that in the aggregate is ten times the area of England and Wales.

This "incoherence," or even antagonism, between town and country is further complicated by incoherence, if not antagonism, between province and province; and recent events have produced more or less chaos in an area where enormous size had already made political coherence a matter of great difficulty. In this case the attempt to push to extremes the doctrine of self-determination had a plausible excuse in the very incoherence of the huge area, and in the existence within it of marked "racial" grouping; for these did call for a wide application of decentralisation, *i.e.* the concentration of local government in each major natural region, with its particular type of people and life. And, as a matter of fact, the various "republics" and "autonomous provinces" do more or less correspond to geographical units and ethnic groups. For there are three main groups in Russia which may be roughly called Russian, Finn, and Tatar; and the Russian peoples are sub-divided into three main branches—Great, Little, and White Russians. Further, the Great Russians have always been essentially the people of the forested morainic plateau, though they now— nominally and politically—reach the Caspian and the Black Sea; their natural capital was always Moscow, and their real sphere of influence was the Volga or Caspian basin. The Little Russians have always been essentially the people of the rich steppe-lands, with their expanses of Black Earth; but they have spread north-westward into the rich forest and south-eastward into the poor steppe, and their sphere is the Black Sea hinterland. The White Russians have always been essentially the people of the forested Baltic lake-land west of the Dvina, where they have been "bleached" by forest-shade and high humidity until they are truly *white*; but nearness to the sea, which maintained that humidity even in winter, and which brought them into touch with the quickening life of the Nordics, led to the intermarriage that accounts for their being taller and longer-headed than either the Great or the Little Russians. For their limestone was more fertile than the morainic platform of Great Russia, and their occupational control did not favour most the survival of the stocky, dwarfed "groom" type, as in Little Russia.

The idea underlying the political subdivisions of the Empire was equality of population, which involved great inequality of area; and the Soviet at once decided to reverse this, giving "independence" to each group of subdivisions that seemed to correspond with a natural geographic region and its ethnic group. Thus emerged "the Russian *Federated* Socialist Soviet Republic." But the possession of power and the experience of the actual working of the arrange-ment revolutionised the ideas of the revolutionists, with the result that since 1922 there has been a determined revival of centralisa-tion, and the title of the political unit has actually been changed to "the Union of Socialist Soviet Republics." Cf. p. 129.

Internal Isolation. Besides the insignificance of the Man compared with the Place, Man is insignificant to Man. For the huge distances involve profound isolation. Roads—such as they are in a land where "metal" is as rare as marsh is common—are measured by the thousand miles; inns are practically unknown; railways are discouraged by the excellent navigation and sledge-traffic on the rivers, and are so short of rolling-stock that they cannot cope with the long distances and interminable delays. In fact, size exercises a physical tyranny from which, to the ordinary peasant, escape is impossible. It is little wonder that his most typical trait is a perfectly pathetic humility, based on a most vivid realisation of his own insignificance; and he is, even when apparently immeasurably degraded, profoundly religious—standing in church, "as in the presence of an earthly king," and minimising the value of any human intermediary between his God and himself.

Relief. But uniformity of relief is as vital a factor as size. The land lies in a rough square, measuring *c.* 1600 miles each way; and from the Caspian to the Baltic, from the White Sea to the Black, from the Urals to the Carpathians, it is practically one boundless plain. Indeed, as far as relief only is concerned, the uniformity is simply paralysing, leaving no possible opening for human variety or human initiative (cf. p. 61). It is only within geologically recent times that the land emerged either from under an arm of the Arctic Ocean or from under a wide mantle of ice; and, therefore, vast areas present an absolutely monotonous surface, the mass being of Tertiary or Quaternary formation and never disturbed by folding or volcanic action. This has a certain political value, for it undoubtedly breeds a unity of political environment and interest, as it has moulded a curious mixture of races into a definite (and unattractive) Russian type—with the ruddiness of hair and the greeny-grey eye that are so typical of hybrids. But the unattractiveness of the type may be the test of the moral and mental harm done to the individual.

Water-parting. Where the relief does rise slightly above the general level, it does so only in the form of broad and gentle swellings, the most important of which forms the main water-parting of the country. It runs right across the country from near Brest Litovsk, maintaining an almost due N.E. direction, *i.e.* parallel with the lie of the great lake-system and with the normal path of cyclonic systems; and its average height—which is also its normal height—is *c.* 800 feet. But, as it reaches a breadth of 700 miles, its actual height is imperceptible. The scenic and topographic effect is exaggerated by the fact that, through the normally horizontal strata in the relatively dry climate, the rivers have cut their beds down almost to sea-level, and now flow at the bottom of a ravine which one cannot see at all until one stands on the brink of the precipice formed by the bank.

Of course, this is most true of the central plateau, with its average height of 800 to 900 feet; and it is least true of the Baltic lowland, which does not often exceed 300 feet, *i.e.* 100 to 200 feet lower than the rest of the lowlands which surround the plateau.

Over this vast area of profound uniformity climatic conditions, **River-** past and present, have imposed an added tyranny. The whole **system.** country north of 50° N. and west of the eastern limits of the Don basin is covered with a thick mantle of boulder clay and other glacial deposits, which radiated from the Scandinavian ice-centre; and the clay is often in long broad ridges which are close together in the north-west, but get wider and wider apart as they advance eastward and southward. Between these ridges, after the melting of the great ice-sheet, immense lakes collected, linked together by actually broad, but relatively narrow, straits; and the sites of these lakes are now covered with lacustrine deposits or with marsh, while their main channels, *e.g.* through the straits, are perpetuated in the existing rivers. South of 50° N. the grass-lands are covered, especially on their upswellings, with Black Earth (cf. pp. 74-76). The loess by itself would be too porous, but the humus enables it to economise the water-supply; the boulder clay is absolutely impervious, but it lies in ridges, and is often mixed with gravel and sand and mud, while a gradual upheaval[1] that is going on towards the north-west materially assists drainage.

These are the conditions under which the relentless uniformity **Climatic** of structure and relief are intensified by a climatic control that **Control.** shows itself in enormous areas of uniform vegetation or absence of vegetation—leagues of tundra followed by leagues of coniferous forest, followed by leagues of deciduous forest, followed by leagues of rich steppe, followed by leagues of poor steppe. The tundras extend over the whole area where there is no sunshine in winter, and where the summer sunshine is "filtered" through ubiquitous fog; and, as these conditions imply temperatures below zero in winter and not much above freezing-point in summer, the soil is permanently frozen — except on the surface for a few weeks in midsummer—and there is very little precipitation. As soon as the latitude allows of the warmest month in the year having a temperature of 50° F., and relief and exposure allow of an annual rainfall of over 10 inches, forests of short-rooted conifers can begin to flourish—stunted towards the tundra frontier, where they merge in the shrubs, dwarf birches, and various "berries" of the southern latitudes of the tundra, and little better than dense thickets in the marshes, but covering thousands of square miles between the Baltic and the Urals. As the summer temperature rises, the need for needle-shaped and evergreen leaves decreases;

---

[1] This is slightly increasing the power of the rivers, especially in the south, to cut cañon-like gorges.

and, as the relatively deficient rainfall is more than compensated—for long-rooted trees—by the water-bearing soil, the land is still largely covered with deciduous forest from the Carpathians to the Urals. Where approach to "Mediterranean" latitudes involves the failure of rain-bearing winds by the time of maximum temperature, while the Ural-Caspian Gap gives easy access to icy winds in winter, grass-land replaces forest ; for, even if the absence of moisture in the hottest season and the presence of wind in the coldest season were not fatal to trees, the latter grow so slowly that they would be—and millions of tiny trees actually are every year—smothered and killed by the quick-growing grasses and bulbous plants. Thus the tyranny of size and the tyranny of relief are supplemented by a climatic tyranny which imposes over thousands of consecutive square miles a monotony of plant life that favours no variety of occupation and interest, and therefore no individuality or initiative to human life.

Temperature. But the tyranny of the climatic control does not stop here. For just as the absence of physical obstacles made political expansion easy, especially eastwards, so it makes rapid distribution of climatic phenomena easy, with the result that the average annual temperature scarcely varies 20° F. between the extreme north and the extreme south—as far as the Crimea. Indeed, the difference between the average annual temperatures of Odessa and Archangel is sometimes not more than that between the top and the foot of Ben Nevis. Even at Archangel the summer temperature reaches 85° F. ; and even on the Black Sea coast the range of temperature exceeds 100° F., frosts lasting till the end of April and returning at the beginning of October.

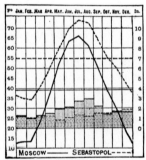

Rainfall and temperature of Moscow and Sebastopol.

No place seems to have an average temperature much lower than that of Archangel (*c.* 33° F.), and none has one very much higher than Odessa (49° F.) ; and the winter isotherms cross the summer ones almost at right angles, Odessa being on about the same (25° F.) as Minsk in winter, while Moscow is on the same (66° F.) as Minsk in summer. So Leningrad and Kharkof are on the same (15° F.), and Archangel and Kazan on the same (7° F.), in winter, while Bobrüisk and Perm are on the same (65° F.), and Ekaterinoslaf and Orenburg on the same (71° F.), in summer.

Winds. The climate is, of course, essentially continental, temperatures being occasionally recorded as low as − 54° F., and as high as 109° F., while most places have an extreme range of from 130° F. to 140° F., and record their minimum in January ; but cyclonic

influences from the Atlantic do reach the country, working across
the great lakes in winter and across the belt of deciduous forest in
summer—much to the advantage of the forest.   It follows that the
regular wind in the west is a westerly or south-westerly one ; but
the contra-clock movement involves a constant inflow from the east
and south-east, while the regular wind in the south-east is almost
always easterly.   This involves many difficulties.   For instance, an
Anti-Trade inflow may cause a temporary thaw which "mires"
felled timber ; or a cold blast from the east may make the flax-pits
too cold for retting purposes.   But the great trouble is the strength
and velocity of the winds, especially in winter, when terrific storms
sweep the country, and cover all the leagues of tundra, forest, and
steppe, with endless leagues of snow.

 The climate is, therefore, in many ways as unfavourable to the **Naviga-**
river-system as the relief is favourable.   The rivers start in lakes or **tion.**

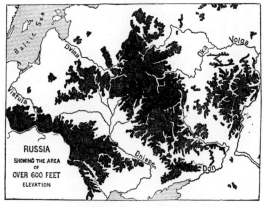

Eastern Europe.   Area above 600 feet in black.

vast marshes, they have a very gentle gradient, and they have to
meander round the central plateau, thus developing enormous basins
and giving every advantage for a circuit of navigation by river and
linking canal round the plateau.   They have, therefore, from very
early times been almost the only channels of movement—for trade
and migration, and have exercised a most potent influence on
national unity.   They have even contributed what little variety of
relief the country does possess, for the "hills" of the more elevated
areas are due simply to the river-erosion ; and they have made it
possible for a country, the mass of which drains naturally away from
the Atlantic, to have its foreign trade concentrated on the Baltic.
The Volga, Dnieper, and Don have lengths respectively of *c.* 2300,
c. 1400, and *c.* 1300 miles, with basins of *c.* 560,000, *c.* 200,000,
and *c.* 170,000 square miles.   But they suffer from ice in winter

and from drought in summer, and their gradient is too slight to give them much power over obstacles in their beds ; and where such disturbances are rarest, other causes greatly affect their value. For instance, the Petchora is navigable for nearly 800 miles, but—until linked by canal to the Kama—it was entirely isolated from Russia by the Timan ridge. The Onega, which has a most useful position, is marsh-girt and spoilt by rapids. The Dvina-Vychegda is navigable for over 800 miles, but flows through almost unpeopled forest to an estuary which it has not strength to keep free from débris. Contrariwise, the Dnieper, with its very important navigable tributaries—Beresina, Pripet, and Desna—serves a relatively dense population in a very rich area that has a relatively favourable climate ; but it has *c.* 50 miles of dangerous rapids just below its chief town, Ekaterinoslaf, which choke up its mouth with débris, while its upper waters for months are either frozen or too shallow for safe navigation. Indeed, it is only during the melting of the snow in spring—when the peasants are too busy on the land to have time for anything else—that the rivers of the country are normally navigable as a system.

Distribution of People. The distribution of population is, however, very closely related to the river-system. In the north the flat swellings that form the water-partings are largely marshy and covered with peat bogs, so that population is attracted to the river banks for lumbering and the growing of barley in cleared areas. In the south the unglaciated water-partings are too dry, and population is attracted to the broad valleys for growing wheat and rye. Even in the mining areas the river is still the prime factor, *e.g.* the Donetz in the southern coal-field and the Chusovaya and the Issek in the platinum and copper districts of the Ural. And, as the trend of almost all the great rivers is essentially southward, the population would have tended to gravitate southward as soon as Turkish rule was driven across the Black Sea, even if the rewards of labour had not also been much greater on the Black Earth.

Centres of Population. Now a proposal has been made to reorganise the land (cf. p. 424) on economic function, the boundaries of the economic regions being drawn in such a way and their capitals being located in such positions as to discourage in every way any separatist (ethnic, political, or economic) aspirations. To-day, Great Russia is the base of the Russian Socialist Soviet Republic ; but, though there are practically no Great Russians north of 60° N., *i.e.* the southern limit of unworked forest, the Republic extends to the White Sea and the Arctic Ocean, and includes more than half the White Russians and a fraction of the Little Russians. Little Russia, *i.e.* the Republic of the Ukraine, is relatively large, and contains Kief, Kharkof, Odessa, and nearly all the great wheat ports except Rostof ; but the White Russia Republic is a mere strip of forest " hanging from "

Minsk.   On each flank of the Archangel province of Great Russia there is a Finn province—"The Workers' Community of the Caulians" and the autonomous Province of the Zyrians ; and on each line of Turko-Tatar movement from Asia there is a group of tiny Tatar Republics, *e.g.* round Ufa and Kazan and in the Crimea.

Whether judged by the density per square mile of the Govern- **Centres of** ments or by the number of towns there have been three centres **Popula-** of population—the largely urban and suburban district round **tion.** Leningrad, with perhaps an average density of 150 per square mile ; the Moscow district, which contains nearly two-thirds of all the chief industries ; and the Black Earth, with, possibly, two-thirds of the total population of the country on less than two-fifths of its total area, the density in parts of Kief, Poltava, and Podolia being over 250 per square mile.   In the Leningrad district the density is a relic of the past, for the importance of the city is steadily declining now that it has been replaced by Moscow as capital—though the change obviously implies no denial of aspirations to intrude into European politics.   But the historical and economic interest of the neighbourhood has been very great, especially in the case of Novgorod and Pskof.   Both were "lake-end" towns, and neither was actually on its lake.   The first Slav forts were, indeed, where the Volkhof leaves Lake Ilmeñ, but Viking intruders built a "New Town" (hence *Nov-gorod*) on the riverside terrace below the lake 1100 years ago.   Thus Novgorod, unlike Pskof, commanded all approach by water from the Baltic to its lake and so to the Volga, and became the "Sovereign" of a number of centres in the safe seclusion of the marshy lake-land.   It was ruled for centuries by a Common Council, and had a population of fully 80,000, possibly 100,000.   This has now fallen to *c.* 25,000, for the Msta Canal joins the Volkhof below the town, and the great railways to the south ignore it in favour of its two old rivals, Pskof and Tver. In the Moscow area, though the land is less favourable to agriculture, there is also mineral wealth, commerce is greatly encouraged by the central site and its relation to the mighty Volga, and the area has been protected from nomad raids and isolated from the Black Earth—by a narrow belt of hillocky rough land (the chief oats-growing area) that runs across the country below Tula.

This Moscow industrial district consists essentially of two **Moscow** large towns, Moscow itself (2,000,000) and Tula (150,000), with **District :** a large number of small towns closely associated with them in **Textiles.** position and economic interest ; but the textile centre of Moscow is, of course, much more important than the hardware centre of Tula.   The most important branch of industry is in cotton, pre-war Russia in this respect coming third in Europe and fourth in the world, mainly because she had an assured home market with a growing population, and because—unlike all her European rivals—she produced more than half the cotton that she used; and the Moscow district has probably about 80 p.c. of all the spindles in Russia to-day, though most of them seem to be idle.   Labour here has always been cheap, partly because supplied by girls and young women (under thirty), the usual proportion of female workers being 41 p.c. in wool, 48 p.c. in cotton, and 62 p.c. in silk.   The cotton industry extends more or less over all the provinces that touch that of Moscow—Vladimir, Tver, Smolensk, Kaluga, Tula, and Riazan; but it was developed specially through Vladimir to the "Volga" provinces of Yaroslaf and Kostroma, which have special facilities for handling the Russian river-borne raw material.   Moscow and Vladimir have been the most important both for spinning, in which the former is slightly the more important (4 : 3), and for weaving, in which Vladimir is the more important (3 : 2), while Kostroma weaves, and Yaroslaf spins; and all four were prospering in 1914—at the expense of the Baltic area—because the consumption of Russian-grown cotton shipped by the Volga had doubled since 1900.[1]   In the linen industry, of course, the raw material is all home-grown, but the "Volga" provinces still have the advantage, especially Kostroma, Yaroslaf, and Vladimir, Kostroma specialising in weaving and Vladimir in spinning.

Moscow District: Hardware.   Though the city of Moscow has a very important hardware industry, the special hardware centre is Tula, with its local supplies of both coal and iron-ore.   The town rose round a marsh-girt fortress in the low valley of the Upa, and it has never shaken off either the military or the marshy environment.   It is still very unhealthy; and, though immense numbers of samovars and other metal "small-wares" are turned out, its special products seem to be—as they were before the war—various kinds of arms and munition.   The coalfield, however, though broadest round Tula, extends northwards in a narrow arc west of Moscow, from the Oka to the Volga; and there are several "confluence" towns on it, *e.g.* Kaluga and Tver, which might seem to have a better site for the capital of a forested area than Moscow has.   But before the rise of St. Petersburg traffic seems to have avoided the long northern détour on the Volga *via* Rybinsk, and to have preferred the Oka and Moskva channels; and it was certainly in the Moskva basin that the Muscovite germ of the Great Russian people had its race-home.

City of Moscow.   The land is relatively infertile, and is still thickly forested (*c.* 40 p.c. of the Moscow province); and where the river drops from the forested plateau on to the "Oka" lowland, there sprang up a shrine to The Saviour in the Wood, vestiges of which still

---

[1] Amongst typical centres are Serpukhof, Bogorodsk, and Kalomna,—Ivanovo, Voznesensk, and Shuya.

survive. On the Borovitsky hill, 130 feet above the river, a fort
was built — the Kremlin, and round this many villages grew,
renowned even in the fifteenth century for the skill and energy
with which they made good the deficiencies of their soil by little
textile, glass, and pottery industries. The conquest of Siberia
brought an immense impulse to the place by the introduction, *via*
Nijni-Novgorod, of the fur-trade ; and the English fur-traders at
Archangel gave Moscow a northern, specially European, connection. From these beginnings the city has spread until it is now
the chief centre of trade in Russia, with a population that was
returned in 1926 as over 2,000,000 ; it does (?) a quarter of

Railways of European Russia

the railway business of the whole country, and is the junction for
six important routes—*via* Borodino to Smolensk for Poland and
the Baltic, *via* Tver for Leningrad, *via* Yaroslaf for Archangel,
via Nijni-Novgorod for Kazan, *via* Samara for the Trans-Siberian
line, and *via* Tula for the Caspian and Black Sea coasts. It is
essentially in the centre of the country, practically equidistant from
all the four seas, and controls a coal-field which underlies 150,000
square miles of " Park " country.

The people of this industrial area are typical Great Russians. **Type of**
The absence of variety in the physical relief of the country generally **People.**
is profoundly unfavourable to variety of human type, but the climatic
control divides the whole mass naturally into Great Russians of the

control divides the whole mass naturally into Great Russians of the forest, Little Russians of the grass-land, and White Russians of the lake-land. All originated in the great Slav offshoot of the Alpine race, which entered Russia from Danubia, driving before them people of more primitive type and more primitive tongue ; but in their turn they were pushed back from the steppes by Mongol-Tatar intruders, who were afraid of forest. Within the forest, therefore, the Slavs were safe, though isolation and infertile soil condemned them to slow progress and stunted stature, as the forest shade bleached them—in hair and eye and skin ; and in time they grew strong enough to bear all the brunt of Asiatic barbarism, to roll it back to the steppe from which it came, and to spread Slav population south-eastward again—to the Black Sea and the Caspian.

Kief.

As the inflow of population came from the south-west, an appropriate site for the earliest political capital was found at Kief, between Black Earth and Forest, and commanding—from heights 300 feet above the broad Dnieper—the convergence of the two great navigable tributaries of Pripet and Desna ; and it became an ecclesiastical capital of Russia. The site is of profound antiquity, its caves having furnished relics even of neolithic troglodytes ; it was the first city in Russia to have a school or a library ; and its golden-domed cathedral of St. Sophia is the oldest in the kingdom. But proximity to " Greek " lands, and the characteristic inability of the Greek Church to abstain from " Hellenising," were as adverse to the city as its proximity to the steppes and its consequent exposure to raids, *e.g.* in A.D. 1240. And so the political capital was removed 500 miles to the north-east, where forested marshes protected it alike from steppe raiders and from Anti-Slav politicians.

Agri-culture.

Agriculture is far the most important activity of the country, though recently it has been carried on largely for export instead of being devoted to supplying the needs of the people themselves. And this seems to have led to decreased consumption and a lower standard of comfort at home, because the price of wheat is practically fixed by the American prairies. Fully 80 p.c. of the total population is engaged in agriculture, and over 90 p.c. in rural industries of various kinds ; and these are conducted under conditions very adverse to the health of the employed, the mortality amongst infants whose mothers do field labour being *c.* 50 p.c. ! The conditions are equally unfavourable to the land. In the forest region there are few areas where the population can live on their own produce, partly because the cleared ground is cropped continuously with oats, rye, and flax, until it is exhausted—when it is left to run wild. Even on the fertile Black Earth things are not very much better than in the forest ; for, owing to the small size of the original lots and the subsequent subdivisions, over 70 p.c. of the peasants cannot raise enough food off their holdings, or vary their crops enough to prevent exhaustion of the soil. Further, in order to pay the taxes, they sacrificed pasture to grain-growing, so that they had not enough animals for their farm work and not enough manure for their soil. The burden of taxation, too, was worst where communal ownership had been most strongly developed. After 1906, however, the peasant did become more or less really free, with right to demand his share in one plot, and to retain it.

The legacy of the past is, however, not easily cast off; and the The Old evils of the old régime will dominate the situation for many years Régime. to come. These were fundamentally based on the fact that, in a country where a hundred million peasants had come into possession of the most fertile areas, agriculture is impossible in the one season when transport is easiest—over snow and ice. For that reason the peasants acquired the habit of migrating townwards in winter,[1] and artisans moved landward in summer—to estates which were inalienable, but liable to such subdivision that from 3 to 5 acres per head was a normal holding. These plots, too, were so situated as to do maximum injury to the general agriculture of the country. For, before the Emancipation, the serfs had lived on the precise places where it suited the landlords best to have them in order to develop the land ; at the Emancipation these precise spots passed into the possession of the peasants ; and, therefore, henceforth the land-lords' domains were much less easily worked. Further, as the result of having little or no capital, the landlords began to pay wages "in kind," which explains why famine did so little harm except where landlords were few, e.g. in Central Russia, or owned only small properties, e.g. in Southern Russia.

At the same time, although the peasants originally got the "Climatic" best land in the country, the average peasant's harvest seldom Ignorance. exceeded one-third of that gathered from a similar area in the same neighbourhood cultivated by a landlord; and the chief causes for this were the absurd subdivision of the plots and gross ignorance, some 77,000,000 of the peasants being unable to read or write. The latter was largely a climatic "control"; for the need for raising food-stuffs while the soil was tillable, caused wages to rise so much in summer that even small children had a very definite value in the field, and the custom grew up of closing all schools in summer. Of course, they were open in winter, but many children could not attend them. For during Advent and Lent, people whose normal expenditure on food did not exceed 1½d. per day *per caput* were—and still seem to act as if they were practically, if not nominally—forbidden by their Church to eat animal food (including e.g. butter and eggs). They were, therefore, so hungry and so cold that there was a premium on improvidence : cattle, utensils, clothes, future labour, were alike

---

[1] Many even went abroad, e.g. with performing bears—the famous Bear Academy being at Vilna, the nearest "forest" town to the Baltic.

sold; byres, barns, and even homes, were burned, two or three families living in one house and burning the houses thus freed from use.   Children could not go out, to school or elsewhere, half-fed and half-clad, and so they did not go out at all.

Coöpera- Under such circumstances coöperation must come to be a
tion. second instinct; and, as a matter of fact, these people can live, work, fight, only in bands (artels).   In 1913 there were *c.* 100,000 small coöperative "works" in the country, and no one dreamt of even trying to dig a ditch by himself.   Conditions were also accentuated by the control exercised over military organisation by a relief that allows invasion as well as expansion.   The whole land was organised as a military unit—unifying scattered items by common service and giving education and good food to the ignorant and the starved, but crushing initiative and thus reinforcing the tyranny of size and relief and climate.

Climatic And, again, it is the climate that is the most tyrannical influence
Tyranny. on the great agricultural lands of the Black Earth, as might be judged from the dark colouring of the Little Russians—*little* in stature only where there is large infusion of Jewish blood, though they all have the "stocky" frames typical of grass-landers—or from the dates of the great fairs.   For instance, the Nijni-Novgorod fair, on the debatable strip of land between Oka and Volga which was the old Slav-Tatar battle-ground, could not be held till the results of the harvest could be known or approximately foretold.   And, like its human product, the climate has no moderation; it varies only between the death-like peace of winter and the fearful struggle of summer.   There is a minimum of spring and autumn—a fortnight of melting snow and a fortnight of drenching rain; and on the lowland both lie about until the one is evaporated and the other frozen.   It is no wonder that the better houses are built on hillocks —often artificial, for labour is dirt-cheap—and built for extremes, with two kitchens, two sets of bedrooms, etc., one for summer and the other for winter.   Of course, they are built of wood—which is warm and cheap, but perishable: the "life" of a house is seldom over sixty years, even if it is not burnt down in winter; and the risk of this in a frozen land is so great that few people care to collect household ornaments, etc., a great check on the development of any historic sense.   But land is abundant and cheap, so that houses—and even the rooms in the same "house"—can be far apart; and, in a land cursed by a monotonous relief and endless distances, few seem to object to a hideously monotonous and straggling house.   Nor are the conditions of life ameliorated by the stubborn canopy of leaden cloud in winter; for, though very little moisture reaches the area then, the temperature is so low that the air is almost always below saturation-point.

Of course, the industrial influence of the Donetz coal and iron, and similar influences on the Dnieper, centred at Kief and **Climate** Ekaterinoslav and Kherson (Krivoi-Rog), must work for good; but **and In-** the adverse conditions[1] affect even the purely industrial progress. **dustries.** Most mills are shut in summer, which means machinery lying idle; change of hands from "rural" to "urban," or *vice versa* in spring and autumn, means that machinery is misused; ignorance on the part of the workers must in any case be always adverse to the use of machinery; and, while girls are willing to work for nothing except their keep, *provided they are kept throughout the whole winter*, human labour must be cheaper than machines. On the other hand, agriculture no longer supports much more than half the people, and does not support even half properly for more than half the year. This is so although in 1913 Russia produced 50 p.c. of the rye in the world, 33 p.c. of the barley, 25 p.c. of the oats, and 22 p.c. of the wheat.

The last quinquennial return published before 1913 showed that the average surplus of grain—above what the Government called "the irreducible minimum of 15 poods *per capita* necessary to maintain life"—had been 4·09 poods (*c.* 147 lb.), *i.e.* a total of 586,000,000 poods (*c.* 9,000,000 tons). But the average export had been 659,000,000 poods (*c.* 10,350,000 tons). Where did this come from? Who went without bread? In 1911 the *per capita* surplus was only 1·18 poods (*c.* 42 lb.), or a total of 199,000,000 poods, but the actual export was 821,000,000 poods (*c.* 13,000,000 tons). Again, where did it come from? Is it surprising that millions of Russian children died of starvation?

There are, indeed, only two vegetable products from which **Timber** Russia has any natural predominance in world markets. They are **and Flax.** timber and flax, and in neither will Russia ever again have the predominance of the past. There are still 700,000 square miles of forest, and there will be a large surplus for export. At the same time some of the subsidiary forest products are becoming less profitable. For instance, organised fur-farming, in Canada and Alaska, is materially threatening the Russian trade, for its furs come from animals that have never had to face starvation.

In recent years Russia has been supplying fully 77 p.c. of the world's flax, for the fibre was more or less a bye-product, subsidiary to the linseed, Russia supplying less than 22 p.c. of the world's linseed against over 77 p.c. of its flax-fibre. For every family had its own patch of flax in order to guarantee a supply of vegetable oil —instead of butter and cheese—during Advent and Lent; but the

---

[1] This paragraph and the previous one represent the conditions at least up to the war. References to "wages," "cheapness of labour," "keep," etc., may be, quite literally, out-of-date; but all reliable evidence tends to suggest that the essential conditions are not in any serious sense better than they were in 1914, and in some ways they seem to be worse.

best quality of flax-fibre was always grown in areas that are now outside Russia, and have better access to outside markets.

The Broad Base. But this vast area surely gives a broad base for life and outlook and growth. Is there any language except Russian that can concentrate in a single word—prostòr—"the opening of the heart to vastness"? Can any consciously scientific constitution, such as the Belgian, compare with the natural growth of the Mir and the Zemstvos—with their inimitable machinery for suppressing the crook and the crank under the disguise of an obligatory unanimous vote in all business? It is no wonder that Russian literature, even when most monotonous, is never mean; and it is obvious that Russia has known for ages the direct rule of the people—hampered only by that lack of initiative for which environment must bear most blame, and which the recent massacres have accentuated terribly, by destroying the only type of people with any gift of initiative or independence. This evolution of a political democracy administered by an autocrat was the work of the forest, not the steppe—of the refuge, not the raiding-ground. And this forest people, even though more backward than forest peoples so often are, had the stability, the tenacity, the persistence of the long-lived forest-tree, while the steppe raiders—Scyths and Sarmatians, Huns and Avars, Mongols and Tatars—were as ephemeral as the short-lived steppe-grasses.

The Frontier of Europe What does the future hold for these people, so intensely religious, so lacking in initiative, so much at the mercy of a tyrannical land, with a tyrannical climate, in which political or priestly tyranny is an unavoidable incident? Some of their essentially natural products —postins and furs, tubs and spoons—suit eastern markets better than western; and even on their typical knives and locks and samovars their work is now often only "second-stage" work, the blocked-out metal being imported from Birmingham and other places! These people in their millions were cut off for ages from all the lessons of Europe—lessons of Roman order, of Teutonic self-respect, of Feudal blending of self-respecting freedom with orderly loyalty to a person or a political ideal, of that inspiring of knowledge by zeal or that directing of zeal by knowledge which Europe learnt from the Renaissance and the Reformation. They therefore became an easy prey to the influence of a land where relief and climate are profoundly adverse to independence, initiative, individuality. And they must be still for ages foredoomed victims of any demand for blind obedience—from a foreign Jew as economic middleman or camouflaged Czar, or from a Slav fanatic as president of a secret Society, if not also from German Romanoffs as rulers. And it is these millions that form a frontier to all that is really Europe.

INDEX

THE END

Printed in Great Britain by R. & R. CLARK, LIMITED, *Edinburgh*.